ADVANCED
OPTICAL TECHNIQUES

WILEY SERIES IN PURE AND APPLIED OPTICS

Advisory Editor
STANLEY S. BALLARD, University of Florida

Lasers, BELA A. LENGYEL

Ultraviolet Radiation, second edition; LEWIS R. KOLLER

Introduction to Laser Physics, BELA A. LENGYEL

Laser Receivers, MONTE ROSS

The Middle Ultraviolet: its Science and Technology, A. E. S. GREEN, *Editor*

ADVANCED OPTICAL TECHNIQUES

EDITED BY

A. C. S. VAN HEEL

Technological University, Delft

1967

NORTH-HOLLAND PUBLISHING CO. – AMSTERDAM

JOHN WILEY & SONS, INC. – NEW YORK

Publishers:

NORTH-HOLLAND PUBLISHING CO., AMSTERDAM

Sole distributors for U.S.A. and Canada:
JOHN WILEY & SONS, NEW YORK

Library of Congress Catalog Card Number 67—20004

PRINTED IN THE NETHERLANDS

FOREWORD

Between the well-known introductions into the theory and the practical side of optics and the often highly specialized articles on particular subjects a gap is to be filled. It is an impossible task to try filling this hiatus in one book. The series 'Progress in Optics' fulfills already an important part of this work. A book presenting modern subjects in a comprehensive form seems helpful in those cases where a connection between the more elementary treatises and the specialized publications is missing. The present volume is an attempt in this direction. Completeness has not been aimed at, neither in the choice of subjects nor within each chapter.

It need not be emphasized that it is unfeasible to be up to date in all subjects treated (lasers, fibers, lens design, transformation function). These branches of the optical science are in full bloom. The respective chapters can be considered as introductions to the pertinent literature.

Some chapters are more or less rounded-off studies of the subject matter (modern spectroscopic methods, coherence and image formation, crystal interferometry, thin films, geometrical optics).

Another group of chapters deals with matters of practical importance that are scattered in different journals and of which even a short but general review has its utility (modern light sources, modern applications of interference, precision measurements, optical glass, fabrication of optical parts, coronagraphy). To this group also three other small chapters may be reckoned, which call attention to special subjects of some importance, but are apt to be overlooked (three-slit method, alignment, optical glass spheres).

Three points must be stressed: each author wrote his text under his own responsibility; there is no uniformity between the different chapters, the subjects (and the authors) being often too wide apart; the reader is supposed to possess a general knowledge of the optical principles. Matter that can easily be found in well-known books is, in many cases, not included.

v

The editor is aware of the fact that the inclusion in or omission from this book of certain subjects will meet criticism from competent workers in the optical field. He can only hope that it will be understood that within the scope of one volume no agreement can be reached between more than a few persons, even if they come from one school.

One of the clearest examples is the area of lens design: each lens designer is perfectly aware of the fact that his methods are the best in the world and it is impossible to convince him by any length of argument that other methods are more rapid or give more easily a larger amount of information. The reader, therefore, either has to comply to the author or to reject his way of thinking. The editor can only declare that he has done his best to assemble a number of writers who have won their spurs in their field, and who devoted their time making a collection of texts which to his opinion will prove useful to those who feel the need of modern optical knowledge. For a long time technical optics has been neglected by the research workers in the domain of space physics, of atomic energy, and of other disciplines with a flavour of actuality and even of romanticism; workers, who begin to feel now the need of a sound optical background for the benefit of their own work.

A. C. S. VAN HEEL

Delft, 1966

PREFACE

As a result of intensive fundamental research since the Second World War, optics, one of the oldest branches of physics, has developed dramatically, not only in the more novel fields, but also in the well-established areas of geometrical and physical optics.

Among the more important advances and discoveries which may be mentioned are:
Computer techniques in lens design and the use of new optical glasses, leading to better corrected lenses.
Extensive use of reflecting optics in X-ray relay cameras, air reconnaissance cameras, microscope objectives, and other new fields.
The laser, which has made holography practicable and has led to new applications of interferometry.
Thin film optics, which now has reached the stage of elaborate computer programmes for automatic design.
Fibre optics.
Application of Fourier transform techniques to spectroscopy and to lens assessment.

These developments indicated to Professor A. C. S. van Heel the need for a new book which gathered together the relevant details and presented new ideas and devices together with all the necessary background information. Although not all the possible topics can be treated within a single volume, the aim of the book is to stimulate physicists, both pure and applied, working on optical problems, and engineers engaged in designing new equipment. The book should also serve as a guide to all who are interested in advanced optical techniques.

In order to ensure that each field was covered by an author with first-hand knowledge of it, Professor van Heel invited outside contributions, though he himself wrote two chapters dealing with his own special interests: alignment and the use of spheres.

Unfortunately these plans were interrupted tragically by his sudden death on 18th May, 1966. We have lost in him a friend as well as an able, prominent and enthusiastic physicist.

I was asked to co-ordinate some of the work which remained to be done; Professor van Heel's staff and North-Holland Publishing Company together performed the greater part of this task.

I am convinced that the volume will constitute an invaluable aid for all who are concerned with optical problems, both in research and in the application thereof.

B. S. BLAISSE

Delft, April 1967   Technological University, Delft

CONTENTS

A detailed contents of each chapter
is given at the pages referred to here

CHAPTER 1

PRECISION MEASUREMENTS

J. B. SAUNDERS

National Bureau of Standards, Washington

CONTENTS

1. Introduction

The development of precision measurements has remained one of the outstanding efforts of scientific research. The term means measurements beyond the realm of ordinary measurements such at those made with a scale and protractor. The Egyptians made precision measurements as early as 4700 B.C. Proof of this currently exists in the geometrical regularity of the great pyramids of Khufu at Gizah.

Precision measurements do not require rigidly defined units. The cubit, used by the Egyptians, is defined as the distance from the elbow to the tip of the middle finger. Obviously the Egyptians must have transferred this unit from some person's arm to a stable scale that was either used throughout the pyramid project or distance measured with it was used to calibrate other standard scales. When multiple measurements are combined, as in modern engineering developments, there must be consistency between the units used and the standards of reference must be stable. The need for consistency between standards used by different countries has led to the establishment of international standards. The need for high precision had led to the selection of standards that have the highest available stability and the values of the standards are specified to a degree of accuracy that is comparable with the most precise measurements that are currently anticipated.

2. Reliability of measurements

If the result of any measurement is to be of value it is necessary to have some numerical estimate or measure of its reliability. The results of a measurement may be rendered almost useless, unless the investigator is able to state the degree of reliance which can be placed upon it. A brief description of the several types of errors that enter into measurements is given by WILSON [1952].

A single measurement can have no precision value. The precision of a measurement depends upon the deviations of several measurements from the mean of these several measurements. The precision measure or reliability of a result is increased appreciably by increasing the number of individual measurements. In general, five measurements yield a precision that is approximately twice that for two observations. However, it does not pay to increase the number of observations beyond a certain limit, say ten or fifteen, as the time and labor involved soon become excessive, with very little increase in the precision.

3. Units and standards

The fundamental quantities used in most optical measurements are length, angle, time (or frequency) and intensity. The meter is defined as 1 650 763.73 wavelengths in vacuum of the transition $2P_{10}$–$5d_5$ in Kr^{86}. The inch is defined as 25.4 millimeters. The length of most reference standards of length is given either in inches or in millimeters. The basic angle (360 degrees) is not an accepted unit. This angle is basic to all angular measurements and is the angle swept over by a straight line while rotating in a plane, about a point in this plane, and making one revolution. There are two units of angle – the degree, which is subdivided into minutes and seconds, and the radian. There are 2π radians or 360 degrees in the basic angle. Most of the standard reference angles are given in degrees and/or subdivisions of it. The unit of time usually used for optical measurements is the second which is 1/31 556 925.974 7 of the tropical year at 12^h E.T. of January 0, 1900. The units of length and time are based on relatively invariant natural quantities. The basic angle is a geometrical concept. The unit for intensity is an arbitrarily chosen unit.

4. Precision optical instruments

Optical instruments for precision measurements may be simple or complex. The basic requirement for most precision optical instruments is that they be made with high quality optics that have been assembled accurately. A poorly aligned system of precision optical elements would not be suitable for a precision instrument. When the instrument depends upon mechanical parts, these parts should be made and adjusted with the same care used in making and mounting the optical elements. Similarly the scales, indexing heads and reference lines that are used in optical instruments must be made with a high degree of accuracy. The precision with which an image of a line can be adjusted to coincide with a reference mark depends as much on the quality of the mark as it does on the quality of the image. The image quality depends upon the quality of the optics and sharpness of the object.

A precision optical instrument should be handled with care. Mechanical and thermal shocks should be avoided. When the instrument is not in use it should be protected from dust, fumes and humidity as far as covers and environmental storage places will permit. Optical surfaces should be cleaned only when this results in significant improvement in its performance.

5. Operation of precision instruments

An instrument will not yield precision results unless it is adjusted precisely and due consideration is given to environmental conditions. Cleanliness and gentleness are essential in making precise adjustments. Small temperature gradients are detrimental to the image forming properties of optical elements because of the relatively large coefficient of thermal expansion in most optical glasses. The shape and size of scales are adversely affected by both temperatures and thermal gradients.

A precision built and properly adjusted instrument will yield best results only when used by a skilled operator. The operator must therefore become familiar with the instrument and its operation. This can only be attained by experience acquired during a period of training.

6. Index of refraction

6.1. GASES

The refractive index of a gas is most precisely measured by interferometry. The interferometers most frequently used for this purpose are the Jamin interferometer and the Rayleigh refractometer. These instruments are described in many textbooks (e.g. JENKINS and WHITE [1957]) on optics. In the Rayleigh refractometer, shown in fig. 1, monochromatic light from a slit source S_1 is collimated by the lens L_1 and

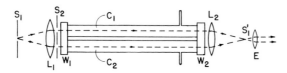

Fig. 1. Rayleigh refractometer.

divided into two beams by two relatively broad slits in the screen S_2. These two slits should be parallel to the slit source. The two gas chambers, C_1 and C_2, are of equal length and are sealed by cementing two glass windows, W_1 and W_2, to their ends. The lens L_2 forms an image of S_1 at S_1'. Fringes of interference are observed in S_1' by means of the eyepiece E. The gas chambers are connected by means of gas lines, with suitable valves, to a pump that permits evacuation of either or both chambers.

The procedure for obtaining the refractive index of a gas is to evacuate both chambers, C_1 and C_2; set the cross-hair of the eyepiece on the zero order of interference; slowly fill one chamber with the gas to the desired temperature and pressure while observing the change in the order of interference, ΔN. The refractive index, n, is computed from the formula $\lambda \cdot \Delta N = L(n-1)$ where λ is the wavelength of the light and L is the length of the gas chambers.

The sensitivity of the test, assuming the temperature and pressure of the gas to be known, is proportional to the length of the gas chambers. The choice for an optimum value for L depends upon the accuracy with which the temperature, pressure and the fractional part of ΔN can be measured. The integral part of ΔN is assumed to be free from error and the errors in λ and pressure are assumed to be negligible, because these are easy to obtain in practice.

In general, the uncertainty in L varies directly with the error in temperature whereas the percentage error in ΔN decreases with increase in L. An optimum choice for L is one that tends to equalize the error due to temperature and the error in reading ΔN.

The index of most gases, in the range of visible wavelengths, is usually known to an approximation that permits the use of the 'method of exact fractions' (PEROT and FABRY [1899]) for ascertaining the integral part of ΔN. Even when ΔN is obtained by counting fringes it is advisable to check the integral part by applying the method of exact fractions to the values computed for three or more wavelengths. If the value of ΔN is known for one wavelength λ_1, the corresponding value for any other wavelength

λ_2 may be obtained by observing the fractional part of ΔN_2 and computing the integral part, which is the integer that most closely approximates $\Delta N_1 \lambda_1 / \lambda_2$.

The modified Michelson interferometer, shown in fig. 2a, is more sensitive than a Rayleigh refractometer of the same length chamber because the light path in the

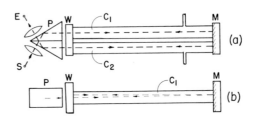

Fig. 2. Gas interferometer. (a) Section normal to the dividing plane.
(b) Section parallel to the dividing plane.

gas chambers is doubled by reflection of the light. This interferometer pemits more light because a larger source can be used. The fringes are localized near the mirror, M, and may be observed without an eyepiece. However, a low power telescope with micrometer eyepiece is preferred. The window, W, should have a 20 to 30 minute wedge between its faces, and the vertex of this wedge should be normal to the beam dividing plane of the Köster's prism P (SAUNDERS [1957]), so as to eliminate unwanted reflected light.

If the pressure and temperature of the gas and the length of the gas chambers are known to a higher accuracy than ΔN, then improved accuracy can be obtained either by increasing the length of the chambers or by using multiple reflection in the chambers. The effective length of the gas chamber may be doubled by having a small (three or four minute) wedge between M and the inner surface of W and having this surface of W coated to reflect and transmit equal amounts of light. See fig. 2b. The prism is adjusted so that the two collimated beam of light, after being first reflected from M, is incident normally onto W, from which it returns to M and then to the prism. A suitable diaphragm, located in the focal plane of the collector lens, permits isolation of all undesirable beams of light; one of which is that reflected from the base of the prism.

6.2. LOW ABSORBING MATERIALS

The minimum deviation method of measuring the refractive index of solids and liquids remains the most practical for precision tests. The principle of this method is described in many textbooks on optics. An accuracy approximating $\pm 2 \times 10^{-6}$ can readily be achieved, in the range of visible wavelengths, if certain goniometrical requirements (TILTON [1929]) are fulfilled and proper techniques (TILTON [1931, 1935]) are adhered to.

This method requires that solid materials be made into the form of prisms with two polished faces and an appropriate included angle which, for highest accuracy, depends upon the refractive index of the material. Liquids may be measured by placing them in prismatic cells that have two plane-parallel windows, with the appropriate angle between them.

6.3. HIGH ABSORBING MATERIALS

The refractive index of liquids in spectral regions of high absorption may be measured by placing a thin layer of the liquid between two identical prisms, as shown in fig. 3. The index of refraction and angles of the prisms may be measured by means of the minimum deviation method. The index of the prisms must exceed that of the liquid. The optimum angles of the prism (fig. 3) are: $\alpha = 90°$ and $\beta \approx \text{arc } \sin(n/n')$ where

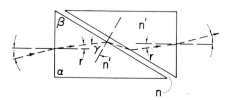

Fig. 3. Prisms for measuring refractive index of high absorption materials.

n and n' are the indices of the liquid and prisms, respectively. Measurement is made by allowing a collimated beam of monochromatic light to fall on the entrance face and measuring the angle of incidence, i, that corresponds to the critical angle of incidence of the light on the glass–liquid boundary. The index of the liquid may be computed by means of the formulas (VINCENT-GEISSE and LECOMTE [1962])

$$\sin i = n' \sin r,$$

$$n = n' \sin \gamma = n' \sin(\beta - r).$$

Thin parallel sheets (or plates) of high absorbing solids may also be measured by this method if a suitable liquid of known index is used between the prisms and sample. The precision obtained with this method is approximately $\pm 1 \times 10^{-3}$.

6.4. OPAQUE MATERIALS

Neither of the above methods permits measurement of the index of refraction of materials in regions of very high absorption, such as metals. Observation must be made by reflection if precision is to be obtained. Methods for measuring the optical constants of solids and liquids are described by VINCENT-GEISSE and LECOMTE [1962]. An ellipsometer, such as that described by ROTHEN [1945], is usually used for studying the optical properties of metals and thin films. A good discussion on techniques in polarimetric measurements is given by WINTERBOTTOM [1946].

7. Wavelength of light in air

Precise measurement of length by interferometry requires that the wavelength of the light be accurately known. If such measurements are to be made in air they should include a measurement of the wavelength of the light under the same conditions. ENGELHARD [1957] enclosed a wavelength and a length measuring interferometer into a single unit. The NBS wavelength interferometer (SAUNDERS [1963a]) is a separate unit and is designed to measure the wavelength of light under the ambient conditions of a gage testing laboratory.

The wavelength interferometer developed at NBS is identical to the gas interferometer shown in fig. 2 except that one chamber is open to ambient conditions. One component beam of light traverses a one meter space two times. This space is either evacuated or filled with standard air. The other component beam traverses an equal space filled with ambient air. The wavelength of light is accurately known for both vacuum and standard air (BARRELL [1951]). If the geometrical path length and the order of interference is known for any spectral line, the corresponding wavelength is known in the enclosed gas chamber. If the enclosed chamber contains standard air, the order will always be relatively small. A calibrated optical wedge, located between the window and the prism, may be used for reducing the order to zero. The fringe count, as the order of interference is reduced to zero, gives the order and consequently the difference in wavelength between ambient and standard air. The zero order of interference is readily identified by replacing the monochromatic light source with a white light source.

8. Testing optical flats

An optical flat is a surface that approximates a plane. Attempts have been made to produce natural surfaces that could be used for master references planes. BARRELL and MARRINER [1948], and VON BÜNNAGEL [1956] have produced liquid surfaces of high quality over small areas. An undeformed liquid surface approximates the curvature of the earth. Since the curvature is known corrections can be applied for correcting these to plane surfaces. These liquid surfaces, however, have not been satisfactory for testing large optical flats.

Optical flats are usually tested by measuring the separation of two surfaces placed close together and nearly parallel to each other. Fig. 4 shows an arrangement that permits the comparison of two optical surfaces. The upper plate, M_1, must be transparent, with both of its surfaces polished for transmitting the light. Usually the upper surface of the lower plate, M_2, is the unknown surface to be tested against the master surface of M_1. Interference is obtained by the combination of light reflected from the two adjacent surfaces of M_1 and M_2.

If the shape of the lower surface of M_1 is known from previous tests it can be considered a primary or secondary standard, depending upon the method used for calibrating it. If the accuracy of its shape depends directly upon the accuracy of the surface with which it was compared then it is a secondary standard. The accuracy of a primary standard flat does not depend directly upon the accuracy of the surfaces used for its calibration. Furthermore, two additional surfaces must be used to calibrate a primary standard flat. This usually results in the simultaneous calibration of three (or more) primary standards. No previous knowledge of the surfaces is required, except that they must be flat enough to produce interference fringes that can be measured accurately.

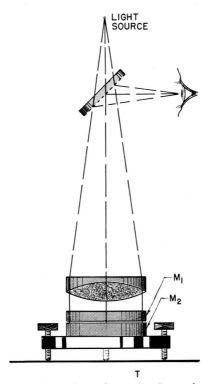

Fig. 4. Fizeau viewer for testing flat surfaces.

The calibration of a primary optical flat is performed by using three surfaces that are approximately plane, testing these by comparing them in pairs, and making an appropriate mathematical analysis of data obtained from the three comparison tests. This mathematical analysis has been discussed by EMERSON [1952], PORTER [1933], and others but the descriptions are incomplete. The procedure for calibrating (or measuring) three primary optical flats will be described. The three surfaces, labeled A, B and C in fig. 5, will be one face of each of three circular glass plates of equal diameter and of sufficient thickness to avoid significant gravitational distortion (EMERSON [1952]). Fig. 5 shows three possible combinations: surface A over B, surface B over C and surface C over A. Equally spaced reference points that are similarly positioned relative to the center, are chosen along one diameter of each plate. The interference fringes produced by each pair of surfaces, are illustrated above the corresponding pair of surfaces. The wavy lines in the sectional views represent diameters of the surfaces. The sections are approximately normal to the surfaces and include all reference points. The projections of the several reference points are indicated on each surface. The shapes of the surfaces are greatly exaggerated for simplification and to avoid crowding of symbols. Note that the plates are always positioned so that the projections of the reference points of one surface coincide with corresponding points of the other plate.

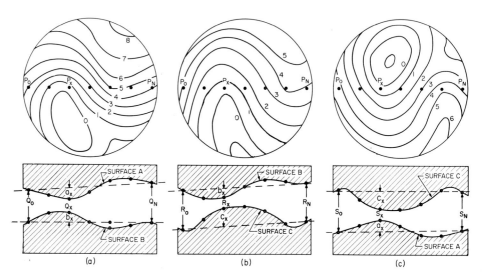

Fig. 5. Arrangement of three surfaces for absolute measurement of shapes. Fringes produced by combining surfaces A and B, B and C, and C and A are shown above each of the corresponding pairs of surfaces.

The order of interference at any point $P_x (x = 0, 1, 2, \ldots N)$ multiplied by the wavelength, λ, of the light, is twice the separation of the two surfaces at this point. The subscript x denotes the distance from P_0 to P_x, in units that equal the separation of the reference points, and $N + 1$ is the number of reference points on each plate. The change in order from point to point is independent of the absolute order, which is unimportant. Therefore, any fringe may be chosen to represent the zero order and all readings may be made relative to this fringe. Accordingly, one fringe in each pattern has been labeled zero. The relative orders of all other fringes can be inserted when the direction of increasing order is known. The direction which the fringes move when downward pressure is added to the top plate is the direction of increasing order. When the added pressure is reduced the fringes move toward the direction of decreasing order.

The reference plane to which any surface is referred must maintain a fixed relation to this surface. For this illustration, we will choose reference planes that are approximately normal to the incident light by passing the planes through the outer reference points of each surface. The reference planes are indicated in fig. 5 by dashed, straight lines.

If we know the vertical separations of the three pairs of curves (surfaces) we can compute the vertical deviations of each curve from the straight line (or reference plane), that passes through its marginal reference points, at all other reference points. Let a_x, b_x, and c_x represent the deviations of surfaces A, B and C, respectively, from their corresponding reference planes at P_x. These deviations are positive if the reference plane is inside the plate at the corresponding points and negative if it is outside. We use relative orders, instead of absolute orders, because they only appear as differences. Let Q_x, R_x, and S_x represent orders of interference at P_x in fig. 5a, 5b, and 5c respectively. Since the optical path difference for any two interfering beams of light, observed with the arrangement of fig. 4, is twice the separation of the two surfaces, it is easily shown that

$$(2a_x + 2b_x + \lambda Q_x - \lambda Q_0)/x = \lambda(Q_N - Q_0)/N$$
$$(2b_x + 2c_x + \lambda R_x - \lambda R_0)/x = \lambda(R_N - R_0)/N$$
$$(2c_x + 2a_x + \lambda S_x - \lambda S_0)/x = \lambda(S_N - S_0)/N$$

which becomes:

$$2N(a_x + b_x) + \lambda N(Q_x - Q_0) = \lambda x(Q_N - Q_0)$$
$$2N(b_x + c_x) + \lambda N(R_x - R_0) = \lambda x(R_N - R_0) \qquad (1)$$
$$2N(c_x + a_x) + \lambda N(S_x - S_0) = \lambda x(S_N - S_0).$$

The solutions of eq. (1) for the several deviations are:

$$a_x = \tfrac{1}{4}\lambda x N^{-1}[(Q_N - Q_0) - (R_N - R_0) + (S_N - S_0)] - \tfrac{1}{4}\lambda[(Q_x - Q_0) - (R_x - R_0) + (S_x - S_0)]$$

$$b_x = \tfrac{1}{4}\lambda x N^{-1}[(R_N - R_0) - (S_N - S_0) + (Q_N - Q_0)] - \tfrac{1}{4}\lambda[(R_x - R_0) - (S_x - S_0) + (Q_x - Q_0)] \qquad (2)$$

$$c_x = \tfrac{1}{4}\lambda x N^{-1}[(S_N - S_0) - (Q_N - Q_0) + (R_N - R_0)] - \tfrac{1}{4}\lambda[(S_x - S_0) - (Q_x - Q_0) + (R_x - R_0)].$$

Thus, the deviations at all points for the three surfaces are given directly as functions of the measurable quantities, x, N, and the relative orders of interference at the several reference points.

The above explanation is enhanced by applying eqs. (2) to the evaluation of the deviations at an arbitrary chosen point, such as P_4, for instance. The measurable quantities for this point are: $x=4$, $N=6$, $Q_0=3.0$, $Q_4=5.0$, $Q_6=4.0$, $R_0=3.9$, $R_4=2.9$, $R_6=3.9$, $S_0=4.3$, $S_4=3.0$, and $S_6=3.9$. When these values are substituted into eq. (2) for the corresponding symbols which they represent, the values for the deviations at P_4 are computed to be: $a_4=-0.33\lambda$, $b_4=-0.30\lambda$, and $c_4=0.84\lambda$.

9. Flatness of surface plates and ways

The testing of large-surface plates, from 30 to 600 cm in length and from 30 to 150 cm wide, have usually been done with an autocollimator and a plane mirror (HUME [1950]). The autocollimator, A, in fig. 6, is preferably mounted just beyond the edge of the surface to be tested and on a support that is rigidly bound to it. Its axis is adjusted approximately parallel to the surface and in a vertical plane that intersects the surface along the line where measurements are to be made. The mirror, M, mounted on a tripod, is adjusted to receive the beam of light from A as close to normal

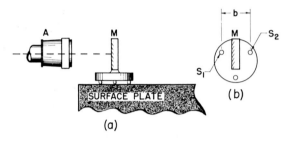

Fig. 6. Autocollimator and mirror for surface plate measurements.

incidence as possible. Two of the tripod supports, S_1 and S_2, (fig. 6b) are located vertically below the normal to M at its center and are separated by a convenient distance b, which is the base for the angular measurements.

Measurements of the flatness of the surface is made by starting with the mirror near one edge of the surface, measuring the vertical component of the angle of incidence at this original position, moving the mirror a distance b to a new position and remeasuring the vertical angle of incidence. This operation is repeated until the entire length (or breadth) of the surface is tested. The change in the vertical component of the angle of incidence of the light, between two adjacent positions of the mirror, multiplied by the base b, is equal to the corresponding change in the distance between the principal ray of the light beam and the surface. A method for determining the topography of the surface from measured changes in height is described by HUME [1950, p. 177].

Measurements are usually made along several lines parallel to the sides and along the two diagonals of the surface. This permits the combination of all measuremens for calculating the deviation of the surface from a plane.

There are two principal sources of error in this test. These are the measurement of changes in orientation of the mirror and the failure of the mirror orientation to represent the corresponding change in the slope of the surface. This latter error, however, is minimized but not eliminated, by having the tripod supports slightly rounded and all contacting surfaces clean. Care should be used to avoid abrasion of the contacting points caused by sliding the tripod on the surface.

The change in orientation of the mirror may be measured more precisely by substituting the interferometric autocollimator (BRITTON and HABELL [1958]), shown in fig. 7, for the autocollimator. This interferometer is well compensated so that bright light sources may be used and good contrast is obtained for all path lengths (distance from prism to mirror). It is insensitive to linear translations of the mirror and is sensitive to rotation of the mirror about one axis only. Thus, the instrument is quite stable and very sensitive to the one orientation for which it is used. If the aperture of this mirror-prism interferometer is 5 cm a change of one second in mirror orientation produces unit change in the order of interference for a wavelength of 0.48 μm.

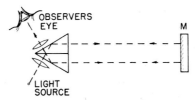

Fig. 7. Interferometric autocollimator.

The flatness of a surface plate can be measured directly in units of the wavelength of light by using the surface as one reflector in an interferometer. The two characteristics of surface plates that prevent them from being tested with conventional interferometers are low reflectivity due to roughness and relatively large deviations from flatness. Both of these difficulties are eliminated by reflecting the light at a large angle of incidence. The interferometer shown in fig. 8 permits ample reflection from

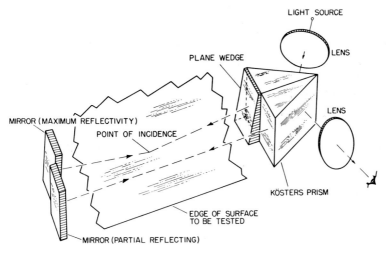

Fig. 8. Interferometer for testing surface plates.

relatively rough surfaces and the sensitivity is reduced so that the interference fringes are quite legible (SAUNDERS and McDERMOTT [1964]). The large angle of incidence permits the testing of the surface along a narrow strip of its entire length or breadth at one setting.

The aperture of this interferometer is not limited by the size of the prism. It can be made relatively large by using a lens with a small prism (SAUNDERS [1963a]). The light from a seven cm aperture interferometer, incident at an angle of 88°, will cover a narrow strip of the surface two meters long; and one fringe departure from straightness corresponds to a departure from flatness of 0.004 mm for a wavelength of 0.56 μm.

10. Measurement of temperatures

When measurements, such as thermal expansion, changes in refraction of glass with temperature, etc., are made by interferometry it is sometimes desirable to measure temperature by interferometry also. The thermometer usually used for this purpose is a transparent solid with two optical surfaces that are plane and almost parallel (LUCKIESH *et al.* [1922]). A small disc or rectangular section cut from a glass plate that has one half minute angle between its surfaces will suffice. If a collimated beam of monochromatic light is incident normally on the surfaces, fringes of interference are produced by light reflected from the two surfaces.

The sensitivity of this thermometer is proportional to the separation of the surfaces. Ordinary line sources, such as helium or mercury, will produce fringes of good contrast for optical path differences up to one cm. Much larger path differences, and consequently interferometers of very high sensitivity, may be used with sources of higher coherene such as Kr^{86}, Hg^{198} and lasers.

The refractive index and separation of the surfaces of this interferometer change with temperature. The thermometer may be calibrated with a thermocouple by noting the temperature corresponding to all integral orders of interference over the temperature range for which it is to be used. The calibration and application require a continuous recording of the change in order of interference. This thermometer is quite practical for interferometer meaurements when the fringes are continuously recorded either with a camera (SAUNDERS [1945]) or by visual observations (TOOL *et al.* [1930]).

Thermometers made of optical glass may be used below 400 °C. For higher temperatures the material should be either fused quartz or sapphire. Because of incandescence, it is difficult to observe interference at high temperatures. Photographic recording may be used, however, if a blue or violet spectral line source is used with a photographic emulsion that is relatively insensitive to green, yellow and red light. An interference filter will help to suppress the incandescent light.

11. Thermal expansion

The optical instrument often used for measuring thermal expansion of solid bodies is an interferometer that was originally described by FIZEAU [1866]. This interferometer may be operated in helium at reduced pressure or in air at atmospheric pressure. When it is operated in air the changes in wavelength due to changes in the refractive index of air must be considered. Change in density due to change in temperature is the dominant factor. Equations for this correction are given by BARRELL [1951] and PÉRARD [1932].

The interferometer (SAUNDERS [1945, p. 167]) shown in fig. 9 provides one set of fringes for measuring expansion and another for measuring temperature. See § 10 above. The thermometer plate, T, has a part of its lower surface rough ground to prevent overlapping of the two sets of fringes. The upper plate, P, is smaller than T and has a 20 minute wedge between its surfaces so as to eliminate light reflected from its top surface. The sensitivity of this interferometer is proportional to the thickness of the thermometer and to the length of the 3 samples S. These can be very large if a gas laser is used for illumination.

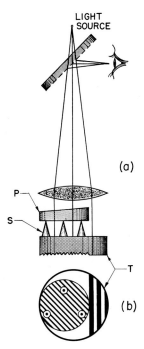

Fig. 9. Viewing apparatus for observing Fizeau interference.

This method of measuring expansion is vulnerable to an error that can be so large as to render the method useless if it is not suppressed. If three separated spacers are used to separate the interferometer plates two of these will usually become tilted during the heating cycle because of differential expansion between plates and specimen. This causes a spurious increase in separation of the plates. Even if the spacer is a ring or T-type tripod (SAUNDERS [1939]), there may be a change in the thickness of the air films at the points of contact between the spaces and plates unless the interferometer is in a vacuum and previously heated for degassing the contact areas. This tilting error may be eliminated (SAUNDERS [1939]) by having one of the contact points bear a major portion of the weight of the top plate and by heating the assembled interferometer to 250 °C before starting the test.

12. Testing lenses and mirrors

There are two principal reasons for testing the image forming properties of optical elements and systems; one is for making corrections during manufacture and the other is for evaluating the quality of the finished product. Several interferometric and noninterferometric methods are available for precision testing.

12.1. THE FOUCAULT KNIFE-EDGE TEST

The Foucault knife-edge test is unsurpassed when testing for spherical or zonal aberrations during the figuring of concave mirrors and aspheric lenses. This is basically a qualitative test. Fig. 10 shows the arrangement for testing a concave mirror. The point

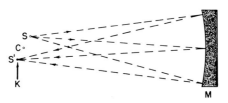

Fig. 10. Foucault knife-edge test.

source, S, is placed slightly off axis, and near the center of curvature, C, of the mirror. The rays from all parts of the mirror converge toward the neighborhood of a point near S'. If the mirror is spherical all rays will pass through a common point as S'. However, because of the wave nature of light, the image is not a point (STRONG [1958]). If S is very close to C and the mirror is spherical, the knife edge, K, can be moved across the beam to obstruct equal parts of all rays simultaneously. This causes the evenly illuminated mirror, as seen by the observer, to fade uniformly. Very small departures from sphericity of the mirror can be detected and located in the resulting nonuniform penumbral shadow produced by the knife-edge. More details of this test are given by PORTER [1933, p. 6].

12.2. THE FILAMENT TEST

The Foucault test is considerably enhanced by replacing the point source with a narrow slit source and the knife-edge with a small filament (SAUNDERS [1954]). This is similar to the Gaviola test (PLATZECK and GAVIOLA [1939]). A suitable slit is produced by scratching a line through an opaque layer of aluminum-on-glass with the sharp point of a razor blade. The filament may be a spider web, a silk fiber or a very fine human hair. The observer sees a diffraction pattern with sharp lines replacing the penumbral shadow of the knife-edge. This test permits accurate measurement on the diameter of the zone corresponding to the axial position of the filament and, consequently, precise measurement of spherical and chromatic aberration.

12.3. LENS TESTING INTERFEROMETERS

Interferometry is the most practical precision method of testing optics for characteristic aberrations and for quantitative analysis of wavefront forms. The Twyman lens testing interferometer produces an interferogram that is a countour map of the wavefront produced by the specimen (lens or mirror) relative to the reference wavefront. The size and number of elements that combine to form a Twyman interferometer limits the accuracy of results obtained with it. The apertures of all elements must approximate or exceed that of the lens or specimen to be tested. Their separation requires very stable mounting to prevent relative vibration of the components, and the air should be homogeneous to prevent fluctuations in the position of the fringes. The convex end-mirror is expensive to manufacture because it is difficult to test. Also, lenses of different focal lengths require convex mirrors of different curvatures if precision results are to be obtained.

The wave front shearing interferometer by BATES [1947] does not require a reference standard. It produces interference by shearing the wave front relative to an image of itself. Since any two interfering rays are separated by a relatively small angular displacement, atmospheric disturbances are greatly reduced. The interferometer elements can be bound together so that vibration of the fringes can be practically eliminated. The Bates interferometer requires two beam dividers, one compensator plate, and two end mirrors. The equivalent of all these elements may be condensed into the small fifteen mm aperture prism (SAUNDERS [1964]) shown in fig. 11a. The small size

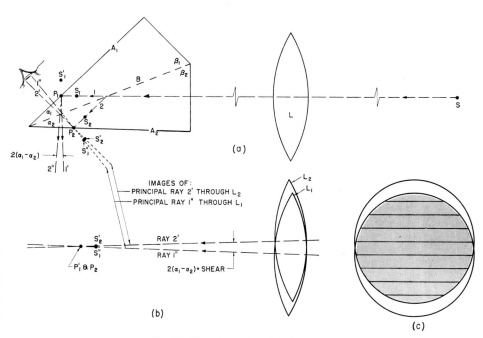

Fig. 11. Shearing prism interferometer.

of the prism permits the elimination of all significant errors in the interferometer because the effects of imperfections in the surfaces and glass are reduced in proportion to its size. The prism is adjusted to receive the principal ray through the center of and normal to its entrance face. The beam is divided into two components, 1 and 2, at the semireflecting surface B. The prism-to-lens separation is adjusted so that the two coherent images of the point source, S_1 and S_2, are located near P_1 and P_2 respectively, where total internal reflections of the beams occur. Light from S_1 and S_2 recombines at surface B to produce nonlocalized interference in the same manner that intereference is obtained with the Fresnel's mirror arrangement. The two components, 1 and 2, of the principal ray redivide at B. The components of 1 are labeled 1' and 1'' and the components of 2 are labeled 2' and 2''. An observer receiving rays 1'' and 2' sees two images, L_1 and L_2, of the lens, L, (fig. 11) with interference of light in the overlapping region. When S_1 and S_2 coincide with P_1 and P_2, respectively, the two virtual images appear to coincide and, if the beams are free from aberrations, the phase difference is the same at all points in the two overlapping beams. When the prism is moved along the principal ray we obtain a separation of the secondary images of S_1 and S_2, which are represented in fig. 11 as S_1'' and S_2', respectively. Thus, the width of the fringes (fig. 11c) may be varied at will. A complementary set of fringes can be seen by using the pair of emergent rays 1' and 2''. The order of interference is changed, without changing the width or direction of the fringes, by moving the prism parallel to surface A_1 and in the plane of the figure. Extremely fine adjustment can be made with relatively coarse screws for moving the prism. If the lens is free from aberrations, the fringes will be straight. Aberrated wave fronts produce curved fringes. The shape of the fringes is a measure of the shape of the wave front relative to a sphere. Measurements made along one diameter of the lens permit a computation of the wave front shape along this diameter.

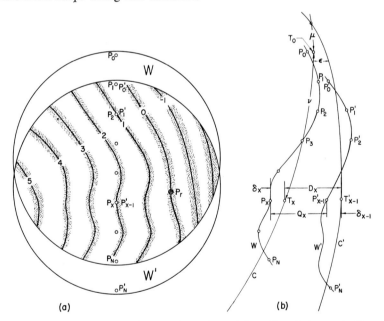

Fig. 12. (a) Two images of a wavefront sheared laterally relative to itself.
(b) Illustration of the two wavefronts relative to the images of a reference circle.

The interferometer remains in permanent adjustment. Preparation for making measurements require only that the specimen and source be arranged to project an image of the source to the proper position in the prism. Either white light or mono-chromatic fringes are immediately visible. The fringes have excellent contrast because the interferometer is fully compensated and the order of interference is always small.

Any convergent wave front may be tested along any chosen diameter. Several reference marks with spacings equal to the shear of the interferometer, are placed along the chosen diameter. The interferometer is rotated about the principal ray until the direction of shear is parallel to the line of reference marks. This arrangement and spacing of the reference marks causes their images, in the region of overlapping wave fronts, to coincide in pairs as is shown in fig. 12a. The $N+1$ reference points in one of the images, W, of the sheared wave front is represented by $P_x(x=0, 1, 2 \ldots N)$ and in the other image, W', they are represented by P'_x. Let δ_x (see fig. 12b) equal the deviations of the wave front at P_x from the corresponding points, T_x, on a reference circle, C, (to be chosen later). Let ε equal the angle between the two images, C and C', of the reference circle at their point of intersection, and μ equal the distance from the intersection point to T_0. The distance μ is positive if P_0 is below the nearest intersection of the two circles (as seen in fig. 12b) and negative if above. The deviation δ_x is positive if P_x is on the concave side of the circle and negative if it lies on the convex side of the reference circle. The distance from T_0 to T_x (or from P_0 to P_x), measured along the circle, is always positive and is represented by x. It can be shown (SAUNDERS [1961]) that the separation D_x of the two images C and C' at any pair of reference points, P_x and P_{x-1}, is closely approximated by the equation

$$D_x = (\mu+x)\varepsilon \tag{3}$$

and it is apparent from fig. 12b that

$$\delta_x + D_x = \lambda Q_x + \delta_{x-1} \tag{4}$$

where Q_x is the order of interference at P_x. The absolute order Q_x is, in general, unknown. If we let q_x represent the difference in order between P_x and some arbitrarily chosen point, P_r, then $Q_x = Q_r + q_x$, where Q_r is the unknown order at P_r. By eliminating D_x from eqs. (3) and (4) and replacing the constant term $\lambda Q_r - \varepsilon\mu$ by r, we obtain the set of observation equations

$$\delta_x = \delta_{x-1} + \lambda q_x + r - \varepsilon x \tag{5}$$

It is shown by SAUNDERS [1961] that eq. (5) is equivalent to

$$\delta_x = \delta_0 + \sum_{\sigma=1}^{x} q_\sigma + rx - \varepsilon \sum_{\sigma=0}^{x} \sigma \tag{6}$$

These N equations represent the δ_x's ($x=1,2,3 \ldots N$) as functions of the parameters δ_0, r and ε and the observed quantities x and q_x. These three parameters define the reference circle, C. They may be evaluated by any of the statistical methods normally used for evaluation of parameters. If the method of averages (SCARBOROUGH [1930]) is to be used with equal weights, for the case illustrated in fig. 12a ($N=7$), the three condition equations

$$3\delta_0 + 3\delta_1 + 2\delta_2 = \delta_2 + 3\delta_3 + 3\delta_4 + \delta_5 = 2\delta_5 + 3\delta_6 + 3\delta_7 = 0 \tag{7}$$

must be added to eq. (6). Eqs. (6) and (7) represent 10 equations with 10 unknowns from which all δ's can be evaluated.

If the method of least squares is used for evaluating the parameters of eqs. (6) the equations of condition, for the case of $N+1$ reference points, are

$$\sum_{\sigma=0}^{N} \delta_\sigma = \sum_{\sigma=0}^{N} \sigma\delta_\sigma = \tfrac{1}{2} \sum_{\sigma=0}^{N} \sigma(\sigma+1)\delta_\sigma = 0 \tag{8}$$

and for the case illustrated above, where $N=7$, they are

$$\delta_0 + \delta_1 + \delta_2 + \delta_3 + \delta_4 + \delta_5 + \delta_6 + \delta_7 = 0$$
$$\delta_1 + 2\delta_2 + 3\delta_3 + 4\delta_4 + 5\delta_5 + 6\delta_6 + 7\delta_7 = 0 \tag{9}$$
$$\delta_1 + 3\delta_2 + 6\delta_3 + 10\delta_4 + 15\delta_5 + 21\delta_6 + 28\delta_7 = 0$$

On solving the 10 equations of (6) and (9), we have the deviations of the wave front from a best fitting reference sphere.

13. Separation of double stars

An interferometer for measuring the separation of double stars is shown in fig. 13

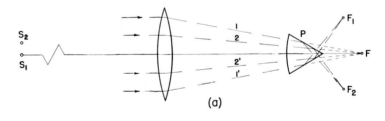

(a)

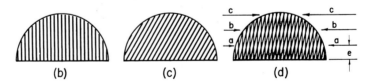

(b)   (c)   (d)

Fig. 13. Double star interferometer.
Figs. b, c, and d represent, respectively, interference fringes by a star on axis, a star off axis and a double star.

It is formed by replacing the eyepiece of an astronomical telescope with a modified Köster's double image prism, P. The center of curvature of the prism's curved entrance face is located near the focus, F, of the telescope. The prism is adjusted so that its dividing plane coincides with the axis of the telescope and is normal to the plane through F and the two stars. When the telescope is pointed at the double star, virtual images of it are formed near F and two real images of both stars are formed at F_1

and F_2. An observer's eye, located at F_1 or F_2 and focused on the objective, will observe fringes of interference. These fringes are produced by the interference of pairs of rays 1 and 1', 2 and 2', etc. which are symmetrical with respect to the dividing plane.

The observer sees the lower half of the lens inverted and coinciding with the upper half. Each star produces its own set of fringes. The angle that the fringes make with the normal to the dividing plane are directly related (SAUNDERS [1963b]) to the angular displacement of the source from the dividing plane. Since the angular displacement is different for the two stars the corresponding fringes will also be at different angles.

A single star, S_1, on the axis and consequently in the dividing plane produces a single set of fringes normal to the dividing plane (fig. 13b). A second star, S_2, that is slightly outside the dividing plane, will produce a second set of fringes that make a small angle with the first mentioned set (fig. 13c). The two stars together form the two sets of fringes shown in fig. 13d.

The two sets of fringes intersect along parallel and equally separated lines aa, bb, etc., where the difference in order of interference is 1, 2, etc., respectively. These lines of intersection remain fixed for changes in the position of the double star relative to the axis of the telescope.

If we let eQ equal the observed distance from the dividing plane to any point at which the difference in order of interference is Q, the corresponding angular separation, θ, between two two stars is (SAUNDERS [1964])

$$\theta = \frac{Q\lambda}{2eQ} = \frac{\lambda}{2e}.$$

Since the resolution of a telescope (ROBERTSON [1929]) is approximately 1.22 λ/A (where A is the aperture), a double star that is barely resolved will produce sets of fringes with their 1st line of intersection, aa, well inside the margin of the objective. Consequently, the angular separation of a double star that is barely resolved by a given objective, can be measured with considerable accuracy. The accuracy of the measured angle is proportional to the accuracy with which the distance e can be measured. Double stars that are easily resolved by a telescope will produce fringes with higher order differences. If the largest observed order difference is Q, the corresponding value eQ can be measured approximately Q times as accurate as for $Q=1$, with a corresponding increase in accuracy of the angle.

The visibility of the fringes in this interferometer differs considerably from that in the Michelson stellar interferometer (CANDLER [1951]). The Michelson fringes are severely affected by variations in the phase of the light from all parts of the two transmitting slits. This variation is due mainly to atmospheric turbidity but, to a lesser extent, to imperfections in the objective. The contrast in the fringes of the double star interferometer is not affected by imperfections in the objective and would not be affected by atmospheric turbidity if an instantaneous photograph could be taken of them. Due to the persistency of vision of the eye, contrast in the fringe pattern appears to be affected by atmospheric turbidity if the resultant movement of the fringes is excessive.

References

BARRELL, H., 1951, J. Opt. Soc. Am. **41**, 295.

BARRELL, H. and R. MARRINER, 1948, Brit. Sci. News **2** (17), 130.

BATES, W. J., 1947, Proc. Phys. Soc. (London) **59**, 940.

BRITTAN, K. W. and K. J. HABELL, 1958, The measurement of angles, in:
    P. MOLLET, ed., Optics in metrology (Pergamon Press, London) p. 141.

CANDLER, C., 1951, Modern interferometers (Hilger and Watts, London) p. 235.

EMERSON, W. B., 1952, J. Res. Natl. Bur. Std. **49**, 241; RP2359.

ENGELHARD, E., 1957, Natl. Bur. Std. Circular **581**, 1.

FIZEAU, H., 1866, Ann. Physik **128**, 564.

HUME, K. S., 1950a, Engineering metrology (McDonald and Co., London) p. 135.

HUME, K. S., 1950b, Engineering metrology (McDonald and Co., London) p. 177.

JENKINS, F. A. and H. E. WHITE, 1957, Fundamentals of optics, 3rd ed. (McGraw-Hill Book Co.,
    New York) p. 256.

LUCKIESH, M., L. L. HALLADAY and R. H. SINDEN, 1922, J. Franklin Inst. **194**, 251.

PÉRARD, A., 1932, Trav. Mém. Bur. Intern. Poids Mesures **19**.

PEROT, A. and CH. FABRY, 1899, Ann. Chim. Phys. **16**, 289.

PLATZECK, R. and E. GAVIOLA, 1939, J. Opt. Soc. Am. **29**, 487.

PORTER, R. W., 1933, in: Amateur telescope making, 3rd ed. (Scientific American Publ. Co., New
    York) p. 55.

ROBERTSON, J. K., 1929, Introduction to physical optics (D. Van Nostrand Co., New York) p. 234.

ROTHEN, A., 1945, Rev. Sci. Instr. **16**, 26.

SAUNDERS, J. B., 1939, J. Res. Natl. Bur. Std. **23**, 194; RP1227.

SAUNDERS, J. B., 1945a, J. Res. Natl. Bur. Std. **35**, 157; RP1668.

SAUNDERS, J. B., 1945b, J. Res. Natl. Bur. Std. **35**, 167; RP1668.

SAUNDERS, J. B., 1954, J. Opt. Soc. Am. **44**, 664.

SAUNDERS, J. B., 1957, J. Res. Natl. Bur. Std. **58**, 21; RP2729.

SAUNDERS, J. B., 1961, J. Res. Natl. Bur. Std. **65B**, 239.

SAUNDERS, J. B., 1963a, J. Res. Natl. Bur. Std. **67C**, 203.

SAUNDERS, J. B., 1963b, J. Res. Natl. Bur. Std. **67C**, 307.

SAUNDERS, J. B., 1964, J. Res. Natl. Bur. Std. **68C**, 155.

SAUNDERS, J. B. and J. V. MCDERMOTT, 1964, J. Res. Natl. Bur. Std. **68C**, 83.

SCARBOROUGH, J. B., 1930, Numerical mathematical analysis (Johns Hopkins Press, Baltimore, Md.).

STRONG, J., 1958, Concepts of classical optics (Freeman and Co., San Francisco) p. 203.

TILTON, L. W., 1929, J. Res. Natl. Bur. Std. **2**, 909; RP64.

TILTON, L. W., 1931, J. Res. Natl. Bur. Std. **6**, 59; RP262.

TILTON, L. W., 1935, J. Res. Natl. Bur. Std. **14**, 393; RP776.

TOOL, A. I., D. B. LLOYD and G. E. MERRITT, 1930, J. Res. Natl. Bur. Std. **5**, 635; RP219.

VINCENT-GEISSE, J. and J. LECOMTE, 1962, Appl. Opt. **1**, 575.

VON BÜNNAGEL, R., 1956, Z. Angew. Physik **8**, 342.

WILSON, Jr., E. B., 1952, An introduction to scientific research (McGraw-Hill Book Co., New York).

WINTERBOTTOM, A. B., 1946, Trans. Faraday Soc. **42**, 487.

CHAPTER 2

ISOTROPIC AND ANISOTROPIC MEDIA

APPLICATION OF ANISOTROPIC MATERIALS TO INTERFEROMETRY

M. FRANÇON

Sorbonne et Institut d'Optique, Paris

CONTENTS

Contents continued overleaf

Contents, continued

Introduction

This first part, on the propagation of waves in isotropic and anisotropic media, deals only with essential points and is not intended as a complete survey of the subject. In it we develop the general ideas and give the results needed for the practical applications described in the second part. The equations required in the general application are not derived but sufficient explanations are given as to how these equations are arrived at.

The second part consists of a detailed study of polarization interferometry. We give formulae and numerical results which can be used in designing apparatus.

THE PROPAGATION OF A PLANE WAVE IN ISOTROPIC AND IN ANISOTROPIC MEDIA

1. Maxwell's equations

According to Maxwell's electromagnetic theory, light is a simultaneous propagation of electric and magnetic fields. This theory depends essentially on the two fundamental equations of electromagnetism. The following symbols will be used in the equations:

E, the electric field,

D, the electric induction,

H, the magnetic field,

B, the magnetic induction

The first equation is a differential form of Faraday's law; it is written

$$\text{rot } E = -\frac{\partial B}{\partial t}. \tag{1}$$

It states that a region containing a field of varying magnetic induction B contains also an electric field E. The second equation expresses the fundamental law of the formation of magnetic fields by currents:

$$\text{rot } H = J, \tag{2}$$

where J is the current density. Maxwell postulated that if there is a dielectric medium forming part of the circuit then a current must be considered to flow through the dielectric in a fictitious form, called the displacement current. This is to be characterized by a displacement current density given by

$$J_{\text{D}} = \frac{\partial D}{\partial t}. \tag{3}$$

The concept of a displacement current is, of course, implied by the view that a condenser does not constitute a break in a circuit in which a varying current is flowing. The magnetic properties of this current are similar to those of an ordinary current; thus it produces a magnetic field and eq. (2) must then be written

$$\mathrm{rot}\ \boldsymbol{H} = \boldsymbol{J} + \frac{\partial \boldsymbol{D}}{\partial t}. \tag{4}$$

Thus a varying electric field in space gives rise to a magnetic field; but the magnetic field which did not previously exist has increased with time, and so according to eq. (1) it produces an electric field. Eqs. (1) and (3) show that the two phenomena, the varying electric and magnetic fields, are complementary. Eqs. (1) and (3) are supplemented by two further equations. If we write that the flux of the vector $\boldsymbol{D}$ across a closed surface S is equal to the sum of the charges inside S we have

$$\mathrm{div}\ \boldsymbol{D} = \varrho, \tag{5}$$

where ϱ is the charge density. Finally we write that the flux of the vector $\boldsymbol{B}$ entering a closed surface S is equal to the outgoing flux (assuming no free magnetic charge), giving

$$\mathrm{div}\ \boldsymbol{B} = 0. \tag{5a}$$

Eqs. (1), (4), (5) and (5a) are Maxwell's equations. They are expressed in the rationalized MKSA system of units and they hold good in all media.

2. Isotropic dielectric media

In dielectric media we have $\boldsymbol{J} = 0$ and $\varrho = 0$. If the medium is isotropic there are linear relations between $\boldsymbol{D}$ and $\boldsymbol{E}$ and between $\boldsymbol{B}$ and $\boldsymbol{H}$, so we have

$$\boldsymbol{D} = \varepsilon \boldsymbol{E}, \qquad \boldsymbol{B} = \mu \boldsymbol{H}, \tag{6}$$

where ε and μ are the permittivity and permeability of the medium. Maxwell's equations are then written

$$\mathrm{rot}\ \boldsymbol{E} = -\mu \frac{\partial \boldsymbol{H}}{\partial t}, \tag{7}$$

$$\mathrm{rot}\ \boldsymbol{H} = \varepsilon \frac{\partial \boldsymbol{E}}{\partial t}, \tag{8}$$

$$\mathrm{div}\ \boldsymbol{E} = 0, \tag{9}$$

$$\mathrm{div}\ \boldsymbol{H} = 0. \tag{10}$$

On eliminating $\boldsymbol{H}$ between eqs. (7) and (8) we have

$$\nabla^2 \boldsymbol{E} = \varepsilon \mu \frac{\partial^2 \boldsymbol{E}}{\partial t^2}, \tag{11}$$

which is the classical equation of wave motion. Maxwell's equations thus show that a varying electric field and its accompanying varying magnetic field do not remain localized in one region of space, i.e. there is a propagation of the electromagnetic field. Several experimental facts, for example polarization by reflection at an air–glass interface, show that the effects of visible light may be ascribed to the electric field vector.

The above results do not involve the functional dependence of E on the time t. We choose a harmonic time dependence which gives a simple explanation of interference phenomena; then E can be written in complex notation as follows:

$$E = E_s e^{j\omega t}, \tag{12}$$

where ω is the angular frequency or pulsation and E_s is a complex number which contains the phase of the vibration. The actual value of E is obtained by taking the real part of (12). The advantage of the complex notation is that complicated mathematical linear operations can be carried out on the complex function and the physical magnitude is always given by the real part of the final expression.

3. Propagation of a plane wave in an dielectric isotropic medium

In what follows we discuss only plane waves parallel to the plane yOz (fig. 1). By a plane wave Σ we mean that E_s is the same at all points of Σ, so that E depends only on the variable x. Then $\nabla^2 E_s$ reduces to $d^2 E_s/dx^2$ and on putting

$$v = (\varepsilon\mu)^{-\frac{1}{2}} \tag{13}$$

the equation of wave motion (11) reduces to the differential equation

$$\frac{d^2 E_s}{dx^2} + \frac{\omega^2}{v^2} E_s = 0; \tag{14}$$

the solution of this equation is

$$E_s = E_m e^{j(\pm \omega x/v + \varphi)},$$

where E_m and φ are two constants. The constant v is the velocity of propagation of the electromagnetic wave. From (12) the light vibration can be written

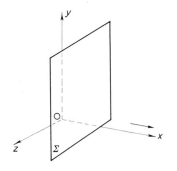

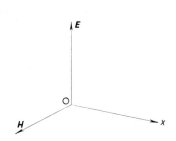

Fig. 1. Plane wave Σ travelling in the direction Ox.

Fig. 2. Configuration of the vectors E and H in the plane of the wave.

$$E = E_m e^{j\varphi} e^{j\omega(t \pm x/v)} = A e^{j\omega(t \pm x/v)}. \tag{15}$$

Furthermore, since E_s is independent of y and z, eq. (9) shows that the component of E_s parallel to Ox is zero: the electric field lies in the plane of the wave, or, the vibrations are transverse.

In eq. (15) we take the negative sign for a wave propagated in the direction Ox, i.e. in the direction of increasing x-values, because we find that a crest which was at the origin at time $t - x/v$ arrives at x at time t. From eq. (15) the components of the vibration in the plane of the wave are

$$E_x = 0, \qquad E_y = A_y e^{j\omega(t - x/v)}, \qquad E_z = A_z e^{j\omega(t - x/v)}; \tag{16}$$

these equations represent a monochromatic plane wave of frequency $v = \omega/2\pi$ propagated in the Ox-direction. This is called a progressive wave. The velocity with which the planes of equal phase are displaced is the velocity of propagation of the wave (the wave or phase velocity). From eq. (7), which relates E and H, it can be seen that H lies in the plane of the wave and is perpendicular to E (fig. 2). We have

$$H = (\varepsilon/\mu)^{\frac{1}{2}} E. \tag{17}$$

The velocity of the wave is given by (13); we have in vacuum

$$c = (\varepsilon_0 \mu_0)^{-\frac{1}{2}} = 3 \times 10^8 \text{m/sec}.$$

It was the equality of the velocities of electromagnetic waves and of light which led Maxwell to conclude that light is an electromagnetic wave motion. In a medium having the constants ε and μ we have $v = (\varepsilon\mu)^{-\frac{1}{2}}$, and the refractive index of the medium, which is the ratio of the velocity c in vacuum to the velocity v in the medium, is given by

$$n = c/v = (\varepsilon\mu/\varepsilon_0 \mu_0)^{\frac{1}{2}}.$$

In practice $\mu \approx \mu_0$ and if ε_r is the relative permittivity of the medium we have

$$n \approx (\varepsilon/\varepsilon_0)^{\frac{1}{2}} = \varepsilon_r^{\frac{1}{2}} \quad \text{or} \quad n^2 = \varepsilon_r. \tag{18}$$

Thus electromagnetic theory yields a relation between the refractive index and the dielectric constant of a medium.

Maxwell's equations as developed to this point do not predict the dispersion of transparent media, i.e. the variation of n with wavelength. In order to explain dispersion phenomena we have to add to Maxwell's equations terms containing frequencies corresponding to the maxima of the absorption bands of the medium. Dispersion and absorption are in fact two linked effects, the former depending closely on the latter.

4. Energy transmitted by a plane wave in a dielectric isotropic medium

It is shown in electrical theory that the electromagnetic energy contained in a volume dV is given by

$$dW = (\tfrac{1}{2}\varepsilon E^2 + \tfrac{1}{2}\mu H^2)dV; \tag{19}$$

from (17) it follows that dW is a function of E^2:

$$dW = \varepsilon E^2 dV; \tag{20}$$

now the amount of energy crossing a surface element dS parallel to the plane of the wave in time dt is that contained in a cylinder of volume $v\,dt\,dS$, so that

$$dW = \varepsilon E^2 v\,dt\,dS. \tag{21}$$

But E is a periodic function of time which can be expressed in the real form $E = E_0 \sin \omega t$. Substituting this in (21) and integrating it follows that the average energy carried by the wave is proportional to E_0^2, that is, to the square of the amplitude of the vibration.

Alternatively, if we calculate the vector product $\boldsymbol{P} = \boldsymbol{E} \wedge \boldsymbol{H}$ we have, from (17),

$$P = \varepsilon E^2 v, \tag{22}$$

but (21) also gives, with $dS = 1$,

$$dW/dt = \varepsilon E^2 v; \tag{23}$$

here dW/dt represents the electromagnetic energy flux per unit area. Comparing this with (22) we see that $\boldsymbol{P}$ is the electromagnetic energy flux vector. The flux lines of the vector $\boldsymbol{P}$ are the trajectories of the energy, i.e., the light rays, and these are normals to the wave surfaces. The vector $\boldsymbol{P}$ is called the Poynting vector and it forms a right-handed system of axes with $\boldsymbol{E}$ and $\boldsymbol{H}$ (fig. 3).

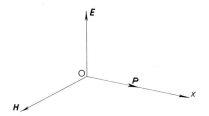

Fig. 3. Configuration of the vectors $\boldsymbol{E}$ and $\boldsymbol{H}$ and of the Poynting vector $\boldsymbol{P}$.

5. The light vibration. Natural light

The end of the vector representing the electric field describes a curve in space of which the projection on the plane of the wave is given by eqs. (16). To obtain the actual electric field we take the real parts of eqs. (16). From (15) we can put

$$A_y = E_{my}e^{j\varphi_y}, \qquad A_z = E_{mz}e^{j\varphi_z}, \tag{24}$$

and on putting $\tau = \omega(t - x/v)$ the actual electric field is

$$E_x = 0, \qquad E_y = E_{my} \cos(\tau + \varphi_y), \qquad E_z = E_{mz} \cos(\tau + \varphi_z). \tag{25}$$

Eqs. (25) represent an ellipse, as can be seen by eliminating the time t. Thus in the most general case the light vibration is elliptical. The light is actually emitted by individual atoms over very short periods of time θ. If we observe for a time which is large compared to θ, as is always the case in practice, the first elliptical vibration is successively replaced by others having no definite phase relation with it. This implies that the quantities E_{my}, E_{mz} and φ_y, φ_z which describe the ellipse vary in a completely random fashion from one ellipse to the next. There is thus no steady relation between

$$E_y = E_{my} \cos{(\tau + \varphi_y)} \quad \text{and} \quad E_z = E_{mz} \cos{(\tau + \varphi_z)} \tag{26}$$

on the scale of possible observing times, since these are long compared to θ, i.e. the vibrations E_y and E_z are incoherent. We are then led to consider time averages in order to represent observable effects. Returning to the expressions given in (16), the intensities of these two vibrations will be proportional to the means

$$\overline{E_y E_y^*} = \overline{E_{my}^2} \quad \text{and} \quad \overline{E_z E_z^*} = \overline{E_{mz}^2}.$$

We describe the natural light emitted by a light source in this way. Since the choice of the two directions Oy and Oz is arbitrary the light can be considered as formed by two perpendicular incoherent vibrations of equal intensity $\overline{E_{my}^2} = \overline{E_{mz}^2}$.

6. The plane-polarized plane wave

The optical devices known as polarizers transmit only one of the two components described above, E_y or E_z. The plane wave is said to be plane-polarized.

7. Anisotropic dielectric media

We consider now a medium which is magnetically isotropic ($B = \mu H$) but electrically anisotropic. Its permittivity depends on the direction of propagation of the wave and, except in certain special directions, D is not parallel to E. There are three such directions for which D is parallel to E in an anisotropic medium; taking a system of coordinate axes along these three directions we have

$$D_x = \varepsilon_x E_x, \qquad D_y = \varepsilon_y E_y, \qquad D_z = \varepsilon_z E_z. \tag{27}$$

Here the quantities ε_x, ε_y, ε_z are not the components of a vector, they are the principal dielectric constants of the medium. For all other directions D and E are not parallel. Maxwell's equations (1), (4), (5) and (5a) are valid in an anisotropic dielectric but we cannot write as before div $E = 0$. Instead we have from (5)

$$\text{div } D = 0, \tag{28}$$

and, as before,

$$\text{div } H = 0. \tag{29}$$

Thus the vectors D and H lie in the plane of the wave but E is no longer in this plane.

In an anisotropic medium the wave velocity is a function of direction and the equation of wave motion no longer takes the simple form (11); this latter is valid only in isotropic media. To illustrate the difference between these two cases we now rewrite eq. (11) in a new form. Since $\nabla^2 E$ reduces to $d^2 E_s/dx^2$ we can calculate this derivative from eqs. (16) and we then write eq. (11) for the component E_y as follows

$$- \frac{\omega_2^2}{v^2} E_y = -\varepsilon\mu\omega^2 E_y, \tag{30}$$

intentionally retaining the negative signs. As might be expected, eq. (30) reduces to an identity.

In the case of anisotropic media the above two terms still occur but in addition the dielectric constant ε depends on the direction considered. Thus in eq. (30) ε must be replaced by the principal dielectric constant ε_y for the axis Oy, but also another term appears since div E is now not zero. Let α, β, γ be the direction cosines (fig. 4) of the normal OM to the plane of the wave Σ. We know that the plane Σ

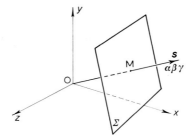

Fig. 4. Plane wave Σ travelling in an arbitrary direction s.

contains D and H but not E. Then classical theory shows that in an anisotropic medium eq. (30) for the component E_y is to be replaced by the following equation:

$$- \frac{\omega^2}{v^2} E_y + \frac{\omega^2 \beta}{v^2}(\alpha E_x + \beta E_y + \gamma E_z) = -\varepsilon_y\mu\omega^2 E_y. \tag{31}$$

There are two similar equations for E_x and E_z. It can be seen that a second term has been added to the left-hand side of eq. (30) to generalize it to anisotropic media. In this term the factor $\alpha E_x + \beta E_y + \gamma E_z$ is the scalar product $E \cdot s$ of the vector E and a unit vector s along OM. This factor is zero for an isotropic medium since E lies in the plane of the wave and is therefore perpendicular to s. In an anisotropic dielectric this factor is not zero and eq. (31) can thus be written

$$- \frac{\omega^2}{v^2} E_y + \frac{\omega^2 \beta}{v^2}(E \cdot s) = -\varepsilon_y\mu\omega^2 E_y, \tag{32}$$

or, using (27),

$$\frac{D_y}{\varepsilon_y v^2} - \frac{\beta}{v^2}(E \cdot s) = \mu D_y. \tag{33}$$

Writing down two similar equations for D_x and D_z we note the occurrence of the expressions

$$v_x^2 = (\varepsilon_x \mu)^{-1}, \qquad v_y^2 = (\varepsilon_y \mu)^{-1}, \qquad v_z^2 = (\varepsilon_z \mu)^{-1}; \tag{34}$$

these are the principal velocities of waves propagated along the three axes; they are not, of course, components of v. On introducing the principal velocities and writing down the other equations analogous to (33) we have

$$D_x = \frac{-\alpha}{v^2 - v_x^2} \frac{E \cdot s}{\mu}, \qquad D_y = \frac{-\beta}{v^2 - v_y^2} \frac{E \cdot s}{\mu}, \qquad D_z = \frac{-\gamma}{v^2 - v_z^2} \frac{E \cdot s}{\mu}; \tag{35}$$

but D is perpendicular to s, so the condition that the scalar product $D \cdot s$ is zero gives

$$\alpha D_x + \beta D_y + \gamma D_z = 0. \tag{36}$$

From eqs. (35) we have therefore

$$\frac{\alpha^2}{v^2 - v_x^2} + \frac{\beta^2}{v^2 - v_y^2} + \frac{\gamma^2}{v^2 - v_z^2} = 0. \tag{37}$$

This is Fresnel's equation giving the phase velocity v of a plane wave travelling in the direction s. It is a second-degree equation with roots $\pm v'$ and $\pm v''$; the ambiguous signs indicate that the wave can travel in either direction.

8. The configuration of the vectors D, E, H and P

Starting from Maxwell's equations (1) and (4) it can be shown that the configuration of the vectors D, E, H and P is as in fig. 5. We saw that the wave surface Σ contains

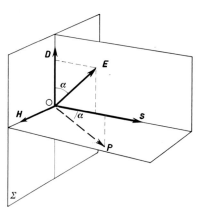

Fig. 5. Configuration of the vectors D, H, E, s and P in an anisotropic medium.

D and H. The vector $P = E \wedge H$, which still represents the magnitude and direction of electromagnetic energy flow, is in the plane (D, s). The vector E is no longer in the wave surface but it is in the plane (D, s). In an anisotropic medium it is preferable to identify the light vibration with D rather than with E in order to preserve transversality to s. The direction of the vector P, which represents the light ray, shows that in an anisotropic medium the ray and the wave-normal are not parallel. Since P is normal to the plane (E, H) and s to the plane (D, H), the angle between s and P is equal to the angle between E and D.

9. Privileged directions

Eqs. (35) show that two possible velocities v' and v'' in general correspond to a given direction s. Two vectors D' and D'' corresponding respectively to v' and v'' are also found. Consequently if the incident disturbance is along D' or D'' it remains plane-polarized on traversing the anisotropic medium and is not changed in any way. Let D'_x, D'_y, D'_z and D''_x, D''_y, D''_z be the components of these two vectors; from eqs. (35) we obtain

$$D' \cdot D'' = D'_x D''_x + D'_y D''_y + D'_z D''_z = 0.$$

The two directions of D' and D'' are therefore perpendicular and they are special or privileged directions in the sense that waves with electric inductions in either of these directions are unchanged on propagation through the medium.

Now consider an incident rectilinear vibration D in an arbitrary direction, D lying in the plane of the wavefront; the incident vibration can be resolved into two components which are initially in phase and which are directed along D' and D'' respectively. A thickness e of the anisotropic medium corresponds to an optical path length

$$n'e = \frac{c}{v'} e \tag{38}$$

for the component along D', where v' is the wave velocity for this direction and n' is the corresponding refractive index. Similarly for the component along D'' the optical path length is

$$n''e = \frac{c}{v''} e. \tag{39}$$

The anisotropic medium thus produces a path difference between the vibrations in the privileged directions which is equal to

$$\delta = (n' - n'')e \tag{40}$$

The corresponding phase difference is

$$\varphi = \frac{2\pi\delta}{\lambda} = \frac{2\pi(n' - n'')e}{\lambda} = \omega e \left(\frac{1}{v'} - \frac{1}{v''} \right). \tag{41}$$

10. Phase velocity and ray velocity

At time t_1 the wave is at Σ_1 (fig. 6) and at time t_2 it is at Σ_2. The path along the normal to the wave is $O_1 O_2$ and the wave velocity is

$$v = \frac{O_1 O_2}{t_2 - t_1}.$$

It is this quantity which occurs in the preceding formulae as the phase or wave velocity. In addition a ray velocity is defined as follows: Along the ray OP, i.e. in the direction of the Poynting vector, the path travelled is OP and the corresponding velocity is

$$v_r = \frac{OP}{t_2 - t_1} = \frac{v}{\cos \alpha}. \tag{42}$$

This is the ray velocity, i.e. the velocity of propagation of the disturbance not along the wave normal but along the ray.

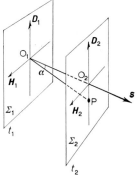 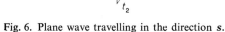 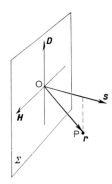

Fig. 6. Plane wave travelling in the direction s.   Fig. 7. Determination of the wave surface from the ray velocity in the direction OP.

11. The wave surface in a uniaxial medium

Instead of calculating the velocity v of the wave along the normal s we can carry out the calculation of section 7 for the ray velocity v_r, along the direction OP (cf. fig. 7). Let r be a unit vector along OP, having components r_x, r_y, r_z; Fresnel's equation is then replaced by

$$\frac{r_x^2 v_x^2}{v_r^2 - v_x^2} + \frac{r_y^2 v_y^2}{v_r^2 - v_y^2} + \frac{r_z^2 v_z^2}{v_r^2 - v_z^2} = 0, \tag{43}$$

an equation giving the velocity v_r as a function of the direction of the light ray OP. Suppose the light to be emitted from a point O: the locus of points reached by the light disturbance after a certain time t is, by definition, the wave surface. In order to obtain this surface we mark off in every direction a length on the ray OP equal to the velocity v_r in that direction as given by eq. (43). Two of the principal dielectric constants are equal for a large number of anisotropic substances; these are the uniaxial media. We consider only such media in what follows.

Suppose, for example, that $\varepsilon_y = \varepsilon_z$ so that

$$v_y = (\mu \varepsilon_y)^{-\frac{1}{2}} = v_z = (\mu \varepsilon_z)^{-\frac{1}{2}}. \tag{44}$$

To find the equation of the wave surface in this uniaxial medium we start from the origin O (fig. 8) and take a distance OV along the light ray OP equal to the velocity v_r in this direction. The coordinates of V are $x=r_x v_r$, $y=r_y v_r$, $z=r_z v_r$ with

$$x^2+y^2+z^2 + (r_x^2+r_y^2+r_z^2)v_r^2 = v_r^2,$$

since $r_x^2+r_y^2+r_z^2=1$. In eq. (43) we replace r_x, r_y, r_z by x/v_r, y/v_r, z/v_r and v_r^2 by $x^2+y^2+z^2$. On putting $R^2=x^2+y^2+z^2$ we have

$$(R^2 - v_y^2)[x^2 v_x^2(R^2 - v_y^2)+y^2 v_y^2(R^2 - v_x^2)+z^2 v_y^2(R^2 - v_x^2) = 0. \tag{45}$$

We take first $R^2 - v_y^2 = 0$ which gives

$$x^2+y^2+z^2 = v_y^2, \tag{46}$$

the equation of a sphere. The factor in square brackets in eq. (45) gives

$$\frac{x^2}{v_y^2} + \frac{y^2+z^2}{v_x^2} = 1, \tag{47}$$

an ellipsoid of revolution. The sphere (46) and the ellipsoid (47) are the two sheets of the wave surfaces. They are illustrated in fig. 9.

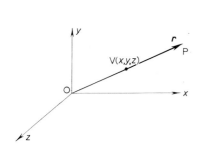

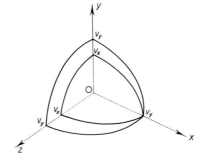

Fig. 8. Location of the point V on the wave surface, OV being the ray velocity.

Fig. 9. Wave surface in a uniaxial medium.

Since x, y, z are the coordinates of the extremity of the vector OV (fig. 8) which represents the ray velocity, it can be seen that along Ox the two ray velocities are equal to the wave velocity v_y. The direction Ox is the optic axis of the uniaxial medium. A plane wave perpendicular to the optic axis Ox is propagated as in an isotropic medium.

The spherical sheet of the wave surface is the ordinary wave surface and the ellipsoidal sheet is the extraordinary wave surface. We put

$$v_y = v_o, \qquad v_x = v_e,$$

and

$$n_o = c/v_o, \qquad n_e = c/v_e. \tag{48}$$

Then n_o is the ordinary index and n_e the extraordinary index. For quartz we have $v_o > v_e$ $(n_o < n_e)$ and it is said to be a positive uniaxial medium; for Iceland spar (calcite), $v_o < v_e$ $(n_o > n_e)$, and the crystal is negative. Figs. 10 and 11 represent the

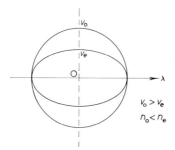

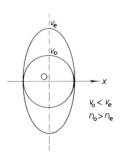

Fig. 10. Section of the wave surface by a plane through the optic axis for a positive medium, e.g. quartz.

Fig. 11. Section of the wave surface by a plane through the optic axis for a negative medium, e.g. calcite.

intersections of the wave surfaces with a plane passing through the optic axis Ox.

In what follows we shall be concerned only with plane waves; we now show how the usual description of wave propagation in isotropic media can be extended to the case of an anisotropic medium. The wavefront Σ_e (fig. 12), corresponding to the

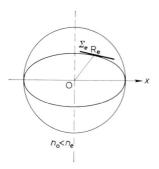

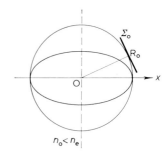

Fig. 12. The plane of the extraordinary wave Σ_e is tangent at R_e to the extraordinary sheet of the wave surface.

Fig. 13. The plane of the ordinary wave Σ_o is tangent at R_o to the ordinary sheet of the wave surface.

direction OR_e of the extraordinary ray is tangent at R_e to the extraordinary wave surface. For the direction OR_o of the ordinary ray (fig. 13) the wavefront Σ_o is obviously normal to OR_o and is tangential to the ordinary wave surface.

12. The index ellipsoid in a uniaxial medium

We now determine how the refractive index varies as a function of the direction of the incident light. By means of eqs. (35), in which we had $v_y = v_z$ (uniaxial medium) we form the scalar product $s \cdot D$. The product vanishes since D is transverse to s, so we have

$$\frac{D_x^2}{n_x^2} + \frac{D_y^2 + D_z^2}{n_y^2} - \frac{D^2}{n} = 0. \tag{49}$$

Here n_x and n_y are the principal indices corresponding to the axes Ox and Oy. The index n is that corresponding to any chosen direction. The principal indices are not,

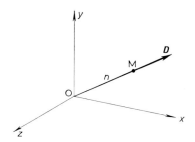

Fig. 14. If $OM = n$, the locus of M is the index ellipsoid.

of course, components of n. We now take a length $OM = n$ along D (fig. 14). If x, y, z are the coordinates of M we have

$$\frac{x^2}{D_x^2} = \frac{y^2}{D_y^2} = \frac{z^2}{D_z^2} = \frac{n^2}{D^2}$$

since $n^2 = x^2 + y^2 + z^2$. This gives

$$\frac{x^2}{n_x^2} + \frac{y^2 + z^2}{n_y^2} = 1,$$

and putting as before $n_o = n_y$ and $n_e = n_x$ we have

$$\frac{x^2}{n_e^2} + \frac{y^2 + z^2}{n_o^2} = 1. \tag{50}$$

This is the refractive index ellipsoid for a uniaxial medium. It gives the index $n^2 = x^2 + y^2 + z^2$ as a function of the direction of vibration D. The ellipsoid has revolution symmetry about the optic axis Ox (fig. 15).

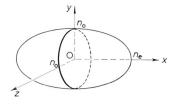

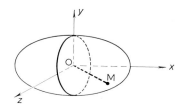

Fig. 15. The index ellipsoid for a uniaxial medium.

Fig. 16. The index ellipsoid for a uniaxial medium.

13. Orientation of a plane wave in relation to the index ellipsoid in a uniaxial medium. Directions of the privileged vibrations

Let OM (fig. 16) be any direction of the vibration vector D; to this direction corresponds a certain refractive index. Also OM must be one of the privileged directions in the plane wave which transports OM, i.e., D. A plane wavefront in an anisotropic medium, i.e. the plane containing D and H, is not normal to the light ray. Thus in fig. 17 the light ray OP for the wave makes an angle α with the normal to the wave surface. Thus this wavefront is called the extraordinary wavefront or wave surface. To find this wavefront we note that the ellipsoid has revolution symmetry and it is therefore permissible to turn fig. 16 round Ox so as to make OM lie in the plane of the figure (fig. 18). The direction of the normal to the wave is given by the vector s.

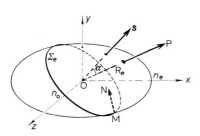

Fig. 17. Section of the index ellipsoid by a plane through the optic axis.

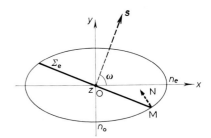

Fig. 18. Section of the index ellipsoid by a plane through the optic axis.

The direction ratios of the normal MN to the ellipsoid are x/n_e^2 and y/n_o^2, these being obtained by differentiating eq. (50) with respect to x and y. But x and y, the projections of OM, are proportional to D_x and D_y, since D lies along OM. Therefore the direction ratios of MN are proportional to D_x/n_e^2 and D_y/n_o^2, i.e. to D_x/ε_x and D_y/ε_y; these are simply the projections of E on Ox and Oy. Consequently E lies along MN and the wave surface is the plane Σ_e which passes through OM (vibration D) and is perpendicular to the plane OMN containing D and E. One of the axes of the ellipse formed by the intersection of E_e with the ellipsoid is OM, which is a special direction. The other privileged direction is the other axis of the ellipse, which falls along Oz. The vibration along Oz is perpendicular to the optic axis (minor axis of the ellipse) and it is therefore the ordinary vibration, (index n_o), as propagated in an isotropic medium. The vibration along OM (major axis of the ellipse) is the extraordinary vibration; to it corresponds an index n which is intermediate between n_o and n_e. The coordinates of M are $x = n \sin \omega$ and $y = n \cos \omega$ since OM$=n$. Substituting these values in eq. (50) we have

$$n^2 \left(\frac{\sin^2\omega}{n_e^2} + \frac{\cos^2\omega}{n_o^2} \right) = 1; \tag{51}$$

this equation gives the extraordinary index n as a function of ω.

14. The angle between the extraordinary ray and the normal to the extraordinary wavefront

Fig. 19 shows the section S_e of the extraordinary wave surface by the plane of the diagram, the same ellipse as was given in figs. 10 and 12. The ellipse $\mathscr{E}$ is the section of the index ellipsoid with the plane of the diagram as in fig. 18. The two ellipses

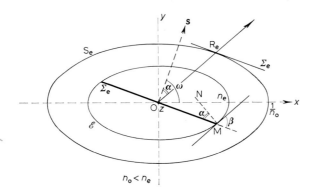

Fig. 19. Sections of the index ellipsoid $\mathscr{E}$ and of the extraordinary wave surface by a plane through the optic axis.

S_e and $\mathscr{E}$ are similar, as can be seen by putting $z=0$ in eqs. (47) and (50). The trace of the wave surface Σ_e is OM and the extraordinary ray is OR_e. The normal s to the wave surface makes an angle α with the ray OR_e. From section 8 (fig. 5) this is also the angle formed by MN (the electric field) and OM (the direction of $\boldsymbol{D}$). Let ω be the angle which the normal to the extraordinary wave makes with the optic axis. According to the classical result for curves in polar coordinates we have

$$\operatorname{tg}\alpha = \operatorname{cotg}\beta = \frac{1}{n}\frac{dn}{d\omega} = -\tfrac{1}{2}n^2\frac{dn^{-2}}{d\omega}, \tag{52}$$

and from eq. (51)

$$\operatorname{tg}\alpha = \frac{n^2}{2}\left(\frac{1}{n_o^2}-\frac{1}{n_e^2}\right)\sin 2\omega, \tag{53}$$

from which we obtain

$$\operatorname{tg}\alpha = \frac{n_e^2-n_o^2}{2(n_o^2\sin^2\omega+n_e^2\cos^2\omega)}. \tag{54}$$

The maximum value α_m of α is reached at $\omega=\tfrac{1}{4}\pi$ to a good approximation; α_m is given by

$$\operatorname{tg}\alpha_m = \frac{n_e^2-n_o^2}{n_e^2+n_o^2}. \tag{55}$$

This equation will be used later on. For quartz and calcite we have $\alpha_m=17'$ and $6°$ respectively.

15. Refracted rays in a uniaxial medium. Ray splitting

We can apply Huygens' construction to find the refracted rays in a uniaxial medium, but this involves three-dimensional geometry, since the two refracted rays are usually not in the same plane. The construction is simplified when the plane of incidence is a plane of crystal symmetry since the two refracted rays do lie in a single plane; this happens when the plane of incidence either contains the axis or is perpendicular to it. A plane containing the normal to the surface and the optic axis is called a principal section of the crystal. We proceed to apply this construction to a plate of calcite with parallel surfaces cut obliquely to the optic axis. We suppose the plane of incidence to contain the optic axis, as in fig. 20, so that the plane of the figure is a

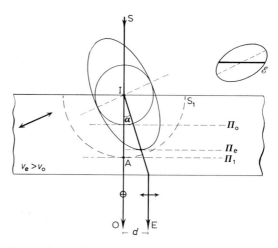

Fig. 20. Path of a ray in a calcite plate cut at an arbitrary angle to the optic axis.

principal section. Let the incident ray SI be normal to the surface and let it meet the wavefront in air S_1 at A. The plane Π_1 which is tangent at A to S is parallel to the surface of the crystal. We construct two planes parallel to Π_1 and tangent to the two sheets of the wave surface in calcite. These are the planes Π_o and Π_e. We thus obtain immediately the ordinary ray O, which is undeviated, and the extraordinary ray E. The two rays become parallel again on emerging from the plate.

We show in the figure the index ellipsoid $\mathscr{E}$ from which the two privileged directions are obtained. One of these corresponds to the ordinary vibration, perpendicular to the plane of the figure, and the other is the extraordinary vibration, parallel to the plane of the figure. If the incident light is natural it can be resolved into perpendicular incoherent component vibrations along the privileged directions. These are transmitted unchanged through the crystal but, as we saw, they travel with different velocities. The two rays O and E are polarized at right angles. The splitting d, i.e., the distance between the two rays when they emerge from the crystal plate, is important in what follows. To calculate d we note that the angle α in fig. 20 is the angle made by the extraordinary ray with the extraordinary wave surface. It is given by eq. (54). If e is the thickness of the plate we then have

$$d = \frac{e(n_e^2 - n_o^2)\sin 2\omega}{2(n_o^2\sin^2\omega + n_e^2\cos^2\omega)}. \tag{56}$$

If the crystal is cut at an angle of 45° to the optic axis we have $\omega = \tfrac{1}{4}\pi$ and if the angle of incidence is non-zero but small we can say that ω is also the angle made by the optic axis with the crystal surface. Then from (55) we have

$$d_m = e\frac{n_e^2 - n_o^2}{n_e^2 + n_o^2}. \tag{57}$$

The values of d_m for calcite and for quartz are $0.106e$ and $5 \times 10^{-3}e$ respectively.

16. Interference between the ordinary and extraordinary rays in a uniaxial crystal plate

Consider a plate of the kind described in section 15, cut at 45° to the optic axis. We saw that the incident ray emerges as two parallel rays after leaving the plate, these being the ordinary and extraordinary rays. These two rays meet at infinity and, according to the classical theory of interference, fringes localized at infinity should be observed. Referring to fig. 21, a uniform extended source S is placed at

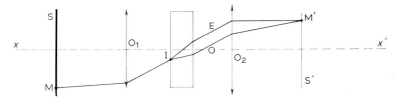

Fig. 21. The two rays O and E from L interfere at M′, giving fringes at infinity.

the focus of an objective O_1. A birefringent plate L is placed between O_1 and a second objective O_2 and the phenomena can be observed on a screen S′ placed at the focus of O_2. Let MI be any incident ray; it is split into two rays O and E by the plate L; these rays are parallel on emerging from the plate and they intersect at M′ in the focal plane of the objective O_2. Thus the disturbances transported by O and E rays should interfere at M′. The classical theory of interference of polarized light shows that this interference can occur if the plate L is placed between polarizers. The disturbances along O and E are then coherent and parallel. In fig. 21, as in the majority of figures that follow, we do not show these polarizers but it is to be understood that they are present as required. The theory of interference in polarized light shows also that the effects have maximum contrast and brightness if the two polarizers are parallel or crossed and if they are oriented at 45° to the privileged directions in the plate. Let Δ be the path difference at M′ between the rays O and E. If the plate L is between crossed polarizers the intensity at M is given by

$$I = \sin^2{(\pi\varDelta/\lambda)}, \tag{58}$$

where λ is the wavelength. Between parallel polarizers we have

$$I = \cos^2{(\pi\varDelta/\lambda)}. \tag{59}$$

We shall in what follows also have to do with crystal plates of which the surfaces are not parallel, as in fig. 22. Here the plate L is illuminated by a collimated beam from a small source S at the focus of the objective O_1. Relative to the incident ray

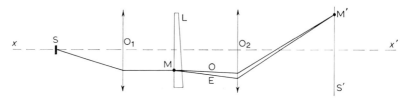

Fig. 22. The two rays O and E from L interfere at M', giving fringes localized at the image of L.

SM, the plate behaves as a prism having different refractive indices for vibrations along the two special directions. The two emerging rays O and E are not parallel; they appear to come from a point somewhere in the plate which can be taken as the point M if the plate is thin. The two rays meet at M', the image of M, after traversing the objective O_2. There is interference at M' as before and the difference between the two cases is only in the localization of the fringes. In the case of the parallel plate they are localized at infinity, i.e., in the focal plane of the objective O_2 in fig. 21. For the wedge plate they are localized at the image of the wedge, i.e., at the plate itself. Let $\varDelta$ be the path difference produced by the wedge between the rays O and E. This is the same as the path difference at M' between these two rays. This path difference $\varDelta$ depends on the position of the point M on the plate L, since the thickness of L is not uniform. The intensity I at M' is given by eq. (58) if the plate is between crossed polarizers or eq. (59) if the polarizers are parallel.

APPLICATION OF ANISOTROPIC MATERIALS TO INTERFERO-METRY

17. Introduction

In all two-beam interferometers an incident wave from the light source is split into two waves; these follow two different paths and are then superimposed, giving interference effects in the region of superimposition. Interferometers differ from each other according to the manner in which this splitting is achieved; for example, in the Michelson and Mach–Zehnder interferometers a semi-reflecting and transmitting plate at 45° to the incident beam is used. It is also possible to use a birefringent plate as a beam-splitter, so that variations in optical path through an isotropic object can be observed through the use of polarization phenomena. The principles and apparatus involved in doing this are usually simple and it is possible to use a white light source. To obtain white light fringes it is, of course, necessary to have substantially zero path difference between the interfering beams; this is quite difficult to manage with the Michelson and the Mach–Zehnder but it is very easily done with polarization interferometers which utilize quartz, because of the very weak birefringence of this material. Thus in order to observe white light fringes in an air film between glass plates (ordinary interference in natural light) the film must be only about one micron thick; a thickness variation of 0.3 μm causes one fringe displacement. With a plate of quartz, however, the thickness must change by 30 μm to produce one fringe shift. The adjustment of the apparatus is therefore much less critical.

The essential part of a polarization interferometer is the birefringent element which produces the splitting of the incident wave; these elements fall into two classes, producing respectively linear and angular splitting. We describe first the main kinds of birefringent elements and we then go on to explain the principles of the various methods of using these elements.

18. Birefringent systems with linear splitting

18.1. THE SAVART POLARISCOPE

The Savart polariscope (fig. 23) is made up of two identical plates of uniaxial material, cut with the optic axis at 45° to the surface and superimposed with the principal sections crossed. In fig. 23 we show the projection of the axis of the second plate on the plane of the figure but in fact it makes an angle of 45° with this plane.

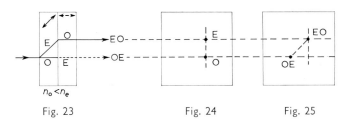

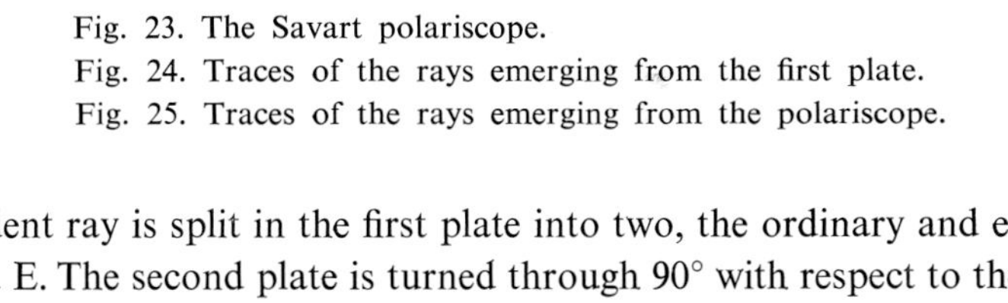

Fig. 23   Fig. 24   Fig. 25

Fig. 23. The Savart polariscope.
Fig. 24. Traces of the rays emerging from the first plate.
Fig. 25. Traces of the rays emerging from the polariscope.

The incident ray is split in the first plate into two, the ordinary and extraordinary rays, O and E. The second plate is turned through 90° with respect to the first, so the ordinary ray in the first plate becomes the extraordinary ray in the second, and vice versa. The dotted line indicates that the ray OE emerging from the second plate is not in the plane of the figure, but it is parallel to the ray EO, which *is* in this plane. These ray paths are more easily comprehended from figs. 24 and 25; a view of the trace of the rays after passing through the first plate is shown in fig. 24, the ordinary ray being at O and the extraordinary ray at E. Fig. 25 shows the trace of the rays as they emerge from the second plate; the ray EO is a prolongation of the ray E but the ray OE is displaced horizontally. The displacement of OE with respect to O is in the horizontal plane but the displacement of E with respect to O is in the vertical plane.

We now consider the system of fringes at infinity produced by the Savart polariscope; we can use fig. 21, simply replacing the plate L by the Savart polariscope Q (fig. 26).

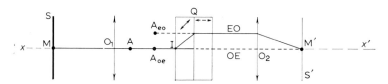

Fig. 26. The two rays OE and EO apparently coming from the two images A_{oe} and A_{eo}.

Consider an incident ray MI along the axis of the system; this involves no loss in generality. This ray is split into two rays EO and OE and, as we saw, OE is parallel to EO but is not in the plane of the diagram. Suppose the incident ray to have come from a point source A; the emerging rays EO and OE appear to have come from two images A_{oe} (corresponding to OE) and A_{eo} (for EO) and these are respectively behind and in the plane of the figure. Both images lie in the same transverse plane, so that the two paths EO and OE are equal and the effect is as if there were no plate and the two rays EO and OE came from the two sources A_{eo} and A_{oe}. The two rays are normal to the polariscope and are in phase. The same is true for any other ray emitted from M (fig. 27): the two rays EO and OE are in phase and the

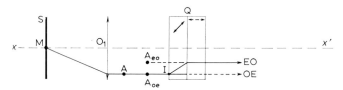

Fig. 27. The two rays OE and EO interfere in the same way, whatever the ray from M in which they originated.

amount of splitting is the same as before. The state of interference at M' (fig. 26) is the same for all rays from M; it is thus possible to study the interference effects at M' by considering only the two rays OE and EO from the two virtual sources A_{oe} and A_{eo} as in fig. 26. The interference effects at M' are as if the polariscope had been removed and the rays had originated at A_{eo} and A_{oe}.

We now consider a ray incident obliquely on the polariscope (fig. 28) from, say, a point A at the same distance from the polariscope as in fig. 26. It can be seen that if the angle of incidence i is small the two emerging rays EO and OE still appear

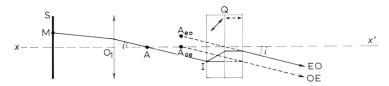

Fig. 28. The two rays OE and EO apparently pass through A_{oe} and A_{eo} if the original ray is obliquely incident.

to originate from the same points A_{eo} and A_{oe} as in fig. 26. We can show as before that the interference effects at infinity are the same for all rays with angle of incidence i, that is, all rays originating at the source point M. We need therefore consider only the two virtual sources A_{eo} and A_{oe} of fig. 28, and these are the same as in fig. 26. Thus the effects at infinity in the direction i are as if the rays came from the sources A_{eo} and A_{oe}.

To summarize, we can describe the interference effects by taking the rays as starting from the two sources A_{eo} and A_{oe} of fig. 26, the polariscope having been removed, and it can be seen from fig. 29 that we now have an analogue of Young's interference

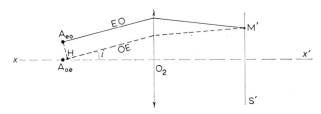

Fig. 29. The rays interfere at M' as if they passed through A_{oe} and A_{eo} for any angle of incidences to the approximation considered.

experiment; in this figure we show only the two sources A_{eo} and A_{oe} and the two rays EO and OE in a certain direction i. As in Young's experiment, the two sources A_{eo} and A_{oe} give parallel equidistant straight fringes at infinity; these fringes appear in the plane S' perpendicular to the direction $A_{eo}A_{oe}$. This is the direction containing the rays OE and EO of fig. 25, so that the fringes are at an angle of 45° to the principal sections of the polariscope plates. This analogy with Young's experiment gives immediately the orientation of the fringes. In order to calculate the angular separation of the fringes we note that the path difference between the rays in the direction i is $\Delta = A_{oe}H$. Now if $d = A_{eo}A_{oe}$ is the linear splitting produced by the polariscope we have

$$\Delta = id. \tag{60}$$

It can be seen from fig. 25 that the splitting d is $\sqrt{2}$ times that produced by a single plate, so that, from eq. (57) the splitting produced by a polariscope of thickness $2e$ will be

$$d = e\sqrt{2}\,\frac{n_e^2 - n_o^2}{n_e^2 + n_o^2}. \tag{61}$$

This gives $7 \times 10^{-3}e$ and $0.15e$ for quartz and calcite respectively. From (60) and (61) we have

$$\Delta = ie\sqrt{2} \frac{n_e^2 - n_o^2}{n_e^2 + n_o^2}. \tag{62}$$

If the polariscope is between crossed polarizers there will be a bright fringe when $\Delta = \frac{1}{2}(2K+1)\lambda$, where $K = 1, 2, 3, \ldots$, according to eq. (58), i.e. when the angle of incidence i takes values given by

$$i = (K + \tfrac{1}{2}) \frac{(n_e^2 + n_o^2)\lambda}{(n_e^2 - n_o^2)e\sqrt{2}} \qquad (K = 1, 2, 3, \ldots); \tag{63}$$

from this the angular separation between two consecutive bright or dark fringes is

$$i_f = \frac{(n_e^2 + n_o)\lambda}{(n_e^2 - n_o^2)e\sqrt{2}}. \tag{64}$$

This gives for quartz $i_f = 0.068/e$ mm

and for calcite $i_f = 0.37 \times 10^{-2}/e$ mm $\left. \right| \quad \lambda = 0.56 \ \mu m.$

18.2. THE MODIFICATION OF SAVART'S POLARISCOPE DUE TO FRANÇON

Eq. (62) is actually an approximation; a more detailed calculation shows that the right-hand side of eq. (62) is only the first term of a series development. The higher-order terms are small and can be neglected for a first approximation but if they are taken into account it appears that the fringes in the Savart polariscope are not perfectly straight. For certain applications which will be discussed later on it is desirable to have the fringes more nearly straight. Fig. 30 shows a polariscope in which the fringes are straight to the third approximation. This polariscope is made up of two identical plates cut at an angle of 45° to the optic axis and having their principal sections parallel; the two optic axes are perpendicular and a half-wave plate with its principal directions at 45° to the principal sections of the plates is interposed between them. It can be seen immediately that the rays remain in the plane of the figure and the splitting is twice that from a single plate, i.e., it is

$$d = e \frac{n_e^2 - n_o^2}{n_e^2 + n_o^2}, \tag{65}$$

or $\sqrt{2}$ times that of the Savart polariscope. From eq. (60) the path difference is

$$\Delta = ie \frac{n_e^2 - n_o^2}{n_e^2 + n_o^2}; \tag{66}$$

this is a good approximation to the third order. The angular separation between two consecutive bright or dark fringes is given by

$$i_f = \frac{(n_o^2 + n_e^2)\lambda}{2(n_o^2 - n_e^2)e}. \tag{67}$$

As in the previous section, the two rays correspond to two points A_{eo} and A_{oe} but since the rays are in the plane of the figure the fringes are oriented perpendicular to the principal sections of the polariscope.

18.3. STEEL'S POLARISCOPE WITH VARIABLE FRINGE SPACING

Let the two plates of the polariscope in fig. 30 be separated and let polarizers P_1 and P_2 be fixed to L_1 and L_2 in the usual orientations (cf. fig. 31). We suppose L_1 and L_2 to rotate about the axis xx' normal to the plates in opposite directions and at the same speed, the polarizers turning with the plates; when each plate has turned through 90° the system is as in fig. 32, and the ray paths shown at the top of the

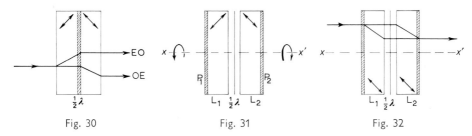

Fig. 30   Fig. 31   Fig. 32

Fig. 30. Françon's modified Savart polariscope.
Fig. 31. Steel's polariscope with variable fringe spacing.
Fig. 32. Adjustment of the polariscope of fig. 31 for zero splitting.

figure make it clear that there is no final splitting, so that the fringes at infinity are in theory infinitely broad (the analogue with Young's experiment is that as the distance between the sources tends to zero the fringe spacing tends to infinity). If we now start with the plates oriented as in fig. 32, i.e. with the principal sections parallel, and turn each through an angle α in opposite directions the angular fringe spacing is given by

$$i_f = \frac{n_o^2 + n_e^2}{n_o^2 - n_e^2} \frac{\lambda}{2e \sin \alpha}. \tag{68}$$

For $\alpha = 0$ the fringe spacing is infinite and for $\alpha = \frac{1}{2}\pi$ it is as for the polariscope of fig. 30, i.e. it is given by eq. (67).

18.4. TSURUTA'S POLARISCOPE WITH VARIABLE FRINGE SPACING

The Tsuruta polariscope is derived from a Savart polariscope divided into four identical prisms and rearranged as in fig. 33. The elements A and B are cemented to each other and similarly for C and D; the whole forms a parallel-sided plate. If the elements were arranged in the order DABC we should have simply a Savart polariscope. The axis xx' crosses the plates where all the thicknesses are equal; if we displace AB and CD through equal distances in opposite directions we find that xx' again crosses the plates where all thicknesses are equal but the thickness of the whole (i.e. the thickness of the equivalent Savart plate) has increased or decreased; in fig. 33 it is shown as increased. We have thus a Savart polariscope of variable thickness $2e$, so from eq. (64) the fringe spacing is variable.

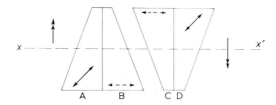

Fig. 33. Tsuruta's modification of the Savart polariscope.

19. Birefringent systems with angular splitting

19.1. THE WOLLASTON PRISM

The Wollaston prism (fig. 34) is made up of two prisms cut parallel to the optical axis and with the axes crossed. The two prisms have the same angle θ and the whole forms a parallel plate. Let xx' be an axis intersecting the Wollaston at C, where the two prisms have equal thickness. Consider an incident ray which meets the Wollaston normally at a distance y from the axis xx'; there is no splitting when the ray enters the first prism but splitting occurs at the interface. To simplify matters we suppose the splitting to be so small that it cannot be shown in the figure, but we know that it occurs. The path difference Δ between the two rays is given by

$$\Delta = 2(n_o - n_e)y \, \text{tg} \, \theta. \tag{69}$$

Since the axes of the two prisms are at right angles the ordinary ray in the first prism becomes the extraordinary ray in the second, and vice versa; thus at C, where the thicknesses are equal ($y=0$), the path difference is zero. If the prisms are displaced parallel to one edge, so that $y=$const., the path difference does not change, but for

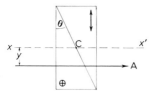

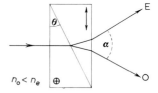

Fig. 34. Wollaston prism.   Fig. 35. Splitting produced by a Wollaston prism.

displacements perpendicular to an edge eq. (69) shows that Δ is a linear function of y. The fringes are equidistant straight lines parallel to an edge of the prisms; they are localized in the Wollaston and the plane of localization is inclined at an angle of about $\frac{2}{3}\theta$ to the outer surfaces. The fringe separation y_f is given by

$$y_f = \frac{\lambda}{2(n_o - n_e)\,\text{tg}\,\theta} . \tag{70}$$

If the Wollaston is placed between crossed polarizers there is a black fringe at C, where the thicknesses are equal; the coloured fringes on either side follow the Newton colour scale with black centre.

Fig. 35 illustrates the angular splitting α produced by a Wollaston; it is given by

$$\alpha = 2(n_o - n_e)\,\text{tg}\,\theta. \tag{71}$$

Eq. (69) is valid for rays incident nearly normally on the Wollaston; consider a normally incident ray M_1I (fig. 36) and another ray M_2I incident at the same point I at an angle i. The change in path difference due to the inclination of the rays can

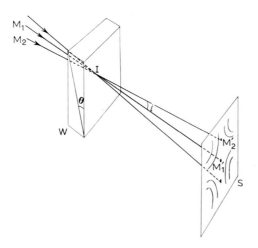

Fig. 36. The path difference changes with the angle of incidence on the Wollaston.

be calculated as follows. If the angle θ of the Wollaston is small we can assume that in the small region I where the rays traverse the Wollaston we are dealing with two parallel plates cut parallel to the axes and with crossed axes. Since θ is small the splitting is negligible and we assume that the two rays O and E which came from a single incident ray are substantially parallel. Now let a screen S be placed at some distance from the Wollaston (for a quartz Wollaston with θ about 5° a suitable distance would be 15 to 20 cm). We are now in effect observing in convergent light two plates cut parallel to the axis and crossed, so that hyperbolic fringes appear on the screen S. We apply eq. (69) to the ray M_1IM_1'. Then for an angle of incidence i in a plane of incidence at 45° to the asymptotes of the hyperbolae the path difference becomes Δ', given by

$$\Delta' = \Delta(1 - i^2/2n_o^2). \tag{72}$$

For example, for a 20 mm thick quartz Wollaston, if θ is small and each prism is 10 mm thick in the region I, we have

$$\Delta' = \Delta(1 - i^2/4.74).$$

For $i = 10°$ the change $\Delta' - \Delta$ amounts to one wavelength, which exceeds what is permissible. Thus the Wollaston must be used with pencils of small angular aperture.

19.2. NOMARSKI'S MODIFICATION OF THE WOLLASTON PRISM

The inclination of the plane of localization of the fringes can be inconvenient for certain purposes. To overcome this disadvantage Nomarski suggested using two Wollastons separated by a half-wave plate, as in fig. 37. The plane of localization is then exactly parallel to the surfaces of the Wollastons.

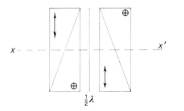
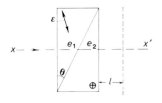

Fig. 37. Nomarski's modified Wollaston with normal fringe localization.   Fig. 38. Wollaston modified by Nomarski.

Another system has the plane of localization of the fringes set right outside the Wollaston. It is a modified Wollaston in which one of the axes is inclined at an angle ε to the exterior surfaces. This is particularly useful in the field of microscopy. In the arrangement shown in fig. 38 the light comes from the left and the fringes are localized in a plane at a distance l from the exit surface, i.e., we have a real plane of localization. Let n be the extraordinary index, corresponding to the extraordinary ray in the first prism, and let the incident ray be normal. There will be zero path difference in the axial direction xx' for different thicknesses e_1 and e_2 of the two prisms on account of the inclination ε of the optic axis. We have

$$e_2 = e_1 \frac{n - n_o}{n_e - n_o}. \tag{73}$$

Let V be the angle between the ordinary and extraordinary rays in the first prism. If α is the splitting angle, as in fig. 35, we find for quartz

$$e_1 = \frac{\alpha\lambda}{V + \alpha \left[1 + \frac{n - n_o}{n_e - n_o} \left(1 - \frac{1}{n_o} \right) \right]}. \tag{74}$$

We can calculate V as a function of ε from the equation

$$\operatorname{tg} V = \frac{0.011\,833 \operatorname{tg} \varepsilon}{1 + 1.011\,833 \operatorname{tg}^2 \varepsilon} \tag{75}$$

and from eq. (51) the extraordinary index n can be obtained, taking $\omega = \frac{1}{2}\pi - \varepsilon$. In this formula ε must be taken as the angle made by the optic axis with a surface parallel to the extraordinary wave surface. If the angle of incidence is zero then ε is also the angle between the optic axis and the first surface. The angular splitting is

$$\alpha = (n + n_e - 2n_o) \, \text{tg} \, \theta, \tag{76}$$

which may be compared with eq. (71). If the axis is inclined as in fig. 39, the light coming from the left as before, then the plane of localization is virtual and is at a distance l from the first surface. In this case we have

$$e_1 = \frac{\alpha\lambda}{V - \alpha \left[1 + \dfrac{n - n_o}{n_e - n_o} \left(1 - \dfrac{1}{n_o} \right) \right]} \tag{77}$$

and eqs. (73, 75) and (76) remain unaltered.

It should here be pointed out that the ordinary Wollaston fringes are straight but this is not so for the systems shown in figs. 38 and 39; the frings are not quite straight when the plane of localization is outside the prism.

Numerical example

As a numerical example we take a quartz prism of the type of fig. 39 with $\varepsilon = 20°$ and $\theta = 34'$. Then we have $n_e - n_o = 0.00911$, $n - n_o = 0.000804$ and the above formulae give

$$V = 3.80 \times 10^{-3} \text{ radian}, \qquad e_1 = 1.352 \text{ mm},$$
$$\alpha = 1.64 \times 10^{-4} \text{ radian}, \qquad e_2 = 1.195 \text{ mm},$$
$$l = 29.6 \text{ mm}, \qquad e_1 + e_2 = 2.547 \text{ mm}.$$

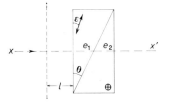
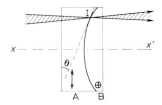

Fig. 39. Wollaston modified by Nomarski.   Fig. 40. Girard's modification of the Wollaston.

19.3. VARIABLE ANGULAR SPLITTING

Girard designed a simple system which was used by Tsuruta for measuring the optical transfer function of objectives; this was in effect a Wollaston with cylindrical elements, as in fig. 40. The two elements A and B are cylindrical lenses, respectively plano-concave and plano-convex, with equal curvatures on the cylindrical surfaces. Comparing fig. 40 with fig. 34, it can be seen that if we use a small region I of the cylindrical Wollaston (by having a pencil converging to I) the effects are the same as for an ordinary Wollaston with angle θ. This angle θ made by the tangent plane to the cylindrical surface with the external surface varies with the distance of I from the axis xx'. We assume that the tangent plane to the cylinder where it meets xx' is normal to this axis. We thus have a Wollaston in which the angle can be varied by changing the region in which it is traversed by the rays. Let y be the distance from I to xx'. Then if R is the radius of the cylindrical surface, the angular splitting α between the ordinary and extraordinary rays is given by

$$\alpha = 2(n_o - n_e)y/R. \tag{78}$$

In this system the fringe spacing varies continuously from the centre to the edge. Nomarski has shown that it is also possible to obtain fringes of variable spacing by means of two Wollastons at some distance from each other and with a half-wave plate between them.

19.4. LARGE WORKING FIELDS

For some purposes it is desired to transmit a wide-angle pencil of rays through a Wollaston. Since the path difference depends on the inclination of the rays, the Wollaston in its original form is not suitable in this case, as was noted in subsection 19.1. Returning to fig. 36, we want to replace the Wollaston by a system which gives uniform illumination on the screen S even when the angle i is fairly large. This can be done by a system devised by Nomarski and shown in fig. 41; the axes of the two plates are parallel and a half-wave plate is placed between them. Another system, which does not have a half-wave plate, is shown in fig. 42; in this system,

Fig. 41. Nomarski's large field Wollaston.   Fig. 42. Françon's large field Wollaston.

due to Françon, the elements A and D are identical plane-parallel plates of quartz and elements B and C form an ordinary Wollaston of calcite. The axes are aligned as in the figure and the thickness of each quartz plate is 17.331 times the mean thickness of each calcite prism.

20. Principle of the polarization interferometer

The principle of the polarizing interferometer is as follows. A wave which is distorted by phase variations in a transparent object is split into two waves by a birefringent system; the waves are caused to interfere by means of a polarizer and an analyzer and thus the phase detail of a transparent object is revealed, the object being itself isotropic.

20.1. INTERFEROMETERS WITH COMPLETE SPLITTING

Consider a transparent object AC, for example the glass plate in fig. 43, which has at M a region of optical thickness different from that of the rest of the plate. This object is illuminated by a collimated beam of light from a small source at S and its

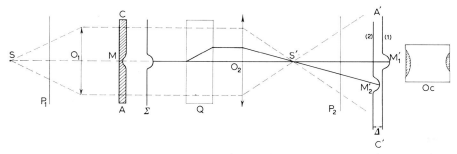

Fig. 43. Principle of a polarization interferometer using a Savart polariscope.

image A'C' produced by the optical system O_2 is observed through the eyepiece Oc. A birefringent system Q with parallel faces is placed between the object AC and the objective O_2, for example the polariscope of fig. 23 or fig. 30. The incident light is plane-polarized by a polarizer P_1, which can be placed in any position in front of the birefringent system Q, and similarly the analyzer P_2 can be placed anywhere after Q. The incident wave Σ is plane before it enters Q except in the central region, where it is slightly distorted by the varying optical thickness of the object in that region. After passing through Q the wave Σ is split into two waves (1) and (2) which are polarized at right angles, as in fig. 44. The relative displacement perpendicular

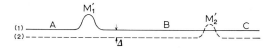

Fig. 44. Configuration of the two waves in the method of total splitting.

to the axis of these two waves is due to the birefringence of Q and the axial displacement corresponds to the optical path difference Δ introduced by Q. For a Savart polariscope the path difference in question is that between the two rays OE and EO in fig. 23; it is given by eq. (62). In fig. 45, as also in fig. 43, the ray OE through P interferes with the ray EO through M. The images of P and M formed respectively by these two rays coincide at P' (or M') in the image A'C' and a difference in the lengths of the optical paths POEP' and MEOM' is produced by the polariscope. This difference, which is equal to Δ, is evidently the optical path difference in the image A'C' between the two rays corresponding to these two images.

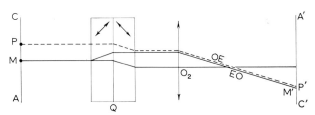

Fig. 45. The two rays OE and EO which interfere at M' (or P').

This optical path difference can be varied by inclining the polariscope relative to the incident beam. Let it be inclined slightly so as to make the path difference between the waves where they are plane (regions A, B, C of fig. 44) equal to 0.565 μm and let the polarizers be crossed. A purple colour is seen at A, B and C, the so-called sensitive tint or sensitive purple. At M_1 and M_2, where the image of M appears, the path difference becomes 0.565 μm plus or minus the path difference introduced by the object, so the sensitive tint is changed and the phase structure of the object is made visible. The colour of the ordinary image differs from that of the extraordinary image because the path differences are respectively 0.565 μm $+ \delta$ and 0.565 μm $- \delta$, where δ is the path difference due to the object itself. The two colours are symmetrically placed on the Newton colour scale with respect to the sensitive tint. It is possible to measure the optical path difference by means of a colour chart; the colours of the image of the phase object and of the uniform background are compared and their places in the colour scale are estimated.

It is usually better to measure phase differences by using straight wedge fringes, as in ordinary interferometers, and this can be done as follows. A second polariscope similar to Q is placed between the eyepiece Oc and the eye; the light through this second polariscope is not parallel, so it superimposes on the field a set of straight fringes at infinity which are loci of constant optical path difference between the waves (1) and (2). The wave deformations produced by the object cause displacements in these fringes which can be measured in orders, i.e. whole fringes and fractions of a fringe, just as in ordinary interferometry. The analyzing polarizer must, of course, be placed after this second polariscope. Fig. 46 shows the field of view with the

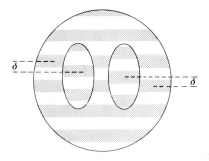

Fig. 46. Wedge fringes in the method of complete splitting.

ordinary and extraordinary images; the two images are separated or sheared and the method is clearly best suited for isolated small objects of such a kind that the two sheared images are not obscured by background detail or overlapping.

20.2. DIFFERENTIAL INTERFEROMETERS

Returning to fig. 43, we now consider a polariscope in which the lateral displacement is small compared to the size of the object, i.e. the polariscope must be much thinner than for the preceding method. Fig. 47 shows how the two waves (1) and (2) emerge

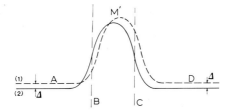

Fig. 47. Configuration of the two waves in the differential method.

in this case and again we suppose that the polariscope Q is adjusted to make the optical path difference between the plane regions of the two waves equal to 0.565 μm. Such plane regions which surround the image M' of the object M, e.g. A and D, again show the sensitive purple tint. On the other hand in the region of the image M', say at B and C, the lateral shear produces a change in optical path difference between the waves (1) and (2) and the outline of the phase object is revealed.

In principle it would be desirable to have a birefringent system suitably matched for every different size of object. Very often, however, the path difference variations are rather rapid, as in microscopy, and we have therefore suggested choosing a thickness for Q which will give a shear of the order of magnitude of the resolving power of the instrument, so that the lateral doubling would not be visible. Thus we have a fixed-adjustment instrument in which the shear is not visible, i.e. there appears to be only one image. This method gives not the optical path itself but its variations, so it is a differential method. Again it is possible to introduce wedge fringes by means of an auxiliary polariscope to facilitate measurement.

20.3. USE OF A BIREFRINGENT SYSTEM WITH ANGULAR SPLITTING

The two preceding methods make use of a system of birefringent plates giving linear splitting of the rays, but we could equally well use a system giving angular splitting, as in fig. 48. Here the Wollaston W or an equivalent system is placed at the focus of the objective O_2; the image S' of the source S is formed at the Wollaston and the rest of the system is as in fig. 43. The splitting of the waves (1) and (2) occurs as in fig. 43; it should be noted that in fig. 48 the splitting of each ray is not shown; the angle $2i$ is the angular aperture of the pencil. We show in fig. 49 how an incident

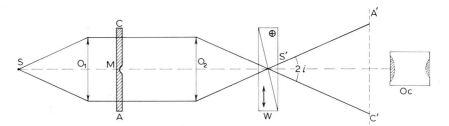

Fig. 48. Principle of a polarization interferometer using a Wollaston prism.

ray is split, the angle α being the same as in fig. 35; the separation $\varDelta$ representing the optical path difference between the rays is obviously considerably exaggerated in scale relative to the rest of the figure. As we saw, the aperture $2i$ of the pencil traversing the Wollaston must be small, otherwise the field will not be uniform in the absence of a phase object; this condition is usually satisfied in microscopy but it may not be easy to satisfy it on a macroscopic scale, in which case one of the devices described in subsection 19.4 must be used.

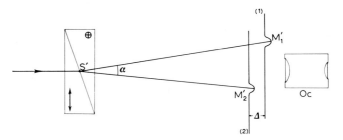

Fig. 49. The waves split by a Wollaston.

21. Image contrast in polarization interferometers

In the preceding account we have not discussed the size or shape of the light source S to be used; to consider this point we return to fig. 43. If there is to be good contrast in the image with an extended source S, the optical path difference $\varDelta$ at a given point of the field must be the same for all points of the source S which illuminate it. In fact, to a given point of S there corresponds a certain angle of incidence at Q and thus a certain optical path difference $\varDelta$ between the interfering waves (1) and (2) where they are plane. For a given wavelength the resulting intensity I is equal to $\sin^2(\pi\varDelta/\lambda)$ or $\cos^2(\pi\varDelta/\lambda)$, depending on whether the polarizers are crossed or parallel, and if $\varDelta$ varies with the point of the source in question this intensity will vary correspondingly. The different points of the source are incoherent, so these different intensities must be added and the result is an overall decrease in contrast. Thus, as stated above, the optical path difference between the two waves must be the same for all source points for optimum contrast.

We can now see what shape the source should be for the Savart polariscope.

We showed that the Savart fringes at infinity are parallel straight lines at 45° to the principal sections of the plates, so they are in effect virtual fringes in the focal plane through S. We therefore use as source a slit parallel to the fringes at infinity and narrow compared to the fringe spacing. Then all the points of this source produce the same optical path difference between the waves (1) and (2), since, as in all cases of interference fringes at infinity, the optical path difference produced by a plane parallel plate is constant if the source point is displaced along a fringe at infinity. It can easily be seen that in fig. 43 the fringes at infinity are formed at the focal plane S' of the objective O_2 and the image S' of the slit S is also formed there, so this image must be set as in fig. 50. With this arrangement all the incoherent points of the slit S give the same interference pattern in the image plane, as seen in the eyepiece Oc.

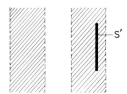

Fig. 50. The image S' of the slit set parallel to the fringes.

Thus the fringes are the same as would be seen with a point source but they are much brighter. If the fringes are displaced perpendicular to the image S' of the slit by tilting the polariscope the contrast of the image changes, and thus the most suitable contrast for a given object can be chosen.

21.1. CONTRAST IN THE COMPLETE-SPLITTING METHOD

Let the polarizers be crossed and suppose the light is monochromatic. If the image S' is projected on to a dark fringe the path difference Δ between the two waves (1) and (2) of fig. 43 is zero and the field of view is dark except at the two images M'_1 and M'_2; in these regions the path difference is δ. If e_o is the depth of the hollow at M and n_0 is the refractive index of the glass plate we have $\delta = (n_0 - 1)e$. If δ is small the intensity in the image M'_1 or M'_2 is

$$I = \sin^2 (\pi\delta/\lambda) \approx (\pi\delta/\lambda)^2, \tag{79}$$

i.e. the intensity is proportional to the square of the phase difference $\varphi = 2\pi\delta/\lambda$ introduced by the object and we have similar conditions to dark-field illumination. Now let the polariscope be slightly inclined, so as to bring the image S' to the region of the fringes at infinity where $\Delta = \frac{1}{4}\lambda$. The intensity in the regions (1) and (2) is now

$$I = \sin^2 (\pi\Delta/\lambda) = \tfrac{1}{2}$$

and at M'_1 the intensity is

$$I' = \sin^2 \frac{\pi(\Delta + \delta)}{\lambda} \approx \tfrac{1}{2} + \pi\delta/\lambda = \tfrac{1}{2}(1 + \varphi). \tag{80}$$

We take the following ratio as a measure of contrast:

$$\gamma = \frac{I_{max} - I_{min}}{I_{max}},$$

so that in the present case we have

$$\gamma = \frac{I' - I}{I} \approx \varphi, \tag{81}$$

i.e. the contrast is proportional to the phase difference introduced by the object, as in the phase contrast method. The required position of the slit source in the fringes at infinity to give $\Delta = \frac{1}{4}\lambda$ is where the intensity distribution has maximum slope, i.e. $x = \frac{1}{4}\pi$ for the function $y = \sin^2 x$.

We now consider the effect of using white light with crossed polarizers. If the image S' is projected on the central dark fringe the path difference Δ between the two waves (1) and (2) is zero and the field of view is dark except at the images M'$_1$ and M'$_2$, as before, and again the arrangement is like dark-field illumination. If the polariscope is very slightly tilted, to produce the grey colour next to the black on the Newton colour scale, the effects are substantially as in the preceding case, where $\gamma = \varphi$ for all wavelengths and so the field appears uniformly grey. Again the image appears as if in phase contrast. If the polariscope is now further tilted, so that S' is projected on to the first-order purple fringe ($\Delta = 0.565$ μm) the entire field appears purple except at the two images M'$_1$ and M'$_2$, where the sensitive purple tint changes. For example, if $\delta = 0.1$ μm the tint of the image M'$_2$ corresponds to $\Delta + \delta = 0.565 + 0.1 = 0.665$ μm, which is sky blue. By displacing the coloured fringes in relation to S' a complete range of contrasts can be obtained. A similar argument applies to the case where the birefringent system is a Wollaston prism, as in fig. 48, except that instead of the fringes at infinity we have the fringes localized in the prism. This is shown in fig. 50; the source (S in fig. 48) must be a narrow slit projected into the plane of localization of the fringes of the Wollaston. The path difference Δ between the two waves (1) and (2) in fig. 49 depends on the position of S', the image of the slit; when working between crossed polarizers this path difference is zero if S' is projected on to the black fringe. Now let the Wollaston be displaced parallel to itself in a direction perpendicular to the axis of the system so as to displace the fringes with respect to S'; the fringe contrast changes in the same way as in a Savart polariscope, the only difference being in the nature of the adjustment needed to change the contrast.

21.2. CONTRAST IN THE DIFFERENTIAL METHOD

Let us take for the object, a plane-parallel plate AC (fig. 51) with a region M with a small wedge angle θ; we take this instead of the conventional object AC of fig. 43. A wave takes the form Σ after traversing this object and the polariscope splits this into two parts (1) and (2) as in fig. 52, which corresponds to $\Delta = 0$. It can be seen that, if v is the slope of the wavefront at M, the path difference is vd, where d is the splitting produced by the polariscope. If the polariscope is slightly tilted the path difference becomes Δ in the flat parts of the wavefronts in fig. 52 and at

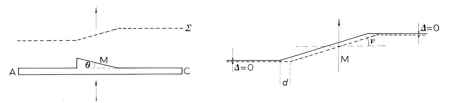

Fig. 51. A conventional phase object for the differential method.

Fig. 52. The waves in the differential method when $\Delta = 0$.

M it becomes $\Delta \pm \delta$. Outside the image of M the intensity with crossed polarizers and monochromatic light is

$$I = \sin^2 (\pi \Delta / \lambda)$$

and in one of the images of M, say that corresponding to $\Delta + \delta$, we have

$$I' = \sin^2 \frac{\pi(\Delta + vd)}{\lambda} ; \tag{82}$$

if $\Delta = 0$ and if vd is small we have

$$I = 0 \quad \text{and} \quad I' = (\pi vd/\lambda)^2. \tag{83}$$

This is similar to dark-field illumination but the intensity is now proportional to the square of the slope v of the wavefront or of the angle θ of the object itself, since $v = (n-1)\theta$. If the polariscope is tilted to make $\Delta = \tfrac{1}{4}\lambda$ we have

$$I = \tfrac{1}{2} \quad \text{and} \quad I' \approx \tfrac{1}{2}(1 + 2\pi vd/\lambda), \tag{84}$$

so the contrast is

$$\gamma = \varphi \approx 2\pi vd/\lambda. \tag{85}$$

This is like a phase contrast image, but the contrast is proportional to the angle v of the wavefront or the angle θ of the surface of the object. If we change to a white light source all that was said in subsection 21.2 applies, except that the angle v (or θ) takes the place of the path difference produced by the object.

22. Compensation in polarization interferometers

The necessity of using a slit as a light source would considerably limit the light-gathering power of polarizing interferometers, but, as we shall show, it is quite easy to arrange matters so that extended sources can be used; this considerably extends the sphere of usefulness of these instruments.

Consider two parallel polariscopes Q_1 and Q_2, which may be for example of the kind shown in fig. 30. They are identical but Q_2 is turned through 180° in relation

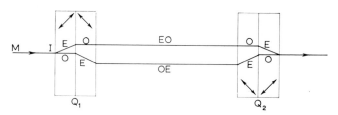

Fig. 53. The two compensating polariscopes Q_1 and Q_2.

to Q_1, as in fig. 53. The two polarizers are not shown in fig. 53 but we always imply that the birefringent elements are placed between polarizers, as in all the following figures; in the present case the first polarizer would be to the left of Q_1 and the second to the right of Q_2. To investigate the fringe system produced, we note first that for an incident ray MI normal to the polariscopes the splitting produced by Q_1 is cancelled by that due to Q_2. If the ray MI is oblique the path difference between the two rays EO and OE on emerging from Q_1 is compensated by an equal and opposite path difference introduced by Q_2. Thus the two rays EO and OE are recombined by Q_2 even at oblique incidence. We can see this in a different way as follows. Let the polariscope Q in fig. 43 be replaced by the two polariscopes Q_1 and Q_2 in fig. 53, so that the result is as in fig. 54. If Q_1 were used alone it would

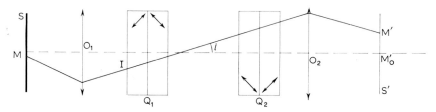

Fig. 54. The fringes at infinity from Q_1 and Q_2 are projected to S′ and compensation is obtained.

give wedge fringes at infinity, at S′ in the focal plane of the objective O_2; similarly polariscope Q_2 alone would give the same fringe system at S′. Now consider the ray MI in fig. 54 again; we assume the splitting to be too small to be shown in the figure, but the ray EO is retarded with respect to OE in Q_1, while the reverse holds in Q_2, which is turned through 180°. The birefringence is cancelled and, since the fringes at infinity of both polariscopes are similar and similarly placed this effect will occur at every point in the plane S′. The path difference will be zero at M'_0, in the centre of the field, and likewise it will be zero everywhere else. Thus the system of two polariscopes gives a fringe system at infinity with infinitely wide spacing, so that there is a uniform tint at S′ (to the third order of approximation in the obliquity i). The path difference Δ is substantially constant for all i and a broad source S can be used. In this connection Q_1 is said to compensate Q_2; the ray diagram in fig. 53 is valid at oblique incidence.

It is clear from fig. 53 that the object must not be placed to the left of Q_1, since there would then be no splitting and no interference effects. It must obviously be placed between the two polariscopes, in accordance with a general rule: *When two birefringent systems compensate each other and permit the use of a broad source the object must be placed between the two systems.* We discuss the detailed arrangement of the polariscopes in the next section, which gives descriptions of specific apparatus.

In figs. 53 and 54 the path difference is zero and we have a dark field of view as with the narrow slit in the previous section; we saw there that the type of contrast obtained with a slit source could be changed by tilting the polariscope and correspondingly in the present case we have to tilt polariscope Q_2 in relation to Q_1 to change the contrast. The effects are the same as in the preceding section, the only difference being in the possibility of using a large source and thus having a very bright system.

The principle of compensation can be applied to all the birefringent systems so far described provided the following two conditions are complied with:

(a) *The two fringe systems of the birefringent elements, which may be either fringes at infinity or localized fringes, must be exactly superimposed in one plane.*

(b) *The two birefringent systems must be so oriented that the splitting produced by one is exactly cancelled by the other.*

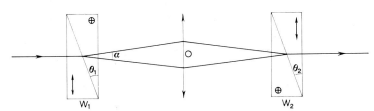

Fig. 55. The two compensating Wollastons W_1 and W_2.

A simplified scheme showing the application to the Wollaston is given in fig. 55, and all that was said above applies again. The fringes of W_1 must fall on those of W_2, so that W_1 and W_2 must be conjugates in O. In fig. 54 there were no lenses between Q_1 and Q_2 and the two fringe systems were identical if the two polariscopes were themselves identical, but in fig. 55 the superimposition of the planes of localization of the fringes is carried out by means of the objective O. The spacing of the Wollaston fringes is inversely proportional to the angles θ_1 and θ_2, so that, if p_1 and p_2 are the distances of W_1 and W_2 from O, the condition for the fringes to be superposed is obviously

$$\theta_1/\theta_2 = p_2/p_1 . \tag{86}$$

Thus if the Wollastons are identical they must be placed at the points of unit magnification. As before, the object must be between W_1 and W_2 to obtain interference contrast.

To recapitulate, using two suitable birefringent systems, an incident ray from the source is split into two rays EO and OE; the second system recombines the two rays and a single ray emerges from the two systems. The same holds if the angle of in-

cidence is changed, and the path difference between EO and OE is constant with
varying angle of incidence, so that a broad source can be used. The object is placed
between the two birefringent systems and a splitting into two waves (1) and (2) in
the image of the object is produced by the second birefringent system. The path
difference at a given point in the image is constant for all angles of incidence and the
contrast of the image is not diminished if a large source is used. Thus the system
has large light-gathering power.

23. Description of the principal polarization interferometers

The preceding survey enables us to understand the principles of the birefringent
apparatus to be described below and it also provides a useful basis for designing
such systems. We shall give brief descriptions of several systems, followed by the
numerical data for the construction of one type. All the systems described can be
used in white light.

23.1. INTERFEROMETERS WITH LINEAR-SPLITTING SYSTEMS

The first polarizing interferometer was made by Jamin (see fig. 56). It consisted of
two identical plates cut at 45° to the optic axis and with a half-wave plate between
them. The function of the half-wave plate is to interchange the O and E vibrations,
so that the rays are recombined after passing through L_2. The object is placed

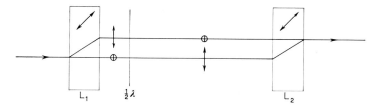

Fig. 56. Jamin's interferometer.

between L_1 and L_2, and the image is split by L_2, so that the apparatus is in effect
like that in fig. 54, but Q_1 is replaced by the half-wave plate and L_1, and Q_2 is
replaced by L_2. Both the conditions stated above for compensation are fulfilled.
Jamin's interferometer was applied by Lebedeff in microscopy.

The present author has described a non-compensated interference eyepiece containing a Savart polariscope as the birefringent element; this is effectively the system
shown in fig. 43 with a slit at S. The Savart Q is now in the eyepiece instead of in
front of the objective, but these positions are equivalent. The Savart is conveniently
placed after a field lens of which the focus coincides with the image S' of the slit.
The present author has also, in collaboration with Yamamoto, investigated the very
simple compensated interferometer shown in fig. 57; in this system the image-side
focal plane of the objective O_1 is made to coincide with the object-side focal plane

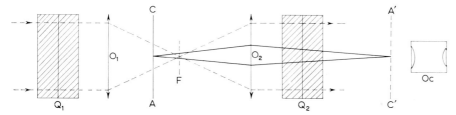

Fig. 57. The interferometer of Françon and Yamamoto.

of the objective O_2 at F. The Savart polariscope Q_1, or one of the type shown in fig. 30, can be placed at any convenient position before O_1 and another similar polariscope can be placed anywhere after O_2. The usual two polarizers, not shown, must be included. The system is illuminated by a broad source, so as to have rays incident over a range of angles, and the polariscope Q_1 forms its fringes at infinity at F. These are parallel equidistant straight fringes, i.e. wedge fringes, and Q_2 also gives (virtual) fringes of the same type at F. The first condition for compensation is that these two fringe systems should be identical; now according to eqs. (64) or (67) the angular spacing of the fringe is inversely proportional to e, so that if f_1 and f_2 are the focal lengths of the objectives O_1 and O_2 the condition for compensation is

$$e_1/e_2 = f_1/f_2. \tag{87}$$

It is furthermore necessary to orient Q_1 and Q_2 so as to spread out the fringes so that the plane F is uniformly illuminated. The object AC must be placed somewhere between O_1 and O_2, but not at F, since its image would then be at infinity and Q_2 would not produce any splitting. The object could be, for example, a little before F and its image A'C' would then be seen conveniently in the eyepiece Oc.

23.2. INTERFEROMETERS WITH ANGULAR-SPLITTING SYSTEMS

The interferometer of F. H. Smith is shown in fig. 58. It consists of two Wollastons W_1 and W_2 at the foci of the objectives O_1 and O_2; the object is at AC and its image A'C' produced by the objective O_2 is observed through the eyepiece Oc. The first condition for compensation is that the two systems of fringes should be congruent at W. If f_1 and f_2 are the focal lengths of O_1 and O_2 eq. (86) gives

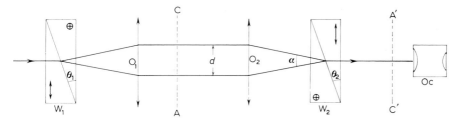

Fig. 58. F. H. Smith's interferometer.

$$\theta_1/\theta_2 = f_2/f_1. \tag{88}$$

The angular splitting is given by eq. (71), from which the linear splitting in the object plane AC is

$$d = 2f_2(n_o - n_e)\,\mathrm{tg}\,\theta_2. \tag{89}$$

The second condition for compensation is that the Wollastons should be orientated to oppose their birefringences and then the system can be illuminated by imaging a large source into W_1. The path difference is varied, i.e. the contrast is controlled, by, e.g., displacing W_2 parallel to a wavefront and in a direction perpendicular to its fringes.

For practical reasons the focal plane of the objective O_2 (fig. 58), and perhaps also that of O_1, may be inaccessible, particularly in microscopy. In such a case Nomarski's modification of the Wollaston (figs. 38 and 39) may be applicable. Fig. 59 shows

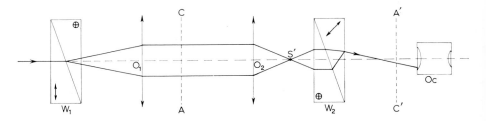

Fig. 59. Nomarski's interferometer.

a prism of the type of fig. 39 used where the focal plane S' of the objective O_2 is inside the objective itself and is thus inaccessible. The fringes of the modified Wollaston W_2 are localized at S', which is conjugate to W_1 in the system comprising O_1 and O_2.

If the focus S' is inaccessible it is possible to use an ordinary Wollaston displaced from O_2 by a suitable distance, as was done by Yamamoto and the present author. This Wollaston produces its fringes near the object AC and compensation can be achieved by another Wollaston in front of the object-side principal focus of the objective O_1. The result is a system similar to that in fig. 57 but with two Wollastons.

23.3. INTERFEROMETERS FOR REFLECTING OBJECTS

In Nomarski's apparatus a single Wollaston traversed twice by the light replaces the two Wollastons needed for compensation, as in fig. 60. To simplify the diagram we show only the path of a pencil of light without indicating the splitting of the rays. An image of the source is formed at the Wollaston after reflection at the semi-reflecting plate G, which is at 45° to the axis. The point I is a point of this image and it is at the focus of the objective O, so that W is also at this focus. After reflection at the object AC the pencil converges to I′ in the Wollaston and then continues to the image A′C′. It is easily seen from fig. 60 that the Wollaston is self-conjugate in the system, so the first condition for compensation is automatically fulfilled. Furthermore, the incident beam goes through I and the reflected beam through I′, as in fig. 58, so the birefringences oppose. The path difference can be varied, and thus the contrast changed, by displacing the Wollaston across the fringe direction in the usual way. We saw that in a Wollaston the plane of localization of the fringes is inclined to the faces, so that for best results the system of fig. 57 should be used. We note also that the Wollaston can be slightly inclined to eliminate reflected stray light.

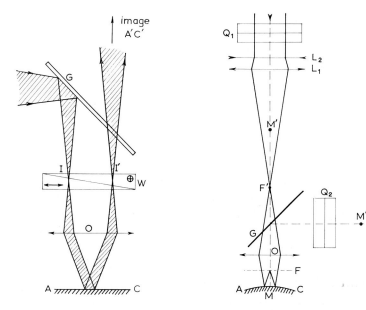

Fig. 60. Nomarski's interferometer for reflecting objects.

Fig. 61. The Nippon Kogaku interferometer for non-plane reflecting objects.

A device based on the system of fig. 57 was applied by Nippon Kogaku to the study of curved reflecting surfaces, as in fig. 61. Compensation is achieved by two Savarts Q_1 and Q_2, which remain the same when the objective is changed or the curvature of the surface AC being examined is varied. The light (from above in the figure) passes through Q_1, the two lenses L_1 and L_2, the semi-reflecting plate G and the objective O; it is then reflected from the object AC and again reflected at G, having passed through O; finally the image M″ is observed in the eyepiece Oc. The fringes of Q_2 are formed virtually in the focal plane F of the objective O. The fringes of Q_1 are also at F since this point is conjugate to the focus F′ of the system $L_1 L_2$ after reflection at AC. Consider the point M′ which is conjugate to M via O and G; if M′ is made to coincide with the focus of L_1 a simple geometrical-optics calculation shows that compensation is achieved by using two identical Savarts Q_1 and Q_2. The only adjustment necessary, apart from focussing, is to displace L_2 in order to make the focus F′ of the system $L_1 L_2$ coincide with the conjugate of F after reflection at AC and after passing through O. This adjustment is obtained by making the field uniform in brightness.

23.4. DYSON'S INTERFEROMETER

Dyson's interferometer is different from those so far described since the splitting is produced by a lens of calcite, as in fig. 62. The triplet L_1 comprises a bi-concave calcite lens cut parallel to the optic axis and cemented to two biconvex glass lenses.

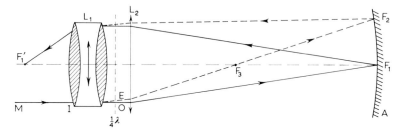

Fig. 62. Path of a ray in Dyson's interferometer.

The power of the triplet is zero for the ordinary ray but it forms a converging system of a few centimetre focal length for the extraordinary ray. A quarter-wave plate is placed next to the triplet and then follows an objective L_2 of which the focus F_1 coincides with a spherical concave mirror A. The centre of curvature of A is at the triplet. The triplet is illuminated with a collimated beam, and a small image of the source is formed on the mirror at F_1. To see how the system works we follow an incident ray MI which is initially parallel to the axis; after traversing the triplet it separates into two rays, O and E; the O ray is not deviated by the triplet and after the quarter-wave plate and the objective L_2 it converges to F_1 and is reflected symmetrically. The O ray emerges from L_2 again parallel to the axis and it passes through the quarter-wave plate again. Since the quarter-wave plate is traversed twice it becomes in effect a half-wave plate and the O ray becomes an E ray in the calcite on the return path; it then converges to F_1' where an image of the point source is formed. We follow now the E ray through the lens L_1 and the quarter-wave plate; after passing through L_2 this ray converges to the focus F_2, is reflected symmetrically, passes through L_2 and then becomes an ordinary ray in the calcite; it converges to the same point F_1' as before. We have thus traced the ray paths from a single incident ray MI but there is in fact an infinity of such rays and a group of these forming a pencil is shown in fig. 63. It can be seen that the ordinary beam from this pencil converges to F_1 on emerging from L_2 and returns to a focus at F_1'; the extraordinary beam converges to F_3, the focus of the combination $L_1 L_2$ for the extraordinary rays; it covers the whole surface of the mirror A and on its return converges to F_1'. There must, of course, be a semi-reflecting plate to the left of the figure, but this is not shown; its function is to reflect the rays back to one side on the return path, so that the fringes can be conveniently observed. Thus we have at F_1' two

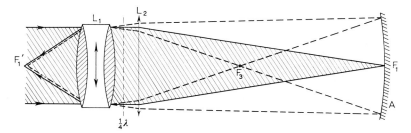

Fig. 63. Ray pencils in Dyson's interferometer.

images of the source from the two beams; one beam covers the entire surface of A and the other covers only a small area at F_1. The object to be studied is placed against the mirror A and it can cover all or most of its aperture. The beam converging to F_1 is the reference beam and as it passes through only a small region of the object it can be assumed that the reference wave is unperturbed by the object. The eye is placed at F_1'; it sees the whole surface of A by the extraordinary beam and it also receives the reference wave, which converges to F_1; it can be seen from fig. 63 that these two waves emerge from F_1' with the same convergence angle. First suppose that there is no object in front of A and that the mirror is perfect; the eye focusses on A through L_1 and L_2 and sees the mirror uniformly illuminated. If now the mirror A is slightly tilted the two images from the two beams no longer coincide at F_1'; they are separated in a plane perpendicular to the axis of the system, so the eye then sees wedge fringes on the surface of A. If an object is placed in front of A or if the mirror is not perfect the departure from straightness of the fringes is a measure of the optical path error, as in classical interferometry. If the two images corresponding to the two beams at F_1' are made to coincide exactly the object is seen in sensitive tints. This apparatus was used by Dyson for work on plasmas.

Addenda on methods of obtaining wedge fringes

In all the systems shown in figs. 57–61 wedge fringes to facilitate measurement can be produced by placing a Savart polariscope after the eyepiece; as always, the birefringent elements must be between two polarizers. A Savart with a thickness $2e$ of 5 mm gives fringes conveniently spaced over the field of view.

Wedge fringes can be obtained in the systems of figs. 58, 59 and 60 by slightly displacing the Wollaston (W in figs. 58 and 59) along the axis of the system. If this is done the image S' of the source (fig. 59) is no longer in the plane of localization of the fringes, so it appears doubled and the fringes seen at A'C' are Young's fringes.

If a Savart polariscope is used it is possible to arrange the fringes parallel to the splitting direction, which is more convenient for some measurement purposes. It is not possible to obtain this condition (i.e. fringes parallel to the splitting or shearing direction) by displacing the Wollaston, so if the object has a straight-edge region of interest this must be set non-parallel to the fringes; the best arrangement seems to be with the edge at 45° to the fringes.

Thᴇ variable fringe systems of figs. 31, 33 and 40 can be used to give variable splitting or shear.

24. Numerical design data.

In this section we give the complete design data for a polarization interferometer of large aperture. In this instrument, shown in fig. 64, an image of the source S is formed by the objective O_1 at S_1', after reflection at a mirror M; the point S_1' is

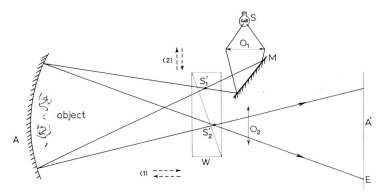

Fig. 64. Example of a polarization interferometer.

near the centre of curvature of the spherical mirror A. This mirror forms an image S_2' which is slightly displaced from S_1'. A large-field Wollaston prism W (as in fig. 41) is placed to contain S_1' and S_2'. The light beam then passes through an objective O_2 which forms an image A' of the mirror A on the screen E. As usual two polarizers are needed to complete the system, one between O_1 and M and the other between W and O_2. In practice it is possible to use one polarizer only, which is placed between W and M and which covers the whole aperture of W; both the incident and reflected beams then pass through this polarizer and the effect is the same as if two separate polarizers were used with their axes parallel.

The Wollaston is displaced along the axis in the directions of the arrows (1) to obtain the sensitive tint, and to vary the type of contrast it is displaced across the axis, as shown by the arrows (2). The object is placed close to the mirror A. The action of the Wollaston on the returning beam produces a shear in the image of A and the two traversals give complete compensation.

The dimensions and other data are given below.

Mirror A: Diameter 20 cm, radius of curvature 70 cm.

Mirror M: About 2 cm by 2 cm; it is inclined at about 45°, and its projected area should cover half the aperture of the Wollaston.

Objective O_1: A good-quality condenser suitable for use in a slide projector. It is required to give uniform illumination over the surface of the mirror A.

Objective O_2: This is a projection objective but the quality is unimportant since it can be used at small aperture; generally a singlet lens will serve the purpose. The focal length depends on the position of the screen E; a focal length of about 60 cm is suitable for projection to a distance of 5 or 6 metres. This will produce an image A′ of A on the screen about 2 metres in diameter.

Light source: An arc is necessary for projecting to several metres but a low-voltage car headlamp can be used if the image A′ needs to be only about 20 to 30 cm in diameter.

Large field Wollaston: If the relative aperture of the mirror A, i.e., the ratio of the diameter to the radius of curvature, exceeds about $\frac{1}{15}$ an ordinary Wollaston is unsuitable because the field would not be uniform. It is then necessary to use a modified Wollaston, as shown e.g. in fig. 41. The choice of angle depends on the method to be applied. This system is convenient for the differential method, for which it would be suitable to take θ about 5°, for quartz, to match the rest of the dimensions. The aperture of 3 by 3 cm could be obtained with a thickness of 5 or 6 mm.

A glass plate with inhomogeneities can be used as a demonstration object, or alternatively convection currents can be produced near A from a source of heat. The effects are very beautiful.

25. Applications of polarization interferometers

We list below some of the numerous applications of polarization interferometers and we give the main references in the bibliography.

Polarization interferometers are particularly important in microscopy; they permit the observation and measurement of transparent or phase objects, which is useful in biology, medicine and chemistry. For example, the dry weight of a cell can be determined by measuring the path difference which it introduces with respect to the surrounding field. Similarly, in microchemistry it is possible the measure the refractive indices of eutectic mixtures, which can be used to identify unknown organic compounds.

In crystallography, polarization interferometers are used in the study of crystal growth. The differential method can be used for the measurement of contact angles and surface tension. It can also be applied to the determination *in vacuo* of the transformation points of radioactive metals.

Polarization interferometers have the particular advantages of compactness and ease of adjustment for work with macroscopic objects; they have been used for the measurement of thickness of thin films deposited *in vacuo*, in the study of polishing defects and inhomogeneities in transparent materials, and in observations on plasmas. Finally they are at present being used for the measurement of aberrations and the determination of the transfer function of optical instruments.

References

BURTIN, R., 1964, Etude des propriétés optiques de certains métaux dans l'infrarouge, Thèse, Paris.

CATALAN, L. and M. FRANÇON, 1960, Rev. Opt. **39**, 1.

DYSON, J., 1957, J. Opt. Soc. Am. **47**, 386.

ERICSSON, J. and L. P. SJÖFALL-JOHNSON, 1960, Opt. Acta **7**, 105.

FRANÇON, M., 1952, Rev. Opt. **31**, 65.

FRANÇON, M., 1957, Bull. Res. Council Israel 5c, 357.

FRANÇON, M. and Y. GANDON, 1958, Opt. Acta **5**, 78

FRANÇON, M. and B. SERGENT, 1955, Opt. Acta **2**, 182.

FRANÇON, M. and T. YAMAMOTO, 1962, Opt. Acta **9**, 395.

GIRARD, A., 1960, Opt. Acta **7**, 81.

JAMIN, J., 1868, Compt. Rend. **67**, 814.

JOHNSSON, L. P., 1957, An interference microscope for rapid measurement of biological objects. Cytochemical methods with quantitative aims (Academic Press, New York) p. 158.

LEBEDEFF, A. A., 1930, Rev. Opt. **9**, 385.

LENOUVEL, L. and F. LENOUVEL, 1938, Rev. Opt. **10**, 350.

NOMARSKI, G., 1955, J. Phys. Radium **16**, 9S.

NOMARSKI, G., I. EPELBOIN and M. FROMENT, 1958, Rev. Mét. no. 3, 260.

NOMARSKI, G. and A. R. WEILL, 1955, Rev. Mét. no. 2, 121.

SMITH, F. H., 1956, Microscopic interferometry. Modern methods of microscopy (Butterworths, London) p. 76.

STEEL, W. H., 1962a, Opt. Acta **9**, 111.

STEEL, W. H., 1962b, J. Opt. Soc. Am. **52**, 1153.

STEEL, W. H., 1964, Opt. Acta **11**, 9.

TSURUTA, T., 1963a, J. Opt. Soc. Am. **53**, 1156.

TSURUTA, T., 1963b, Appl. Opt. **2**, 371.

VAN HEEL, A. C. S., 1958, Interferometry with Savart's plate, appendix D, *in*: J. Strong, ed., Concepts of classical optics (Freeman, San Francisco).

VAN HEEL, A. C. S. and A. WALTHER, 1958, Opt. Acta **5**, 47.

CHAPTER 3

PRINCIPLES OF
INSTRUMENTAL METHODS IN SPECTROSCOPY

A. GIRARD

Office National d'Etudes et de Recherches Aérospatiales, Paris

AND

P. JACQUINOT

Centre National de la Recherche Scientifique, Paris

CONTENTS

1. Introduction

In order to establish clearly the purpose of this chapter we set out a few preliminary remarks. The spectroscopist, although primarily interested in the use to be made of the spectrum, ought nevertheless to take some interest in the means of obtaining it. It is this latter aspect with which we are here concerned; we shall not discuss spectroscopy as such, this is an entirely different field. We shall try to answer the questions, which method and which apparatus should be chosen. The most important criteria are resolution and luminosity but there are other considerations which in some circumstances are also important although less fundamental, for example convenience in use, portability, speed in obtaining the results, cost, etc. Thus, the conclusions of this discussion are subject to a wide range of interpretation according to the relative importance of these factors in each particular application.

Our main purpose is to describe the trends of modern developments in instrumental spectroscopy and explain the principles of the apparatus concerned. There are two main trends:

The first is concerned with developments in instruments which may be called classical, since they depend on the use of a slit and a dispersing system, as in the earliest spectroscopes. Spectroscopy as a research tool has achieved spectacular successes by means of such instruments and this has led to instrumental improvements, usually in the direction of further specialization. Nonetheless, beneath the differences of spectral range and nature of application, a common principle underlies such diverse systems as the simple pocket spectroscope and the most elaborate spectrograph.

The second developmental trend is in non-classical devices, with which we shall deal in detail later; these are of three kinds, the Fabry–Perot spectrometer, the Fourier transform spectrometer, and instruments utilizing selective spectroscopy by amplitude modulation. The latter method may be called (for brevity) selective modulation spectroscopy.

We do not suggest that either of these two lines of development is superior to the other. Progress in the development of classical systems has been so rapid that any new type of instrument must have a performance of extremely high quality to be competitive but, on the other hand, classical instruments have fundamental limitations due to the nature of their principle of operation. To overcome these limitations is now a major objective of instrumental spectroscopy.

At times we shall distinguish between industrial apparatus and research apparatus. We make this distinction purely for practical convenience; research apparatus is designed to be flexible and adaptable to a variety of different problems and there is little use of automatic systems; industrial apparatus is adapted to specialized problems and much use is made of automation in the interests of speed and simplicity in use. It is pointless to attempt a rigid demarcation between the two kinds of apparatus but it can be said that usually research apparatus are developed first and the industrial forms follow after an interval of several years.

In this chapter we aim to explain the basic principles, so as to make clear the domains of application of the different spectroscopic techniques and the best methods of applying them; we do not give detailed technical descriptions of various apparatus, since this would result in a chapter which, though perhaps more instructive, would be necessarily incomplete. Thus in the first section we shall review certain fundamental notions relating to the detectors associated with spectroscopic instruments. Then, after enumerating the main problems which arise in spectroscopy, we shall introduce a generalized concept of luminosity in a form which will permit comparisons between widely differing cases. The second section will deal with classical apparatus; the principles will be briefly recalled and the relation between luminosity and resolution will be studied; short descriptions of apparatus must suffice here owing to the great diversity which exists. The third section will deal with non-classical systems; their possibilities will be examined and compared with those of the classical systems.

1.1. DETECTORS OF IMAGES AND DETECTORS OF FLUX. SPECTROGRAPHS AND SPECTROMETERS

The photographic plate together with the technique of densitometry was for a long time the only means of measurement in spectroscopy. Until about 1940 only specialist workers in research laboratories made use of photoelectric detectors. The importance of this historical fact should not be underestimated. The long predominance – and almost exclusive use until recent years – of image receptors still exerts a strong influence on the development of spectroscopic instrumentation. The availability of photoelectric detectors, which are flux detectors, marks a stage as important as the introduction of photography. The gradual evolution of new techniques which is now occurring may fairly be said to be due to the realization of the profound differences between the use of flux detectors and image detectors.

These two kinds of detectors respond in fundamentally different ways to incident light energy. We suppose the incident energy to be a function $F(x, y, t)$ of time and of two spatial coordinates in the plane of the sensitive surface. Then the image detector integrates over time but conserves the dependence on the spatial variables, so that it gives a response which may be written

$$S(x, y) = \int_0^T F(x, y, t)\,dt$$

where T is the exposure time.

For a photoelectric detector, such as a photomultiplier or a thermal detector for the infrared, the effects on the space and time coordinates are interchanged and the response is represented by

$$S(t) = \iint_\Sigma F(x, y, t)\,dx\,dy.$$

The integral is taken over the surface Σ of the detector. Obviously certain simplifying hypotheses are implied, such as uniform sensitivity of the surface Σ and the reciprocity law for emulsions.

These two equations express the facts that the photographic emulsion responds to illumination whereas the photoelectric detector responds to flux. The emulsion gives spatial resolution within limitations imposed by its granularity and the flux detector gives time resolution within limitations imposed by its time constant. We cannot decide on this basis alone that one or the other type is superior, but we note that because the space coordinates are two in number the photographic emulsion has a greater information capacity. The optical design of the apparatus must depend on the type of receptor to be used; to change from one to the other simply by replacing the plate by a photocell could introduce serious disadvantages.

Systems using flux detectors will be called spectrometers and those using photographic emulsions will be called spectrographs; the latter can only be used at wavelengths below 1.2 μ, so that in the infrared we have only spectrometers. By the term monochromator we mean a spectrometer which is used to produce a monochromatic emerging beam of variable wave length. The monochromator, as thus defined, does not include a detector; it may form part of a complex optical system. The table in fig. 1 shows the kinds of receptors used in different spectral regions.

1.2. PHOTON NOISE AND DETECTOR NOISE (JONES [1953], VAN DER ZIEL [1954], FREEMAN [1958])

Light energy arrives at a detector discontinuously in photons carrying energy hv. An ideal radiation detector would therefore be an error-free photon counter. Suppose we could count the photons arriving in unit time in a frequency band Δv. Then the statement that the luminous flux is constant means that, if this measurement were repeated at different times, the result would vary about a mean value N with mean square deviation $\overline{\Delta N^2} \propto N$. This is a result of classical mechanics which is not rigorously true for a beam of radiation, but it is important to remember that a 'constant' luminous flux is really a mean value and that analysis in time of such a beam would reveal random fluctuations; these constitute photon noise. This noise imposes an ultimate limit on the sensitivity of the best detectors. In addition to photon noise we have also noise originating in the detector, which may be due to Johnson noise, current noise, etc.

The detector is said to be limited by detector noise or by photon noise according to which of these predominates. If photon noise is the greater the noise level is a function of the incident flux; in the most sensitive detectors, e.g. a cooled photomultiplier, the r.m.s. noise level is proportional to the square root of the signal level. If, on the other hand, the system is limited by detector noise then the incident flux does not affect the noise level.

From the expression hv for the quantum energy we may infer that it is easier to approach the ideal detector in the ultraviolet, i.e. the domain of high energy photons, than in the infrared. In practice the performances of photomultipliers are not usually limited solely by photon noise; in the infrared this kind of noise is hardly ever noticed with either quantum or thermal detectors. In the latter case the noise level can be minimized by observing certain general rules: (1) Use a detector with as small

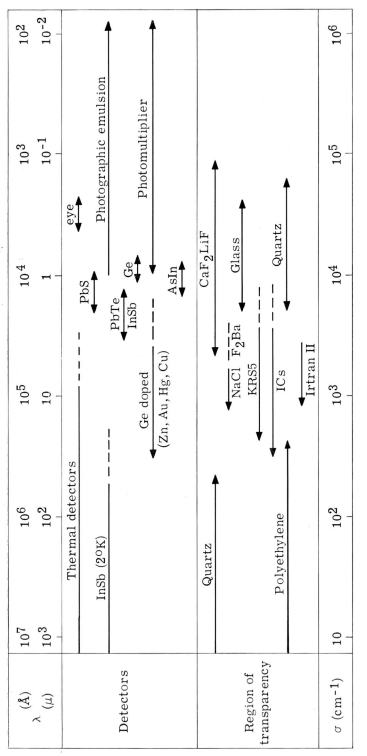

Fig. 1

a sensitive surface as possible. The detectivity varies inversely as the square root of the sensitive area of the detector, so that the emerging pencil must be concentrated onto a small area by a system of large numerical aperture. (2) Use a carrier frequency, i.e. chopper speed, which matches both the time constant and the noise spectrum of the detector; this is usually about 10 Hz for thermal detectors and some hundreds of cycles for quantum detectors. (3) Reduce the thermal noise by surrounding the detector with cooled surfaces to reduce radiation heating and by using filters which are themselves cooled (MCARDLE [1961]) to limit the spectral region transmitted to that being studied.

It will be seen that these two kinds of noise lead to two different principles for non-conventional instruments.

1.3. THE ESSENTIALS OF A PROBLEM OF SPECTROSCOPY

The initial data in a problem of spectroscopy can be expressed by four numerical values, corresponding to the following factors: the spectral region to be studied, the breadth of this region, the limit of resolution and lastly the speed at which the spectrum is to be recorded. The spectral region is characterized by a wavelength λ or by a wave-number σ. The relation between the most frequently used units is $\lambda = 10^4/\sigma$ (λ, wavelength in microns; σ, wave number in cm^{-1}).

The breadth or extent $\Delta\lambda$ of the spectrum to be studied is expressed by the limiting wavelengths λ_1 and $\lambda_2 = \lambda_1 + \Delta\lambda$.

The limit of resolution is the smallest interval $\delta\lambda$ between two just distinguishable wavelengths. There are several different definitions of this quantity, none exactly equivalent. The Rayleigh criterion was established for the theoretical case of pure Fraunhofer diffraction. $\delta\lambda$ is defined as the distance between the maximum and the first zero of the diffraction pattern or, alternatively as the width of the central maximum at the point where the intensity is 0.405 of its maximum valve. In practice it is

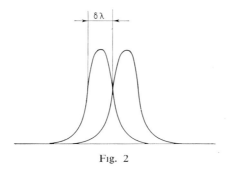

Fig. 2

often preferable to adopt a simple criterion which applies to all forms of the instrumental function (cf. § 2.1.2), which is that the resolution limit $\delta\lambda$ is equal to the width at half-height of the central maximum (fig. 2). In fact the difference between these definitions is negligible since $\delta\lambda$ can usually only be determined with poor precision. Elaborate calculations of this quantity are pointless.

In any case, we require only a conventional value since the effective resolution will depend on the signal-to-noise ratio. Certain techniques for dealing with the information to obtain resolution beyond the theoretical limit are available when the signal-to-noise ratio is high (TORALDO DI FRANCIA [1950], ARSAC [1960]). If the signal-to-noise ratio were infinite the resolution limit would be zero. However, methods of this kind are extravagant in terms of signal-to-noise ratio. It is always preferable to achieve the required result by using apparatus with a resolving limit (conventionally defined) corresponding to the resolution desired.

It is convenient to use the following dimensionless parameters in place of $\Delta\lambda$ and $\delta\lambda$:

Number of spectral elements $M = \Delta\lambda/\delta\lambda$,

Resolving power $\mathscr{R} = \lambda/\delta\lambda = \sigma/\delta\sigma$.

After λ, M and $\mathscr{R}$ the last datum needed to define the problem is the time T in which all the information is to be collected. Here T is the time for which the detector is actually in operation; it does not include the time needed for other operations such as development, reduction of data, etc.

The time reduced to a single spectral element $t = T/M$ expresses the speed of operation better than T. It is well known that if a measurement is subject to errors due to statistical fluctuations the accuracy can be increased according to the square root of the time taken over the observations. In the case of a spectrograph, T is the exposure time and all the spectral elements are treated simultaneously. For a spectrometer the band-width Δf of the complete measuring system (detector, amplifier, recorder, etc.) must satisfy the relation $\Delta f \geq 1/2t$. Generally speaking, the study of rapidly varying phenomena is particularly difficult in the infrared. In fact, thermal detectors, which are still the most used detectors beyond 6 μ have time constants which are limited by their thermal capacities to about 0.01 second, whereas many quantum detectors have time constant less than a microsecond.

1.4. INTRODUCTION TO THE CONCEPT OF LUMINOSITY

We now consider how best to obtain the spectrum thus specified with maximum accuracy. If we take the general term noise to include all random or non-systematic sources of error, the accuracy can be specified by the signal-to-noise ratio. This ratio, which controls, as we have already noted, the effective resolution, expresses the quality of the final result.

For a classical spectrometer we define the luminosity $\mathscr{L}$ as the ratio of the flux emerging from the exit slit to the energetic luminance of the source, $\mathscr{L} = \phi/B$. By definition, the luminance is the flux emitted from unit surface area in unit solid angle, so that $\phi = BS\Omega = BU$. The product $U = S\Omega$ is a measure of the 'étendue' of the beam accepted by the apparatus and we shall call it the optical acceptance of the apparatus. The two preceding relations show that the luminosity of a spectrometer is equal to its optical acceptance.

For a spectrograph the luminosity is the ratio of the illumination of the plate to the luminance of the source, $\mathscr{L} = E/B$.

In both these cases, spectrometer and spectrograph, the signal reaching the detector is the product of the luminosity by the luminance of the source; the signal produced is proportional to this to the extent that the detector and the rest of the measuring channel are linear.

The extension of the notion of luminosity to non-classical systems can present some difficulties because the effect of noise depends largely on the nature of the method itself; thus an increase in the signal, resulting from an increase in the luminosity as defined above, is of no value if it is accompanied by a greater increase in the noise level. It is therefore desirable to include the detector and its recording channel in the estimate of luminosity, rather than to discuss the optical system in isolation. Thus we shall say that, among many possible systems for dealing with a given spectroscopic problem (with given λ, M, $\mathscr{R}$, T) *that* one has the greatest luminosity which yields the required spectrum with the greatest signal-to-noise ratio after all data reduction. In other words, this apparatus shall give, under the required conditions of resolution and speed, the desired result with the weakest light source. We shall use this generalized definition of luminosity mainly in the third part of this chapter. For classical systems this definition reduces to the earlier one.

2. Systems using a slit

2.1. THE PRINCIPAL RESULTS IN THE GENERAL THEORY

The theory given sytematically here has only partially been published (JACQUINOT [1954b, c]). Reduced to bare essentials, the classical system comprises an entrance slit at the focus of a collimator, which may be either a mirror or a lens system, and an exit collimator, at the focal surface of which is the exit slit in the case of the spectrometer, or the photographic plate of the spectrograph. The dispersing system, which

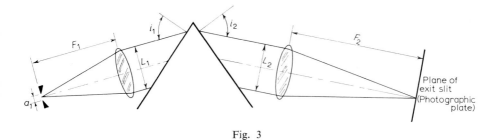

Fig. 3

may be either a prism or a plane grating, is between the two collimators; in the case of the concave grating the functions of the two collimators are taken over by the dispersor. The schematic diagram in fig. 3 applies to all cases; the dispersion occurs in the plane of the figure and the slits are perpendicular to this plane.

Notation

F focal length of the collimator
a slit width
b slit height
α angular width of the slit: $\alpha = a/F$
β angular height of the slit: $\beta = b/F$
i angle of incidence at the dispersor
L width of the beam

For all these symbols the subscript 1 refers to parts before the dispersor and subscript 2 to parts after the dispersor.

e half width of the central maximum of the diffraction pattern
ε angular half width of the central maximum of the diffraction pattern
g granularity of the emulsion
τ transmission factor of the system
H height of the dispersing system
W width of the dispersing system

2.1.1 *General properties*

Dispersion: The incident beam and the dispersor being fixed, the angular dispersion is the ratio of the difference between the angles of deviation of two neighbouring wavelengths to the difference between their wavelengths,

$$D_2 = (\partial i_2/\partial \lambda)_{i_1}. \tag{1}$$

The angular width $\varDelta i_2$, after the dispersor, of an incident monochromatic beam of width $\varDelta i_1$ is $\varDelta i_2 = G\varDelta i_1$, where G is the angular magnification of the dispersor, and we have also $L_1 = GL_2$. On the other hand, in the plane perpendicular to the plane of dispersion, the magnification of the dispersor is always equal to unity; thus the entrance slit and its image at the plane of the plate have the same angular height, apart from possible effects of astigmatism. From this it follows that the dispersor gives in general an anamorphotic effect. Neglecting diffraction, the width of the monochromatic image of the entrance slit is

$$a_1' = Ga_1 F_2/F_1. \tag{2}$$

In the Littrow mounting G is approximately unity, since L_1 and L_2 are nearly equal.

   The reduced slit width. It is convenient to express the slit width in terms of the width of the diffraction pattern:

$$u = \alpha/\varepsilon = a/e. \tag{3}$$

It can be shown that it is always best to have the exit slit the same width as the geometric image of the entrance slit, so that $a_2 = a_1'$ and $u_1 = u_2$.

   The case of a spectrograph is more complex; when the image of a point is formed on a photographic emulsion the developed image is a disc of finite size with a blackening curve of roughly Gaussian shape. The shape and size of this curve depend on the maximum density; we can take it as a first approximation that its diameter g at half-height is a characteristic of the emulsion. Thus the plate "grain" can be taken as the equivalent of an exit aperture of width g; the light incident in this area is integrated to produce the same final effect whatever its distribution within the region g. The blackening depends only on the flux received by each "grain" in the plate, so that we can imagine a photographic plate as a mosaic of independent detectors, contiguous, distributed at random and of diameter g. This is a crude approximation but it will serve for our discussion.

As for the spectrometer, the most favourable conditions for luminosity and resolution are

$$u_1 = u_2 \quad \text{and} \quad a_1/F_1 = g/F_2 \quad \text{(assuming } G = 1\text{).} \tag{4}$$

2.1.2. Resolving power

We shall treat the case of the spectrometer; the conclusions can be applied to the spectrograph with the reservations implied by the preceding subsection.

The instrumental function or apparatus function. This is the spectrum registered by the system when the source is a single line of negligible width (monochromatic line). For various reasons both fundamental and non-fundamental (diffraction, slit width, grain size, aberrations, mechanical faults) the recorded spectrum is not infinitely narrow; its shape is an essential characteristic of the system.

If the entrance and exit slits were infinitely narrow and if the system were aberration-free and perfectly made and adjusted, the instrumental function would be the diffraction pattern of a uniformly illuminated pupil, usually rectangular, of width L:

$$D(x) = F_2 \left[\frac{\sin (\pi x/e)}{\pi x/e} \right]^2 \tag{5}$$

with half width

$$e = \varepsilon F_2 \quad \text{and} \quad \varepsilon = \lambda/L_2. \tag{6}$$

Theoretical resolution. The theoretical resolution limit $\delta\lambda_0$ is the spectral interval corresponding to the width of the diffraction pattern:

$$\delta\lambda_0 = \varepsilon/D_2 = \lambda/L_2 D_2 \tag{7}$$

and the theoretical resolving power is

$$\mathscr{R}_0 = \lambda/\delta\lambda_0 = L_2 D_2. \tag{8}$$

In practice this value can be closely approached but it can never be exceeded.

Effect of slit width. The instrumental function which is obtained under practicably realizable conditions, that is, with slits of finite width, is very different. For an entrance slit of width a the light distribution in the final focal plane is given by the integral

$$F(x) = \int_{x-\frac{1}{2}a'_1}^{x+\frac{1}{2}a'_1} D(x)\mathrm{d}x. \qquad (9)$$

To obtain the flux emerging from the exit slit as a function of its position as the spectrum is scanned a second integration over the exit slit is necessary:

$$G(x) = \int_{x-\frac{1}{2}a_2}^{x+\frac{1}{2}a_2} F(x)\mathrm{d}x. \qquad (10)$$

For $u \gg 1$ the effects of diffraction are negligible and $F(x)$ is a rectangular (top-hat) function of width a, while $G(x)$ is a triangular function of base $2a = 2ue$. The width at half-height is thus ue, u times greater than the theoretical diffraction pattern, so that the resolving power $\mathscr{R}$ is related to $\mathscr{R}_0$ by

$$\mathscr{R} = \mathscr{R}_0/u \qquad (u \gg 1). \qquad (11)$$

For smaller values of u it can be shown that $\mathscr{R}_0/\mathscr{R}$ varies as in curve 1 of fig. 4. For $u = 1$ we have $\mathscr{R} = 0.65\,\mathscr{R}_0$.

2.1.3. *Luminosity*

The spectrometer. The luminosity is the ratio of the flux received by the detector to the monochromatic luminance for the spectral element considered; it is equal to the optical acceptance (cf. § 1.4). $\mathscr{L} = \phi/B = \tau S\Omega$, where S is the area of the exit slit and Ω the solid angle subtended by the dispersor at the exit slit. On putting S and Ω in terms of the geometry of the system we have (assuming $u_1 = u_2 = u$)

$$\mathscr{L} = \tau a_2 b_2 H L_2 / F_2^2 = \tau H \beta a_2 L_2 / F_2.$$

Using eqs. (3) and (6) we have

$$\mathscr{L} = \tau H \beta \lambda u. \qquad (12)$$

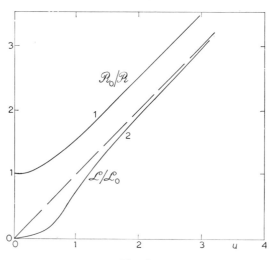

Fig. 4

From curve (1), fig. 4, the reduced slit width u can be put in the form $u = K(u)\mathscr{R}_0/\mathscr{R}$ with $K(u) = 1$ for $u \gg 1$ and $K(u) = 0$ for $u = 0$.

The general expression for the luminosity of a spectrometer is finally

$$\mathscr{L} = \tau H\beta\lambda(\mathscr{R}_0/\mathscr{R})K(u). \tag{13}$$

On putting $\mathscr{L}_0 = \tau H\beta\lambda$, eq. (13) can be written

$$\mathscr{L}\mathscr{R} = \mathscr{L}_0\mathscr{R}_0 K(u). \tag{14}$$

For given resolution $\mathscr{R}$ the luminosity or acceptance is a maximum when the product $\mathscr{L}_0\mathscr{R}_0$ is a maximum.

For $u \gg 1$ the product $\mathscr{L}\mathscr{R}$ is constant. Curve 2 of fig. 4 shows the behaviour of $\mathscr{L}/\mathscr{L}_0$ as a function of u; it departs from the straight line $\mathscr{L}/\mathscr{L}_0 = u$ for small u because the image of the entrance slit is spread by diffraction. Fig. 5 shows the variation of $\mathscr{L}\mathscr{R}/\mathscr{L}_0\mathscr{R}_0$ as a function of u.

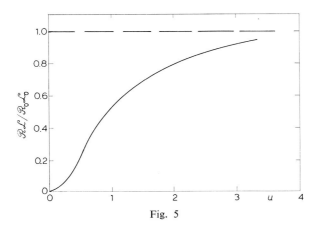

Fig. 5

The following deductions can be made from these equations: (1) For given resolving power $\mathscr{R} < \mathscr{R}_0$ the acceptance of the system is proportional to the theoretical resolving power $\mathscr{R}_0$ of the dispersor. Thus it is an advantage to use a dispersing system of which the theoretical resolution $\mathscr{R}_0$ is as great as possible, even if the desired resolving power $\mathscr{R}$ is much smaller. (2) The theoretical resolving power can only be approached at considerable expense in luminosity; for $\mathscr{R}/\mathscr{R}_0 = 0.8$ the loss in luminosity is about 70%. (3) The acceptance is proportional to the height H of the dispersing system and the angular height β of the slit; it is independent of the focal lengths F_1 and F_2 and of the dispersion D of the prism or grating.

The spectrograph. The luminosity is the ratio of the illumination at the plate to the luminance of the element of spectrum considered: $\mathscr{L} = E/B$. We saw (§ 2.1.1) that the plate grain can, to a first approximation, be regarded as having the effect of an exit slit of appropriate width in a spectrometer. Thus, to obtain near theoretical resolving power, g must be less than or equal to the diffraction pattern in size, that is:

$$g \leqq \lambda F_2 / L_2. \tag{15}$$

The relative aperture $n_2 = F_2/L_2$ must thus be very small, about $1 : 40$ for $\lambda = 0.5\ \mu$ and $g = 20\ \mu$. This condition is rarely fulfilled, so that the plate grain sets an upper limit to the resolving power:

$$\mathscr{R} = \mathscr{R}_0 e/g = \mathscr{R}_0 n_2 \lambda / g. \tag{16}$$

Furthermore, the optimum slit width is such that its image has a width a'_1 approximately equal to g, for if the slit is narrower the resolution is not improved, being limited by g; if on the other hand the slit is wider the resolving power is decreased without any resultant increase in luminosity, since the illumination at the plate is hardly changed for a line spectrum.

The luminosity is governed by the usual law of photographic optics, that it is proportional to the solid angle subtended by the second collimator at the plate,

$$\mathscr{L} = \tau L_2 H / F_2^2. \tag{17}$$

From eqs. (16) and (17) it can be shown that the product $\mathscr{L}\mathscr{R}^2$ is constant for a system of given dispersion. We can modify $\mathscr{L}$ or $\mathscr{R}$ and obtain the wanted resolution–luminosity compromise by a suitable choice of F_2; if F_2 is decreased the luminosity is increased, since the relative aperture of the second collimator is increased, but at the same time the plate grain limits the resolution more severely. Another parameter is the type of emulsion and here the width of the entrance slit must be chosen to suit the grain size in each case.

Even more than in the case of a spectrometer, it is advantageous to use a dispersor with as high a theoretical resolving power as possible. It can be shown that the case of the spectrograph is analogous to that of the spectrometer from the point of view of diffraction: as long as the inequality (15) holds, the luminosity approaches zero as the resolving power $\mathscr{R}$ approaches the theoretical value $\mathscr{R}_0$.

2.2. GENERAL PROPERTIES OF DISPERSORS

The most important property of a dispersor is its theoretical resolution $\mathscr{R}_0$, given by eq. (8). Another general expression for $\mathscr{R}_0$ can be obtained as follows. Let $\varDelta$ be the optical path difference between two rays of a parallel pencil emerging from the dispersor, the rays being at opposite edges of the dispersor. Suppose that for wavelength λ there is constructive interference between all the rays of the beam parallel to these two rays. Let λ' be the closest wavelength for which there is destructive interference. Then the path difference at λ' is $\varDelta_{\lambda'} = \varDelta_{\lambda} + \lambda' \approx \varDelta_{\lambda} + \lambda$; for if these two extreme rays are in phase, one extreme ray and one ray in the centre of the beam are exactly in opposition and the whole width of the beam can be arranged in pairs of rays in phase opposition thus giving a resultant amplitude of zero. Applying the Rayleigh criterion, the interval between two wavelengths that are just resolved is

$$\delta\lambda_0 = \lambda' - \lambda$$

Thus

$$\mathscr{R}_0 = \lambda/\delta\lambda_0 = \frac{\varDelta'_\lambda - \varDelta_\lambda}{\lambda' - \lambda} = \frac{\partial \varDelta}{\partial \lambda}. \tag{18}$$

2.2.1 The prism

The extreme rays in this case are those near the refracting edge and the base of the prism. It is easily seen that for an increment dn of the refractive index of the prism the increment in optical path between these two rays is $d\varDelta = E\,dn$, where E is the width of the base of the prism. Then from eq. (18) we have

$$\mathscr{R}_0 = E\,dn/d\lambda. \tag{19}$$

Table 1 lists the spectral regions for which present-day materials can be used. Fused silica is the only material used in the ultraviolet. There are no materials suitable for dispersing systems for wavelengths below 2000 Å or above 50 μ.

TABLE 1

Material	Region (μ)
F²Ca	0.2–8
Quartz	0.2–3.5
Glass	0.4–2.5
NaCl	< 15
KBr	< 25
CsBr	< 25
CsI	< 45

2.2.2. Plane reflecting gratings

The use of the plane grating as dispersor has grown considerably in recent years as a result of progress in their manufacture and testing (HARRISON [1949], STROKE [1963]). The basic grating formula is obtained by writing down the condition for constructive interference between two parallel rays diffracted by two consecutive lines of the grating (fig. 6)

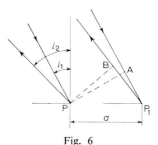

Fig. 6

$$S = PA + PB = a(\sin i_1 + \sin i_2) = p\lambda \tag{20}$$

where p is an integer and a is the spacing between lines. If W is the ruled width then $a = W/N$ where N is the number of lines.

The path difference Δ between extreme rays from opposite sides of the grating may similarly be written

$$\Delta = W(\sin i_1 + \sin i_2) = Wp\lambda/a. \tag{21}$$

From (18), (20) and (21) $\mathscr{R}_0$ can be expressed in various forms:

$$\mathscr{R}_0 = \partial\Delta/\partial\lambda = Wp/a, \tag{22}$$

$$\mathscr{R}_0 = pN, \tag{22'}$$

$$\mathscr{R}_0 = W(\sin i_1 + \sin i_2)/\lambda. \tag{22''}$$

Eq. (22'') can be used to obtain the resolution limit $\delta\sigma_0$ in wave numbers: $\delta\sigma_0 = W^{-1}(\sin i_1 + \sin i_2)^{-1} = \sigma/\mathscr{R}_0$.

The quantity $\sin i_1 + \sin i_2$ generally lies between 1 and 1.5, so that we have

$$W^{-1}(\text{cm}^{-1}) > \delta\sigma_0(\text{cm}^{-1}) > \tfrac{2}{3}W^{-1}(\text{cm}^{-1}). \tag{23}$$

The theoretical resolving limit of a grating (in cm^{-1}) is thus roughly equal to the reciprocal of the ruled width in cm. For a 20 cm wide grating we have $0.05 > \delta\sigma_0 > 0.033 \text{ cm}^{-1}$.

It follows from (22'') that high resolution grating must have a large ruled width and must be operated at a large angle of incidence. A given wavelength λ may be investigated with a grating used in the first order to obtain a certain resolving power, the grating spacing being then of order λ, or a different grating with spacing much larger than λ may be used in a higher order to give the same resolving power. If the two gratings are the same size and are used at the same angles of incidence and diffraction the resolution and luminosity are independent of the spacing and the order of interference. Under the condition $\mathscr{R} \ll \mathscr{R}_0$ it is possible to express $\mathscr{R}$ very simply in terms of the angular width of the slit:

$$\mathscr{R} = \frac{\sin i_1 + \sin i_2}{\alpha \cos i_2} = \mathscr{R}_0/u.$$

A modern development is the echelette grating (STROKE [1963]) which has a sawtooth ruling profile (fig. 7). Such a grating is characterized by the angle φ, the blaze

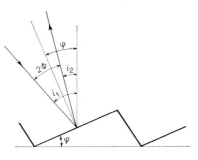

Fig. 7

angle, which is the angle between the effective surfaces of the profile and the general plane of the grating surface. An echelette grating should be used with the incident and diffracted rays as close as possible to the normal to these facets, i.e. preferably in an autocollimating mounting. Under such conditions a large proportion of the light is concentrated in a single order. The 'transmission factor' or, more appropriately, efficiency can be higher than 70%, a value approaching the transmission factor of the best prisms.

Let θ be the angle between the normal to the reflecting facets and the bisector of the incident and diffracted rays and let 2ϕ be the angle between the incident and diffracted rays, as in fig. 7. Then from eq. (20) and (22) we have

$$p\lambda = 2a \cos \phi \sin(\theta+\varphi),$$
$$\mathcal{R}_0 = 2W \cos \phi \sin(\theta+\varphi)/\lambda. \tag{24}$$

The angle θ measures the departure from the blaze condition and it should be kept as small as possible. These equations show also the advantage of using a grating with a large blaze angle. Finally, it can be seen that the angle of deviation 2ϕ should be kept as small as possible. These formulae and conclusions are also valid for concave gratings.

2.2.3. Comparison of the luminosity of prism and grating spectrometers (JACQUINOT [1954])

The general conclusions in this section also apply to spectrographs. From eq. (13) the effect of the dispersing system on luminosity is given by the product $H\mathcal{R}_0$. All other things including the τ's being equal, the ratio of luminosities can be written

$$P = \mathcal{L}_{pr}/\mathcal{L}_{gr} = H_{pr}\mathcal{R}_{0,pr}/H_{gr}\mathcal{R}_{0,gr}.$$

On using the expressions (19) and (22'') for the resolving powers of the prism and the grating we have

$$P = \frac{H_{pr}E\lambda(dn/d\lambda)}{H_{gr}W(\sin i_1 + \sin i_2)}. \tag{25}$$

It is reasonable to compare the luminosities of a prism and a grating of equivalent dimensions; assuming that the prism has a projected area equal to the area of the grating ($H_{pr}E = H_{gr}W$) and that $\sin i_1 + \sin i_2$ is little different from unity the expression for P reduces to

$$P = \lambda \, du/d\lambda. \tag{26}$$

The curves in fig. 8 show P as a function of wavelength for various materials. From this it can be seen that for a dispersive system of given dimensions and resolving power a grating spectrometer has at least ten times greater luminosity than a prism instrument. In other words, for the same luminosity a prism can be replaced by a grating with P times less area.

The development of grating instruments has for a long time been slow because of the poor directivity of the gratings; if the energy is distributed roughly equally among the various orders the transmission coefficient τ which appears in the expression for the luminosity will be low. However, for echelette gratings the efficiency (cf. § 2.2.2) can reach 70%, which is near the value for the best prisms.

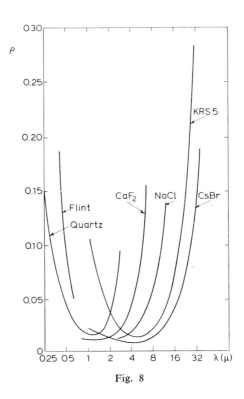

Fig. 8

The question now arises, how can the superiority of the grating be realized in practice? Although gratings are widely used in all branches of spectroscopy there can be no question of simply doing without prisms. The main difficulty in the use of gratings is separating the orders and one of the ways of overcoming this difficulty is to use a prism in combination with a grating. Apart from this point, the prism is still the most convenient system for spectroscopy when only modest performance is required and it is thus the logical choice for certain industrial apparatus *. On the other hand, research apparatus must be capable of being used under conditions demanding considerable resolution and speed. This, then, is where luminosity is a prime consideration and it would be difficult to justify the use of a prism, at any rate as the principal dispersor.

* The terms 'research apparatus' and 'industrial apparatus' used here are explained in the introduction.

2.2.4. *Separating the orders of a grating*

Eq. (20) is satisfied by a series of wavelengths obtained by giving p a sequence of integer values. The pth order wavelength is given by $\lambda_p = a(\sin i_1 + \sin i_2)/p$, so that we have $\lambda_1 = 2\lambda_2 = \cdots = p\lambda_p$.

There are several possible ways of isolating one order of a grating and eliminating the others. The problem becomes more difficult, however, when a high order is to be isolated.

Use of filters. Either band-pass or low-pass filters can be used to eliminate orders higher than the one required; any transparent material will generally form a low-pass filter; interference filters offer a wide range of possibilities for band-pass filters.

Pre-monochromators. Grating spectrometers are often preceded by simplified prism spectrometers of low resolving power; the exit slit of this pre-monochromator serves also as the entrance slit of the grating spectrometer and it passes a wavelength range less than the interval $\lambda_p - \lambda_{p+1}$ between the orders of the grating. The coupling of the scanning mechanisms of the two monochromators needs considerable care. As a result of progress with filters of various types there has been a decline in the use of prism pre-monochromators in the infrared.

Crossed dispersion. A relatively weak dispersion is used in a plane perpendicular to the dispersion plane of the grating. This is the preferred solution for spectrographs; it arranges the spectra of different orders one under the other within the field covered by the photographic plate, thus utilizing to the full the information recording capacity of the plate all over its surface. The spectrum is spread out in rows like printed lines of text on a page. As many as several hundred rows can be obtained with an echelle grating (HARRISON [1949, 1952]) as these work in very high orders. Crossed dispersion can be obtained by means of transmission or reflection gratings or prisms.

2.2.5. *Use of dispersors in series*

Dispersors can be arranged in series for two different purposes:

(a) To obtain very great reduction of parasitic light in spectrometers and more particularly monochromators. For this purpose two monochromators, usually identical, are combined by means of an intermediate slit. Such a system can be very efficient, for if the level of stray light for each system on its own is 1 % the combined systems will give only 1 in 10^4. Double monochromators are usually made with prisms; they are classified as additive or subtractive according as the dispersions add or subtract.

The problem of parasitic radiation is particularly acute in the infrared; to see this it is only necessary to note that a black body at 1500 °K emits 500 times more radiation at 2 μ than at 20 μ. Fig. 9 shows an example of a double monochromator for the infrared.

(b) To increase the theoretical resolving power of the spectrometer as well as the spectrograph. In the classic case of a train of prisms, for example, the theoretical resolving power of the ensemble is the sum of the resolving powers of the individual prisms. The same holds for gratings (STROKE [1963]). Another method is to use the same dispersor twice or more, as in the Littrow prism mounting (see § 2.3); this method of double-passing can be used with very large gratings and gives very good

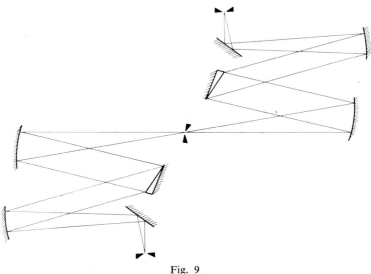

Fig. 9

results both in the visible and in the infrared (RANK [1959]). However, in double-passing it can happen that stray light which is not removed after the first reflection from the grating may reach the exit slit and be superimposed on the wanted spectrum. This stray light can be eliminated in various ways but none of these is entirely satisfactory, at least in the region where photon noise predominates.

2.3. PRINCIPLES OF THE MOST GENERALLY USED SYSTEMS

Considerations of space must limit our present summary to the principles of the systems in most common use, with reference in each case to the most recent publications.

2.3.1. *Prism systems*

Minimum deviation mounting. This is the most classic of the mountings used in spectroscopy; fig. 3 shows the general arrangement. It can be shown that the reasons for using a prism at minimum deviation are, in fact, only reasons of practical convenience. The product of luminosity and resolution (cf. § 2.1.3) does not depend on the angle of incidence or on the refracting angle of the prism, but only on the size of the base of the prism. The generally adopted angle of 60 degrees is a good compromise between various factors, none of fundamental importance; among these the reflection losses at the faces of the prism rank high.

The Littrow mounting (fig. 10). In this mounting the rays are reflected by a plane mirror after traversing the prism and return substantially along the original paths. The double passing gives a factor of two increase in theoretical resolving power and consequently also in luminosity and effective resolving power. Thus a single prism of base E is optically equivalent to a prism of base $2E$. Furthermore the same collimator,

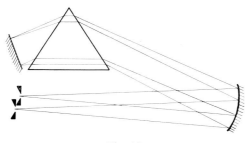

Fig. 10

reflecting or refracting, is used for the incident and refracted beams. When the collimator is a mirror, as is always the case in the infrared, correction for spherical aberration and coma can be obtained by using an off-axis paraboloid mirror. In this case the system is rigorously stigmatic at the focus of the mirror but the usable slit height is severely limited by field curvature.

The Féry mounting (fig. 11). This consists of a prism with spherical surfaces, the rear surface having a reflecting coating. As in the case of the concave grating, the

Fig. 11

dispersor serves also as a collimator. The small number of surfaces and the simplicity of mounting make this system useful for apparatus of modest performance. This mounting has been employed commercially in simple monochromators for the visible or near ultraviolet.

2.3.2. *The plane grating*

Littrow mounting. This is similar to the Littrow prism system described in § 2.3.1, but the prism and plane mirror are replaced by the grating. Most of what was said in § 2.3.1 is equally applicable here.

Ebert–Fastie system (fig. 12; EBERT [1889], FASTIE [1952, 1953, 1958], CROSSWHITE [1956]). This is mainly used for spectrometry; the entrance and exit slits S and S′ are in the focal plane of the spherical mirror, on either side of the grating. The slits are arcs of a circle in the focal plane of the mirror, the centre of this circle lying on the line joining the centres of the grating and the mirror. In this way the effects of astigmatism and spectrum line curvature are compensated for all angles of incidence on the grating. The angular height of the slits β can be about 0.1 in this system; it is widely used, particularly for efficient spectrometers for the infrared.

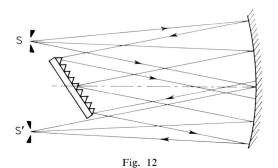

Fig. 12

Czerny–Turner system (CZERNY and TURNER [1930]). In its original form this system comprised two identical spherical mirrors placed symmetrically with respect to the grating (fig. 13). This symmetry gives coma correction but in fact this is only rigorously true if the grating is replaced by a plane mirror; in practice, as in the

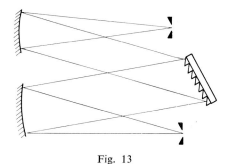

Fig. 13

preceding cases, the geometry is changed by the inclination of the grating so that there is some residual coma. An improvement can be obtained by abandoning the strict symmetry to an extent governed by the inclination of the grating (LEO [1958, 1962], SHAFFER *et al.* [1964])]).

2.3.3. *The spherical concave grating* (ROWLAND [1882, 1883])

If the grating is ruled on a concave spherical mirror it functions simultaneously as dispersor and collimator. Certain interesting properties of the concave grating are associated with the 'Rowland circle', a circle whose *diameter* is equal to the *radius* of the concave mirror: if the entrance slit is placed on and the grating tangent to this circle then all the monochromatic images of the slit are focussed on the circle.

In the far ultraviolet the poor reflecting power of mirrors dictates a reduction in the number of reflecting surfaces. The concave grating serves simultaneously as dispersor and entrance and exit collimator, so that it can be used to make a spectrograph with only a single reflection; for this reason the concave grating is the only kind of dispersor used in the far ultraviolet. It is used throughout the photographic region, that is, to 1 μ, but hardly ever in the infrared.

Many concave grating mountings have been suggested; we shall not describe the Rowland and Abney mountings as these are now only of historical interest.

Paschen–Runge mounting (fig. 14; RUNGE [1902], DIEKE *et al.* [1945]). The entrance slit and the grating are fixed and the angle of incidence is usually small. As a spectro-

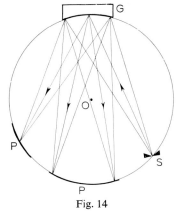

Fig. 14

graph, a series of photographic plates can be arranged along the Rowland circle. The mounting is very bulky and very great mechanical precision is needed in making the Rowland circle. However, this mounting can give simultaneously a large amount of information about a complex, extended spectrum; very large mountings of this type (10 metres) have been set up in specialized laboratories devoted to the classification of atomic and molecular spectra (HARRISON *et al.* [1948], TOMKINS and FRED [1956]).

Eagle mounting (fig. 15; EAGLE [1910], BAIR [1953]). In this arrangement the angle

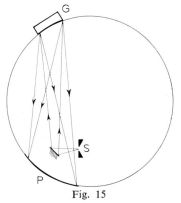

Fig. 15

between the incident and returning beams is always small. The entrance slit and the plate are fixed and in order to change the spectral region under investigation it is necessary to rotate the grating (to change the angle of incidence), to displace it (in order to change the slit–grating distance) and to rotate the plate. This mounting is more compact than the Paschen–Runge but only a limited spectral range can be covered in a single exposure.

Wadsworth mounting (fig. 16; WADSWORTH [1896], JARRELL [1942]). This mounting does not use the Rowland circle; the incident beam is collimated and the spectrum

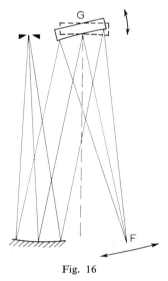

Fig. 16

is formed near the normal to the grating ($i_2 = 0$) at its focus F, i.e. at a distance $\frac{1}{2}R$ from the grating. The image at F is stigmatic. The spectrum can be scanned by rotating the arm FP round the point P; the plate or exit slit is thus displaced along an arc of a circle of radius $\frac{1}{2}R$.

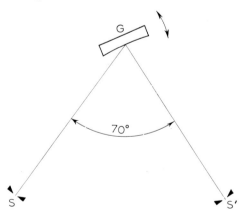

Fig. 17

Seya–Namioka mounting (SEYA [1952], NAMIOKA [1954, 1959]). In this system the spectrum is scanned by simply rotating the grating, the same convenient method of adjustment as that of a plane grating instrument. This is achieved as in fig. 17; the entrance and exit slits S and S′ subtend an angle of 70 degrees at the centre P of the grating and the distances SP and S′P are respectively $0.8181R$ and $0.8176R$, where R is the radius of the grating. It was shown by the above-named authors that under these conditions the spectral images of the entrance slit at S′ are of acceptable quality over a wide range of angles of the grating.

Other mountings have been proposed using aspherical gratings, but these have not been used to any great extent (HABER [1950], SHCHEPETKIN [1959]).

2.3.4. *Notes on the choice of mounting*

Spectrographs. It seems preferable to use a system with separate entrance and exit collimators, so that the focal distance F_2 can be chosen as required. This is particularly useful for research instruments. The spectrograph used with the large telescope of the Observatory of Haute Provence is a good example of such flexibility; it has five exit collimators, the maximum and minimum focal length being 2 m and 16.5 cm (FEHRENBACH [1959]). The plane grating mounting is of the Czerny–Turner type, which is convenient for these conditions.

On the other hand, one important parameter of a spectrograph is the number of spectral elements obtained on the plate. From this point of view the Paschen–Runge mounting is very attractive, although it cannot realize the full possibilities of echelette gratings; as we saw, these gratings are very efficient only when used under well-defined conditions.

Spectrometers. The question of the mode of scanning the spectrum is basic here. In the case of a plane grating spectrometer and the Seya–Namioka mounting of the concave grating, scanning is achieved by simplying rotating the grating. For other mountings of the concave grating the scanning procedure is more complex. Of the various plane grating mountings the Ebert–Fastie is as compact as the Littrow and it offers the great advantage of exact correction of the spectrum line curvature. However, because of its flexibility, the Czerny–Turner offers the best possibilities for correction of the geometrical aberrations due to oblique incidence at the grating.

2.4. INDUSTRIAL APPARATUS

Apart from ordinary spectrographs and spectrometers, usually of prism type, the need for simple and rapid operation has given rise to two new types, spectrophotometers and multichannel direct reading spectrometers. Both types rely on flux detectors.

2.4.1. *Multichannel direct-reading spectrometers*

The optical system is that of a spectrograph with plane or concave grating, usually very large, in which the photographic plate is replaced by a series of slits of which the positions can be adjusted to correspond to the characteristic lines of the material to be tested. The signal given by the photomultiplier following each slit is proportional to the intensity of a spectral line and, hence, the concentration of the element in question. As many as fifty channels are used in some commercial apparatus. Apparatus of this type is used particularly in metallurgical control work; the results are given directly, in less than a minute after the specimen is tested. Such systems are coupled to an electronic computer for automatic control and regulation. The same equipment can equally well be used as a spectrograph.

2.4.2 *Double beam spectrometers*

These instruments are needed in industrial laboratories concerned with atomic or molecular absorption spectroscopy. Rapid automatic measurements of spectral transmission or reflection coefficients for solid, liquid or gaseous specimens have to be made. With an ordinary spectrometer two measurements would be necessary. The transmission curve would be obtained as the ratio of the intensities of the spectra with and without the sample, so that the measurement of the two spectra must be followed by a calculation.

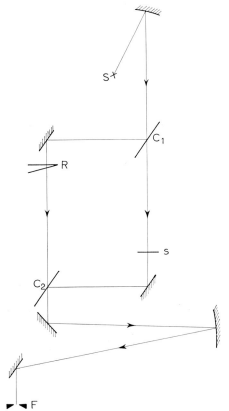

Fig. 18. S = source; C_1, C_2 = choppers; R = optical attenuator; s = sample; F = entrance slit of the spectrometer.

Nowadays spectrometers for this purpose are made as 'double-beam' systems; a single detector is used and the sample and reference spectra are scanned simultaneously, using an optical commutator (fig. 18). In the course of one cycle the detector receives energy from the sample and reference beams for equal periods of time. Clearly the commutation cycle must be short compared to the time required to scan a single spectral element. Apparatus of this kind falls into two classes according to the method used for determining the ratio of the energies:

(1) The ratio between the sample and reference signals can be determined by a recording potentiometer after isolation and amplification of these signals. This 'sequential' method seems to need more care in construction and adjustment but it gives more precise results than the second method. It is used in some systems where high precision is required.

(2) An optical attenuator is introduced into the reference beam; this is used to equalize the two beams, thus reducing the differential signal to zero. The pen recorder can be then coupled to the attenuator to give directly the absorption coefficient of the sample. This technique of 'optical zeroing' is in wide use.

2.5. COMPARISON BETWEEN SPECTROMETERS AND SPECTROGRAPHS

The advantages to be gained from the use of photomultipliers can be enumerated as follows: (1) Linearity of response. (2) Possibility of immediate recording of the reading. (3) Very high sensitivity for a single spectral element; the quantum efficiency can be as much as 100 times that of a photographic plate (FELLGETT [1958], JONES [1959]).

Of these the first two are advantages of convenience, but they do not in principle affect precision of measurement, since they are not concerned with luminosity as defined in § 1.4. Thus they are more important advantages for industrial apparatus than for research apparatus, using these terms in the sense explained earlier. We shall now be concerned with the latter class in comparing the luminosity of spectrometers and spectrographs.

The fundamental advantage of a spectrograph lies in its ability to record simultaneously a large amount of information. Some tens of thousands of spectral elements are recorded in one exposure. With the notation of § 1.3 we can say that to obtain the same information in the same time with a spectrometer the scanning time for a single spectral element must not exceed $t = T/M$. For equal quantum efficiencies of detectors the ratio of luminosities is equal to the square root of the ratio of the time required for a single spectral element by the two methods. In the present case the advantage would lie with the spectrograph, but there are two other factors which must be taken into account; first, as we have just seen, the quantum efficiency of photomultipliers is considerably greater than that of photographic plates, and secondly not all the spectral elements are of equal interest. The spectrum to be investigated is not in any practical case completely unknown, as is illustrated by the selection of information in multichannel spectrometers; nevertheless the photographic plate enjoys a unique position by virtue of its capacity for information. Finally the possibilities of the electronic camera (LALLEMAND *et al.* [1960]), of which the quantum efficiency is equal to that of the best photomultipliers, lend a new interest to spectrographic methods. The resolution limit of the camera itself is several microns over a field of 30 mm. Furthermore its response is linear: the opacity measured on the nuclear plate is proportional to the illumination.

A spectrograph with a large grating used at a high blaze angle, with crossed dispersion for separating the orders and an electronic camera would undoubtedly be the conventional system offering the greatest possibilities in its own field.

2.6. SPECIAL PROBLEMS OF THE FAR ULTRAVIOLET (TOUSEY [1962], 150 references)

This is the region between 2000 Å and 100 Å and we meet three special difficulties in this domain:

(1) The atmosphere is opaque, so the apparatus has to be used in a vacuum of about 10^{-5} Torr; obviously under these conditions the system must be as compact as possible. It follows also that such systems are of special interest for astrophysical experiments outside the atmosphere in this wavelength range, in particular in studies of the Lyman line of hydrogen at 1216 Å (NAMIOKA [1961]).

(2) There are few transparent materials. Fluorite can be used down to 1200 Å in thicknesses of a few mm. Below 1000 Å no known material is transparent in macroscopic thicknesses.

Windowless photoelectric detectors are used (BRUNET *et al.* [1963]). This is feasible because of the vacuum in the whole system. Photomultipliers having a window covered with a fluorescent material, most commonly sodium salicylate, are also employed.

Gelatine as used on ordinary plates is itself opaque, so special films or plates are used (SCHOEN [1952], AUDRAN [1956], TOUSEY [1960]).

(3) It is difficult to get mirrors with high reflectivity. This has long been a major obstacle in the study of this spectral region and it justifies the almost exclusive use of the concave grating, since in its most simple mountings only one surface is involved. Considerable progress is at present being made in the improvement of reflectivity in the far ultraviolet (MADDEN [1963]); as much as 80% can be obtained at 1200 Å with certain coated aluminium films and some non-oxidizing metals are also being used. On account of this progress plane grating systems with two extra reflections are now beginning to be used.

The separation of orders is done by the means described in § 2.2.4: the use of a prism (WILKINSON and ANGELL [1963]) or crossed dispersion with another grating (DOUGLASS *et al.* [1957], DETWEILER *et al.* [1961], TOUSEY [1961]). The selectivity of certain detectors can also be used (DUNKELMAN [1962]).

Below 400 Å the concave grating is used at a high angle of incidence (about 80 degrees) primarily because of its poor reflectivity at small angles of incidence. The entrance slit and the plate (or exit slit) are thus on the Rowland circle on either side of the grating. Such systems have been made as spectrographs (WILLIAMS [1958],

AUSTIN [1962]) and as spectrometers (BEHRING *et al.* [1962], ROMAND and VODAR [1962]). A comparative study of different mountings for use in space (NAMIOKA [1961]) suggests that the Eagle mounting is superior to the others.

2.7. SPECIAL PROBLEMS OF THE FAR INFRARED

Two of the difficulties mentioned in connection with the far ultraviolet, atmospheric absorption and the lack of transparent materials, are also present at the other extreme of the spectrum ($\lambda > 50 \mu$).

Several papers have been published recently on the few materials which can be used in the far infrared (DECAMPS *et al.* [1960], GENZEL [1964], McCUBBIN *et al.* [1950]). Quartz is the most important; it becomes transparent again beyond 50 μ.

The atmospheric absorption is due to rotation bands of water vapour. Spectrometers are used in vacuum or, less frequently, in a carefully dried atmosphere.

In this region the main difficulties come from the feebleness of useable radiation from conventional light source, combined with much stronger parasitic radiation of shorter wavelengths. Only plane grating systems are used; the main instrumental problem is the elimination of unwanted higher orders of the grating while retaining good transmission for the wanted order. Many different filtering methods have been used and the best results have been obtained by combining several of them. These filtering techniques are: depolished mirrors (PLYLER [1947]), selective reflection from meshes (MITSUISHI *et al.* [1963]), selective reflection from monocrystals (MITSUISHI *et al.* [1962]), use of auxiliary gratings with small spacing ($< \frac{1}{2}\lambda$) which operate as plane mirrors (HADNI [1960]), use of materials that are transparent at low temperature (HADNI [1964]), transmission through polyethylene sheets containing powders of crystals (YAMADA *et al.* [1962]). In this way it is possible to isolate the first order of a grating with a transmission coefficient near 50%.

In this spectral range, the detectors most generally employed are thermal detectors. (For exceptions see PUTLEY [1960] and BESSON *et al.* [1965].) The sensitive surface is usually not more than a few tens of square millimetres. The choice is in practice restricted to two or three types, the most used being the Golay pneumatic detector. On the other hand the optical acceptance (see § 1.4) of the apparatus is usually quite large in this region and is in fact often limited by the detector, because all the flux from the exit slit must be concentrated on the sensitive area of the detector. Thus spectrometers for the far infrared are specialized systems which must be adapted to suit best the available detector (HADNI [1956]). The optical system which is placed between the exit slit and the detector is generally of very large relative aperture and it is more difficult to design and make than the collimator. It would seem that progress in the development of far infrared spectrometry must depend on the development of detectors with large sensitive surfaces.

Much more so than in the near and middle infrared, the use of light choppers and synchronous rectifiers has resulted in major progress in the far infrared. The chopper disc is always placed before the entrance slit, mainly so that its own radiation is dispersed by the grating along with that of the source.

3. Non-classical systems

3.1. FABRY–PEROT SPECTROMETERS AND SPECTROGRAPHS

3.1.1. *Introduction*

Fabry–Perot interferometers or etalons have been in use for many years. Until 1950 these instruments were used almost exclusively for high-resolution spectroscopy, in particular in the study of hyperfine structure, which reveals the effect of the atomic nucleus on optical spectra. Furthermore, they were always used photographically. Since then considerable progress has been made in the use of these interferometers; in particular they are now used with flux detectors (the Fabry–Perot spectrometer) thus extending their range well into the infrared. In this chapter we shall restrict ourselves to indicating briefly the various methods of use and the advantages of each. Several more detailed accounts have recently been published (e.g. JACQUINOT [1960]) and we refer to these to further information and more detailed and rigorous treatment of the theory. For the moment we only point out that the Fabry–Perot spectrometer is the prototype of the high-acceptance system: the solid angle of the beam which it can accept for given resolving power gives it under certain conditions a product $\mathscr{L}\mathscr{R}$ much greater than that of the conventional instruments considered above. Since then other systems with the same properties of high acceptance have evolved; we shall consider these in later sections.

3.1.2. *General properties of a Fabry–Perot element*

Structure. We use the term *Fabry–Perot element,* or FP for brevity, to denote the arrangement of two transparent plates with the facing surfaces exactly plane and parallel; these surfaces are coated with semi-transmitting films of reflectance R and transmittance T and are separated by a distance e which may range from a few hundredths of a millimetre to a few centimetres. Each incident beam is divided by multiple reflections into an infinity of parallel beams of which the amplitudes form a decreasing geometrical progression with ratio R. The transmitted rays are collected by a lens and they recombine in its focal plane to interfere according to the path difference $\Delta = 2ne \cos i$ between successive rays.

There is constructive interference betweeen the beams if $\Delta = p\lambda$ where p, the order of interference, is an integer; in practice p can range over several orders of magnitude, from about unity to 10^5. The relation $2ne = p\lambda$ (assuming $\cos i \approx 1$) holds only for certain discrete values of λ; thus the FP is a filter, but a filter with several pass-bands.

Resolving power. If there were an infinite number of interfering beams of equal amplitude the filter would be infinitely selective; for if the equation $\Delta = p\lambda_p$ were satisfied for λ_p then for another wavelength $\lambda = \lambda_p + d\lambda$ we could associate with each beam another of equal amplitude and opposite phase, so that the resultant of all beams would be zero. In practice the transmitted beams 1, 2. 3, ... have decreasing amplitudes and such a completely destructive interference cannot occur for any wavelength. A more detailed analysis, to be found in the standard texts, shows that the selectivity of the filter is such that it would be given by a finite number N of beams all of equal amplitude; here N increases as the reflectivity of the coatings approaches unity and its value is actually given by $N = \pi R^{\frac{1}{2}}/(1-R)$. In this way it is possible to express the resolving power by a formula similar to that used for the grating $\mathscr{R}_0 = pN$. The theoretical width of the pass-band is then $\delta\lambda_0 = \lambda/pN$. Although this expression is formally similar to that for the grating the practical consequences are quite different, since the two terms of the product, N and p are independent of each other, contrary to the case of the grating, where we have $Np = W(\sin i_1 + \sin i_2)/\lambda$; it is thus possible in principle to use one or the other to increase the product indefinitely.

p can be increased by simply increasing the spacing e between the plates since $p = 2ne/\lambda$; in principle this distance can be increased without limit, so that from this point of view there is no limit to the resolving power whatever the value of N. In practice, however, the use of very large values of p involves certain difficulties, as we shall see later. The following table shows how N varies with R according to theory:

R	0.60	0.70	0.80	0.90	0.95	0.98	1.0
N	6	9	14	30	60	150	∞

The preparation of reflecting coatings, usually multilayer dielectrics, with R as high as 0.97 is now well understood, but the values found in practice for N are not as high as predicted by theory, because of lack of perfect flatness of the plates, a question which we cannot pursue here. A value of N of about 30 is fairly easily obtained in practice.

Transmission coefficient. When radiation satisfying the condition $2ne \cos i = p\lambda$ falls on the FP there is perfectly constructive interference and the resultant amplitude is simply the sum of the individual amplitudes (fig. 19), since all the transmitted beams

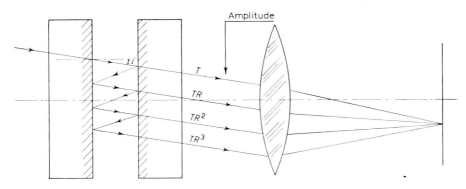

Fig. 19

are in phase. The sum of a geometrical progression with ratio R and first term T is equal to $T/(1-R)$, so the fraction of intensity transmitted is $\tau = T^2/(1-R)^2$.

If there is a loss of energy in the reflecting films we have $T < 1-R$ and so $\tau < 1$. With modern techniques for preparing the reflecting films it is possible to obtain values of τ considerably in excess of 0.5 together with values of R giving N about 40 or 50.

Multiple pass-bands. It has been shown that the FP is a filter which can have any desired selectivity, but also it transmits many pass-bands of which the wavelengths satisfy the relation

$$2ne = p_1\lambda_1 = p_2\lambda_2 = p_3\lambda_3.$$

The distribution of these pass-bands is more easily understood in terms of wave-numbers $\sigma = \lambda^{-1}$ instead of wavelengths; we then have:

$$\sigma_1/p_1 = \sigma_2/p_2 = \sigma_3/p_3 = \Delta\sigma$$

where $\Delta\sigma$ denotes the *constant difference* of wave-number between two consecutive pass-bands.

There is no band transmitted in an interval which we may call the *free spectral range*, given by $\Delta\sigma = \sigma/p = 1/2ne$;* the free spectral range decreases as the order of interference increases and at the same time the multiple pass-bands become increasingly troublesome.

It is interesting to compare the free spectral range $\Delta\sigma$ with the theoretical resolution limit $\delta\sigma_0$, which is, from the preceding equations, equal to σ/Np. Thus we find $\Delta\sigma = N\delta\sigma_0$.

The transmission curve of the complete FP filter is shown in fig. 20; it consists of a series of identical peaks which are equidistant on a wave-number scale; the width of a

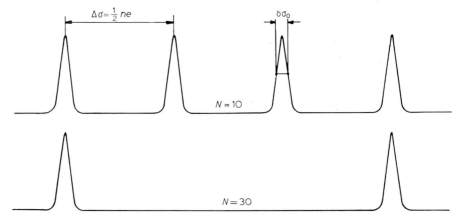

Fig. 20

peak is N^{-1} times the distance between peaks, from which fact the number N is called the *relative finesse*, or more frequently simply the *finesse*. In this figure are compared two FP's of the same resolving power; the first has a finesse one third as great as the second (10 and 30) but a thickness three times greater so that $R_0 = pN$ is the same for each.

---

* If p is large then $\Delta\sigma$ is small and we can write $\Delta\sigma/\sigma = \Delta\lambda/\lambda$ and $\Delta\lambda/\lambda = \lambda/p$. In this case all these relations involving the spectral ranges or the resolution limits may be expressed equally well in terms of λ or σ.

Before considering the question of the unwanted multiple bands and their removal we give some numerical examples:

(a) 'Interference filters' of low resolving power: Here p is small and there is only one pass-band, or at most two or three, in the visible region. For example we might have $\lambda_1 = 10\ 000$ Å, $\lambda_2 = 5000$ Å, $\lambda_3 = 3333$ Å.

(b) FP of high resolving power, $\mathcal{R} = 10^5$: on taking a finesse N of 50 (on the limit of present possibilities) we find $p = 10^5/50 = 2000$; thus for $\lambda = 5000$ Å we have $\varDelta\lambda = \lambda/2000 = 2.5$ Å.

It can thus be seen that for high resolving powers the free spectral range becomes very small. Now it would be exceptional to find that the spectrum to be investigated did not contain any radiation at all outside a certain domain $\varDelta\lambda$, particularly if the latter were very narrow. It is therefore necessary to remove the light extraneous to this domain by means of a pre-monochromator. This system must have a pass-band at most $\varDelta\lambda$, that is, N times larger than that of the FP itself. Fig. 21 shows how this monochromator is arranged to eliminate the unwanted pass-bands and so prevent

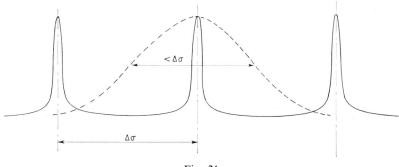

Fig. 21

overlapping orders. The pre-monochromator can be of either the prism or grating type, or it can even be another FP with pass-band and free spectral range k times larger ($k \ll N$) i.e. of optical thickness ne k times smaller; the free spectral range of the whole is then equal to $k\varDelta\lambda$.

Obliquity of the incident beams. At normal incidence the wavelengths transmitted are given by $\lambda = 2ne/p$. At oblique incidence, for an angle of incidence on the reflecting coatings i, the wavelength of maximum transmission is changed to $\lambda' = (2ne \cos i)/p$. A small change in the angle i equal to di gives a corresponding change in the wavelength transmitted d$\lambda = \lambda$d$(\cos i)$.

We now seek the change δi from normal incidence corresponding to a change in λ of $\delta\lambda_0$, the resolution limit: this will tell us the angular aperture of the beam which we can use in the FP without sensibly degrading the resolving power. This is equivalent to the case $u = 1$ in conventional systems (cf. § 2.1), so that

$$\mathcal{R} = 0.65\ \mathcal{R}_0 \text{ approximately.}$$

We have then $\delta(\cos i) = \mathscr{R}_0^{-1}$ but $\delta(\cos i) = \frac{1}{2}\delta i^2$ so that $\delta i = (2/\mathscr{R}_0)^{\frac{1}{2}}$.* The angular aperture of the beam which can be used with a FP thus decreases as the required resolving power increases.

The effect of obliquity of illumination appears in other ways also: if we illuminate a FP with a wide-angle monochromatic beam of wavelength λ, the light transmitted at different angles i corresponds to different values of p in the equation $2ne \cos i = p\lambda$. The system has revolution symmetry, so that the well-known ring system is produced in the focal plane of a lens placed behind the FP. The increment $\varDelta(\cos i)$ in $\cos i$ between two successive rings is given by

$$2ne\varDelta(\cos i) = \lambda \quad \text{or} \quad \varDelta(\cos i) = \lambda/2ne = p^{-1},$$

thus the rings are packed closer with increasing order p of interference. If several wavelengths are present there are several concentric ring systems; the photographic use of the FP depends on this principle.

3.1.3. *Fabry–Perot spectrometers and monochromators*

The use of the FP with a flux detector is more recent (DUFOUR and JACQUINOT [1948]) than the photographic use, but we consider the former first as it is much simpler in principle.

Principle of the Fabry–Perot monochromator. This system consists simply of an etalon, a lens and an exit aperture. The etalon is illuminated by beams at angles ranging from zero to at least the angle δi calculated above. A screen with a circular hole is placed axially at the focal plane of the lens (fig. 22), so that only rays at an

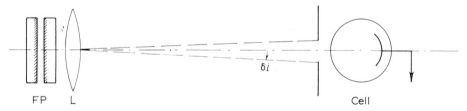

FP   L   Cell

Fig. 22

angle less than δi are accepted and the resolving power is not sensibly degraded; the diameter of this hole is therefore $F\delta i = F(2/\mathscr{R}_0)^2$ where F is the focal length of the lens and $\mathscr{R}_0$ is the theoretical resolving power of the etalon. The photocell is placed behind the hole. Thus we have a monochromator transmitting a spectral band of width $\delta\lambda$; in fact, there are many bands, but a single one can be isolated, as discussed above.

The interference filter is a simplified form of this monochromator, often used for low resolving powers ($\mathscr{R}$ between 30 and a few hundreds). It is a FP in which the

---

* In this calculation we have assumed that the refractive index between the reflecting surfaces is unity.

space between the reflecting surfaces is filled by a thin dielectric film of optical thick-
ness $\frac{1}{2}\lambda$ or a small multiple of $\frac{1}{2}\lambda$. The reflecting layers and the spacer are deposited
together on a glass plate. In this case δi is so large that it is not necessary to limit the
angle of incidence by means of a lens and diaphragm.

The acceptance and the product $\mathscr{L}\mathscr{R}$ for a Fabry–Perot monochromator. The solid
angle Ω defined by the exit aperture of the monochromator is (cf. § 1.4)

$$\Omega = \pi \delta i^2 = 2\pi/\mathscr{R}_0 = 1.3\pi/\mathscr{R}.$$

In computing the flux transmitted in this solid angle we must take account of the
fact that there is not maximum transmission of the beams for all angles of inclination;
it turns out that an additional factor $\frac{1}{4}\pi$ must be introduced. The luminosity $\mathscr{L} = \phi/B$ of the FP is thus $\mathscr{L} = 1.3\pi^2\tau S/4\mathscr{R}$, so that the product $\mathscr{L}\mathscr{R}$ is equal to $3.2\,\tau S$,
where S is the area of the FP. This should be compared with the expression obtained
for the grating (cf. § 2.1.3)

$$\mathscr{L}\mathscr{R} = \tau \beta S \text{ *.}$$

The coefficients τ are of the same order of magnitude for the best gratings and the
best FP's, so the ratio of the products $\mathscr{L}\mathscr{R}$ or of the acceptances for the same $\mathscr{R}$
is thus:

$$G = (\mathscr{L}\mathscr{R})_{FP}/(\mathscr{L}\mathscr{R})_{gr} = 3.2(S_{FP}/S_{gr})\beta^{-1}.$$

This ratio evidently depends on β, the angular height of the slit used with the grating,
which may be between 0.01 and 0.05 but rarely more. Thus for the same area we have
a ratio G between 70 and 350 in favour of the FP. The areas of gratings are usually
larger than those of FP plates, which latter rarely exceed $50\ \text{cm}^2$, but even if we compare
a FP with a grating of ten times the area there is still a gain of 7 to 35 in favour of the
FP. It should, however, be pointed out that the FP must usually be used with an
auxiliary system for eliminating overlapping orders, and this system may decrease the
transmission coefficient of the whole or limit the acceptance so as to lose part of the
advantage of the FP over the grating. It is nevertheless true that for all ranges of
resolving power the FP may give an important gain in luminosity and compactness
(see, for example, RENK and GENZEL [1962] for a case in the far infrared).

The Fabry–Perot spectrometer. A spectrometer is a monochromator with a detector
at the exit aperture and a means for displacing the pass band. For the FP it follows
from the formula $p\lambda = 2ne$, which is valid near normal incidence, that λ can be
changed while keeping p constant by changing either n or e.
(a) Variation of n. The space between the plates of a FP normally contains air,
of which the refractive index is given by $n = 1 + 3 \times 10^{-4}H$ where H is the pressure
in atmospheres. By varying this pressure between zero and one atmosphere it is
possible to change λ by the free spectral range if $p \geq 0.33 \times 10^4$. Putting $N \approx 30$
this gives $\mathscr{R}_0 = pN \geq 10^5$, an average resolving power. If an interval of at least $\Delta\lambda$
can be scanned in this way it is possible to scan the whole spectrum by making use of

---

 * To obtain this expression from the formulae (13) and (22″) we put $\sin i_1 + \sin i_2 = 1$ and
$WH_{gr} = S$ (area of the grating).

the multiple pass-bands. To do this it is necessary that the pre-monochromator have a wavelength scan which is continuous and in synchronism with that of the FP through the range $\Delta\lambda$. At the end of this interval the pre-monochromator continues its scan while the FP returns to its original value of n, changing p by one unit. We obtain in this way a saw-tooth scan (CHABBAL and JACQUINOT [1955]). Thus for sufficiently high resolving powers, pressure scanning is very convenient; the apparatus is easy to design, construct and operate (CHABBAL [1958]).

(b) Variation of e. For lower resolving powers, where the FP offers great advantages, particularly in the infrared, it is necessary to vary the distance e between the plates by mechanical means. The requirements of parallelism of the plates are very stringent so that such mechanical systems are difficult to make. In some cases purely elastic deformation has been used (CHABBAL and SOULET [1958], GREENLER [1958], BRADLEY [1962]); other systems have utilized piezoelectric movement (e.g. KOLOSHNIKOV et al. [1961]) or magnetostriction (SLATER [1964]). The techniques are still developing in this field and further advances may be expected in the near future.

Practical realization. There are no commercially available complete FP spectrometers except for very high resolving power instruments. A complete description of such a system has been given by CHABBAL and JACQUINOT [1961]. Systems of medium or low resolving power but very high luminosity have also been described. Although these examples are still rather rare and designed for special purposes, it seemed desirable to inform the reader of the possibilities of the FP, especially at a time when the techniques are developing so rapidly.

3.1.4. *Spectrographic use of the FP*

This method of use, which is primarily for very high resolution, will be only briefly described here; full details can be found in standard texts.

It is usual to project the rings (§ 3.1.2) produced by the FP on to the slit of a spectrograph; thus each spectrum line gives a diametral section of the ring system corresponding to the spectral region covered by this line. The hyperfine structure thus appears along each line with non-linear dispersion. Very high resolving power can be obtained by this method and it gives high luminosity if correctly used (cf. JACQUINOT [1960]).

In conclusion we mention a recent device (CHABBAL and PELLETIER [1964]) which offers the advantages of both the spectrometric and spectrographic methods.

3.2. FOURIER TRANSFORM SPECTROMETRY

Conceived only about a decade ago, this entirely different method is still undergoing rapid development. As with any new technique a full account would need more space than we have available here, and we therefore restrict ourselves to a general account, omitting some possibly essential points to ensure a clear explanation of the general method. In particular it should be mentioned that some technical details concerned with obtaining good accuracy have been omitted. Our purpose is to indicate the possibilities of a method which is probably destined to achieve great successes in the near future.

3.2.1. *Principle of the method* (FELLGETT [1951, 1958], JACQUINOT [1954a], STRONG [1957]).

In this method, the different radiations are not separated at all but are received simultaneously by a single detector. Each radiation is marked or coded by a sinusoidal modulation whose frequency is proportional to the frequency or wave-number of that radiation. Then the spectrum can be obtained by analyzing the frequencies contained in the complicated electrical signal from the detector. From a mathematical point of view this analysis of frequencies is simply a Fourier transformation, from which the method takes its name.

3.2.2. *The multiplexing property of the method and its advantages. Domain of application*

All the spectral elements are present in the flux at the detector, each with a different coding to permit its eventual identification, so that we have an analogue of the method of multiplex transmission. It is immediately obvious that this method confers great economy in the use of the information in the spectrum, since no information is rejected, whereas in conventional spectrometers only one spectral element out of M can be studied at a given instant. From this point of view there is something in common with spectrographic methods; we saw that the photographic plate could be considered as comprising independent detectors for all M spectral elements, thus realizing a gain $M^{\frac{1}{2}}$ in efficiency over a conventional spectrometric method using a detector of the same quantum efficiency.

However, if the detector is such that its own noise is negligible compared to the photon noise, then the photon noise for all the spectral elements is added at the detector and *these contributions from the different spectral elements cannot be separated in the subsequent analysis of frequencies.* Thus if all the spectral elements have equal intensity each will be affected by M times the photon noise appertaining to itself; thus all the above-mentioned advantage is lost.

Without further analysis we do, however, assert that in the frequently occurring case where the detector noise is the limiting factor this method gives a gain in efficiency, or in 'luminosity' *in the sense defined in* § 1.4, equal to the square root of the number M of spectral elements in the domain studied; clearly this gain can be quite considerable.

It is in the infrared, especially the far infrared (although here for other reasons), that the method of Fourier spectroscopy finds and will continue to find its field of application.

3.2.3. *Mathematical theory*

Here we give a brief summary, referring the reader to more complete explanations given elsewhere (see, e.g. JACQUINOT [1960]).

The spectral elements are modulated by sending the light through a two-beam interferometer (e.g. the Michelson) in which the path difference Δ can be varied continuously and usually linearly with time from zero to a maximum value Δ_{max}. Under these conditions each radiation of wave-number σ gives, at the exit, a flux proportional to $\cos^2 \pi \sigma \Delta$, which comprises a constant part and a part varying sinusoidally as $\cos 2\pi\sigma\Delta$. Each domain $d\sigma$ of spectral luminance $B(\sigma)d\sigma$ thus gives a modulated contribution $B(\sigma) \cos 2\pi\sigma\Delta \, d\sigma$ and the total signal or 'interferogram' is

$$I(\Delta) = \int_0^\infty B(\sigma) \cos 2\pi\sigma\Delta \, d\sigma.$$

This relation between interferogram and spectrum of the source $B(\sigma)$ implies that I is the cosine Fourier transform of B. It can be shown that the inverse relation holds

$$B(\sigma) = \int_0^\infty I(\Delta) \cos 2\pi\sigma\Delta \, d\Delta.$$

Thus we can obtain the desired spectrum by calculating the Fourier transform of the interferogram, recorded as a function of Δ under any form whatsoever. This calculation is the analysis of frequencies proposed in § 3.2.1; we shall show in § 3.2.4 how it is carried out.

The resolving power of the method is not infinite; it is limited by the maximum path difference Δ_{max}. In fact the decoding equation written above does not give $B(\sigma)$ rigorously unless the limits of integration are 0 and ∞, that is, unless the interferogram $I(\Delta)$ is recorded for Δ between 0 and ∞. The complete mathematical theory shows that the spectrum obtained,

$$B'(\sigma) = \int_0^{\Delta_{max}} I(\Delta) \cos 2\pi\sigma\Delta \, d\Delta,$$

is that which would be given by any system characterized by an instrumental function (cf. § 2.1.2). The instrumental function in this case is

$$W(\sigma) = \sin 2\pi\sigma\Delta_{max}/2\pi\sigma\Delta_{max}$$

corresponding to a resolution limit $\delta\sigma_0 = 1/2\Delta_{max}$.

Various techniques known as apodisation allow this function to be modified. For example it may be transformed to the function $(\sin \pi\sigma\Delta_{max})^2/(\pi\sigma\Delta_{max})^2$ which is identical to the instrumental function of an ideal classical spectrometer with a resolution limit $\delta\sigma_0 = 1/\Delta_{max}$. *

Acceptance. The above analysis assumes that all the beams traversing the system have the same path difference Δ, but this is not so since they are not all parallel; if they were the acceptance would be zero. In fact the solid angle Ω of the pencil entering the system is far from zero. The way in which Δ varies with the inclination i of the beams obviously depends on the kind of interferometer used. For example, in the

---

* We note here that the theoretical resolving power is $\mathcal{R}_0 = \sigma/\delta\sigma_0 = \Delta_{max}/\lambda$ in accordance with the general formula $\mathcal{R}_0 = \partial\Delta/\partial\lambda$ of § 2.2.

Michelson interferometer, as in the case of the Fabry–Perot, $\Delta = \Delta_0 \cos i$. Since the resolving power is also related to the path difference in the same way as for the FP the relation between resolving power and solid angle must be, again, $\Omega \mathcal{R} \approx 2\pi$. Thus this method also gives large acceptance, in addition to the advantage of multiplex action.

3.2.4. *Calculating the spectrum*

In contrast to all other methods, this does not give the spectrum directly; the direct, experimental readings, namely the interferogram, must be transformed to obtain the spectrum.

Use of digital computers for the computation. This is the method generally employed today. Most frequently (GEBBIE [1961], RICHARDS [1964]) the values $I(\Delta_n)$ of the interferogram at evenly spaced points $\Delta_n = nh$ are digitized and punched on paper tape. This operation is carried out automatically each time the path difference reaches a value nh, as shown either by purely mechanical means (see, e.g. RICHARDS [1964]), by Moiré fringes (GEBBIE [1961]) or by interference fringes produced by the interferometer itself from a monochromatic reference beam. The punched tape thus obtained is fed directly into a digital computer with a suitable programme. * The calculation is very rapid if M is not too large, for example, a few minutes for a spectrum with 1000 elements.

In this procedure the transformation $I \to B$ is made after the determination of I. Very recently YOSHINAGA et al. [1964] described a method by which the spectrum is obtained immediately.

Analogue computation. Various analogue procedures are possible most of which are only suitable for low resolving powers. The most commonly used procedure is to record the spectrum on magnetic tape and then to read off into a conventional harmonic analyzer by means of the reading head of an ordinary tape recorder; if the recording is on a closed loop, each point of the spectrum is found on one turn of the tape (MERTZ [1963]). The overall resolving power of the system cannot exceed that of the harmonic analyser, which therefore limits this method to low resolving power. Other methods are suitable for higher resolving powers (JACQUINOT [1965]).

3.2.5. *Types of interferometer used*

The Michelson interferometer (fig. 23) is almost universally used, with many minor variations to achieve smooth control of Δ, insensitivity to mal-adjustment, or larger solid angle than that quoted above (cf. JACQUINOT [1964]). The beam-splitter poses some problems in the far infrared, but these have been fairly satisfactorily solved

---

* In fact the computer does not give the value of $B'(\sigma) = \int I(\Delta) \cos 2\pi\sigma\Delta \, d\Delta$ but rather the sum $\Sigma I(nh) \cos 2\pi\sigma nh$; it can be shown that this does not give any serious errors if h is small enough; the effect is similar to that produced by the superposition of orders in a grating (CONNES [1961], JACQUINOT [1962]).

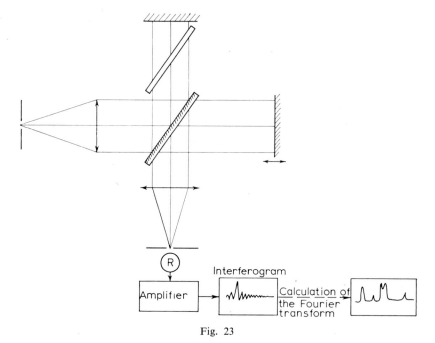

Fig. 23

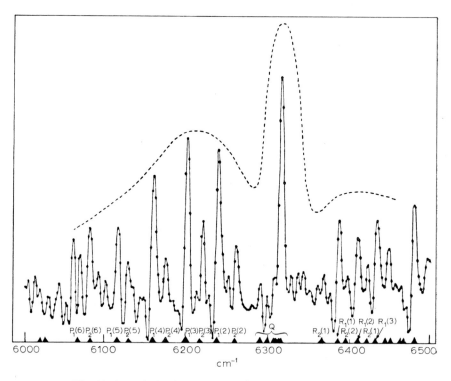

Fig. 22. (.....) Grating: $R = 150$; (———) Fournier: $R = 900$.

(RICHARDS [1964]). Another kind of interferometer, which does not use a beam-splitter, has been proposed by STRONG [1958]; it uses a laminar grating. It does not have such a high acceptance as the Michelson, but this is less important in the very far infrared, where the required resolving power is usually rather small; a good comparison of the two systems has been made by Richards.

3.2.6. *Some complete systems and applications*

One of the first striking applications of this method was made by J. CONNES and GUSH [1959]. Fig. 24 shows a comparison of their results with results previously obtained by means of a grating on the spectrum of the night sky in the 1.6 μm region. GEBBIE [1961] has made considerable contributions to instrumentation in the 10–500 μm region; several applications have been published (e.g. GEBBIE and ADAMS [1963]). A complete system, comprising an interferometer and all the electronics needed to give the interferogram in the form of a punched tape, is now available commercially and others will certainly follow. In the very far infrared, out to 3 cm^{-1}, RICHARDS [1964a, b] has obtained very fine results and has given a good description of the method.

3.3. SELECTIVE MODULATION SPECTROMETERS

The methods described in this subsection does not offer the fundamental advantage of Fourier transform spectroscopy but it does give the spectrum directly, without computation. The spectral elements are measured sequentially in time, as in the classical spectrometer or the Fabry–Perot etalon. In these latter systems the detector receives only the radiation from the spectral element being measured *at the moment*, but this is not so in the systems now to be described. The essential property of these systems is as follows: the radiation received at each instant by the detector comes from several spectral elements only one of which is being modulated at a given instant. The amplitude of the alternating signal amplified by the measuring channel which follows the detector is proportional to the luminance of this spectral element.

The flux received by the detector can thus be separated into two parts:
(1) The useful, modulated flux, which is characteristic of the element under consideration.
(2) The non-modulated flux, which comes from neighbouring spectral elements and which does not register in the final signal. This flux is frequently much larger than the modulated flux and it can thus considerably increase the noise level if photon noise is predominant (cf. § 1.2). This kind of system must therefore be applied with caution in the visible and ultraviolet and its principal application must be in the infrared. Nevertheless, it has certain possibilities below 1 μm in the particular case of the spectra of weak isolated lines, e.g. Raman lines.

By means of this method of selective modulation it is possible to dispense with the slits of classical systems and so to increase considerably their acceptance.

Various methods have been proposed for realizing the principle of selective modulation; some of these are purely interferential and do not involve any dispersing system

(GUILINO [1958], PRAT [1964]). It would appear that it is possible in this way to make low resolving power systems which are very simple and have very high luminosity. The better-known systems however, use a dispersing element. The first approach to this method of selective modulation is due to GOLAY [1951]. In his apparatus the entrance and exit slits of a classical system were replaced by suitable combinations of slits; the theory is involved and it will not be explained here as it has not been further developed, probably because of technical difficulties, not because of the principle.

3.3.1. *SISAM** (P. CONNES [1959])

The optical system of this apparatus is that of a Michelson interferometer in which the two mirrors are replaced by two identical gratings at the same angle of incidence (fig. 25). To each position of the gratings there corresponds a wavelength λ, given by

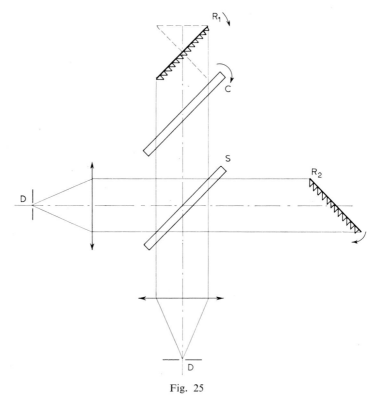

Fig. 25

the equation for the Littrow mounting, such that the two incident beams return exactly on their paths in both arms of the interferometer. For this wavelength the system functions as a Michelson interferometer in which the two mirrors are normal

---

* This name is an abbreviation of Spectromètre Interférentiel à Sélection par Amplitude de Modulation (Interference spectrometer with selective amplitude modulation).

to the incident pencils. If we vary the path difference between the beams linearly with time, by, e.g., a small rotation of the compensating plate, the emerging light is modulated 100% for this wavelength. For other wavelengths, however, the pencils returning from the grating are inclined to the optical axis and the system behaves like a Michelson in which the two mirrors make equal and opposite angles with the incident pencils; thus equidistant fringes due to an air wedge will be seen at the plane of the mirrors instead of a uniform tint. The degree of modulation due to the varying optical path difference decreases very rapidly for wavelengths different from λ and we thus have selective modulation limited to a narrow element around λ. It can be shown that the width of this element corresponds to the theoretical resolution limit of the grating. The diaphragms D and D' are circular and it can be shown that, as in Fourier transform spectroscopy (and for the same reasons) the solid angular aperture Ω, and consequently the acceptance, is the same as in the case of the Fabry–Perot etalon. On the other hand it is easy to separate the different orders of the gratings with this apparatus, since different orders have very different modulation frequencies. Radiation from a given order may thus be conveniently selected by choice of the frequency to be amplified.

The complete theory of this system has been described in several publications (CONNES [1959], JACQUINOT [1960]). So far no commercial version has appeared but several SISAMs are working satisfactorily in research laboratories.

3.3.2. *The grill spectrometer* (GIRARD [1963])

The aim of this system is the same as that of the multislit system of Golay, to retain the general configuration of the classical systems but to remove the slit and so make the acceptance independent of the resolving power. In spite of its superficial similarity to the Golay system the grill spectrometer stems from thoughts related to those which gave rise to the SISAM of Connes.

Structure of the grills. The slits of a classical system are replaced by grills which are conjugate to each other through the system; the area of each grill is not dependent

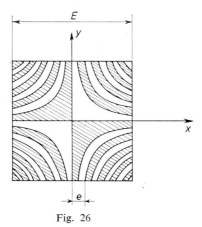

Fig. 26

on the resolution and it may be many hundreds of times greater than that of the single slit which it replaces. The structure of the grills is as follows: the opaque and transparent zones are limited by equilateral hyperbolas having the general equations $y = N/kx$, where N is an integer. The Ox and Oy axes are the common asymptotes to all the hyperbolas of the grill (fig. 26). This family of curves cuts off equal segments, from any line parallel to one of the asymptotes, the length of a segment varying inversely with the distance of the line from the asymptote. The number of zones is actually much larger than that shown in fig. 26. Some which have been made are on squares 30 mm by 30 mm and contain 600 hyperbolas. Each gap is 0.05 mm wide and the slit of equivalent resolving power would be 0.07 mm wide. The grills are made by photogravure from a photographic reduction of a large-scale drawing. The theory leading to this shape for the grills is given by GIRARD [1963].

Taking only the first term of a series, the function $f(x, y)$ expressing the transmission at a point (x, y) is

$$f(x, y) = \tfrac{1}{2}(1 + \cos 2\pi kxy).$$

In fact, other spatial distributions of transparent and opaques zones can be used. For example, in an arrangement described by GIRARD [1960] the slits are replaced by birefringent compensators which produce, in polarized light, a system of localized, circular interference fringes having the same spatial distribution as a Fresnel zone plate. Such a compensator acts as a virtual grill. This distribution of zones can also be utilized for a real grill. More recently, TINSLEY [1965] has experimented with another arrangement of concentric zones.

The hyperbolic grills, nevertheless, have the advantage of permitting a precise control of the spatial distribution of frequencies on which the reduction of secondary maxima (side-lobes) depends.

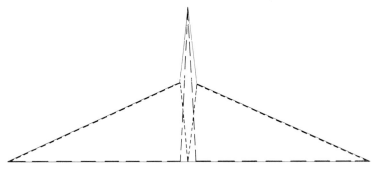

Fig. 27. (———) curve A; (. . . . .) curve B; (– – – –) curve C.

It can be shown that the instrumental function $A(x)$ is of the form shown in fig. 27. It is the sum of two functions:
(1) A triangular function, similar to the instrumental function of a spectrometer with slits of width about $\tfrac{3}{4}e$ where e is the smallest spacing of the grill.

(2) A shallow peaked function of width $2E$, very slowly varying; it is the correlation function of the boundaries of the two grills. It is of the nature of a parasitic signal which should be eliminated in order to reduce the instrumental function to the central peak; there are two ways of doing this.

Commutative operation. If one of the grills is replaced by the complementary grill (i.e. the opaque zones of one are the transparent zones of the other), the function $f(x, y)$ becomes:

$$f(x, y) = \tfrac{1}{2}(1 - \cos 2\pi kxy).$$

The instrumental function obtained is shown in curve B of fig. 27. The desired instrumental function is the difference between the signals when the grills are identical (curve A) and complementary (curve B). This difference can be obtained in practice by making the opaque regions of the entry grill reflecting; it can then be made to function alternately in transmission and reflection by means of an optical commutator (fig. 28). The signal is the modulated part of the emergent flux. In order to ensure

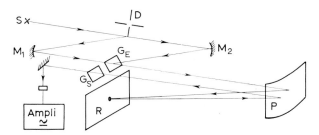

Fig. 28. D = chopper; G_E = entrance grill; G_S = exit grill; P = collimating mirror; R = grating.

that this differential measurement shall give exactly the intensity corresponding to the spectral element, the paths DM_1G and DM_2G must be made perfectly symmetrical. The precautions taken to reduce residual dissymmetry, which include the use of an attenuator comb behind M_1, make the technique of adjusting and using this system difficult.

Alternating operation (GIRARD [1964]). If the Ox axes of the two grills are displaced along Oy by an amount equal to or greater than e, instead of being superimposed, the instrumental function has no central maximum and it reduces to the second of the two functions of which $A(x)$ is the sum. When the two grills are displaced parallel to Oy there is no privileged position along Ox; the effect occurs only in the immediate neighbourhood of coincidence of the image of the entry grill with the exit grill.

It can thus be seen that an alternating movement of the image of the entry grill parallel to the direction of the slit of a classical system produces selective modulation of a single spectral element: the instrumental function (curve C of fig. 29) is the difference of ordinates of curves A and B. An instrument of this kind has been made commercially for high resolving power infrared work.

This method of operation gives only half the luminosity of the previous method (commutation). However, a single grill can be used, in reflection at entry and in

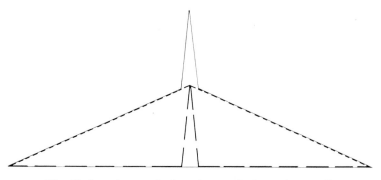

Fig. 29. (——) curve A; (.....) curve B; (– – – –) curve C.

transmission at exit, or *vice-versa*. The centre of symmetry of the grill is at the focus of the collimator mirror of the Littrow mounting (fig. 30). This system is very simple; the whole available field can be used, which compensates for the loss of 50 % in luminosity as compared with the previous method.

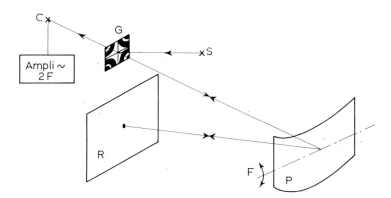

Fig. 30. P = collimating mirror oscillating at frequency *F*.

4. Conclusion

The classification in this chapter is based on the chronological development of spectroscopic methods. Considering only the principles involved we can distinguish three groups of methods:

(1) Methods in which monochromatic luminous flux is isolated. These we may call therefore, 'spectroscopy by spatial isolation' and they are embodied in spectrometers and spectrographs with slits, and the Fabry–Perot. These systems have an overall luminosity which is equal to the acceptance (cf. § 1.4). To the extent that a photographic emulsion can be considered to be a mosaic of contiguous flux detectors, a spectrograph is a multichannel flux detector.

(2) Spectrometry by selective modulation: here the acceptance is increased at the price of the presence of unwanted radiation, which, it is true, has no effect on the

signal; nevertheless, it increases the photon noise and the overall luminosity is not equal to the acceptance in the visible and ultraviolet (cf. § 1.1). In the infrared this system has great possibilities, in fact it may be noted that the principle of selective modulation has been used for several years in infrared tracking systems; it is, in fact, the extension to spectrometry of a general principle which is particularly well adapted for use with infrared flux detectors. Clearly the method is not of much interest in cases where the light source has an angular extent less than that acceptable by the system, for instance in stellar spectrometry.

(3) Fourier transform spectrometry. Again the presence of radiation of other wavelengths may increase the photon noise level and render illusory the gain in luminosity obtained in the encoded signal in the interferogram. Nevertheless this method is theoretically the most powerful of all the spectrometric methods, since it makes most efficient use of the available energy. It is of interest even for point sources. Despite the cumbersome computations involved in decoding the interferogram it is without doubt the method of the future, particularly for the far infrared region.

References

ADAMS, D. M., and H. A. GEBBIE, 1963, Spectrochim. Acta **19**, 925.

ARSAC, J., 1961, Transformation de Fourier et théorie des distributions (Dunod, Paris).

AUDRAN, 1956, *in*: Intern. Konf. Wiss. Phot. (Köln) p. 179.

AUSTIN, W. E., J. D. PURCELL and R. TOUSEY, 1962, J. Opt. Soc. Am. **52**, 597.

BAIR, E. J., P. C. CROSS, T. L. DAWSON, E. A. WILSON and J. W. WISE, 1953, J. Opt. Soc. Am. **43**, 681.

BEHRING, W. E., N. M. NEUPERT and W. A. NICHOLS, 1962, J. Opt. Soc. Am. **43**, 681.

BESSON, J., R. CANO, M. MATTIOLI, R. PAPOULAR and B. PHILIPPEAU, 1965, L'onde électrique. p. 45.

BRADLEY, 1962, *in*: K. T. HABELL, ed., Proc. Conf. Opt. Instr. Tech., 1961 (Chapman and Hall, London).

BRUCE, C. F. and R. M. HILL, 1961, Australian J. Phys. **14**, 64.

BRUNET, M., M. CANTIN, C. JULLIOT and J. VASSEUR, 1963, J. Phys. **24**, 53A.

CHABBAL, R. and P. JACQUINOT, 1955, Nuovo Cimento Suppl. [10] **2**, 661.

CHABBAL, R., 1958, Rev. Opt. **37**, 49.

CHABBAL, R. and P. JACQUINOT, 1961, Rev. Opt. **40**, 157.

CHABBAL, R. and R. PELLETIER, 1965, Principe et réalisation d'un spectromètre Fabry–Perot–multicanal: le SIMAC, *in*: Proc. Conf. Phot. Spectr. Opt., Tokyo and Kyoto, 1964. Japan. J. Appl. Phys. **4**, suppl. 1, p. 445.

CHABBAL, R. and M. SOULET, 1958, J. Phys. Radium **19**, 274.

CONNES, J., 1961, Rev. Opt. **40**, 45.

CONNES, J. and H. GUSH, 1959, J. Phys. Radium **20**, 915.

CONNES, P., 1958, J. Phys. Radium **19**, 262.

CONNES, P., 1959, Rev. Opt. **38**, 157.

CROSSWHITE, H. M. and W. G. FASTIE, 1956, J. Opt. Soc. Am. **46**, 110.

CZERNY, M. and A. F. TURNER, 1930, Z. PHYSIK **61**, 792.

DECAMPS, E. and A. HADNI, 1960, Compt. Rend. **250**, 1827.

DETWILLER, C. R., T. D. PURCELL and R. TOUSEY, 1961, Mém. Soc. Roy. Sci. Liège [5] **4**, 253.

DIEKE, G. H. and H. M. CROSSWHITE, 1945, J. Opt. Soc. Am. **35**, 471.

DOUGLAS, A. E. and G. HERZBERG, 1957, J. Opt. Soc. Am. **47**, 625.

DUFOUR, C. and P. JACQUINOT, 1948, J. Rech. Centre Natl. Rech. Sci. **2**, 91.

DUNKELMAN, L., 1962, Quant. Spect. Rad. Transf. **2**, 533.

EAGLE, A., 1910, Astrophys. J. **31**, 120.

EBERT, H., 1889, Wiedemann Ann. **38**, 489.

FASTIE, W. G., 1952, J. Opt. Soc. Am. **42**, 641.

FASTIE, W. G., 1953, J. Opt. Soc. Am. **43**, 1174.

FASTIE, W. G., H. M. CROSSWHITE and P. GLOERSEN, 1958, J. Opt. Soc. Am. **48**, 406.

FELLGETT, P., 1951, Thesis, Cambridge University.

FELLGETT, P., 1958a, Monthly Notices Roy. Astronom. Soc. **118**, 395.

FELLGETT, P., 1958b, J. Phys. Radium **19**, 187, 237.

FEHRENBACH, 1959, Publ. Obs. Haute Provence **5**, no. 1.

FREEMAN, J. J. 1958, Principle of noise (Wiley and Sons, New York).

GEBBIE, H. A., 1961, in: Proc. 2nd Intern. Conf. Quantum Electronics, Berkeley (McGraw-Hill Book Co., New York).

GENZEL, L., 1965, Far infrared spectroscopy, in: Proc. Conf. Phot. Spect. Opt., Tokyo and Kyoto, 1964. Japan. J. Appl. Phys. **4**, suppl. 1, p. 353.

GIRARD, A., 1960, Opt. Acta **7**, 81.

GIRARD, A., 1963, Appl. Opt. **1**, 79; J. Phys. Radium **24**, 139.

GIRARD, A., 1965, Récents développements du spectromètre ONERA, in: Proc. Conf. Phot. Spect. Opt., Tokyo and Kyoto, 1964. Japan. J. Appl. Phys. **4**, suppl. 1, p. 379.

GOLAY, M. J. E., 1951, J. Opt. Soc. Am. **41**, 468.

GREENLER, R. G., 1958, J. Phys. Radium **19**, 375.

HABER, H., 1950, J. Opt. Soc. Am. **40**, 153.

HADNI, A., 1956, Ann. Phys. (Paris) **13**, 765.

HADNI, A., E. DESCAMPS, D. GRANDJEAN and C. JANOT, 1960, Compt. Rend. **250**, 2007.

HADNI, A., X. GERBAUX, G. MORLOT and P. STIMER, 1965, Far infrared electronics transitions in rare earth and transition elements ions embedded in crystals, in: Proc. Conf. Phot. Spect. Opt., Tokyo and Kyoto, 1964. Japan. J. Appl. Phys. **4**, suppl. 1, p. 574.

HARRISON, G. R., 1949, J. Opt. Soc. Am. **39**, 522.

HARRISON, G. R., J. E. ARCHER and J. J. CAMUS, 1952, J. Opt. Soc. Am. **42**, 706.

HARRISON, G. R., R. C. LORD and J. R. LOOFBOUROW, 1948, Practical spectroscopy (Prentice Hall, New York).

JACQUINOT, P., 1954a, Perspectives d'avenir en spectroscopie instrumentale. in: XVIIème congres du GAMS (Paris) p. 25.

JACQUINOT, P., 1954b, J. Opt. Soc. Am. **44**, 761.

JACQUINOT, P., 1954c, Rev. Opt. **33**, 12, 653.

JACQUINOT, P., 1960, New developments in interference spectroscopy, Rept. Progr. Phys. **23**, 267.

JACQUINOT, P., 1964, Progrès récents en spectroscopie interférentielle, in: Proc. Conf. Phot. Spect. Opt., Tokyo and Kyoto, 1964. Japan. J. Appl. Phys. **4**, suppl. 1, p. 401.

JARREL, R. F., 1942, J. Opt. Soc. Am. **32**, 666.

JONES, R. C., 1953, Performance of detectors for visible and infrared radiation, in: Advan. Electron. **5** (Academic Press, New York).

JONES, R. C., 1959, in: Advan. Electron. **11** (Academic Press, New York).

JONES, R. C., 1963, Appl. Opt. **2**, 4, 351.

KOLOSHNIKOV, W. G., M. A. MAZING, S. L. MANDEL'SHTAM and Y. P. MARASANOV, 1961, Opt. Spectry. (USSR) (English Transl.) **11**, 302.

LALLEMAND, A., M. DUCHESNE and G. WLERICK, 1960, in: Advan. Electron. **12** (Academic Press, New York) p. 5.

LEO, W., 1958, Z. Instrumentenk. **66**, 240.

LEO, W., 1962, Z. Instrumentenk. **70**, 9.

MADDEN, R. P., 1963, in: Physics of thin films, vol. 1 (Academic Press, New York) p. 1123.

MCARDLE, 1961, Infrared Phys. **1**, 146.

MCCUBBIN, T. K. and SINTOR, 1950, J. Opt. Soc. Am. **40**, 537.

MERTZ, L., 1963, Infrared Fourier transform spectrometry for space vehicles, *in*: Les spectres infrarouges des astres. Mém. Soc. Roy. Sci. Liège [5] **9**, 120.

MITSUISHI, A., Y. OTSUKA, S. FUJITA and H. YOSHINAGA, 1963, Japan. J. Appl. Phys. **12**, 574.

MITSUISHI, A., Y. YAMADA and H. YOSHINAGA, 1962, J. Opt. Soc. Am. **42**, 14.

NAMIOKA, T., 1954, Sci. Light (Tokyo) **3**, 15.

NAMIOKA, T., 1959, J. Opt. Soc. Am. **49**, 446.

NAMIOKA, T., 1961, Choice of grating mountings suitable for a monochromator in a space telescope, *in*: W. Liller, ed., Space astrophysics (McGraw-Hill Book Co., New York) p. 228.

PLYLER, E. K., 1947, J. Chem. Phys. **15**, 885.

PRAT, R., 1964, Nouvelle méthode spectrométrique interférentielle, *in*: Proc. Conf. Phot. Spectr. Opt., Tokyo and Kyoto, 1964. Japan. J. Appl. Phys. **4**, suppl. 1, p. 448.

PUTLEY, E. H., 1960, Proc. Phys. Soc. (London) **76**, 802.

RANK, D. H., G. D. SAKSENA, G. SKORINKO, D. P. EASTHAN, T. A. WIGGINS and T. K. McCUBBIN, 1959, J. Opt. Soc. Am. **49**, 1217.

RENK, K. F. and L. GENZEL, 1962, Appl. Opt. **1**, 643.

RICHARDS, P. L., 1964a, High resolution far infrared interferometry, *in*: Proc. Conf. Phot. Spect. Opt.. Tokyo and Kyoto, 1964. Japan. J. Appl. Phys. **4**, suppl. 1, p. 417.

RICHARDS, P. L., 1964b, J. Opt. Soc. Am. **54**, 1474.

ROMAND, J. and B. VODAR, 1962, Opt. Acta **9**, 371.

ROWLAND, H. A., 1882, Phil. Mag. **13**, 469.

ROWLAND, H. A., 1883, Phil. Mag. **16**, 179, 210.

RUNGE, C. R. and F. PASCHEN, 1902, Abhandl. Akad. Wiss. Berlin, Ank. **1**.

SCHOEN and HODGE, 1952, J. Opt. Soc. Am. **42**, 84.

SEYA, M., 1951, Sci. Light (Tokyo) **1**, 1.

SHAFFER, A. B., L. R. MEGILL and L. DROPPLEMAN, 1964, J. Opt. Soc. Am. **54**, 879.

SHCHEPETKIN, P., 1958, Opt. i Spektroskopiya **4**, 383, 513.

SLATER, P. N., H. T. BETZ and G. HENDERSON, 1964, A new design of a scanning Gabry–Perot interferometer, *in*: Proc. Conf. Phot. Spectr. Opt., Tokyo and Kyoto, 1964. Japan. J. Appl. Phys. **4**, suppl. 1, p. 440.

STROKE, G. W., 1963, Ruling, testing and use of optical gratings for high-resolution spectroscopy, *in*: E. Wolf, ed., Progress in optics, vol. 2 (North-Holland Publ. Co., Amsterdam) p. 3.

STROKE, G. W. and H. H. STROKE, 1963, J. Opt. Soc. Am. **53**, 333.

STRONG, J., 1957, J. Opt. Soc. Am. **47**, 354.

STRONG, J. and A. G. VANASSE, 1958, J. Phys. Radium **19**, 192.

TOMKINS, F. S. and M. FRED, 1954, Spectrochim. Acta **6**, 139.

TORALDO DI FRANCIA, G., 1950, Ann. Real Soc. Espan. Fis. Quim. **17** L (A).

TOUSEY, R., 1960, Sci. Ind. Phot. **31**, 301.

TOUSEY, R., 1961, J. Opt. Soc. Am. **51**, 384.

TOUSEY, R., 1962, Appl. Opt. **1**, 679.

VAN DER ZIEL, A., 1958, Noise (Prentice Hall, New York).

WADSWORTH, F. L. O., 1896, Astrophys. J. **3**, 47.

WHITE, S. U., 1947, J. Opt. Soc. Am. **37**, 713.

WILKINSON, P. G. and D. W. ANGEL, 1963, J. Opt. Soc. Am. **53**, 941.

WILLIAMS, S. E., 1958, Opt. Acta **5**, 31.

YAMADA, Y., A. MITSUISHI and H. YOSHINAGA, 1962, J. Opt. Soc. Am. **52**, 17.

YOSHINAGA, H., 1965, Recent techniques in far infrared spectroscopy, *in*: Proc. Conf. Phot. Spectr. Opt., Tokyo and Kyoto, 1964. Japan. J. Appl. Phys. **4**, suppl. 1, p. 420.

Notes added in proof

Since this chapter has been written, research in instrumental spectroscopy has been active: this activity has been reflected in an international colloquium held in Paris in May 1966. The proceedings of this colloquium will be published and will constitute a general review of the most recent progress in this field.

This evolution involves both a development of known methods and the introduction of new methods.

1. NEW METHODS

Some of these new methods are more or less derived from the "mock interferometer" of MERTZ [1960]; they permit the simultaneous measurement of a great number of spectral elements ("multiplexing"); their principle may be very far (KLAGES [1966]) or even totally different (GRAINGER et al. [1966]) from the interference spectroscopy by Fourier transformation.

In another method the old principle of focal isolation has been used and combined with the principle of selective modulation (JAMES and STERNBERG [1966]).

The interest of the use of Girard's grills in spectrographs has been examined by BOUCHAREINE and JACQUINOT [1966]. If the slit of a spectrograph is replaced by such a grill, the photographic plate records a superposition of the images of the grill, produced by all the wavelengths and, of course, this superposition is totally unintelligible. But the same grill can be used to produce the physical process of decoding the plate. The spectrum obtained is the correlation function of the grill and the photographic image. Under certain conditions this spectrum has a signal-to-noise ratio much better than if it were obtained with a single slit.

Moreover very new perspectives in absorption spectroscopy might be open by the use of lasers, the wavelength of which could be continuously varied in a wide range (BESSON [1966]). The lasers studied use semiconductors: GaAs from 0.78 μm to 0.9 μm, and PbSc from 7μm to 22μm, the variation of the wavelength being produced by the effect of high pressure. This technique presents difficulties inherent to the use of high pressures at low temperatures.

2. DEVELOPMENTS OF KNOWN METHODS

Further developments have been made in the use of the Fabri-Perot spectrometer: multichannel spectrometers (namely HIRSCHBERG [1966]) and an all-Fabry–Perot spectrometer consisting of three pressure scanned etalons in series (ROESSLER and MACK [1966]).

The most striking developments concern the interference spectroscopy by Fourier transformation and cover all aspects of this new method: step by step displacement of the moving mirror of the Michelson interferometer (P. CONNES and J. PINARD [1966]); improvements of the digital (J. and P. CONNES [1966a], FORMAN [1966]) or analog (PRITCHARD et al. [1966], EDGAR et al. [1966], HOFFMAN and VANASSE [1966]) computation of the spectrum.

The spectacular results recently obtained by this method in planetary astronomy (J. and P. CONNES [1966b]) ensure that it will be widely used in forthcoming years, as was announced in the conclusion of the chapter.

In addition, the general evolution involves a more extensive use of automatic adjustments (see for example LAUDE [1966]) and an increasing attention paid to the extraction of information in digital form for its subsequent numerical treatment (see for example HUEHNERMANN [1966]).

REFERENCES ADDED IN PROOF

BESSON, J. M., 1966, *in*: Colloque du CNRS: Méthodes nouvelles de spectroscopie instrumentale (Paris, avril 1966), to be published in J. Phys. (Paris) (1967).

BOUCHAREINE, P. and P. JAQUINOT, 1966, *in*: Colloque CNRS.

CONNES, J. and P. CONNES, 1966a, *in*: Colloque CNRS.

CONNES, J. and P. CONNES, 1966b, J. Opt. Soc. Am. **57**, 7, 896.

CONNES, P. and J. PINARD, 1966, *in*: Colloque CNRS.

EDGAR, R. F., B. LAWRENSON and J. RING, 1966, *in*: Colloque CNRS.

FORMAN, M. L., 1966, *in*: Colloque CNRS.

GRAINGER, J. F., J. RING and J. H. STELL, 1966, *in*: Colloque CNRS.

HIRSCHBERG, J. G., 1966, *in*: Colloque CNRS.

HOFFMAN, J. E. and G. A. VANASSE, 1966, *in*: Colloque CNRS.

HUEHNERMANN, H., 1966, *in*: Colloque CNRS.

JAMES, J. F. and R. S. STERNBERG, 1966, *in*: Colloque CNRS.

KLAGES, H., 1966, *in*: Colloque CNRS.

LAUDE, J. P., 1966, *in*: Colloque CNRS.

MERTZ, L., 1960, J. Opt. Soc. Am. **50**, 11.

PRITCHARD, J. L., H. SAKAI, W. H. STEEL and G. A. VANASSE, 1966, *in*: Colloque CNRS.

CHAPTER 4

INTERFEROMETRY: SOME MODERN TECHNIQUES

K. M. BAIRD

National Research Council, Ottawa

CONTENTS

1. Introduction

The technique of optical interferometry, long recognized as a powerful tool in physics, has recently experienced markedly increased attention and development. Even before the advent of the laser, which is providing the subject a strong new stimulus, notable advances in technique were made. Some examples of these advances will be discussed in the following sections; the particular emphasis will be on methods of setting on interference fringes; i.e. on methods of observing the precise relation between an optical wavelength and some physical distance.

If light from a suitable source is split into two or more beams, which are allowed to combine again after traversing separate optical paths, the resultant intensity shows variations which arise from the variations in relative phases of the light in the recombining (or interfering) beams. The variation of intensity as a function of the path difference between the paths traversed is periodic with the wavelength of the light, λ. As λ for visible light is very short (0.5 μm) the phenomenon has proven very useful in the detection and measurement of small changes in physical lengths. Also, since the wavelengths produced by some sources are very precisely reproducible, interferometric techniques make possible the measurement of physical lengths with very great precision – a characteristic which lead to the adoption of the wavelength of a Kr^{86} line as the basic standard for the International Metre. Similarly, one can use such techniques to measure wavelengths themselves or small shifts in wavelengths, if the physical structure which determines the optical path difference between the beams is suitably controlled.

There are many arrangements for using optical interference for measurement. One very important arrangement is typified in the Twyman interferometer shown schematically in fig. 1a. The intensity at O due to the interference of the overlapping beams, reflected from M_1 and M_2 respectively, is given by

$$I = I_0 \cos^2 \left[(2\pi\sigma)(S_1 M_1 - S_1 M_2) \cos \theta \right] \tag{1}$$

where θ is the angle at which a beam travels with respect to the normal to M_1; $\sigma = 1/\lambda$ is the number of waves per centimetre; and $S_1 M_1$ and $S_1 M_2$ are the optical distances from the beam splitter, S_1, to the reflectors, M_1 and M_2.

A typical appearance of the field at O is shown in fig. 1b which shows the familiar bands of light and dark, called interference fringes, due in this case to the variation in θ. Fringes can also be observed as a result of variation in $S_1 M_1$ by the use of light passing through an aperture at O.

Another important example of the application of interference is the Fabry–Perot interferometer shown in fig. 2a. In this case there are a large number of successively retarded beams due to multiple reflections between the highly reflecting mirrors, M_1 and M_2. These, on recombination after transmission through M_2, give rise to an intensity variation (at O, for example) given by:

$$I = I_0 \frac{T^2}{(1-R)^2} \frac{1}{1 + F \sin^2 \frac{1}{2}\delta} \tag{2}$$

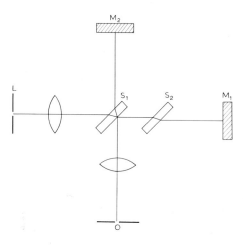

Fig. 1a. Michelson interferometer. M_1, M_2, reflectors. S_1, beam splitter. S_2, compensator. L, source. O, observer.

Fig. 1b. Interference fringes formed in a Michelson interferometer.

where T is the transmission, R is the reflectivity, and $F = 4R/(1-R)^2$ is the coefficient of fineness; δ, the phase retardation between the interfering beams, is a function of the separation of the plates, the refractive index and the angle to the normal.

In this case because of the large number of interfering beams, the light bands or fringes are very narrow, separated by relatively wide distances as shown in fig. 2b;

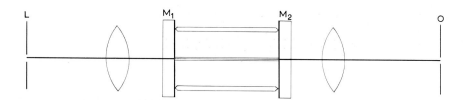

Fig. 2a. Fabry–Perot interferometer. M_1, M_2, reflectors. L, source. O, observer.

Fig. 2b. Interference fringes formed in a Fabry–Perot interferometer.

in this figure, too, the variation in intensity is due to a variation of the angle of incidence on the reflectors.

One of the simplest means for observation of interference fringes is by the arrangement shown in fig. 3a, which is the system very often used in testing or measuring the form of surfaces, both in optical workshops and in microscopic topography. The intensity contour of the fringes can be made to resemble in sharpness either those of fig. 1b or those of fig. 2b, depending on the reflectivity of the surfaces; the higher the reflectivity, the narrower are the dark fringes. Fig. 3b shows the appearance of

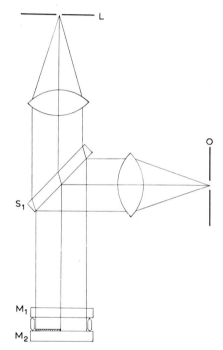

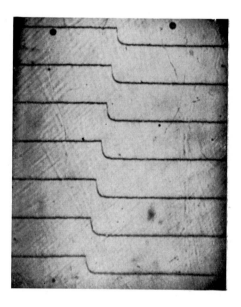

Fig. 3a. Fizeau interferometer. M_1, M_2, reflectors. S_1, beam-splitter. L, source. O, observer.

Fig. 3b. Interference fringes formed in a Fizeau interferometer.

fringes formed in the plane of M_1 due to the inclination of M_1 relative to M_2 and viewed through the aperture at O.

The above basic instrumental arrangements have been known for upwards of sixty years. They, and other types of interferometers, are described in detail in many textbooks, e.g. CANDLER [1951]; BORN and WOLF [1959]. Under the stimulus of new requirements, however, recent important improvements in technique have resulted from relatively minor elaboration and from the use of new aids, such as photoelectric detection of the fringes. The new requirements have been connected with the study of topography of wave fronts; with the measurement of physical lengths and wavelengths (which is the main topic of this chapter); with spectroscopic studies (see ch. 3); and, finally, with the development of the laser.

2. Topography

In a broad range of applications of interferometry, observations are made on fringe shapes to determine the topography of the interfering wave fronts; this in turn gives the topography of some optical surface which has reflected or transmitted one of the beams. Such is the case in workshop testing of surfaces by the method of fig. 3a; in fig. 3b the small step observed in the otherwise straight fringes corresponds to a step of height 0.25λ deposited on one of the optical flats. Another example is the use of the Twyman interferometer (fig. 1a) in the testing of the form of the wave fronts produced by optical instrument components (CANDLER [1951]). A very important field in interference topography is the subject of interference microscopy in which there have been recent notable advances due to Tolansky, Linnik, Françon and others (see KRUG et al. [1964]).

Advances in this type of interferometry are well covered in the references cited and will not be further discussed here. However, it is perhaps not inappropriate to note how improvements can be made on the old technique for testing optical flats where it is necessary to achieve high sensitivity. Very good flats are required to fully realize the advantages of the new fringe setting techniques, described in the next sections, and in connection with laser technology.

The standard technique of testing has been to lay the surfaces together (as in fig. 3a but with very thin separators) and observing the approximately sinusoidal fringes which result largely from only one reflection from each surface. It is very difficult by such fringes to detect less than 0.05λ variation, especially if the variation is over small areas. SAUNDERS [1951] introduced an improvement by silvering the surfaces, giving very sharp fringes similar to those in fig. 3b. In order to cover the relatively broad areas between the fringes, Saunders took a number of exposures on the same film, displacing the fringes a small amount (0.1λ for example) between each exposure by introducing successive small changes in the density of the atmosphere surrounding the flats. These produced corresponding changes in the optical separation of the surfaces and therefore in the position of the fringes. The resultant composite showed sharp fringes whose interval corresponded to about 0.1λ.

An improvement was introduced by HERRIOT [1961] who took a single exposure but illuminated the flats simultaneously with a number of different wavelengths of suitable values to give a similar picture. The different wavelengths were produced by the use of a multiple entrance slit on a monochromator. When illuminated with white light, the monochromator passed a number of wavelengths through its exit slit. Their spacing was controllable by the use of a zoom lens system to image the multiple entrance slit onto the aperture of the monochromator.

A disadvantage of these systems lies in the fact that the flats must be silvered (or aluminized) in order to test them. This almost precludes their use for control during the making of the flats; the length of the operation tends to restrict its use to testing the finished object.

It is possible, however, to increase the sensitivity to topographical variation of the sinusoidal fringes which are used in the usual testing procedure. Although the sensitivity which can be realized is not as great as with multiple beam techniques, such as those described above, the fact that the surfaces do not need treatment makes the methods interesting.

The increase in sensitivity can be accomplished by observing the fringes in a way whereby the contrast sensitivity is enhanced. This can be done by observation of the fringes by means of closed circuit television, in which case the contrast can be increased electronically, or it can be done by photography, by the use of high contrast film. By the use of a suitable exposure, the high contrast can be used to make the fringes appear much narrower, approaching in appearance those of fig. 3b.

This technique requires precise means for supporting and adjusting the test surfaces and requires fairly high intensity in collimated, monochromatic light. A laser provides a suitable source.

In another technique, which can be used either with direct visual observation or in conjunction with the above devices, a wire screen grid is placed between the flats, the wires blocking off light from lower flat from reaching the exit aperture. Thus the positions occupied by the wires of the grid appear uniformly illuminated by light reflected from the upper surface only, whereas interference will cause variation with optical separation in the positions corresponding to the openings of the screen. By observation of the positions of photometric matching between the areas occupied by the wires and those corresponding to the openings, variation of the optical path of as little as 0.01λ can be detected by direct visual observation. This system is most effectively used when the flats are adjusted to be parallel so that, with perfect flats, the intensity of the combined interfering beams would be equal to the intensity of the partially blocked areas over the whole surface. Clearly the reflectivity must not vary over the surfaces, i.e. they must be very clean.

3. Setting on fringes

An important development in modern interferometry has been in the refinement of techniques for the detection to a very great sensitivity of the number of wavelengths in some optical path. The optical path may correspond to the separation of two optical surfaces, or to the displacement of one optical surface with respect to another. Such a measurement requires, in the main, the determination of the amount by which the path exceeds some whole number of wavelengths, that is the determination of what is called the *excess fraction* of the order of interference. The whole number of wavelengths can be inferred fairly easily by the method of exact fractions (CANDLER [1951]) or it can be counted directly. The important and precise measurement is the determination of the excess fraction, which may be required to better than 0.001λ.

This sort of measurement is involved in the comparison of wavelengths and in the measurement of physical lengths in terms of wavelengths. It is also used in the measurement of small changes in wavelengths (resulting, for example, from changes in the conditions of excitation of a given spectral line) and in the measurement of small changes in physical lengths. The techniques involved are usually quite different from those required in the analysis of the fine structure of spectral lines such as are discussed in ch. 3.

In older techniques, the excess fraction was measured by direct setting of cross wires on fringe patterns, or on photographs of fringe patterns – a process that was usually laborious and yielded a sensitivity of from 0.1λ to 0.01λ depending on the fringe contrast, the statistics of observation, etc.

The modern techniques are rapid, often automatic, and can yield a sensitivity of the order of 0.0001λ in a path of length greater than $10^5\lambda$. There are numerous alternative techniques which achieve more or less the same sensitivity but which have specific advantages in certain applications. However, as an idea of the new techniques is best given by considering a specific example, we shall describe the apparatus which was used in the author's laboratory for some years to measure the slight shifts introduced by changes in the operating conditions on the wavelengths of spectral lines of Hg^{198}, Cd^{114} and Kr^{86}; these were being considered for adoption as the International Length Standard. Some alternative techniques will be discussed more briefly later.

3.1. AN EXAMPLE OF PRECISE SETTING ON FRINGES

The very small wavelength shifts were observed by making precise settings on the order of interference in light passing normally through a Fabry–Perot etalon, and observing the changes in the settings required to compensate for perturbations in the wavelengths as the operating conditions of the source were changed. The direct setting gave only the excess fraction; as mentioned earlier, the whole number part of the order of interference was determined by measuring the excess fractions for several wavelengths or by other means.

The intensity of the light passed normally by the etalon, that is, through the small aperture at O in fig. 2a, is given by eq. (2). In the present case, it was advantageous to use films of relatively high transmission; the resultant variation did not show such narrow peaks as one would expect from fig. 2a, but had the form shown

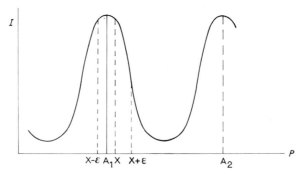

Fig. 4. Variation of intensity with path difference in an interferometer.

graphically in fig. 4, which gives I as a function of optical path between the plates.

Normally the intensity, I, passed by the etalon, corresponded to some point such as at X, removed from one of the peaks.

The method for measuring the excess fraction, $A_1 X/A_1 A_2$ in fig. 4, consisted of (1) the introduction of a change in the order of interference which could be precisely known as a fraction for an order and, (2) means for determining when the total order was exactly integral, i.e. had a value corresponding to the point A_1. The amount by which the order was changed gave the excess fraction.

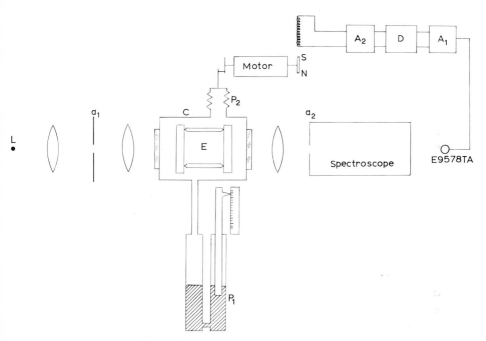

Fig. 5. Fringe scanning apparatus. P_1, P_2, pistons. a_1, a_2, apertures. A_1, signal amplifier. A_2, reference amplifier. C, etalon chamber. D, dynamometer milliammeter. E, etalon.

The apparatus is shown schematically in fig. 5. The etalon, E, was supported on four points in a metal cylinder which was sealed at the ends by optical windows and whose temperature was controlled by circulating water to within a few thousandths of a degree Celsius. The water temperature cycle was short (about 1 minute) so that the etalon, having contact at only four points, was relatively unaffected and, being of invar, suffered no proportional length changes greater than 10^{-8} per minute. The room temperature was controlled to 0.01°C and the end windows were no larger than necessary for the aperture of the etalon. Such precautions were obviously necessary since the sought-for measurement precision was of the order of one part in 10^{10}. No sudden changes could be tolerated; uniform slow drifts could be taken into account by the choice of a proper sequence of reading.

Light from the source under study was focussed on a small aperture, a_1, collimated, passed through the etalon, E, and focussed on a second aperture, a_2, in front of the slit of a two-prism double pass spectrograph in whose film plane was mounted an E9578TA photomultiplier tube. The two apertures and a procedure of careful centring ensured that only light within about $10^{-4}\pi$ radians of normal passed through the system. The two apertures and the spectroscope eliminated unwanted reflections and unwanted spectral lines.

The smooth known adjustments to the optical separation of the etalon plates were effected by air pressure changes introduced by the use of the adjustable mercury displacement piston P_1. This consisted of 25 mm internal diameter U-tube half-filled with mercury, into one side of which was fitted a precision ground steel rod. As the latter was moved up or down, it displaced an equivalent amount of mercury into the other side of the U-tube, which was connected to the etalon chamber. In this way the air density in the chamber, hence the optical separation of the plates, could be adjusted very smoothly by any desired amount.

The displacement of the piston could be measured by the use of an attached precise scale to about 10^{-4} of the movement required to change the optical separation by one fringe (a movement of about 15 cm in the case considered). The diameter of the rod and the bore of the tube into which it was fitted were constant along their length to within 0.025 mm. The gap between them was made as small as possible, consistent with free movement, so as to have negligible effects resulting from atmospheric pressure changes. The mercury surface was covered with a very low vapour pressure oil to eliminate mercury vapour effects in the etalon space.

The piston position was controllable either manually or automatically. The temperature of P_1 had also to be controlled to avoid air density changes in C which otherwise would have occurred. The piston displacement corresponding to one whole order was observed by measuring the movement from one maximum of I to the next, the maxima being detected as described below. From this, the fractional order change corresponding to any wavelength change could be known. In cases where it mattered, e.g. where a large excess fraction was measured, the non-linearity of the density change in the chamber, C, with the displacement of P_1 could be taken into account from the known relation between the volumes of P_1, P_2, and C.

The maxima in I were detected as follows: a sylphon bellows, used as a piston P_2 in the chamber, was imparted a reciprocating motion by means of a synchronous motor operating through a suitable gear system. This system was very carefully constructed and provided with a counterbalancing bellows so as to avoid any parasitic vibration or oscillation; the gear system also permitted the amplitude of oscillation to be varied at will.

As a consequence of the movement of P_2, the air density, hence the optical separation of the etalon plates, suffered an oscillation as indicated by $X-\varepsilon$, $X+\varepsilon$ in fig. 4. When these points were symmetrically spaced about the maxima, i.e. the mean optical path difference corresponded to a maximum I, the fundamental oscillation in the light output was zero. This condition was detected as follows:

A reference phase was generated by the use of a small magnet mounted on the shaft of the motor driving P_2 so that an ac voltage was induced in a small coil mounted near it. The phase of this voltage with respect to the pressure oscillations in C could be adjusted by moving the coil about the shaft; this adjustment was required only to obtain the highest precision of setting.

This reference ac voltage was amplified and filtered by A_2 and impressed on the *fixed* coils of a zero-centre dynamometer, D. The ac in the photomultiplier anode current was amplified by A_1 and impressed on the *moving* coil of D. Both A_1 and A_2 utilized large amounts of negative current feedback to linearize the field variations in the meter and to eliminate transformer effect.

The meter, D, thus read zero (except for noise) when the fundamental in-phase oscillation of the anode current was zero, i.e. when the mean optical path was at maximum or a minimum. Measurement of the average anode current by a micro-microammeter made it possible to distinguish between maxima and minima. Offset from a maximum resulted in a meter deflection in a direction which indicated the direction in which P_1 had to be moved to set on the maximum.

In earlier work the setting was done manually. Later, in order to reduce the tendency to overshoot, the piston P_1 was operated by means of a servo system which detected the offset and drove P_1 in the appropriate direction. A bridge circuit was used to translate the 15 c.p.s. offset signal into a 400 c.p.s. signal which was more suitable for the servo motor operation and yet retained the narrow band filter characteristic of the meter.

This apparatus was used to measure small wavelength shifts induced by changes in the source operating conditions by a systematic observation of the setting position of P_1 corresponding to a suitably programmed set of changes in the source conditions (current density, temperature, etc.).

In the earlier method of manual setting, the r.m.s. deviation of the setting points from the smooth curve resulting from temperature drift, etc. was $2 \times 10^{-4}\lambda$ with a path difference of $2.4 \times 10^5 \lambda$, i.e. about one part in 10^9, where the time constant was about 10 sec. With the servo operated system it was slightly improved; a one-minute time constant yielded a precision of a few parts in 10^{10}.

The shifts which had to be observed in the experiments referred to were only very small parts of a fringe (or order); however, it was also practical to observe differences of large fractions of an order to the same precision. In the latter case, however, close attention had to be paid to such second-order corrections as the non-linear calibration curve of piston P_1. The observation of the excess fraction for different wavelengths could also be used to intercompare wavelengths; also the absolute separation of the mean optical surfaces of the plates could be determined to the same sort of precision. In the latter cases, however, sources of systematic error such as lack of flatness of the plates, lack of uniformity of illumination, etc., become particularly significant.

3.2. ALTERNATIVE METHOD OF SETTING ON FRINGES

A number of alternative methods for very precise setting on interference fringes have been developed and these yield more or less the same sensitivity as has the method just described. They were developed mainly at National Laboratories and at the International Bureau of Weights and Measures in connection with the previously mentioned program of investigation of wavelengths and wavelength shifts prior to the re-definition of the International Metre in 1960.

At the International Bureau, MASUI *et al.* [1958] made use of the Michelson interferometer and a longer path difference than in the experiment described above. The very fine adjustment of the optical path for setting on the fringe was effected, not by means of a pressure change, but by means of a change in the tilt of the compensator plate (S_2 in fig. 1a). The change was made very smoothly by the use of a differential spring arrangement in which the fringe fractions could be read from a drum which advanced the tension of the weaker spring.

The centre or peak of the fringe was detected by observation of the current of the photocathode (in the exit beam) at several intervals during a change or 'scan' across the peak of the fringe from one half-intensity point to the next; the scans were repeated many times. The relatively slow alternation from one side of the peak to the next required very careful control of drifts such as those due to temperature and atmospheric pressure changes, and demanded a suitable symmetry in the program of readings so as to eliminate as much as possible their effect.

At the National Standards Laboratory in Australia, BRUCE and HILL [1961] made use of electromagnetic deflection of a spring mount, which supported one of the interferometer mirrors, in order to introduce the scan of the fringes; it is shown schematically in simplified form in fig. 6. This system used a Fabry–Perot inter-

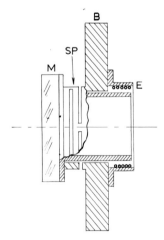

Fig. 6. Fringe scanning mirror mount. M, mirror. Sp, Spring. B, base. E, electromagnet.

ferometer in vacuum; control of the parallelism of the interferometer plates was also by electromagnetic control of the supports. The heating due to the current in the electromagnets was very steady and did not contribute inaccuracy to the measurements. The displacement was found to be linear with current to within the accuracy of measurement, and could be made as great as four fringes.

The scan was alternated at a relatively high frequency (20 c.p.s.) in a fashion similar to that described in the preceding section. The peak of the fringe was detected by the use of a tuned amplifier and oscilloscope as a synchronous detector: observation of the Lissajous figure indicated when the extremes of the alternating scan were symmetrical with respect to the peak of the fringe.

COOK [1959], at the National Physical Laboratory in England, used a Fabry–Perot interferometer in conjunction with scanning by atmospheric pressure change. However, in his apparatus two radiations were scanned, in effect simultaneously, by the use of a rotating sector which allowed the intensity of light from the two to be recorded in rapid alternation during the scan over the two line profiles. In addition to the slow direct scan, an alternating pressure scan was superimposed. The output of the photomultiplier was transformed to digital readout so that by direct computer analysis the record could be used to give such information as the line profile, the difference in excess fraction for two wavelengths, etc. The system made possible the convenient recording of very much information but it suffered a disadvantage in some applications in that the use of two optical channels increased the likelihood of systematic errors due to geometrical effects, such as those resulting from the illumination of different parts of the etalon by the different radiations.

It is of interest that during the period of the measurements which stimulated these new techniques (1954 to 1960) Engelhard at the P.T.B. in Germany, measured wavelengths and shifts visually by the use of a technique which had been in use at the P.T.B. in its basic form for thirty years (ENGELHARD [1952]). The precision of individual setting was less than with photoelectric techniques but this was compensated for by taking a very large number of readings. If the variations in settings are random, this method, with the correct application of statistics, ought to yield as high precision as the other methods. However, the long time and labour required make it impractical by this means to investigate as many parameter changes as can be done with electronic techniques and therefore make it much more difficult to detect systematic errors. Engelhard used atmospheric pressure change in an enclosed chamber to adjust the fringes so that the apparent optical length in air of a metal standard was an integral number of wavelengths; a position that was judged by the eye as the point where fringes due to light reflected from the near end of the standard matched those due to light reflected from a reflector in contact with the far end of the standard.

3.3. A COMPARISON OF METHODS OF SETTING ON FRINGES

It will be noted that all the systems described for setting on fringes depend on two essential features: a device for smoothly changing the path difference by small amounts which can accurately be known as a fraction of a fringe and, means for detecting, with great sensitivity, when the path difference is an exact whole number times λ, i.e. for detecting the centre of the fringe. It is of interest to sum up and compare the various ways for realizing these.

3.3.1. *Changing the optical path*

(i) The use of an adjustment of the density of the atmosphere is one of the simplest ways to introduce a change in the path difference and does not require a physical displacement of the optical surfaces. The rate of change in optical path as a function of density will depend on the path difference if the change in atmosphere affects the whole interferometer. A rate of change independent of path difference can be introduced in the case of interferometers having separated paths (such as the Michelson type, fig. 1), by the introduction of a cell in one of the arms within which the air or gas density is changed. One has a choice of rates of change of path with pressure (or density) by the use of different gases. Helium, for example, will give about 1 order/cm path/atmosphere; air gives about 10 orders/cm path/atmosphere. Pressure scanning is very smooth and can be made to alternate with an amplitude approaching one order at a rate of several tens of cycles per second; or it can be made very slowly in one direction by the use of a controlled slow leak. If the pressure change introduced is very large, the non-linearity of the change in optical path (density) with piston displacement or with time must often be taken into account. A disadvantage of this method is that corrections for the dispersion of the atmosphere must be made where different wavelengths are involved.

(ii) Changing the path by slight rotation of a plate through which an interfering beam passes is most suitably applied to interferometers with separated paths. The change in path can also be very smooth with this technique, provided the mounting is correctly designed and is not subject to vibration; the differential spring system was found to be very good. The change in optical path is, of course, not linear with angle but the corrections are small over a range of several orders and are easily calculated. This system is most suitable for a slow rate of scan. A variation on the method is the use of a very small angle optical wedge whose introduction into one beam by a slow linear translation can be used to produce the change in path difference.

(iii) Electromagnetic distortion of spring mounts, as used by BRUCE and HILL [1961] was shown to be satisfactory in their very precise work. It is usable at relatively high speeds and in vacuum and can be very linear over changes in path of several wavelengths. Very simple arrangements can be made using, for example, inexpensive loudspeaker assemblies, especially if the reflector is light in weight. However, a more elaborate system, such as Bruce's or a parallelogram spring arrangement, gives best linearity and is less likely to suffer error due to tilting during displacement.

(iv) The phenomena of electrostriction and magnetostriction can be used to provide very smooth displacement of an interferometer reflector and give the convenience and ease of control associated with electrical systems. They can be used at high frequency but the amplitude of scan, and the extent of static displacement possible, is ordinarily not great. For example, a typical barium titanate crystal of 6 mm thickness gives a displacement of about 0.3 μm with 1.5 kV between its faces. The displacement is not linear with voltage but typically is proportional to $40V + V^2$ where V is in kV.

The small displacement is not a disadvantage in the application to angle control of interferometer reflectors and the small size of piezoelectric elements make them particularly suited for this purpose. COOK [1961] and MARZETTA used piezoelectric mounts for the continuous servo control of parallelism during translation of an interferometer mirror for measurement by electronic counting of fringes.

Greater displacements without excessive voltage can be obtained by mounting several piezoelectric crystals 'back-to-back'. Another way to get greater displacement is by the use of a *tube* of a piezoelectric material such as lead zirconium titanate (PZT) in which the field is applied between the inner and the outer cylindrical surfaces; the mirror is attached to the end of the tube. The electrostriction is in the direction of the electric field but there is also a dimensional change of opposite sign in a perpendicular direction, i.e. along the axis of the tube, of magnitude about one-third as great. As the tube can be made long, quite large displacements are possible.

Magnetostriction requires considerable space (length of rods) to obtain displacement of practical magnitude without an excessive current; however, in many applications the space is available anyway. In some cases the heating due to the current may be troublesome.

(v) A deliberate temperature drift, with the consequent thermal expansion or contraction of the interferometer, is sometimes used to produce a very slow scan. This method is sometimes used in recording the profile of spectral lines but is not adaptable to the sort of application described above.

3.3.2. *Detecting the fringe peak*

The detection of the point where the path difference becomes an exact whole number of wavelengths, involves finding when the intensities of two points, having a fixed difference in path differences, (2ε in fig. 4) become equal. If the fixed difference approaches zero, this means finding where the slope of the intensity profile of the fringe becomes zero. However, the sensitivity is very much higher if the fixed difference is large enough so that the two points are on the steep sides of the profile and if the detector actually samples a relatively large part of the fringe at the points $X-\varepsilon$, $X+\varepsilon$ in fig. 4; this was shown in the theoretical analysis discussed in § 4.

The comparison of the intensities at the two points can be made by observation during a relatively slow scan as done at N.P.L. and B.I.P.M. or by a rapid alternation between the sampling points as done by SMITH [1960] and by BRUCE [1961]. The latter is less likely to be affected by drift due to temperature or other causes. The two points can also be observed simultaneously as, for example, in the photometric matching used in a comparator for measuring line standards at N.R.C., Canada (BAIRD [1961]) and to a certain extent in Koester's comparator (ENGELHARD [1952]).

3.3.3. *Fringe counting*

An important exception to the class of systems that introduce a known change in path difference, in order to determine the excess fraction, is the method used in photoelectric counting of fringes pioneered by PECK and OBETZ [1953]. In these, the passage of fringes is counted as the interferometer mirrors are moved through many thousands of fringes and when the mirror is stopped, the fraction is indicated directly. The principle is as follows: Two signals are taken from the interferometer which are 90° out of phase as regards the periodic fluctuation due to the passage of the fringes. These signals are obtained, for example, by having a layer of thickness 0.125λ on part of one of the reflectors and separating the parts of the beam corresponding to the two areas; the two parts of the beam are fed to separate photomultipliers. The two signals can be used to discriminate the direction of travel of the distance measuring reflector. The photomultiplier outputs are also separately fed to the X- and Y-axis of an oscilloscope with the result that the spot follows a circular sweep with passage of the fringes; the angular coordinate of the spot at any distance indicates, as a fraction of 2π radians, the excess fraction in the path difference.

3.4. THE DETECTOR

In choosing a detector (which may be the eye, a photographic film or a photoelectric detector) several aspects of a specific experiment must be considered. Where sensitivity is the prime consideration, photoelectric detectors are generally superior, having a quantum efficiency approaching 20% (a value related to the efficiency of conversion of photons into a usable signal but complicated by random fluctuations arising in the detector itself). This is to be compared with about 2% for photographic film and for the eye in their respective spectral regions of highest sensitivity (CLARK JONES [1958, 1959]). Photoelectric detectors are often much more convenient and lend themselves best to direct servo control systems or to systems for automatic analysis of results. On the other hand, photographic films are best adapted to the recording of many readings simultaneously, such as required in the determination of large numbers of wavelengths (cf. BAIRD and SMITH [1963]). Visual methods generally have the lowest sensitivity but often this is more than compensated for by the ability to discriminate against false signals due to misalignment, stray light or dust, etc. Where the eye is sufficiently sensitive, and where automatic recording is not required, it is pointless to use a more elaborate detector.

4. Limit to sensitivity in setting on fringes

It is of interest to consider the limit to the precision of setting on fringes that can be obtained when all possible practical steps have been taken to eliminate experimental uncertainties. A fundamental limit arises because of the finite number of photons available in a given time interval from a source of given average power. These will produce a smaller finite number of photoelectrons, developed photographic grains, etc. depending on the quantum efficiency of the detector. The number of photoelectrons, or photographic grains produced in a given time interval will fluctuate in accordance with statistical laws, and the fluctuations ('noise' or graininess) will tend to mask very small signals. These fluctuations are fundamental and must be distinguished from practical sources of noise, such as variation in the lamp current, which in principle can be eliminated.

Since the detection of the fringe peak depends on the comparison of intensities of the two sides of the fringe peak, and determining the points where they are equal (fig. 4), such fluctuations will limit the precision with which one can set on the peak, i.e. with which one can determine the wavelength.

A number of authors have considered the theoretical limit imposed by such considerations (TERRIEN [1958]; HANES [1959]; SMITH [1960]; HILL and BRUCE [1962]); the subject has been reviewed by HANES [1963] who generalized the treatment for all types of spectrometers. He gives the following expression for the limiting precision P, defined as the ratio of the wave number to the root mean square fluctuation in the observed wave number:

$$P = \left[\frac{2Z}{hc} A\tau\theta P \frac{S}{V^2} \right]^{\frac{1}{2}}$$

where:

Z is characteristic of the spectrometer

h and c are Planck's constant and the velocity of light

τ is the observing time

θ is related to the quantum efficiency of the detector

P is the radiance of the source

S is the half width of the instrumental profile

V is the half width of the convolution of S and the spectral line profile.

Hanes applied this formula to a number of spectrometers. He found that a Fabry–Perot interferometer of 4 cm aperture, having optimum spacing and reflectivity, gave a theoretical precision of 10^{10} for setting on the primary standard Kr^{86} 0.606 μm line with a time of one second. A Michelson interferometer of similar aperture gave about the same precision.

SMITH [1960] investigated the precision of his fringe setting apparatus and found in practice (with a Fabry–Perot interferometer) that it was possible to attain a precision 20 % as high as the theoretical (in fact about 0.3×10^{10}). This agreement was considered reasonable because in the theoretical treatment it was necessary to make certain assumptions which were not realized in practice, concerning for example the degree of extraneous noise in the source.

It should be noted that, insofar as random fluctuations are concerned, the attainment of higher setting sensitivity depends only on the time of reading. A time constant of a minute or so is practical and can yield a precision of the order of 10^{10} with spectral sources such as the Kr^{86} standard lamp. For such a precision, however, certain other considerations are usually of over-riding importance, as for example the presence of systematic errors and the effects of ambient conditions such as temperature.

The nature of the line profile itself has an important bearing on the significance of the sought-for precision. One part in 10^{10} corresponds to about 10^{-4} of the width of the 0.606 μm line of Kr^{86}, the fundamental standard. Even this very good spectral line can suffer wavelength shifts, due to operating conditions, of several parts in 10^8, and a degree of asymmetry which can result in a wavelength difference of the order of $10^{-8} \lambda$ depending on whether it is measured with respect to the peak of the line profile (with a Fabry–Perot interferometer, for example) or with respect to the centre of gravity of the line profile (as in the case when a Michelson interferometer is used). (Cf. BAIRD and SMITH [1962].)

This does not mean that these wavelengths cannot be specified to a precision better than 10^8 but it does mean that a better precision requires careful specification of the part of the profile used, i.e. the interferometer, as well as the source operating conditions. This has been shown by the measurements made in different national laboratories, of the wavelength corrections for practical sources. If the part of the spectral line profile is included in specification, the line can be ascribed a wavelength that is significant to $10^{-9} \lambda$ and perhaps better. It should be noted that such considerations apply also to spectral lines on which laser radiations may be stabilized.

5. Extension to other problems

The techniques described in the preceding sections were developed, in the main, for the specific purpose of measuring optical wavelengths and very small wavelength shifts. However, they are clearly applicable, with slight modifications, to other problems, notably to the measurement of physical lengths and very small changes in length. For such application light is used whose wavelength is constant and precisely reproducible.

Small changes in absolute length can be measured to a sensitivity similar to that referred above, viz. approaching 10^{-9} of the total length, by the use of wavelengths of light in vacuum as a reference standard. Where a relative change only is to be measured, so that the interferometer path difference can be very short, displacements as small as 10^{-8} mm could be detected in the average position of the optical surface, giving the possibility of a very great sensitivity in the proportional length change.

The techniques are also applicable to the absolute measurement of physical lengths, such as required in the calibration of length standards, the measurement of the velocity of light and so on. However in such applications the likelihood of systematic error is very great; the effects of ambient conditions, as well as the imprecise nature of the physical length to be measured, rather than the sensitivity of setting, generally imposes the limitation to the accuracy that can be achieved. Nevertheless, comparators are in use or under construction at several national laboratories and at the International Bureau of Weights and Measures for the routine measurement of length standards to an accuracy which is expected to approach one part in 10^8 (cf. BAIRD [1963]). It will require time and numerous international intercomparisons to find out whether these expectations can be realized.

Interferometry has felt the impact of a great new stimulus with the development of the laser, which promises to extend greatly interferometry's usefulness. Considerable invention has resulted; some of it is not dissimilar to the techniques described above for controlling the separation of optical surfaces; other developments involve a completely new kind of technique, such as the observation and use of beats between separate laser sources (BENNETT and KINDLMANN [1962]; ENLOE and RODDA [1965]). An example of the increased possibilities of interferometry brought about by the laser is the fact that it already appears practical to measure by *direct* interferometry distances as great as several hundred metres, as compared to the limit of less than one metre with sources previously available *.

References

BAIRD, K. M., 1961, Rev. Sci. Instr. **32**, 549.

BAIRD, K. M., 1963, Appl. Opt. **2**, 471.

BAIRD, K. M. and D. S. SMITH, 1962, J. Opt. Soc. Am. **52**, 507.

BAIRD, K. M. and D. S. SMITH, 1963, Appl. Opt. **2**, 167.

BENNETT, W. R. and P. J. KINDLMANN, 1962, Rev. Sci. Instr. **33**, 601.

BORN, M. and E. WOLF, 1959, Principles of optics (Pergamon Press, London).

BRUCE, C. F. and R. M. HILL, 1961, Australian J. Phys. **14**, 64.

CANDLER, C., 1951, Modern interferometers (Hilger and Watts Ltd., London).

CLARK JONES, R., 1958, Phot. Sci. Eng. **2**, 57.

CLARK JONES, R., 1959, J. Opt. Soc. Am. **49**, 645.

COOK, A. H., 1959, in: Symposium on interferometry (National Physical Laboratory, England) p. 389

COOK, H. D. and L. A. MARZETTA, 1961, J. Res. Natl. Bur. Std. **65C**, 129.

ENGELHARD, E., 1952, Recent developments and techniques in the maintenance of standards (National Physical Laboratory, England).

ENLOE, L. H. and J. L. RODDA, 1965, Proc. IEEE **53**, 167.

HANES, G. R., 1959, Can. J. Phys. **37**, 1282.

HANES, G. R., 1963, Appl. Opt. **2**, 65.

HERRIOT, D. R., 1961, J. Opt. Soc. Am. **51**, 1142.

HILL, R. M. and C. F. BRUCE, Australian J. Phys. **15**, 194.

KRUG, W., J. RIENITZ and G. SCHULZ, 1964, Contribution to interference microscopy (Hilger and Watts Ltd., London).

MASUI, T., J. TERRIEN and J. HAMON, 1958, Proces-Verbaux Scéances, Comité Intern. Poids Mesures **26**, M157.

PECK, E. R. and S. W. OBETZ, 1953, J. Opt. Soc. Am. **43**, 505.

SAUNDERS, J. B., 1951, J. Res. Natl. Bur. Std. **47**, 148.

SMITH, D. S., 1960, Can. J. Phys. **38**, 983.

TERRIEN, J., 1958, J. Phys. Radium **19**, 390.

* *Note added in proof:* The techniques described in the foregoing were largely developed previous to 1960 for the specific applications mentioned. In spite of the many great advances in interferometry since 1960, notably, in connection with laser technology (ch. 3) there has been no significant improvement in these techniques. This is not surprising in view of the fact their limitations were fundamental in nature, due largely to the characteristics of the receivers and the sources. Improvements in the latter should make possible corresponding improvements over the examples cited.

CHAPTER 5

OPTICS OF THIN FILMS

F. ABELÈS

Institut d'Optique, Paris

CONTENTS

1. Uncoated surfaces. Reflection and refraction

1.1. MAXWELL'S EQUATIONS

From a theoretical point of view, the investigation of the optical properties of a system of thin films is equivalent to the study of the propagation of plane electromagnetic waves through a stratified medium. We shall begin, therefore, our investigations by recalling briefly Maxwell's equations, which are governing all our further results. They can be written in the following form:

$$\operatorname{curl} \boldsymbol{E} + \frac{1}{c} \dot{\boldsymbol{B}} = 0 \tag{1}$$

$$\operatorname{curl} \boldsymbol{H} - \frac{1}{c} \dot{\boldsymbol{D}} - \frac{4\pi}{c} \boldsymbol{J} = 0, \tag{2}$$

the dot denoting differentiation with respect to time. These vector equations relate the space and time derivatives of five vectors: the electric vector $\boldsymbol{E}$, the magnetic induction $\boldsymbol{B}$, the magnetic vector $\boldsymbol{H}$, the electric displacement $\boldsymbol{D}$, the electric current density $\boldsymbol{J}$. Eqs. (1) and (2) are supplemented by relations which describe the properties of matter under the influence of the field and are called material equations. We shall limit ourselves in what follows to isotropic substances. The material equations take then the simple form:

$$\boldsymbol{J} = \sigma \boldsymbol{E}, \tag{3}$$

$$\boldsymbol{D} = \varepsilon \boldsymbol{E}, \tag{4}$$

$$\boldsymbol{B} = \mu \boldsymbol{H}. \tag{5}$$

Here σ is called the conductivity, ε is the dielectric constant and μ is the magnetic permeability.

We use the Gaussian system of units throughout this chapter, i.e. the electrical quantities ($\boldsymbol{E}$, $\boldsymbol{D}$ and $\boldsymbol{J}$) are measured in electrostatic units, and the magnetic quantities ($\boldsymbol{B}$ and $\boldsymbol{H}$) in electromagnetic units. The constant c is the velocity of light in vacuum and is approximately equal to 3×10^{10} cm/sec.

In order to be able to study the reflection and refraction of an electromagnetic wave at a surface of discontinuity for σ, ε and μ, it is necessary to apply boundary conditions. We shall make use of the following: the tangential components (i.e. parallel to the plane of discontinuity) of the electric and magnetic vectors are continuous across the surface. These two boundary conditions are sufficient for our purpose, because substitution of (3), (4) and (5) into (1) and (2) allows us to write Maxwell's equations in the following form:

$$\operatorname{curl} \boldsymbol{E} + \frac{\mu}{c} \dot{\boldsymbol{H}} = 0, \tag{6}$$

$$\operatorname{curl} \boldsymbol{H} - \frac{\varepsilon}{c} \dot{\boldsymbol{E}} + \frac{4\pi\sigma}{c} \boldsymbol{E} = 0, \tag{7}$$

which is a system of two partial differential equations relating the two vectors E and H.

Finally, we must introduce the Poynting vector S, the magnitude of which represents the amount of energy which crosses per second a unit area normal to the directions of E and H.

1.2. PROPAGATION OF PLANE WAVES

We consider now monochromatic waves of angular frequency ω, i.e. we suppose that the electric and magnetic vectors are of the form $E(x, y, z) \exp(i\omega t)$ and $H(x, y, z) \exp(i\omega t)$ respectively. Eqs. (6) and (7) can be written now

$$\operatorname{curl} E(x, y, z) + \frac{i\omega\mu}{c} H(x, y, z) = 0 \tag{8}$$

$$\operatorname{curl} H(x, y, z) - \frac{i\omega\varepsilon'}{c} E(x, y, z) = 0 \tag{9}$$

with $\varepsilon' = \varepsilon + 4i\pi\sigma/\omega$. Elimination of either $E(x, y, z)$ or $H(x, y, z)$ shows that any of these vectors verifies a wave equation:

$$\Delta E(x, y, z) + \frac{\varepsilon'\mu\omega^2}{c^2} E(x, y, z) = 0, \qquad \Delta H(x, y, z) + \frac{\varepsilon'\mu\omega^2}{c^2} H(x, y, z) = 0. \tag{10}$$

We suppose now that this monochromatic wave is a plane wave propagating in the z-direction. Then E and H are functions of z only and eqs. (10) read now

$$\frac{d^2 E}{dz^2} + \frac{\omega^2\varepsilon'\mu}{c^2} E = 0, \qquad \frac{d^2 H}{dz^2} + \frac{\omega^2\varepsilon'\mu}{c^2} H = 0, \tag{11}$$

which shows that the components of both vectors are of the type $a \exp(-i\kappa z) + b \exp(i\kappa z)$, a and b being constants and $\kappa = (\omega/c)\sqrt{(\varepsilon'\mu)}$.

It can be shown that, for plane waves at least, E and H are perpendicular to the direction of propagation (the z-direction, in our case). Moreover, E, H and the z-direction form a right-handed orthogonal triad of vectors. The magnitudes E and H of the electric and magnetic vectors are such that $\mu^{\frac{1}{2}} H = \varepsilon'^{\frac{1}{2}} E$. In a nonabsorbing medium ($\sigma = 0$), we have $\varepsilon' = \varepsilon$, and the magnitude S of the Poynting vector is given by

$$S = (\varepsilon/\mu)^{\frac{1}{2}} cE^2/4\pi = (\mu/\varepsilon)^{\frac{1}{2}} cH^2/4\pi.$$

1.3. REFLECTION AND REFRACTION OF A PLANE WAVE AT A PLANE BOUNDARY BETWEEN TWO MEDIA

1.3.1. Snell's laws

Maxwell's equations together with their boundary conditions are all that is necessary in order to derive the laws of reflection and refraction of a plane wave incident on a plane boundary between two homogeneous isotropic media. We suppose first that both are nonabsorbing, i.e. they are characterized by real ε and μ. We discuss the case of oblique incidence from the beginning. The direction of the Poynting vector, i.e. the direction of propagation of the wave, is not the same as the direction of the normal to the plane boundary. Fig. 1 indicates our notations. The plane xOy separates the two media, which are characterized by ε_0, μ_0 and ε_1, μ_1. The plane xOz is the plane of incidence, which means that the electric and magnetic vectors of the incident wave have a space and time dependence which may be written

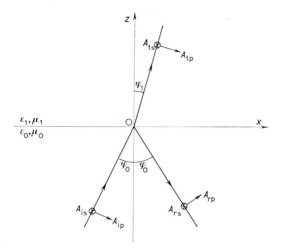

Fig. 1. Illustration of the notations used for the study of the reflection and refraction of a plane wave.

$\exp\,[\mathrm{i}(\omega t - \kappa_0\,(x\sin\phi_0 + z\cos\phi_0))]$, ϕ_0 being the angle of incidence. The reflected and transmitted waves propagate in the directions (l_r, m_r, n_r) and (l_t, m_t, n_t) respectively. Their vectors contain the factors $\exp\,[\mathrm{i}(\omega t - \kappa_0(l_r x + m_r y + n_r z))]$ and $\exp\,[\mathrm{i}(\omega t - \kappa_1(l_t x + m_t y + n_t z))]$, κ_0 and κ_1 being the κ-coefficients defined above, i.e. $\kappa_0 = (\omega/c)\sqrt{(\varepsilon_0\mu_0)}$ and $\kappa_1 = (\omega/c)\sqrt{(\varepsilon_1\mu_1)}$.

At the boundary between the two media (plane $z = 0$), we must write the continuity of the tangential components of the electric and magnetic vectors in the two media. This implies first that the same coefficients of x, y and t must appear in each of the exponentials already written. Equating coefficients of y, we get $0 = m_r = m_t$, which signifies that the directions of the propagation vectors are in the same plane, containing the normal to the boundary. Equating the coefficients of x and writing $l_r = \sin\phi'_0$, $l_t = \sin\phi_1$, we have $\sin\phi_0 = \sin\phi'_0$ and $\kappa_0\sin\phi_0 = \kappa_1\sin\phi_1$. We have thus obtained the laws of reflection and refraction (Snell's laws). It may be noticed that we did not use yet the amplitudes of the vectors.

1.3.2. Fresnel's formulae

We shall do so now in order to find the Fresnel formulae. We can avoid using the exponentials already discussed, because Snell's laws ensure their equality in the plane

$z=0$. We resolve each vector into components parallel (subscript p) and perpendicular (subscript s) to the plane, and use the equality $\varepsilon^{\frac{1}{2}}|E|=\mu^{\frac{1}{2}}|H|$ together with the fact that E, H and the Poynting vector form a right-handed orthogonal triad of vectors. The components of the electric and magnetic vectors of the incident reflected and transmitted wave are, the exponential factors being let aside,

$$E_x^{(i)} = A_{ip}\cos\phi_0,\qquad E_x^{(r)} = A_{rp}\cos\phi_0,\qquad E_x^{(t)} = A_{tp}\cos\phi_1,$$

$$E_y^{(i)} = A_{is},\qquad\qquad E_y^{(r)} = A_{rs},\qquad\qquad E_y^{(t)} = A_{ts},$$

$$H_x^{(i)} = -(\varepsilon_0/\mu_0)^{\frac{1}{2}}A_{is}\cos\phi_0,\; H_x^{(r)} = (\varepsilon_0/\mu_0)^{\frac{1}{2}}A_{rs}\cos\phi_0,\; H_x^{(t)} = -(\varepsilon_1/\mu_1)^{\frac{1}{2}}A_{ts}\cos\phi_1,$$

$$H_y^{(i)} = (\varepsilon_0/\mu_0)^{\frac{1}{2}}A_{ip},\qquad H_y^{(r)} = -(\varepsilon_0/\mu_0)^{\frac{1}{2}}A_{rp},\qquad H_y^{(t)} = (\varepsilon_1/\mu_1)^{\frac{1}{2}}A_{tp}.$$

The boundary conditions are $E_x^{(i)}+E_x^{(r)}=E_x^{(t)}$, $H_x^{(i)}+H_x^{(r)}=H_x^{(t)}$, etc. Solving them, we obtain the amplitudes of the reflected and transmitted waves:

$$A_{rs} = \frac{Y_0\cos\phi_0 - Y_1\cos\phi_1}{Y_0\cos\phi_0 + Y_1\cos\phi_1}A_{is},$$

$$A_{ts} = A_{is}+A_{rs} = \frac{2Y_0\cos\phi_0}{Y_0\cos\phi_0 + Y_1\cos\phi_1}A_{is},$$

$$A_{rp} = \frac{Y_0\cos\phi_1 - Y_1\cos\phi_0}{Y_0\cos\phi_1 + Y_1\cos\phi_0}A_{ip},$$

$$A_{tp} = (A_{ip}+A_{rp})\frac{\cos\phi_0}{\cos\phi_1} = \frac{2Y_0\cos\phi_0}{Y_0\cos\phi_1 + Y_1\cos\phi_0}A_{ip}.$$

$Y_0=(\varepsilon_0/\mu_0)^{\frac{1}{2}}$ and $Y_1=(\varepsilon_1/\mu_1)^{\frac{1}{2}}$ are the admittances of the two media, which reduce to their respective indices of refraction when $\mu_0=\mu_1=1$. In that case, the amplitudes can be written in terms of ϕ_0 and ϕ_1 only, viz.

$$A_{rs} = -\frac{\sin(\phi_0-\phi_1)}{\sin(\phi_0+\phi_1)}A_{is},\qquad A_{ts} = \frac{2\sin\phi_1\cos\phi_0}{\sin(\phi_0+\phi_1)}A_{is},$$

$$A_{rp} = -\frac{\mathrm{tg}(\phi_0-\phi_1)}{\mathrm{tg}(\phi_0+\phi_1)}A_{ip},\qquad A_{tp} = \frac{2\sin\phi_1\cos\phi_1}{\sin(\phi_0+\phi_1)\cos(\phi_0-\phi_1)}A_{ip}.$$

These are the Fresnel formulae (or equations), which have been derived first by Fresnel in 1823 on the basis of his elastic theory of light. We may notice that $A_{rp}=0$ when $\phi_0+\phi_1 = \frac{1}{2}\pi$, that is for an angle of incidence ϕ_{0P} defined by $\mathrm{tg}\,\phi_{0P} = n_1/n_0$ and called the polarizing or Brewster angle.

We examine now how the energy of the incident wave is divided between the reflected and the transmitted waves. We have already indicated that the energy transported by a wave is given by the Poynting vector. It follows that the amount of energy incident on a unit area of the boundary per second is

$$I^{(i)} = S^{(i)}\cos\phi_0 = \frac{cn_0}{4\pi}A_i^2\cos\phi_0,$$

and the same quantities for the reflected and transmitted waves are

$$I^{(r)} = S^{(r)} \cos \phi_0 = \frac{cn_0}{4\pi} A_r^2 \cos \phi_0,$$

$$I^{(t)} = S^{(t)} \cos \phi_1 = \frac{cn_1}{4\pi} A_t{}^2 \cos \phi_1.$$

We have omitted the indices s and p, because these expressions are valid either for the s- or for the p-vibration.

We shall call reflectance and transmittance the ratios $R = I^{(r)}/I^{(i)}$ and $T = I^{(t)}/I^{(i)}$ respectively. From the preceding equations it may be seen that

$$R_s = \frac{I_s^{(r)}}{I_s^{(i)}} = \left(\frac{Y_0 \cos \phi_0 - Y_1 \cos \phi_1}{Y_0 \cos \phi_0 + Y_1 \cos \phi_1}\right)^2 = \frac{\sin^2(\phi_0 - \phi_1)}{\sin^2(\phi_0 + \phi_1)},$$

$$T_s = \frac{I_s^{(t)}}{I_s^{(i)}} = \frac{4Y_0 Y_1 \cos \phi_0 \cos \phi_1}{(Y_0 \cos \phi_0 + Y_1 \cos \phi_1)^2} = \frac{\sin 2\phi_0 \sin 2\phi_1}{\sin^2(\phi_0 + \phi_1)},$$

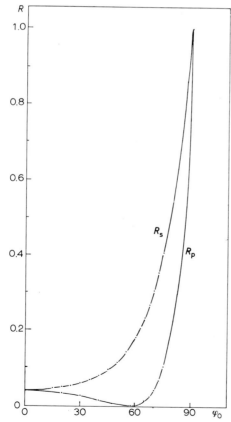

Fig. 2. R_s and R_p vs. ϕ_0 for reflection at the plane boundary between two media with indices of refraction $n_0 = 1$ (air) and $n_1 = 1.516$ (glass).

$$R_p = \frac{I_p^{(r)}}{I_p^{(i)}} = \left(\frac{Y_0 \cos \phi_1 - Y_1 \cos \phi_0}{Y_0 \cos \phi_1 + Y_1 \cos \phi_0}\right)^2 = \frac{\text{tg}^2 (\phi_0 - \phi_1)}{\text{tg} (\phi_0 + \phi_1)},$$

$$T_p = \frac{I_p^{(t)}}{I_p^{(i)}} = \frac{4 Y_0 Y_1 \cos \phi_0 \cos \phi_1}{(Y_0 \cos \phi_1 + Y_1 \cos \phi_0)^2} = \frac{\sin 2\phi_0 \sin 2\phi_1}{\sin^2 (\phi_0 + \phi_1) \cos^2 (\phi_0 - \phi_1)}.$$

It can be verified that energy is conserved, because $R_s + T_s = R_p + T_p = 1$. Fig. 2 shows the variations of R_s and R_p with ϕ_0 for reflection at the plane surface limiting two media with indices of refraction $n_0 = 1$ (air) and $n_1 = 1.516$ (glass).

1.3.3. The second medium is absorbing

Fresnel's formulae are valid even when the second medium is absorbing. The only difference with the situation already discussed is the appearance of a complex dielectric constant ε_1' for such a medium. We shall put now $\mu_0 = \mu_1 = 1$ and $n_1' = \sqrt{\varepsilon_1'} = n_1 - ik_1$. Snell's law reads $n_0 \sin \phi_0 = (n_1 - ik_1) \sin \phi_1$, which shows that ϕ_1 must be a complex angle. It would take us too far to enter the discussion of the type of wave we have in the absorbing medium. In order to write Fresnel's equations, we must know the value of $n_1' \cos \phi_1$, which will be a complex quantity called $p_1 - iq_1$. We have

$$(p_1 - iq_1)^2 = (n_1' \cos \phi_1)^2 = n_1'^2 (1 - \sin^2 \phi_1) = n_1'^2 - n_0^2 \sin^2 \phi_0$$

which is equivalent to two equations in the two unknowns p_1 and q_1:

$$p_1^2 - q_1^2 = n_1^2 - k_1^2 - n_0^2 \sin^2 \phi_0,$$

$$p_1 q_1 = n_1 k_1.$$

The (complex) amplitudes of the electric vector of the reflected wave become

$$A_{rs} = \frac{n_0 \cos \phi_0 - p_1 + iq_1}{n_0 \cos \phi_0 + p_1 - iq_1} A_{is},$$

$$A_{rp} = \frac{n_0(p_1 - iq_1) - [(p_1 - iq_1)^2 + n_0^2 \sin^2 \phi_0] \cos \phi_0}{n_0(p_1 - iq_1) + [(p_1 - iq_1)^2 + n_0^2 \sin^2 \phi_0] \cos \phi_0} A_{ip}.$$

The use of p_1 and q_1 in order to characterize the absorbing medium for the angle of incidence ϕ_0 is not a necessity. It is convenient, because A_{rs} and A_{rp} are thus algebraic functions of the characteristics of this medium instead of being irrational functions of n_1 and k_1. We are not interested now in the amplitudes of the electric vectors of the transmitted wave. The amplitudes A_{rs} and A_{rp} are complex even when A_{is} and A_{ip} are real. The arguments of the complex quantities $A_{rs} = |A_{rs}| \exp (i\delta_{rs})$ and $A_{rp} = |A_{rp}| \exp (i\delta_{rp})$ are the phase changes on reflection. The reflectances are given now by the squares of the moduli of the complex quantities A_{rs}/A_{is} and A_{rp}/A_{ip}. Fig. 3 shows the variations of R_s and R_p with the angle of incidence for two different metals: Ag ($n = 0.055$, $k = 3.32$) and Cu ($n = 0.76$, $k = 2.46$) in the visible ($\lambda = 5460$ Å). It may be noticed that we have always $R_p \neq 0$, but whereas R_s is an increasing function

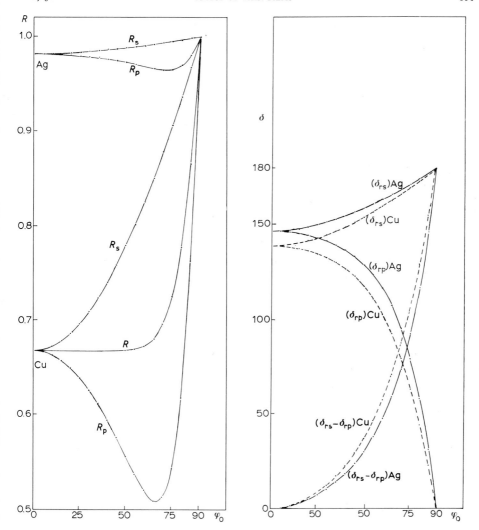

Fig. 3. R_p and R_s vs. ϕ_0 for reflection at the plane boundary air–metal. Two metals with very different normal reflectance for green mercury light ($\lambda=5460$ Å) have been chosen: Ag ($n=0.055$, $k=3.32$) and Cu ($n=0.76$, $k=2.46$). $R=\frac{1}{2}(R_s+R_p)$.

Fig. 4. Phase shifts δ_{rs} and δ_{rp} vs. ϕ_0 for the same metals as in fig. 3. The phase shifts $-\Delta=\delta_{rs}-\delta_{rp}$ are also shown.

of ϕ_0, R_p decreases first until it reaches a minimum and then increases. For grazing incidence ($\phi_0=90°$), both R_s and R_p are equal to unity.

The minimum of R_p occurs always for a large angle of incidence, at least in the visible and the infrared ($\phi_0 \geq 65°$). The intensity of $R_{p\,min}$ is largely a function of k/n, which increases with k/n.

The fact that $\delta_{rs} \neq \delta_{rp}$ has an important practical consequence: a linearly polarized incident light, which is neither s- nor p-polarized, will become, after reflection on an absorbing substance, elliptically polarized. The analysis of the reflected light is commonly used for determining the complex index of refraction of metals. Fig. 4 shows, for the same metals and the same wavelength the variations with ϕ_0 of δ_{rs}, δ_{rp} and $\Delta = \delta_{rp} - \delta_{rs}$. It will be noticed that $\Delta \approx -90°$ when R_p is near its minimum.

For natural unpolarized light, the same intensity is transported by both s- and p-vibrations. The reflectance is, therefore, the average of R_s and R_p: $R(\phi_0) = \frac{1}{2}[R_s(\phi_0) + R_p(\phi_0)]$. Fig. 3 shows the values of R for Cu. It is useful to notice that R keeps the same values from normal incidence to $\phi_0 \approx 50°$.

1.3.4. Total reflection

Total reflection deserves a special mention. Here, although the second medium is nonabsorbing ($k_1 = 0$), we have a complex angle ϕ_1 ($n_0 \sin \phi_0 > n_1$, which gives $\sin \phi_1 > 1$, i.e. ϕ_1 is imaginary). The preceding formulae are still valid, with the following modifications: $p_1 = 0$, $q_1^2 = n_0^2 \sin^2 \phi_0 - n_1^2$. This shows that

$$A_{rs} = \frac{n_0 \cos \phi_0 + iq_1}{n_0 \cos \phi_0 - iq_1} A_{is} = A_{is} \exp(i\delta_{rs}),$$

$$A_{rp} = \frac{-in_0 q_1 - n_1^2 \cos \phi_0}{-in_0 q_1 + n_1^2 \cos \phi_0} A_{ip} = A_{ip} \exp(i\delta_{rp}).$$

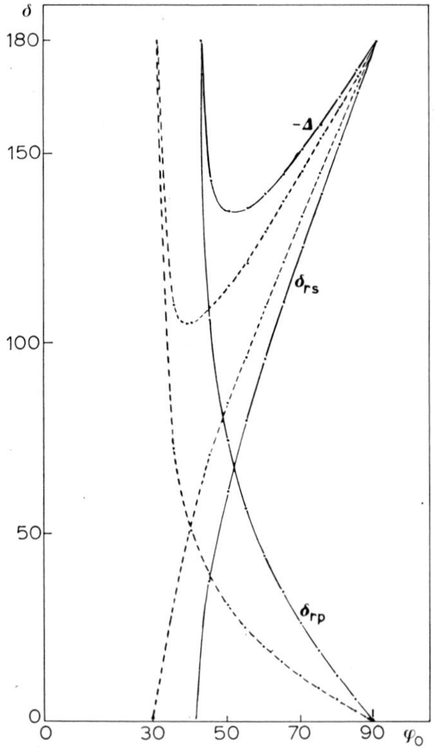

Fig. 5. δ_{rs}, δ_{rp} and $-\Delta$ vs. ϕ_0 for total reflection. Full lines: $n_0 = 1.5$, dashed lines: $n_0 = 2$. For all the curves $n_1 = 1$.

There is total reflection because $R_s = R_p = 1$, but there are phase-shifts on reflection which are given by δ_{rs} and δ_{rp}. Fig. 5 shows the variations of δ_{rs}, δ_{rp} and $\Delta = \delta_{rp} - \delta_{rs}$ with ϕ_0 for $n_0 = 1.5$ and $n_0 = 2$, n_1 being equal to unity. It must be stressed that all the values are given with our conventions for the origins of the phases, i.e. there may be some $\pm 180°$ differences with the values given by other authors.

2. Fabrication of thin films

The most widely used method for fabrication of thin films is evaporation in high vacuum. It is not our purpose to give here a description of the methods of production of such films. There is a constant progress in the techniques and the most advanced method today will become obsolete in a short time. Until a few years ago, for instance, high vacuum meant pressure of the order of 10^{-6} Torr (1 Torr = 1 mm of Hg). Since then, and mostly due to the needs of space research, we have entered the era of ultra-high vacuum and commercially available systems can offer vacuum chambers of large dimensions with vacua of the order of 10^{-11} Torr. It is very probable that even lower pressures will become available in not too remote future. For a description of ultra-high vacuum evaporators, the reader is referred to the article by CASWELL [1963]. The classical high vacuum systems, which are still in use in the majority of the laboratories, are composed of a glass (pyrex) or stainless steel bell-jar which is evacuated by means of a primary (mechanical) pump, followed by a diffusion pump, generally an oil-diffusion pump with liquid nitrogen trap to avoid oil contamination of the vacuum chamber. It is probable that some of the residual gases which can be found in the vacuum chamber are much more active than others, which means that it is not only important to have a low pressure, but also that for a given pressure the nature of the vacuum is important. One of the advantages of ultra-high vacuum equipment is the possibility of obtaining a 'clean' vacuum, that is free of oil and water vapour, due to the use of pumps based on an ionization principle.

There are different methods of cleaning the substrate and, in every laboratory, there are some special tricks used for this purpose.

It is important to notice that every substance has its own evaporating technique, and that there is always some difference between the evaporating procedures of even two closely related substances. Some general considerations are, nevertheless, appropriate for the techniques relating to the evaporation of metals or dielectrics. Metals should be evaporated very rapidly, whereas the same is not necessarily true for dielectrics. Use of a heated substrate is preferable for most dielectrics, but metals should be evaporated on cooled substrates, or, at least maintained at room-temperature, with possible vacuum annealing afterwards. The factors affecting the optical properties of thin films are: purity of the product to be evaporated, rate and pressure during the evaporation, substrate temperature, residual gas and vapour-incidence angle. In fact, the evaporation conditions are function of the subsequent use of the films.

There are different methods for preparing thin films, those which are mainly used being: a) heating by Joule effect of the substance to be evaporated; b) cathode sputtering; c) induction heating; d) use of an electron gun. Some new methods have been proposed, e.g. use of a laser beam. It is generally necessary to control the thickness of the film during its deposition. Many methods have been proposed for this purpose. We shall mention a few of them only: a) measurement of the reflectance and/or of the transmittance of the film; b) measurement of its electrical resistance; c) use of an auxiliary vibrating quartz, the frequency of which is modified by the mass of the deposited film; d) measurement of the ionization current, which gives information concerning the rate of evaporation; e) use of a polarization interfero-meter (Savart plate), as suggested by VAN HEEL and WALTHER [1958]. In all cases, care should be taken in order to ensure uniformity of the thickness of the films. For that purpose, it is possible either to rotate the substrate, or to use several evaporating sources, and, in any case, it is recommended to keep the distance between source and substrate as large as possible. More details concerning these problems can be found in the book by HOLLAND [1958].

3. Theory of the properties of thin films

The theory of the optical properties of thin films is not a difficult subject, but it would take us too far to discuss all of its implications and particularities. There are several books on the subject, to which the reader is referred for further details (HEAVENS [1955], MAYER [1950], METHFESSEL [1953], VAŠIČEK [1960], WOLTER [1956]). We shall give here only a short account of the principles of the theory, sufficient in order to understand how thin films work and to be able to prepare computations of their optical properties.

3.1. NORMAL INCIDENCE

3.1.1. *Representation of a thin film by an equivalent matrix*

We shall use plane, time-harmonic waves, and suppose that the z-axis is in the direction of the normal to the planes limiting the films, which are supposed to be unbounded in the x- and y-directions. The neglect of the finite areas of the films is not critical, except when dealing with total reflection (see IOGANSEN [1961]). It is convenient to discuss first the normal incidence (propagation in z-direction), because oblique incidence is easily deduced from this case. The films are supposed to be isotropic and they are characterized by the complex dielectric constant $\tilde{\varepsilon} = \tilde{n}^2 = (n - ik)^2$ ($\tilde{n}$ being the complex index of refraction), the magnetic permeability μ and the thickness d. The factor $\exp(i\omega t)$, ω being the angular frequency of the wave, will be omitted, because it enters all the expressions of the fields. Maxwell's equations lead to a second-order differential equation (the wave equation) for the (complex) amplitude of the electric field E, the solution of which is, in a plane $z = $ constant,

$$E(z) = ae^{-i\kappa z} + be^{i\kappa z}$$

a and *b* being the two constants of integration, which will be fixed by the boundary or initial conditions, and

$$\kappa = \frac{\omega}{c} (\tilde{\varepsilon}\mu)^{\frac{1}{2}} = \frac{2\pi}{\lambda} (\tilde{\varepsilon}\mu)^{\frac{1}{2}}$$

We neglect any dependence on *x* or *y*, for the same reason we omitted the time dependence, and we take the *x*-axis in the direction of the electric vector.

The magnetic field **H** is related to the electric field, via Maxwell's equations, and it may be shown that

$$H(z) = g(ae^{-i\kappa z} - be^{i\kappa z})$$

with $g = \sqrt{\tilde{\varepsilon}/\mu}$, **H** being parallel to the *y*-direction.

Our first problem is to find the relation between the amplitudes of **E** and **H** at the entrance and the exit of a given thin film. We follow here a method which has been suggested by HERPIN [1947]. It is convenient to use the matrix vector [*A*(*z*)], the components of which are *E*(*z*) and *H*(*z*), so that it is defined by

$$[A(z)] = \begin{bmatrix} E(z) \\ H(z) \end{bmatrix}.$$

Our problem is to find the relation existing between [(*A*(*z*)] and [*A*(*z*+*d*)]. Let us construct the matrix vector [*Z*], defined by

$$[Z(z)] = \begin{bmatrix} X(z) \\ Y(z) \end{bmatrix}$$

with

$$X(z) = gE + H = 2gae^{-i\kappa z}, \quad Y(z) = gE - H = 2gbe^{+i\kappa z}.$$

$$[Z(z+d)] = [P][Z(z)]$$

with

$$[P] = \begin{bmatrix} e^{-i\beta} & 0 \\ 0 & e^{+i\beta} \end{bmatrix} \quad \beta = \kappa d.$$

The relation between *X*, *Y* and *E*, *H*, can be written in matrix form:

$$[Z(z)] = [T][A(z)], \tag{13}$$

the matrix [*T*] being given by:

$$[T] = \begin{bmatrix} g & 1 \\ g & -1 \end{bmatrix}.$$

Reversing eq. (13), we can write, for the plane *z*+*d*,

$$[A(z+d)] = [T]^{-1}[Z(z+d)].$$

We have, therefore,

$$[A(z+d)] = [T]^{-1}[Z(z+d)] = [T]^{-1}[P][Z(z)] = [T]^{-1}[P][T][A(z)].$$

This is the relation we were looking for. It is more convenient to write it in a slightly different form:

$$[A(z)] = [T]^{-1}[P]^{-1}[T][A(z+d)].$$

It is now a matter of matrix multiplication only, to show that

$$[A(z)] = \begin{bmatrix} \cos\beta & (i/g)\sin\beta \\ ig\sin\beta & \cos\beta \end{bmatrix} [A(z+d)] = [M(d)][A(z+d)]. \tag{14}$$

Eq. (14) is very important because it solves, in fact, the problem of computing the optical properties of thin films. It is known, indeed, that the tangential components of the electric and magnetic vectors are continuous across a surface of discontinuity of $\tilde{\varepsilon}$ and μ. Let us imagine that we have a thin film extending from z to $z+d$, i.e. a film of thickness d. Then $[A(z)]$ represents the fields in the plane z, either in the film, or in the medium of incidence. Similarly, $[A(z+d)]$ represents the same vectors in the plane $z+d$, either in the film or outside. We shall always designate by n_0 and n_s the indices of refraction of the first and last (semi-infinite) media.

3.1.2. Equivalent matrix for a pile of films

Consider now two adjacent films, characterized by the quantities $\tilde{\varepsilon}_1$, $\tilde{\varepsilon}_2$, μ_1, μ_2 and extending, the first one from $z=0$ to $z=z_1$ and the second from $z=z_1$ to $z=z_1+z_2$. If $[M_1(z_1)]$ and $[M_2(z_2)]$ are the $[M]$-matrices for the films, then

$$[A(0)] = [M_1(z_1)][A(z_1)] \quad \text{and} \quad [A(z_1)] = [M_2(z_2)][A(z_1+z_2)]$$

with an obvious notation, so that

$$[A(0)] = [M_1(z_1)][M_2(z_2)][A(z_1+z_2)].$$

This result may be generalized to the case of a succession for N films extending from $0 \leq z \leq z_1$, $z_1 \leq z \leq z_1+z_2$, $z_1+z_2 \leq z \leq z_1+z_2+z_3$, and we obtain the final result:

$$[A(0)] = [M_1(z_1)][M_2(z_2)] \cdots [M_N(z_N)][A(z_1+z_2+\cdots z_N)].$$

This is the result we were looking for in this section. It shows that, for the purposes of determining the propagation of a plane monochromatic wave in a direction perpendicular to the planes limiting the film, the latter is specified by the two by two matrix $[M]$, which is called the characteristic matrix of the film.

It is useful to notice that $[M]$ is unimodular, its determinant being equal to one. When we have a superposition of films, their characteristic matrix, obtained by the rules of matrix multiplication, is still unimodular. The fact that the modulus of $[M]$ is constant is related to the conservation of energy.

Matrix multiplication being non-commutative, it is clear that the order of the factors in the product giving $[M]$ is important. That could be expected for physical grounds: there is no reason, indeed, for the system of films to be insensitive to the order of its constituents.

For propagation in the reverse direction, the characteristic matrix of the same system of thin layers will be:

$$[M'] = [M_N][M_{N-1}] \ldots [M_2][M_1].$$

It may be shown that the only difference between $[M]$ and $[M']$ is the interchange of the elements of the principal diagonal.

In our discussion, we have characterized every medium by two optical parameters $\tilde{\varepsilon}$ and μ, besides its thickness d. In fact, it is well known that in the optical region of the spectrum we have $\mu = 1$. The explicit use of μ was motivated by our intention to make it clear that $\tilde{\varepsilon}$ (or $\tilde{n}$) enters the field equations in two different ways: via κ and via g. The former is the propagation constant of the wave, whereas the latter is its admittance. This distinction becomes important when we go to oblique incidence, even if we put $\mu = 1$, as we shall do from now on. The propagation constant is a function of the direction in which the wave is progressing, whereas the admittance is a function of the polarization of the wave. Snell's law of refraction, which is valid for propagation through thin films too, is related to κ only, and reads $\kappa \sin \phi = $ constant, ϕ being the angle of the normal to the plane of the wave with respect to the z-direction.

3.2. OBLIQUE INCIDENCE

We must examine separately the two cases where the electric vector is perpendicular to the plane of incidence (s-polarization) or in the plane of incidence (p-polarization). In either situation, it is easily conceived that, for reasons of symmetry, a linearly polarized incident wave gives rise to a reflected and transmitted wave of the same type. Any other type of polarized wave may be obtained from a linear combination of a s-polarized and a p-polarized wave. We shall, therefore, limit ourselves to the study of these two types of waves only.

3.2.1. s-*polarization*

[A] is the matrix vector found by taking together the electric vector and the projection of the magnetic vector on planes $z = $ constant. The characteristic matrix of a film is still given by eq. (14), with g replaced by $g \cos \phi$ and β given by $(2\pi d n \cos \phi)/\lambda$. The definition of ϕ has already been given. For numerical computations, it is convenient to use the 'effective index' defined by $\tilde{n} \cos \phi$. If the film is absorbing, the angle ϕ is complex and we have

$$\tilde{\varepsilon} \cos^2 \phi = \tilde{\varepsilon} - n_0^2 \sin^2 \phi_0$$

which is a consequence of Snell's law of refraction. We use the following notations: $\tilde{n} \cos \phi = p - iq$, with $p^2 - q^2 = n^2 - k^2 - n_0^2 \sin^2 \phi_0$ and $pq = nk$. It must be remembered that the 'effective index' $p - iq$ is a function of the angle of incidence ϕ_0 in the first medium, which is always supposed to be nonabsorbing. For nonabsorbing films, $p^2 = n^2 - n_0^2 \sin^2 \phi_0$ and $q = 0$, except when total reflection takes place (see § 1.3.4).

3.2.2. p-*polarization*

We consider now only the x-component of the electric vector, which may be written

$$E_x = E \cos \phi = (ae^{-i\kappa z \cos \phi} + be^{i\kappa z \cos \phi}) \cos \phi.$$

The magnetic vector is in the y-direction

$$H_y = g(ae^{-i\kappa z \cos \phi} - be^{i\kappa z \cos \phi}).$$

It is obvious that we may, as well, use instead quantities which are proportional to the preceding ones, viz.

$$E_x = ae^{-i\kappa z \cos \phi} + be^{i\kappa z \cos \phi}$$

$$H_y = \frac{g}{\cos \phi} (ae^{-i\kappa z \cos \phi} - be^{i\kappa z \cos \phi}).$$

This shows that we shall obtain the formulae for p-polarization if we replace the g's of the media by $g/\cos \phi$, whereas the β's will be given by $(2\pi dn \cos \phi)/\lambda$. It is convenient to put $\tilde{n}/\cos \phi = A - iB$ and compute A and B from the following relation:

$$\frac{\tilde{n}}{\cos \phi} \tilde{n} \cos \phi = \tilde{n}^2,$$

i.e.

$$(A - iB)(p - iq) = (n - ik)^2 = (p - iq)^2 + n_0^2 \sin^2 \phi_0$$

which enables the computation of A and B in terms of p and q:

$$A = p \left(1 + \frac{n_0^2 \sin^2 \phi_0}{p^2 + q^2}\right), \qquad B = q \left(1 - \frac{n_0^2 \sin^2 \phi_0}{p^2 + q^2}\right).$$

3.3. REFLECTED AND TRANSMITTED AMPLITUDES

We have shown how it is possible to find the relations between the fields in the first and the last medium. Practically, the problem is the following: given the amplitude of the incident wave (taken as unit), to find the (complex) amplitudes of the reflected and transmitted waves. We shall discuss first normal incidence. Let $r = R^{\frac{1}{2}} \exp (i\delta_r)$ and $t \exp (-i2\pi n_0 D/\lambda) = \tau \exp (i\delta_t)$ be the amplitudes of the reflected and of the transmitted waves. The system of thin films is characterized by the matrix $[M]$, the elements of which are m_{ij} ($i, j = 1, 2$). Eq. (14) is equivalent to the following two equations:

$$1 + r = (m_{11} + g_s m_{12})t \exp (-2\pi i n_0 D/\lambda),$$
$$g_0(1 - r) = (m_{21} + g_s m_{22})t \exp (-2\pi i n_0 D/\lambda),$$

(15)

g_0 and g_s being the values of g for the first and the last (substrate) medium, and D the sum of the thicknesses of the films. We have made use of the continuity of the tangential components of the fields across the first and last surface of the films. Solving (15), we get

$$r = \frac{g_0(m_{11}+g_s m_{12})-(m_{21}+g_s m_{22})}{g_0(m_{11}+g_s m_{12})+(m_{21}+g_s m_{22})}, \tag{16}$$

$$t = \frac{2g_0 \exp\,(2\pi i n_0 D/\lambda)}{g_0(m_{11}+g_s m_{12})+(m_{21}+g_s m_{22})}. \tag{17}$$

We shall call reflectance and transmittance the ratios of the reflected and trans-mitted energy to the energy carried by the incident wave. With these definitions, and making use of Maxwell's equations (Poynting vector), it can be shown that the reflectance of the pile of thin films is R and its transmittance is $T=(n_s/n_0)\tau^2$.

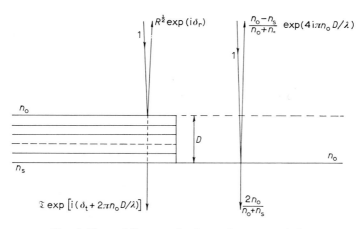

Fig. 6. Phase shifts on reflection and on transmission.

Formulae (16) and (17) give also the phase-shifts on reflection (δ_r) and transmission (δ_t). These can be measured by interferometric methods. Fig. 6 shows why these measurements do not furnish exactly these quantities, but rather $\psi_r = \delta_r + (4\pi n_0 D)/\lambda + \delta_0$ and $\psi_t = \delta_t + (2\pi n_0 D)/\lambda$, δ_0 being the phase shift on reflection at the interface $n_0 - n_s$.

It is clear from the value of the matrix $[M']$ that we shall have, for the propagation of the wave from the last medium (g_s) to the first (g_0).

$$r' = \frac{g_s(m_{22}+g_0 m_{12})-(m_{21}+g_0 m_{11})}{g_s(m_{22}+g_0 m_{12})+(m_{21}+g_0 m_{11})}, \tag{18}$$

$$t' = \frac{2g_s \exp\,(2\pi i n_0 D/\lambda)}{g_s(m_{22}+g_0 m_{12})+(m_{21}+g_0 m_{11})}, \tag{19}$$

the primes denoting the values of the amplitudes for propagation from the substrate to the first medium. If $r'=R'^{\frac{1}{2}} \exp\,(i\delta_{r'})$ and $t' \exp\,(-2\pi i n_0 D)/\lambda=\tau' \exp\,(i\delta_{t'})$, it is readily seen than $\delta_{t'}=\delta_t$ if the extreme media are nonabsorbing (n_0 and n_s real). Here, the measured phase-change is $\psi_{r'}=\delta_{r'}$ i.e. an interferometric measurement gives $\delta_{r'}$ directly.

All the formulae obtained in this subsection can be easily transposed to oblique incidence and either s- or p-polarization, following the indications already given in § 3.2. There is no limitation concerning the substrate, which may be absorbing or not. We give here only the expressions for the reflectance and transmittance on a single film on nonabsorbing substrate:

$$R = R' = \frac{(n_0 - n_s)^2 \cos^2 \beta + [(n_0 n_s/n) - n]^2 \sin^2 \beta}{(n_0 + n_s)^2 \cos^2 \beta + [(n_0 n_s/n) + n]^2 \sin^2 \beta}, \tag{20}$$

$$T = 1 - R = \frac{4 n_0 n_s}{(n_0 + n_s)^2 \cos^2 \beta + [(n_0 n_s/n) + n]^2 \sin^2 \beta}. \tag{21}$$

3.4. GENERAL THEOREMS

It may be useful to know some general properties of systems of thin films, which are easily established.

(a) For a given system of thin films and a given polarization of the wave, $T = T'$, provided the angles ϕ_0 and ϕ_s are related by the law of refraction.

We shall prove this property for normal incidence, the result being easily transposed to the case of oblique incidence. From (16) and (17) it is easily seen that

$$T = (n_s/n_0)|t|^2 = (n_0/n_s)|t'|^2 = T'.$$

It must be stressed that the equality $R = R'$ does not hold generally. It is verified only when all the media are nonabsorbing, and it is, then, only a consequence of $T = T'$. (Indeed, when the media are nonabsorbing, conservation of energy requires that $R = 1 - T$ and $R' = 1 - T'$.)

(b) A nonabsorbing film behaves as if it were non-existing whenever $\sin \beta = 0$. In other words, a film having an optical thickness $nd \cos \phi$ which is an integral multiple of $\frac{1}{2}\lambda$ has no effect on the propagation of a plane wave. This property is obvious from the fact that the characteristic matrix of such a film is the unit matrix.

(c) Another general property of systems of thin films is not so easily established, so we shall only quote the result. Consider (fig. 7) a system of thin absorbing and nonabsorbing films (S_1) which is bounded by two nonabsorbing semi-infinite media n_1 and n_s, and let R_0 and T_0 be its reflectance and transmittance. Replace now the

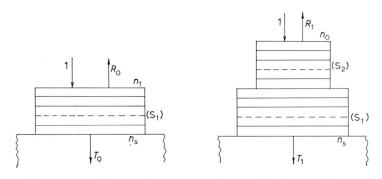

Fig. 7. Illustration of the notations deriving the used in theorem $A_0/T_0 = A_1/T_1$.

medium n_1 by a system of nonabsorbing films (S_2) limited by the nonabsorbing semi-infinite medium n_0, and let R_1 and T_1 be the reflectance and transmittance of $(S_2)+(S_1)$. We have

$$\frac{T_0}{1-R_0} = \frac{T_1}{1-R_1}.$$

If $A=1-(R+T)$ is the absorptance of a medium, we can write

$$\frac{A_0}{T_0} = \frac{A_1}{T_1}.$$

This property is valid for oblique incidence too, provided the angles of incidence are related by the law of refraction: $n_0 \sin \phi_0 = n_1 \sin \phi_1 = n_s \sin \phi_s$ and the same polarization is used to compute the various quantities.

(d) Consider a pile of nonabsorbing films between two nonabsorbing semi-infinite media. The following relation holds between the various phase shifts

$$\delta_r + \delta_{r'} - 2\delta_t = \pm \pi.$$

The origins of the phases are: in the first plane of discontinuity encountered by the incident wave for δ_r and $\delta_{r'}$ and in the last plane of discontinuity for δ_t.

This theorem is readily verified by noticing that rr'/t^2 is real.

3.5. COMPUTING METHODS

We shall indicate briefly some of the different methods which have been used for computing the properties of single or multiple films. For a more complete description of these methods, the reader can consult the following articles or books: COTTON [1950], MALÉ [1950], LEURGANS [1951], KARD [1956], BERNING and BERNING [1960], HEAVENS [1960], BERNING [1963].

3.5.1. *Vector diagrams*

For nonabsorbing film combinations, and especially for two- or three-layer low reflecting coatings, it is possible to use an approximate method. All multiple internal reflections are disregarded. The complex amplitude of the reflected wave is written

$$r = r_1 + r_2 e^{-i2\beta_1} + r_3 e^{-i2(\beta_1+\beta_2)} + \ldots$$

where the r_i are the Fresnel coefficients for reflections at the first, second, etc. boundary. For normal incidence, we have

$$r_1 = (n_0-n_1)/(n_0+n_1), \qquad r_2 = (n_1-n_2)/(n_1+n_2), \quad \text{etc.}$$

These diagrams were found useful for the design of achromatic antireflection film combinations (TURNER [1950]). We give here such a diagram with $n_0=1, n_1=1.41$, $n_2=2.00$, $n_s=1.62$ and $\beta_1=72.5°$, $\beta_2=2\beta_1=145°$. V_1, V_2 and V_3 are the amplitudes of the Fresnel coefficients r_1, r_2 and r_3 (fig. 8).

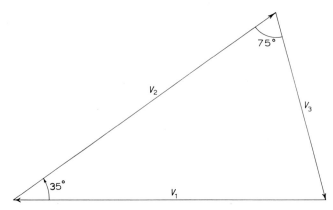

Fig. 8. Vector diagram used for the design of a two-layer anti-reflection coating.

3.5.2. *Admittance charts*

These are based on the use of the admittance concept, which is defined at any given point of the multilayers as the ratio of the tangential components of the field vectors at that point: H_{tan}/E_{tan}. It follows from the continuity of E_{tan} and H_{tan} that the admittance is also continuous across boundaries. Various charts have been suggested, such as, for instance, the Smith chart, which was developed originally for solution of certain electrical engineering problems (SMITH [1939] and [1944]). For a detailed discussion of the use of admittance charts, the reader is referred to the article by BERNING [1963].

3.5.3. *Digital computer methods*

Little must be said here concerning them. It should only be mentioned that one such program has been described in the literature (BERNING and BERNING [1960]) and another one can be obtained quite easily, which enables the computation of the ellipsometric properties of multilayer films (McCRACKIN and COLSON [1964]).

3.5.4. *Analog computer methods*

Three descriptions of analog computers may be found in the literature: one by McNEILLE and DIXON [1954], another by BADOUAL and GIACOMO [1964] and the most recent one by PAPINI and PERROT [1964].

4. Optical properties of a single layer

4.1. NONABSORBING LAYER ON NONABSORBING SUBSTRATE

4.1.1. *Anti-reflection coatings*

The reduction of undesirable reflections from windows and lenses by using thin films has become common practice in the field of optics. For normal incidence, and one nonabsorbing layer, it is clear, from eq. (20), that we must have $\cos \beta = 0$ and $n_0 n_s = n^2$. The first equation indicates that the optical thickness of the layer is an odd multiple of $\frac{1}{4}\lambda_0$, λ_0 being the wavelength for which $R=0$. The second equation enables the choice of the film material. For the most frequently used glasses, with $n_s \approx 1.5$, a film material with $n_1 = 1.23$ would make an ideal anti-reflection coating. Unfortunately, durable film materials with such low indices of refraction are not available. Magnesium fluoride, with $n_1 = 1.38$ is most frequently used for preparing anti-reflection coatings on glass. Films of MgF_2 are very durable and decrease the surface reflectance of ordinary glass from 4 % to 1.2 %. Fig. 9 shows the chromatic effect of the layer, the dispersion of the two media being neglected. The scale of the abscissas is λ/λ_0 but we give also the values of λ when $\lambda_0 = 5520$ Å. The same curve represents also the variation of R with the thickness of the layer, provided λ/λ_0 is replaced by d_0/d, with $d_0 = \lambda_0/4n$.

Fig. 10 shows the influence of the angle of incidence and the polarizing effects of oblique incidence for a MgF_2 layer ($n = 1.38$) on glass ($n_s = 1.52$). Curve 1 corresponds to a thickness $d_1 = 1000$ Å and curve 2 to $d_2 = 2000$ Å, the wavelength being

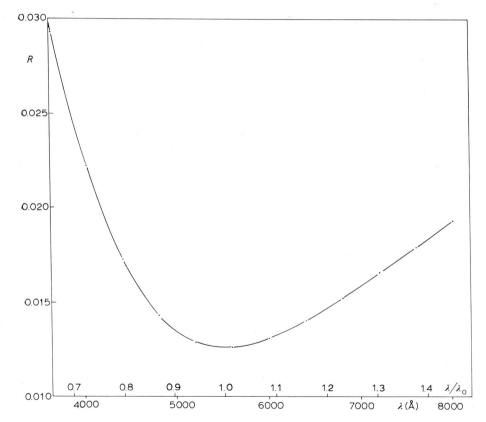

Fig. 9. R vs. λ/λ_0 and λ for a MgF_2 layer ($n=1.38$) on glass ($n_s=1.52$). The thickness of the layer is $d=\lambda_0/4n$. The scale for λ is obtained by taking $\lambda_0=5520$ Å ($d=1000$ Å).

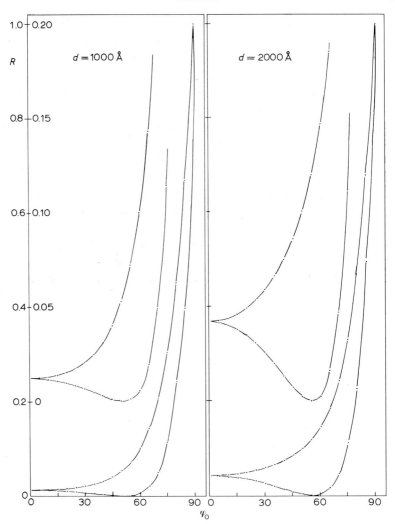

Fig. 10. Influence of the angle of incidence for MgF$_2$ ($n=1.38$) layers on glass ($n_s=1.52$). Left, curve corresponds to an optical thickness of the layer equal to $\frac{1}{4}\lambda$. Right, curve corresponds to a layer having a thickness twice that of the preceding layer. The scale for the ordinates of the complete curves is on the outside. The inside scale is related to the inserts, which show a magnified portion of the same curves, but for moderate angles of incidence only.

5520 Å. The thicknesses have been chosen in order to have $nd_1=5520/4=nd_2/2$. Cryolite, which has a refractive index somewhat smaller than MgF$_2$, is also used ($n=1.34$ in the middle of the visible spectrum), but MgF$_2$ is preferred, because it results in harder and more durable coatings.

4.1.2. *Reflectance increasing coatings*

When it is necessary to increase the reflectance of the substrate, without inducing any absorption, it is common practice to use a layer of a high refractive index material.

The reflectance of a substrate covered with a single layer, the optical thickness of which is an odd multiple of the quarter wavelength, is given by the following expression

$$R_M = \left(\frac{n_0 n_s - n^2}{n_0 n_s + n^2}\right)^2. \tag{22}$$

For $n^2 > n_0 n_s$, R_M is an increasing function of n. Table 1 shows the variation of R_M as a function of n, for $n_s = 1.52$ and $n_0 = 1$.

TABLE 1

n	1.233	1.414	1.732	2	2.236	2.449	2.646	2.828	3	3.162
R_M	0	0.0183	0.1072	0.2019	0.2848	0.3549	0.4137	0.4634	0.5055	0.5418

We see that a film with $n = 3$ deposited on glass can increase the reflectance of the substrate up to about 0.5.

The most commonly used substances for the deposition of reflectance increasing coatings are ZnS and TiO_2. Rutile is more difficult to evaporate and one usually evaporates pure titanium, which is oxidized afterwards by heating in an atmosphere of oxygen. Although its index of refraction is high ($n \approx 2.75$ in the middle of the visible spectrum), the complicated method of preparation has encouraged the use of ZnS. Thin films of ZnS are evaporated from a 'howitzer' source which was developed by TURNER and co-workers at Bausch & Lomb Optical Company, and which has

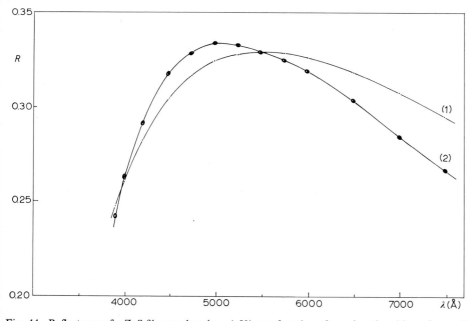

Fig. 11. Reflectance of a ZnS film on glass ($n_s = 1.52$) as a function of wavelength, without (curve 1) and with consideration of the dispersion index of refraction (curve 2).

been described by Cox and Hass [1958]. Fig. 11 shows the reflectance of a ZnS film ($n=2.37$, $d=580$ Å, $nd=\frac{1}{4}\lambda_0$ for $\lambda_0=5500$ Å) on glass ($n_s=1.52$) as a function of λ, neglecting the dispersion effects in the two media. This is not a very good approximation in the visible, but is quite tolerable in the infrared. A high index of refraction for a dielectric substance is due to the vicinity of an absorption band. It is well known that close to such a band n and k are increasing rapidly with decreasing wavelength. Therefore, it is not always permitted to neglect the variations of n with λ. On the same fig. 11, we have also shown the real variations of R with λ, the dispersion of n being taken into account. It is unnecessary to allow for the dispersion of n_s, which is here about two orders of magnitude smaller than the dispersion of n. Table 2 shows the values of n as a function of λ, used in the calculation, and which are due to HALL and FERGUSON [1955].

TABLE 2

λ	3900	4000	4200	4500	4750	5000	5250	5500	5750	6000	6500	7000	7500
n	2.55	2.51	2.47	2.44_5	2.42	2.40_5	2.38_5	2.37	2.36	2.35	2.33	2.31	2.29_5

Two important conclusions are reached, which are of general validity for such layers of high refractive index and high dispersion:

(a) The value of n computed from the maximum R_M of R supposing that it corresponds to a quarter-wavelength optical thickness is not very different from the

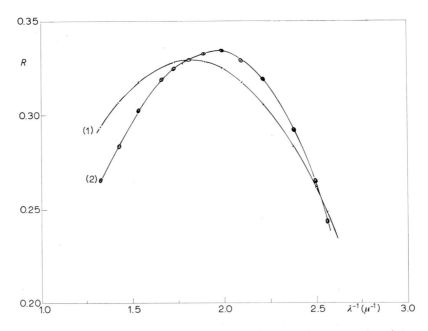

Fig. 12. Same curves as in fig. 11, the abscissas being now the wavenumbers λ^{-1}.

true value. Using eq. (22), we obtain $n=2.38_4$, instead of $n=2.40_5$ for $\lambda=5000$ Å. The error is less than 1 %.

(b) The maximum of R is displaced towards shorter wavelengths. When dispersion is neglected, this leads to an underestimate of the thickness d of the film. In our case, the maximum of R occurs for $\lambda=5000$ Å, which gives $d=5000/(4\times2.38_4)$ $=524$ Å instead of 580 Å. The error on d is of the order of 10 %.

In order to recognize whether the dispersion of the layer is important, it is only necessary to use the representation R vs. $1/\lambda$, which, without dispersion, should be symmetrical with respect to $\lambda=\lambda_M$, λ_M being the wavelength for which R is maximum. Fig. 12 shows the two preceding curves in this representation. The curve obtained when the dispersion of n is taken into account is clearly asymmetrical, the other one being perfectly symmetrical. It is impossible, in principle, to compute n and d for a film from the measurement of R_M only, when $dn/d\lambda$ cannot be neglected, because we have thus only two relations ($R=R_M$ and R is a maximum) in order to determine three unknowns: n, $dn/d\lambda$ and d.

4.2. NONABSORBING LAYER ON ABSORBING SUBSTRATE

Nonabsorbing films on metallic substrates are sometimes used in order to protect the latter. For instance, aluminium front surface mirrors, which are used as solar energy collectors and reflectors in solar simulators, are protected with layers of SiO, SiO_2 or Al_2O_3. It is, therefore, often necessary to be able to compute their optical properties. Let n_s-ik_s be the complex index of refraction of the substrate, the film being specified, as previously, by its index of refraction n and its thickness d. From the formula (16) we obtain, after having made the necessary substitutions:

$$R = \frac{(n_0-n_s+n_0k_sn^{-1}\,\text{tg}\,\beta)^2+[(n_0n_sn^{-1}-n)\,\text{tg}\,\beta+k_s]^2}{(n_0+n_s+n_0k_sn^{-1}\,\text{tg}\,\beta)^2+[(n_0n_sn^{-1}+n)\,\text{tg}\,\beta-k_s]^2}.$$

It is sometimes preferable to use another expression for R, which is written in terms of the Fresnel amplitude coefficients at the two planes limiting the layer: $r_1=(n_0-n)/(n_0+n)$ and $r_2=\varrho_2\exp(i\delta_2)=(n-n_s+ik_s)/(n+n_s-ik_s)$. It is found then that

$$R = \frac{r_1^2+\varrho_2^2+2r_1\varrho_2\cos(2\beta-\delta_2)}{1+r_1^2\varrho_2^2+2r_1\varrho_2\cos(2\beta-\delta_2)}.$$

With the adjunction of a nonabsorbing layer of convenient thickness, it is always possible to increase the reflectance of the metal, for a given wavelength. The chromatic effect of the layer may be such as to decrease the reflectance of the metal for other wavelengths. We give here, fig. 13, the reflectances of two metals covered with a high-index film of various thicknesses. We have chosen Al, which is highly reflecting, and Cu, which is poorly reflecting, for $\lambda=5500$ Å. It is seen that the influence of the same substance (here, ZnS) is more marked when Cu is used as substrate. This is due to the fact the amplitudes r_1 and ϱ_2 for reflection at the two surfaces of the layer have values which are closer to each other for Cu than for Al.

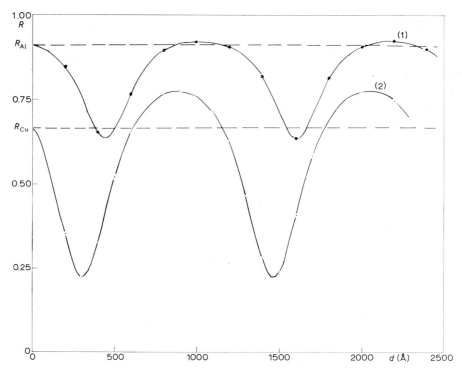

Fig. 13. Reflectance of a metallic mirror covered with a nonabsorbing layer ($n=2.37$, $\lambda=5500$ Å) of various thicknesses. Curve 1: aluminium ($n_s=0.85$, $k_s=6$). Curve 2: copper ($n_s=0.76$, $k_s=2.46$)

Quite often, surface films are spontaneously formed on metal surfaces (oxides, sulfides, etc.). Information concerning their optical parameters (index of refraction and thickness) is usually obtained by using ellipsometric measurements, i.e. analyzing the elliptical vibration resulting from the reflection of linearly polarized light on the filmed surface. The reader interested in this subject will find a thorough discussion of the problems concerning 'ellipsometry in the measurement of surfaces and thin films' in the proceedings of the symposium with this title [1964].

4.3. ABSORBING FILMS

4.3.1. *General formulae*

We give below the formulae allowing the computation of the optical properties of absorbing films, in normal incidence, when deposited on nonabsorbing substrate. They can be deduced from eq. (16), (17), and (18). Following the indications given there, the formulae for oblique incidence are easily written down, by making the proper substitutions for n_0, n, k and n_s.

$$R = \frac{ab\,e^{2k\eta}+cd\,e^{-2k\eta}+2r\cos 2n\eta+2s\sin 2n\eta}{bd\,e^{2k\eta}+ac\,e^{-2k\eta}+2t\cos 2n\eta+2u\sin 2n\eta},$$

$$R' = \frac{cd\,e^{2k\eta} + ab\,e^{-2k\eta} + 2r\cos 2n\eta - 2s\sin 2n\eta}{bd\,e^{2k\eta} + ac\,e^{-2k\eta} + 2t\cos 2n\eta + 2u\sin 2n\eta}$$

$$T = \frac{16n_0 n_s(n^2 + k^2)}{bd\,e^{2k\eta} + ac\,e^{-2k\eta} + 2t\cos 2n\eta + 2u\sin 2n\eta},$$

with

$$\frac{a}{d} = (n\mp n_0)^2 + k^2, \qquad \frac{b}{c} = (n\pm n_s)^2 + k^2,$$

$$\frac{r}{t} = (n_0^2 + n_s^2)(n^2 + k^2) - (n^2 + k^2)^2 - n_0^2 n_s^2 \mp 4n_0 n_s k^2$$

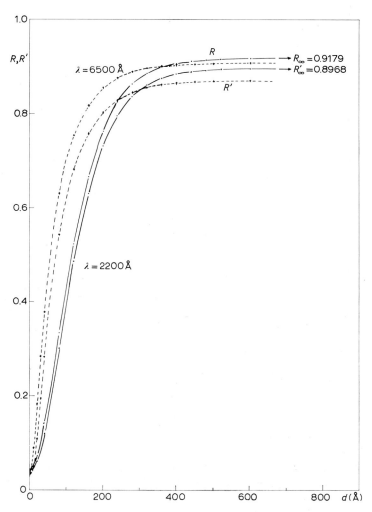

Fig. 14. Reflectance of aluminium films of various thicknesses for two different wavelengths ($\lambda = 2200$ Å, $n = 0.14$, $k = 2.35$, $n_s = 1.534$ and $\lambda = 6500$ Å, $n = 1.30$, $k = 7.11$, $n_s = 1.4565$).

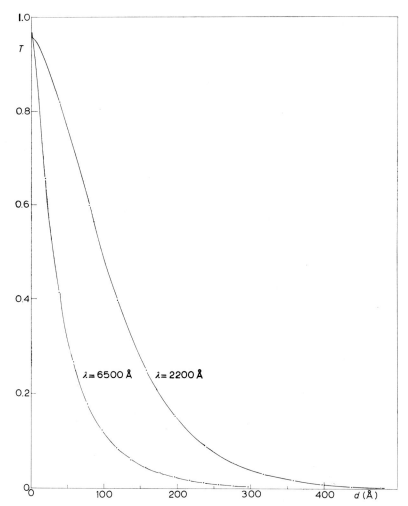

Fig. 15. Transmittance of aluminium films ($\lambda=2200$ Å and $\lambda=6500$ Å, same indices of refraction as in fig. 14) of various thicknesses.

$$\frac{s}{u} = 2k(n_s \mp n_0)(n^2 + k^2 \pm n_0 n_s)$$

$$\eta = 2\pi d/\lambda.$$

These formulae can be simplified when the film is not too thin and multiple reflections inside it can be neglected.

Absorbing films may be made either of metals or of compounds (ionic crystals, etc.). Their properties may be somewhat different.

4.3.2. Highly reflecting metals

They are used for the fabrication of mirrors and interference filters and for inter-

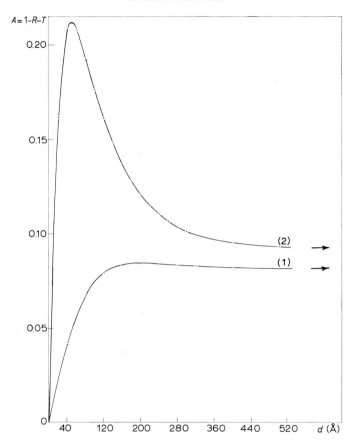

Fig. 16. Variations with thickness of the absorptances $A = 1 - R - T$ of the same films as in fig. 14. Curve (1): $\lambda = 2200$ Å, curve (2): $\lambda = 6500$ Å.

ferometry. The most frequently used metal is aluminium. The reflectance and absorption of Al films are a function of the evaporation conditions. A pressure of 10^{-5} Torr is sufficient, provided the deposition rate is at least 500 Å/sec and purest grade aluminium is used (HASS and WAYLONIS [1961]). We give here, table 3,

TABLE 3

λ (mμ)	220	260	300	340	380	436	492	546	578	650
n	0.14	0.19	0.25	0.31	0.37	0.47	0.64	0.82	0.93	1.30
k	2.35	2.85	3.33	3.80	4.25	4.84	5.50	5.99	6.33	7.11
R (%)	91.8	92.0	92.1	92.3	92.6	92.6	92.2	91.6	91.5	90.7

the values of the optical constants of this metal as a function of wavelength, following these authors, together with the values of the reflectance for an opaque film.

The optical constants of a metal should vary very little with the thickness of the film if the latter is prepared under good conditions. HASS and WAYLONIS [1961] find that, for aluminium films, calculated values of R, using n and k measured on thick layers, agree with directly measured ones for film thicknesses larger than 100 Å. In order to have good mirrors, it is preferable to use just opaque films, never thicker than 0.1 μm. We can get an idea of the effect of thickness variations on the optical properties of thin highly reflecting films from figs. 14 and 15 which show the variations of R and T with d, for normal incidence and for two different wavelengths $\lambda = 2200$ Å and 6500 Å. Fig. 16 gives the absorptance $A = 1 - (R + T)$ for the same films. It should be noticed that A is never very high, so that even semi-transparent films show low absorption.

4.3.3. *Moderately reflecting metals*

Most of the metals are only moderately reflecting in the visible region of the spectrum. Fig. 17 shows the computed variations with thickness of the reflectances of such a metal deposited on glass compared with those of a slightly reflecting mirror. We have chosen palladium: $n = 1.8$, $k = 4$, $n_s = 1.52$, $\lambda = 5500$ Å. Fig. 18 shows, for the

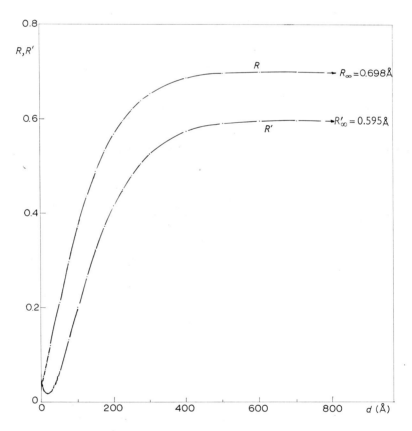

Fig. 17. Reflectance of palladium films of various thicknesses ($\lambda = 5500$ Å, $n = 1.8$, $k = 4$, $n_s = 1.52$).

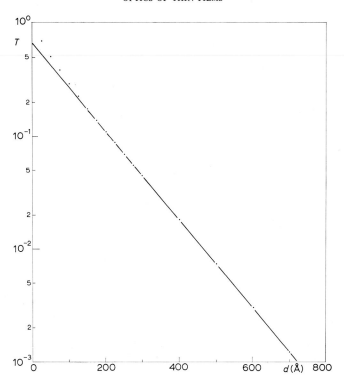

Fig. 18. Transmittance of the same palladium films as in fig. 15, on a semi-logarithmic scale, illustrating the exponential variation of T with thickness for films which are not too thin.

same metal, the transmittance as a function of the thickness of the film. A few remarks of rather general validity can be made concerning these figures:

(a) $R' < R$, generally. Moreover, for very small thicknesses R' shows a minimum, which may be less than 0.01. In fact, one should not forget that films which are so thin (a few tens of angstroms) do not have the same optical constants as thicker films.

(b) R and R' go through a flat and unpronounced maximum for a thickness $d \approx 0.1\ \lambda$.

(c) When k is large enough, T is decreasing continuously, when d increases and does not show any extremal value.

4.4. MEASUREMENT OF OPTICAL PARAMETERS OF THIN FILMS

It is impossible to discuss here even a fraction of the methods which have been proposed and used in order to determine the optical parameters (index of refraction and thickness) of a thin film. We shall mention only those which are the most easily accessible to a non-specialist in the field. For a more thorough discussion, the reader is referred to the articles by HEAVENS [1964] or by ABELÈS [1963].

4.4.1. *Nonabsorbing film*

4.4.1.1. *Spectrophotometric measurements in normal incidence.* If we can neglect the dispersion of the indices of refraction of the layer and of the substrate, the position and the intensity of the extremum of $R(\lambda)$ are sufficient for determining n and d of the layer. The general formulae show that for $\beta = K\pi + \frac{1}{2}\pi$, i.e. $d = \lambda_M(1 + 2K)/4n$ and $K = 0, 1, 2, \ldots$, R reaches an extremum value

$$R_M = \left(\frac{n_0 n_s - n^2}{n_0 n_s + n^2} \right)^2$$

It follows that for $n^2 > n_0 n_s$, which is practically always the case

$$n^2 = n_0 n_s \frac{1 + \sqrt{R_M}}{1 - \sqrt{R_M}}.$$

R_M is a maximum or a minimum depending on whether $n > n_s$ or $n < n_s$. It is only necessary that the optical thickness of the layer is at least equal to $\frac{1}{4}\lambda_M$, i.e. the film is not too thin. There is no difficulty in ascertaining the value of K from the spectral variation of R.

If the thickness of the layer is such that the extremum of R occurs for a wavelength λ_M rather far from the wavelength λ where it is desired to know the value of n, it is always possible to use the measurement of $R_M(\lambda_M)$ in oder to get d and then to measure $R(\lambda)$, which gives n for that wavelength.

It is generally possible to obtain a relative precision of 10^{-2} on n, if R_M is measured to an accuracy which may be attained ($\Delta R_M \geq 0.002$).

4.4.1.2. *Photometric measurements in oblique incidence.* When the angle of incidence is the Brewster angle ϕ_{0B} for the reflection at the first surface of the film, i.e. if $\text{tg } \phi_{0B} = n/n_0$, there is no reflection at this surface and the film behaves as if it did not exist, whatever its thickness may be, for incident light polarized in the plane of incidence (p-vibration). If R_{0p} is the reflectance of the bare substrate, we have $R_p(\phi_{0B}) = R_{0p}(\phi_{0B})$, whatever is the nature of the substrate (absorbing or not). This suggests a simple method for the determination of the indices of refraction of nonabsorbing substances which are deposited on any substrate. We compare the relative reflectances R_p at the uncovered surface and at the surface covered with the thin film. When they are equal, the equality $n = n_0 \text{ tg } \phi_{0B}$ is verified. The method is valid only for homogeneous and isotropic nonabsorbing films. Its sensitivity is a maximum when the optical thickness of the layer is an odd multiple of $\frac{1}{4}\lambda$ and a minimum when $nd \approx \frac{1}{2}K\lambda$, K being an integer. Using this method, n can be measured with an error of about ± 0.001.

4.4.2. *Absorbing film*

The measurement of n, k and d for an absorbing film is a difficult task. The formulae for a thin absorbing film are much more complicated than those for a nonabsorbing one and it is almost always necessary to resort to lengthy computations. They simplify only when the film is sufficiently thick in order to make inoperative the multiple reflections inside it. The transmittance is then an exponential function of thickness

$$T = \frac{16 n_0 n_s (n^2 + k^2) \exp(-4\pi k d/\lambda)}{[(n_0 + n)^2 + k^2][(n_s + n)^2 + k^2]}.$$ (23)

The domain of validity of the formula (23) is rather extended, as can be seen from fig. 18 above. It can be seen that, for $d \geq 175$ Å, $\ln T$ is a linear function of d. Thus, in this example, already for a transmittance as large as 0.14 it is permissible to neglect multiple reflections in the layer. This would seem rather surprising, because $4\pi k d/\lambda = 1.6$ only for $d = 175$ Å, and a more stringent condition would seem necessary, as neglect of multiple reflections in the film is equivalent to neglect of $\exp(-4\pi k d/\lambda)$ with respect to unity.

When formula (23) is valid, the measurement of the thicknesses and of the transmittances of at least two films enables drawing the straight line of $\ln T$ as a function of $4\pi d/\lambda$, the slope of which is $-k$, and the ordinate at the origin

$$\ln \frac{16 n_0 n_s (n^2 + k^2)}{[(n_0 + n)^2 + k^2][(n_s + n)^2 + k^2]}$$

The latter allows to calculate n.

4.4.3. *Weakly absorbing films*

It is often important to know whether a thin film is absorbing. The most straight-forward method for that purpose is the measurement of R and T, because the absorption of a film is given by $A = 1 - (R + T)$. For metal films, there is no problem, because A is generally definitely larger than the experimental errors on R and T. The difficulty arises when $k \ll 1$, because A can have a very small value then. Two methods may be used, both requiring reflection measurements only. The first one has been suggested by KOPPELMANN and KREBS [1959]. A slide as substrate, made of glass or quartz, Tr, is partially covered on one side with the film to be studied, S, and on the other side, with a metallic film having the highest possible reflectance,

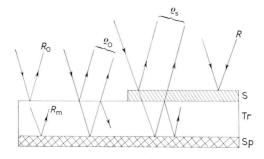

Fig. 19. Illustrating the method of KOPPELMANN and KREBS [1959] for the measurement of small absorptances.

Sp. One measures the reflection of the part which is covered with S, ϱ_s, and of the uncovered part, ϱ_0 (see fig. 19). Let us denote by R_0 the reflectance of the uncovered substrate, by R_m the reflectance of the highly reflecting mirror Sp, by R the reflectance of the film to be studied and by τ the transmittance of the substrate Tr. It can be shown that the absorption $A = 1 - R - T$ of the film is given by

$$A = \left[\varrho_0 - \varrho_s - \varepsilon^2 \left(\frac{R_0}{1-R_0} - \frac{R}{1-R} \right) \right] \frac{1}{2[1 - \varepsilon/(1-R)]^2}, \tag{24}$$

where $\varepsilon = 1 - R_m \tau^2$. The equation (24) is only approximate, powers of A and εA higher than the first and those of ε higher than the second having been neglected.

For antireflection layers, where $R < 0.04$, it is possible to use the simpler relation

$$A = \frac{\varrho_0 - \varrho_s}{2(1-\varepsilon)}.$$

On the other hand, if $2\pi kd/\lambda$ is sufficiently small, it may be shown that

$$\frac{A}{1-R} \approx \frac{4\pi kd}{\lambda}.$$

The method is convenient, because it leads to the comparison of the reflectances ϱ_0 and ϱ_s which are very close to each other. The index of refraction and the thickness of the film may be determined by any of the methods which are in use for nonabsorbing films.

The second method has been suggested by ABELÈS and BAZIN [1962]. It makes use of the attenuated total reflection (ATR). The thin film to be studied is deposited on the base of a total reflection prism. If the film is nonabsorbing ($k = 0$), we still have total reflection, i.e. $R = 1$, whatever may be the values of d and the polarization of the incident light. If $k \neq 0$, we have ATR and $R < 1$. The arrangement shown in fig. 20 enables the detection of very small absorptions in the film by merely comparing the reflectances of the bare substrate ($R_0 = 1$) and filmed substrate (R). The method is of high sensitivity because it compares two light beams which have neighbouring intensities. Fig. 21 shows the variations of R_s and R_p with thickness for a very weakly

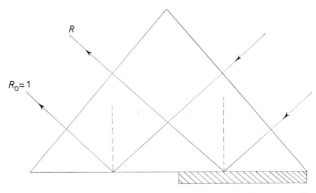

Fig. 20. Use of attenuated total reflection for the detection of very small absorptions.

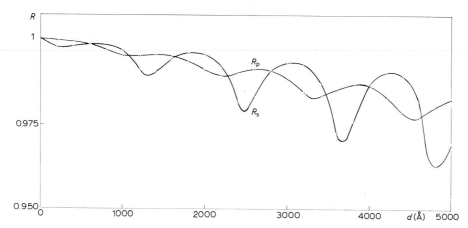

Fig. 21. Example demonstrating the sensitivity of the ATR method: R_p and R_s for various thicknesses of a weakly absorbing film ($n=2.35$, $k=0.001$) on a glass prism ($n_0=1.52$, $n_s=1$, $\phi_0=45°$).

absorbing film ($n=2.35$, $k=0.001$) deposited on glass of index of refraction 1.52 ($\lambda=5000$ Å). It gives information concerning the sensitivity of the method, which is quite high ($4\pi k/\lambda=251$ cm^{-1} here, and it can already be detected for films 200 Å thin).

5. Multiple alternate layers. A formulary

It is common practice to use combinations of alternate high- and low-index non-absorbing films, such that $\beta_H=\beta_L$, L and H referring to the low- and high-index layers. Their usefulness comes from the fact that such combinations of quarter-wave films ($\beta_H=\beta_L=90°$) can reach very high reflectances, being still nonabsorbing. They are now the most commonly used films for Fabry–Perot interferometers, lasers, etc. It might be useful to have some simple formulae enabling the quick computation of their most important properties.

When all the layers have the same optical thickness, their properties can be computed without too much work on a desk computer by using the Chebyshev polynomials, which make their appearance whenever one uses the powers of a two-by-two matrix. We shall give here the main formulae and results, without any indications concerning their derivation. For further details, the reader is referred to the papers by ABELÈS [1950], DUFOUR and HERPIN [1953], and MIELENZ [1959].

We shall state our results for normal incidence only. They may be transposed without difficulty to oblique incidence, by following the procedure which has been described previously (§ 3.2).

The formulae are given separately for an even ($2m$) or odd ($2m+1$) number of layers. The Chebyshev polynomials S_m which we use are defined as follows:

$$\text{when} \quad |x| \leqq 2, \quad \text{put} \quad x = 2\cos\theta, \quad \text{then} \quad S_m(x) = \frac{\sin(m+1)\theta}{\sin\theta}.$$

when $|x| \geq 2$, put $x = 2 \cosh \theta$, then $S_m(x) = \dfrac{\sinh (m+1)\theta}{\sinh \theta}$

S_m are polynomials in x, the properties of which, together with numerical tables can be found in 'Tables of Chebyshev polynomials' [1952].

For an odd number of layers $(2m+1)$, with indices of refraction n_1 and n_2 alternately $(n_1, n_2, n_1, n_2, \ldots, n_1)$, the characteristic matrix is

$$\begin{bmatrix} (S_m - S_{m-1}) \cos \beta & i(S_m n_1^{-1} + S_{m-1} n_2^{-1}) \sin \beta \\ i(n_1 S_m + n_2 S_{m-1}) \sin \beta & (S_m - S_{m-1}) \cos \beta \end{bmatrix}.$$

The system having a plane of symmetry, the matrix is symmetrical $(m_{11} = m_{22})$.

For an even number of layers $(2m)$, $n_1, n_2, n_1, \ldots, n_2$, the characteristic matrix is

$$\begin{bmatrix} b_{11} S_{m-1} - S_{m-2} & i b_{12} \\ i b_{21} & b_{22} S_{m-1} - S_{m-2} \end{bmatrix}$$

the b_{ij} being the elements of the characteristic matrix of the double layer n_1, n_2, i.e.

$$b_{11} = \cos^2 \beta - n_2 n_1^{-1} \sin^2 \beta, \qquad b_{12} = (n_1^{-1} + n_2^{-1}) \sin \beta \cos \beta,$$

$$b_{21} = (n_1 + n_2) \sin \beta \cos \beta, \qquad b_{22} = \cos^2 \beta - n_1 n_2^{-1} \sin^2 \beta.$$

The polynomials are functions of the variable

$$x = b_{11} + b_{22} = 2 \cos^2 \beta - (n_1 n_2^{-1} + n_2 n_1^{-1}) \sin^2 \beta,$$

the number of layers being either even or odd.

Maximum reflectance. It occurs when $\beta = \tfrac{1}{2}\pi$. We can write

$$R_{\max} = \left(\frac{n_0 - N}{n_0 + N} \right)^2$$

with

$$N = n_s (n_1 n_2^{-1})^{2m} \qquad \text{for } 2m \text{ layers}$$

$$N = n_1 n_2 n_s^{-1} (n_1 n_2^{-1})^{2m+1} \qquad \text{for } 2m+1 \text{ layers}$$

Slope of the phase-shift on reflection for $\beta = \tfrac{1}{2}\pi$. It may be useful to know this quantity when the multilayers are used in interferometric devices.

$$\left(\frac{\mathrm{d}\delta_{r,2m}}{\mathrm{d}\beta} \right)_{\beta = \frac{1}{2}\pi} = 2 n_0 (n_1 + n_2) \frac{(n_s^2 n_2^{-2} - n_2 n_1^{-1}) S_{m-1} + (n_s^2 n_1^{-1} n_2^{-1} - 1) S_{m-2}}{n_0^2 (n_2 n_1^{-1} S_{m-1} + S_{m-2})^2 - n_s^2 (n_1 n_2^{-1} S_{m-1} + S_{m-2})^2} S_{m-1},$$

$$\left(\frac{\mathrm{d}\delta_{r,2m+1}}{\mathrm{d}\beta} \right)_{\beta = \frac{1}{2}\pi} = 2 n_0 \frac{(n_s^2 n_1^{-1} - n_1) S_m + (n_s^2 n_2^{-1} - n_2) S_{m-1}}{n_0^2 n_s^2 (S_m n_1^{-1} + S_{m-1} n_2^{-1})^2 - (n_1 S_m + n_2 S_{m-1})^2} (S_{m-1} - S_m),$$

$$\lim_{m \to \infty} \left(\frac{\mathrm{d}\delta_{r,2m}}{\mathrm{d}\beta} \right)_{\beta = \frac{1}{2}\pi} = \lim_{m \to \infty} \left(\frac{\mathrm{d}\delta_{r,2m+1}}{\mathrm{d}\beta} \right)_{\beta = \frac{1}{2}\pi} = \frac{2 n_0}{n_2 - n_1}.$$

The first Chebyshev polynomials are:

$$S_0 = 1,$$
$$S_1 = x,$$
$$S_2 = x^2 - 1,$$
$$S_3 = x^3 - 2x,$$
$$S_4 = x^4 - 3x^2 + 1,$$
$$S_5 = x^5 - 4x^3 + 3x,$$

and $x = -(n_1 n_2^{-1} + n_2 n_1^{-1})$ here.

Boundaries of the high reflection region. The reflectance of the multilayers is high when $|x| \geq 2$. The boundaries of the high reflection region correspond to $x = -2$. It is readily seen from the formula giving x as a function of β, that $x = -2$ when $\beta = \beta_L$, β_L being defined by $\cos^2 \beta_L = [(n_1 - n_2)/(n_1 + n_2)]^2 = r_{12}^2$, where r_{12} is the Fresnel coefficient for reflection at the interface between media n_1 and n_2. We give here the expressions for the transmittance and for the phase-shift in reflection. From these, it is easy to compute the reflectance $(R = 1 - T)$ and the phase-shift in transmission $(2\delta_t = \pm \pi + \delta_r + \delta_{r'})$. The indices $2m$ and $2m+1$ indicate the total number of layers

$$\frac{4n_0 n_s}{T_{2m}(\beta_L)} = \left\{ \left[(n_1 + n_2) \left(\frac{n_0}{n_1} + \frac{n_s}{n_2} \right) r_{12}^2 + (n_1 - n_2) \left(\frac{n_0}{n_1} - \frac{n_s}{n_2} \right) \right] m - (n_0 + n_s) \right\}^2$$
$$+ m^2 \left(\frac{n_0 n_s}{n_1 n_2} + 1 \right)^2 (n_1 + n_2) r_{12}^2 (1 - r_{12}^2),$$

$$\frac{4n_0 n_s}{T_{2m+1}(\beta_L)} = (2m+1)^2 (n_0 + n_s)^2 r_{12}^2 + \left[m(n_1 - n_2) \left(1 - \frac{n_0 n_s}{n_1 n_2} \right) \right.$$
$$\left. + \left(n_1 + \frac{n_0 n_s}{n_1} \right) \right]^2 (1 - r_{12}^2);$$

$$\operatorname{tg} \delta_{r, 2m}(\beta_L) = \frac{4n_0(n_1 - n_2)m}{(n_1 n_2)^{\frac{1}{2}}} \frac{2(n_2 - n_1)(n_s^2 + n_1 n_2)m + (n_1 + n_2)(n_1 n_2 - n_s^2)}{A_{2m} m^2 + B_{2m} m + C_{2m}}$$

with

$$A_{2m} = 4(n_1 - n_2)^2 (n_0^2 - n_1 n_2)(n_s^2 n_1^{-1} n_2^{-1} + 1),$$
$$B_{2m} = 4(n_0^2 + n_s^2)(n_2^2 - n_1^2),$$
$$C_{2m} = (n_0^2 - n_s^2)(n_1 + n_2)^2 ;$$

$$\operatorname{tg} \delta_{r, 2m+1}(\beta_L) = \frac{n_0(n_1 n_2)^{\frac{1}{2}}}{n_1 - n_2} \frac{(2m+1)[(n_2 - n_1)(n_s^2 n_1^{-1} n_2^{-1} + 1)m + n_s^2 n_1^{-1} - n_1]}{A_{2m+1} m^2 + B_{2m+1} m + C_{2m+1}}$$

with

$$A_{2m+1} = \left(n_0^2 - n_1 n_2\right)\left(\frac{n_s^2}{n_1 n_2} + 1\right),$$

$$B_{2m+1} = n_0^2 - n_s^2 + \frac{2}{n_2 - n_1}\left(\frac{n_0^2 n_s^2}{n_1} + n_1^2 n_2\right),$$

$$C_{2m+1} = \frac{n_0^2 - n_s^2}{4} + \frac{n_1 n_2}{(n_1 - n_2)^2}\left(\frac{n_0^2 n_s^2}{n_1^2} - n_1^2\right).$$

$$\lim_{m \to \infty} \mathrm{tg}\, \delta_{r, 2m}(\beta_L) = \lim_{m \to \infty} \mathrm{tg}\, \delta_{r, 2m+1}(\beta_L) = \frac{2n_0(n_1 n_2)^{\frac{1}{2}}}{n_1 n_2 - n_0^2}$$

We give here a numerical example illustrating the preceding formulae. It corresponds to a multilayer made of ZnS ($n_1 = 2.3$) and MgF$_2$ ($n_2 = 1.38$) deposited on glass ($n_s = 1.52$)

TABLE 4

m	0	1	2	3	4	5	∞
$R_{2m}(\beta = \frac{1}{2}\pi)$		0.381	0.711	0.884	0.957	0.984	1
$R_{2m+1}(\beta = \frac{1}{2}\pi)$	0.3065	0.660	0.862	0.948	0.981	0.993	1
$\left(\dfrac{\mathrm{d}\delta_{r,2m}}{\mathrm{d}\beta}\right)_{\beta = \frac{1}{2}\pi}$		−0.3725	−0.783	−0.971	−1.044		−1.087
$\left(\dfrac{\mathrm{d}\delta_{t,2m+1}}{\mathrm{d}\beta}\right)_{\beta = \frac{1}{2}\pi}$		−0.726	−0.947	−1.035			−1.087
$R_{2m}(\beta_L)$		0.358	0.624	0.771	0.850	0.895	1
$R_{2m+1}(\beta_L)$	0.294	0.585$_5$	0.750	0.838	0.888	0.919	1

We give also the variations with β of the reflectance for a slightly different multilayer ($n_1 = 2.4$, $n_2 = 1.38$) deposited on glass ($n_s = 1.52$) (fig. 22). The curves show, for odd numbers of layers, the regions of high reflection, extending between $\beta/\beta_0 = 0.826$ and $\beta/\beta_0 = 1.174$, and the oscillations of R outside this region. They are periodic in β, with period π, and symmetric with respect to $\beta = \frac{1}{2}\pi = \beta_0$.

6. Practical uses of thin films

6.1. ANTIFLECTION COATINGS

We have already discussed the possibilities of single antireflection layers on transparent media. In order to produce a reflectance which is much lower over the entire visible region, or over a portion of the infrared, it is necessary to use two- or, better, three-layer coatings. A discussion of these coatings is given by Cox et al. [1954] for two-layer coatings and by Cox et al. [1962] for three-layer coatings. The latter are the most efficient. It is possible to prepare durable coatings which have a reflectance of less than 0.01 from 4200 to 8400 Å, with a corresponding range for the near in-

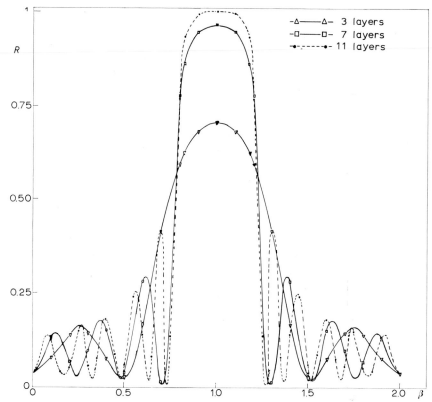

Fig. 22. Reflectance of odd numbers of alternate multilayers ($n_1 = 2.4$, $n_s = 1.38$) on glass ($n_s = 1.52$) vs. β (in units of $\frac{1}{2}\pi$).

frared. The most suitable combination is made of layers whose thicknesses in wavelengths at λ_0 are (starting with the layer next to air): quarter-half-quarter. Cox *et al.* used the following materials: MgF_2 for the outside layer; SiO, ZrO_2, ZnS, CeO_2 and Nd_2O_3 for the middle layer; CeF_3 and SiO for the inside layer. A very thorough discussion of antireflection coatings useful for the visible and infrared optical materials has been given by Cox and Hass [1964].

6.2. MIRRORS

The most commonly used mirrors for ultraviolet and visible (2000 Å $\leq \lambda \leq$ 7000 Å) are front surface aluminium mirrors. Their properties have already been described (§ 4.3.2). The reflectance of all other important mirror metals drops rapidly in the visible or ultraviolet. Fig. 23 shows the spectral reflectance of some metals, following Hass and Hadley [1963]. Silver is not used for mirror coatings, although it is highly reflecting in the visible, because it tarnishes in air. Aluminium is protected by its natural oxide film, but this is sometimes too thin to be sufficient. It is then covered with hard protective coatings: evaporated SiO, or anodically prepared Al_2O_3 (see also § 4.2).

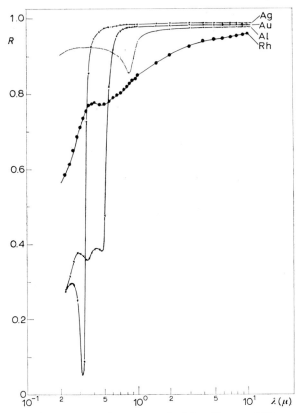

Fig. 23. Spectral reflectance of some metals (after HASS and HADLEY [1963]).

In infrared equipments, front surface mirrors are used as reflectors and image forming devices. Aluminium is extensively used in this region too.

The films need not be thicker than 1000 Å, but they must always be evaporated at a high deposition rate. For aluminium films in the infrared, it was found that there is generally an excellent agreement for the reflectance of films prepared in various vacuum systems and measured on different instruments: this is evidence that the infrared reflectance of aluminium films is very reproducible. The influence of the oxide layer and of surface roughness is negligible for Al films in the infrared, but it becomes very serious in the ultraviolet.

There is a dip in the reflectance of Al near 0.8 μm. We give here (table 5) the results

TABLE 5

$\lambda(\mu m)$	0.7	0.75	0.8	0.825	0.85	0.9	0.95
R (Al, fresh)	0.890	0.876	0.860	0.857	0.862	0.892	0.919
R (Al, aged)	0.889	0.876	0.860	0.856	0.860	0.889	0.915
R (Au)	0.970	0.974	0.977		0.978	0.980	0.981

of BENNETT *et al.* [1962] and, in the same table, those of HASS [1955] on gold, which we would suggest for use if the reflectance of Al is estimated to be too low. Table 6 shows the most recent results obtained by BENNETT *et al.* [1962] on fresh and aged evaporated aluminium films.

TABLE 6

$\lambda(\mu m)$	1	1.2	1.5	2	3	4	5	10	20	32
R(fresh)	0.936	0.960	0.968	0.972	0.976_5	0.979_5	0.981	0.984_5	0.988	0.990
R(aged)	0.932	0.958_5	0.966	0.970	0.974	0.976	0.977	0.981	0.985	0.987

Multiple alternate dielectric layers are commonly used for making highly reflecting nonabsorbing mirrors. Their properties were described in § 5.

6.3. INTERFERENCE FILTERS

An interference filter is a solid and compact Fabry–Perot interferometer made of thin films only. It may be defined also as a thin nonabsorbing layer enclosed between two strongly reflecting systems of thin films, I and II. A very thorough discussion of the properties of some of these filters has been given by HERMANSEN [1955], which will be partly followed here. Fig. 24 shows the principle of an interference filter

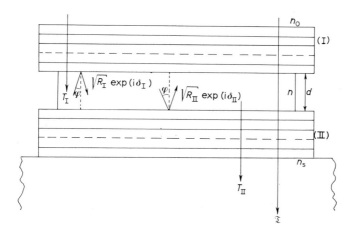

Fig. 24. Schematic of an interference filter with the notations used in the text.

and some of the notations which will be used. We designate by $R_{\mathrm{I}}^{\frac{1}{2}} \exp(\mathrm{i}\delta_{\mathrm{I}})$ and $R_{\mathrm{II}}^{\frac{1}{2}} \exp(\mathrm{i}\delta_{\mathrm{II}})$ the reflected amplitudes at the interfaces between the medium n and the stacks I and II, light being incident from the former. In fact, we shall use the average reflectance R of the stacks defined by $R^2 = R_{\mathrm{I}} R_{\mathrm{II}}$. The transmittances of the layers I and II when limited by the media n_0 and n, and n and n_{s}, will be called T_{I} and T_{II}. The transmittance of the filter is given by

$$\mathcal{T}(\lambda) = \frac{T_{\mathrm{I}} T_{\mathrm{II}}}{1 - 2R \cos y + R^2},$$

or, in a more classical way, by

$$\mathcal{T}(\lambda) = \left(\frac{T}{1-R}\right)^2 \left(1 + \frac{4R}{(1-R)^2} \sin^2 \tfrac{1}{2}y\right)^{-1}. \tag{25}$$

We use the following notations: $T^2 = T_{\mathrm{I}} T_{\mathrm{II}}$ and $y = 2\beta - \delta_{\mathrm{I}} - \delta_{\mathrm{II}}$, β being defined, as usual, by $(2\pi n d \cos \phi)/\lambda$.

$\mathcal{T}(\lambda)$ reaches a maximum for the wavelengths λ_m for which y is a multiple of 2π, i.e.

$$y = (m-1)2\pi \qquad (m = 1, 2, 3, \cdots)$$

and a minimum for the wavelengths $\lambda_{m+\frac{1}{2}}$, for which $y = (2m-1)\pi$.

An interference filter is characterized by means of the following quantities:

1. The values of λ_m;
2. The values of the maximum of its transmittance

$$\mathcal{T}_{\max} = \mathcal{T}(\lambda_m) = \left(\frac{T(\lambda_m)}{1 - R(\lambda_m)}\right)^2, \tag{26}$$

which might be called the 'luminosity' of the filter;

3. The 'contrast factor' defined as the ratio of maximum to minimum transmittance:

$$F = \frac{\mathcal{T}_{\max}}{\mathcal{T}_{\min}} = \frac{\mathcal{T}(\lambda_m)}{T(\lambda_{m+\frac{1}{2}})} = \left(\frac{T(\lambda_m)}{T(\lambda_{m+\frac{1}{2}})} \frac{1 + R(\lambda_{m+\frac{1}{2}})}{1 - R(\lambda_m)}\right)^2$$

If R and T may be considered to be independent of wavelength between λ_m and $\lambda_{m+\frac{1}{2}}$, the contrast factor is given by the simpler espression

$$F = \frac{\mathcal{T}_{\max}}{\mathcal{T}_{\min}} = \left(\frac{1+R}{1-R}\right)^2.$$

4. The bandwidth: the half intensity bandwidth W_2 is defined by

$$\mathcal{T}(\lambda_m \pm \tfrac{1}{2}W_2) = \tfrac{1}{2}\mathcal{T}(\lambda_m).$$

It is sometimes convenient to define the kth intensity bandwidth W_k, by

$$\mathcal{T}(\lambda_m \pm \tfrac{1}{2}W_k) = \mathcal{T}(\lambda_m)/k.$$

If we introduce the small angle γ_k in order to have $y = (m-1)2\pi + \gamma_k$, then, by definition,

$$\mathcal{T}(\lambda_m \pm \tfrac{1}{2}W_k) = \left(\frac{T}{1-R}\right)^2 \frac{1}{1 + \dfrac{4R}{(1-R)^2} \sin^2 \tfrac{1}{2}\gamma_k} = \frac{1}{k}\left(\frac{T}{1-R}\right)^2.$$

It follows that

$$\sin \tfrac{1}{2}\gamma_k = \frac{(1-R)\sqrt{(1-k)}}{2\sqrt{R}} \approx \tfrac{1}{2}\gamma_k.$$

It is convenient to put

$$f = -\left(\frac{dy}{d\lambda}\right)_{\lambda=\lambda_m} \frac{\lambda_m}{2\pi},$$

with $f=m$ for silver layers, but different from an integer when I and II consist of several layers. It can be shown that, because in the neighbourhood of λ_m we have

$$y = 2\pi[m-1-f(\lambda-\lambda_m)/\lambda_m],$$

we get

$$W_k = \frac{\lambda_m}{f} \frac{1-R}{\pi\sqrt{R}} \sqrt{(1-k)}.$$

In particular, we get

$$W_2 = \frac{\lambda_m}{f} \frac{1-R}{\pi\sqrt{R}}$$

and $W_{10}=3W_2$.

An interference filter must have a high luminosity. Eq. (26) shows that $\mathcal{T}_{max}=1$ when the stacks I and II are nonabsorbing. Even a small absorptance reduces drastically the maximum transmittance of the filter. For instance, if I and II are silver films and $R=0.9$, $T=0.05$ for $\lambda=6000$ Å, $\mathcal{T}_{max}=0.25$ only.

The contrast factor and the bandwidth are functions of the reflectance of the reflecting stacks I and II only. They increase with R, so that it is necessary to have highly reflecting films in order to produce filters with high contrast factor and narrow bandwidth. In the preceding example, $F=360$ and $W_2=200/f$ in Å.

An increase of the contrast factor can be obtained, not only through an increase of R, but also by using two interference filters in series. It is preferable, instead, to prepare a contracted double filter, which contains three highly reflecting and slightly transmitting systems I, II and III, separated by two nonabsorbing films of the same effective optical thickness.

The bandwidth is decreased when f is increased. As we have seen that $f\approx m$, this indicates that an increase of the order m of the filter decreases the bandwidth. But m is also related to the number of the transmitted bands, which are closer when it is larger. For instance, a filter which is second order ($m=2$) for $\lambda=6000$ Å, is third order ($m=3$) for $\lambda=4000$ Å (neglecting the variation with wavelength of R, T, δ_{I} and δ_{II}.

The spectrum of white light reflected from an interference filter is roughly complementary to the spectrum of transmitted light and shows narrow minima of reflection which are hardly of practical value. If, however, the thicknesses of I and II are conveniently chosen, it is possible to have minima of reflection which are zero (TURNER [1950]).

If the filter is used in convergent or divergent light, the deviation $\Delta\phi_0$ from $\phi_0=0$,

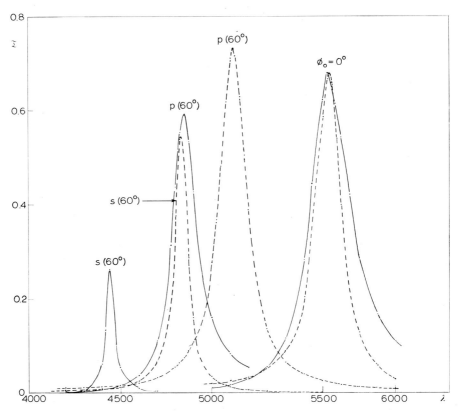

Fig. 25. Transmittance of an interference filter Ag–ZnS–Ag. The thicknesses are: 360 Å for the silver layers and 1900 Å for the middle layer. Dashed line: with dispersion of the indices of refraction taken into account. Full line: the indices of refraction of all the media are kept constant. Computed values are given for $\phi_0 = 0°$ and 60° (s- and p-polarization).

gives rise to a shift $\Delta\lambda_m$ towards the blue. In a first approximation, we can write

$$\Delta\lambda_m/\lambda_m = \tfrac{1}{2}(\Delta\phi_0/n)^2.$$

When the angle of incidence ϕ_0 is increased from $\phi_0 = 0$, there are two main effects: a shift of λ_m towards shorter wavelengths and a splitting up in two components $\lambda_m^{(s)}$ and $\lambda_m^{(p)}$. The s-component is shifted more than the p-component. It is difficult to give approximate formulae which are reasonably accurate, therefore we shall, instead, examine an example which shows the features of the influence of the angle of incidence.

Fig. 25 shows $\mathcal{T}(\lambda)$ computed for an interference filter of the type Ag–ZnS–Ag comprised between identical extreme media ($n_0 = n_s = 1.52$). We have chosen ZnS, because the shift of λ_m is smaller when the index of refraction of the nonabsorbing material is higher. The interrupted line curves are computed by taking into account the dispersion of the indices of refraction of the materials, whereas the full lines give the results obtained with neglect of dispersion. In the latter situation, we have taken

$n = 0.057$, $k = 3.443$ for the Ag films (thickness: 360 Å) and $n = 2.363$ for the ZnS film (thickness: 1900 Å). For Ag, we have used the data of SCHULZ and TANGHERLINI [1954] and of SCHULZ [1954]. The data for ZnS are given in table 2. It is interesting to notice the effect of dispersion, which narrows the pass-band for normal incidence, lessens the shift of λ_m and keeps the luminosity higher for oblique incidence. It may be seen that such a filter can make a good polarizer if used in oblique incidence ($\phi_0 \geq 60°$) and for the wavelength $\lambda_m^{(p)}$ or $\lambda_m^{(s)}$ of the peak transmittance.

References

ABELÈS, F., 1950, Ann. Phys. (Paris) **5**, 596, 706.

ABELÈS, F., 1963, *in*: E. Wolf, ed., Progress in optics, vol. 2 (North-Holland Publ. Co., Amsterdam) p. 250.

ABELÈS, F. and C. BAZIN, 1962, Compt. Rend. **254**, 2310.

BADOUAL, R. and P. GIACOMO, 1964, J. Phys. Radium **25**, 268.

BENNETT, H. E., J. M. BENNETT and E. J. ASHLEY, 1962, J. Opt. Soc. Am. **52**, 1945.

BERNING, J. A. and P. H. BERNING, 1960, J. Opt. Soc. Am. **50**, 813.

BERNING, P. H., 1963, *in*: Physics of thin films, vol. 1 (Academic Press, New York) p. 69.

CASWELL, H. L., 1963, *in*: Physics of thin films, vol. 1 (Academic Press, New York) p. 1.

COTTON, P., 1950, J. Phys. Radium **11**, 321.

COX, J. T. and G. HASS, 1958, J. Opt. Soc. Am. **48**, 677.

COX, J. T. and G. HASS, 1964, *in*: Physics of thin films, vol. 2 (Academic Press, New York) p. 239.

COX, J. T., G. HASS and R. F. ROWTREE, 1954, Vaccuum **4**, 445.

COX, J. T., G. HASS and A. THELEN, 1962, J. Opt. Soc. Am. **52**, 965.

DUFOUR, C. and A. HERPIN, 1953, Rev. Opt. **32**, 321.

Ellipsometry in the measurement of surface and thin films, 1964, Symp. Proc. Natl. Bur. Std. Miscellaneous Publ. 256.

HALL, J. F. and W. F. C. FERGUSON, 1955, J. Opt. Soc. Am. **45**, 74.

HASS, G., 1955, J. Opt. Soc. Am. **45**, 945.

HASS, G. and L. HADLEY, 1963, *in*: Am. Inst. Phys. Handbook (McGraw-Hill Book Co., New York) p. 6.

HASS, G. and J. E. WAYLONIS, 1961, J. Opt. Soc. Am. **51**, 719.

HEAVENS, O. S., 1955, Optical properties of thin solid films (Butterworths, London).

HEAVENS, O. S., 1960, Rept. Progr. Phys. **23**, 1.

HEAVENS, O. S., 1964, *in*: Physics of thin films, vol. 2 (Academic Press, New York) p. 193.

HERMANSEN, A., 1955, Kgl. Danske Videnskab. Selskab, Mat.-Fys. Medd. **29**, no. 13.

HERPIN, A., 1947, Compt. Rend. **225**, 182.

HOLLAND, L., 1958, Vacuum deposition of thin films (Chapman and Hall, London).

IOGANSEN, L. V., 1961, Opt. Spectry. (USSR) (English transl.) **11**, 292.

KARD, P. G., 1956, Soviet Phys.-Doklady **1**, 256.

KOPPELMANN, G. and K. KREBS, 1959, Z. Physik **156**, 38.

LEURGANS, P. J., 1951, J. Opt. Soc. Am. **41**, 714.

MACCRACKIN, F. L. and J. COLSON, Natl. Bur. Std. (U.S.) Tech. Note, 242.

MACNEILLE, S. M. and E. O. DIXON, 1954, J. Opt. Soc. Am. **44**, 805.

MALE, D., 1950, J. Phys. Radium **11**, 332.

MAYER, H., 1950, Physik dünner Schichten, vol. 1 (Wissenschaftliche Verslagsgesellschaft, Stuttgart).

METHFESSEL, S., 1953, Dünne Schichten (VEB Wilhelm Knapp Verlag, Halle).

MIELENZ, K. D., 1959, J. Res. Natl. Bur. Std. A**63**, 197.

NOMARSKI, G. and A. R. WEILL, 1955, Rev. Métallurgie III (2), 121.

NOMARSKI, G., I. EPELBOIN and M. FROMENT, 1958, Rev. Métallurgie (2), 260.

PAPINI, F. and M. PERROT, 1964, Compt. Rend. **259**, 2984.

SCHULZ, L. G., 1954, J. Opt. Soc. Am. **44**, 357.

SCHULZ, L. G. and F. R. TANGHERLINI, 1954, J. Opt. Soc. Am. **44**, 362.

SMITH, P. H., 1939, Electronics **12**, 29; 1944, **17**, 130.

Tables of Chebyshev polynomials $S_n(x)$ and $C_n(x)$, 1952), Natl. Bur. Std. (U.S.) Appl. Math. Ser. no. 9.

TURNER, A. F., 1950, J. Phys. Radium **11**, 444.

VAN HEEL, A. C. S. and A. WALTHER, 1958, Opt. Acta **5**, 47.

VASICEK, A., 1960, Optics of thin films (North-Holland Publ. Co., Amsterdam).

WOLTER, H., 1956, *in*: S. Flügge, ed., Encyclopedia of physics, vol. 24 (Springer-Verlag, Berlin) p. 461 (in German).

CHAPTER 6

THE THEORY OF COHERENCE
AND ITS APPLICATIONS

H. H. HOPKINS

Imperial College of Science and Technology, London

CONTENTS

1. The nature of light emitted by sources

At optical frequencies the electromagnetic field produced by a light source may be considered as arising from each atom radiating as a simple electric dipole. The field components of the radiation from an oscillating dipole are illustrated in fig. 1. The dipole, of moment p and frequency v, has its axis along the direction of Z. At any

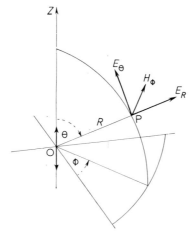

Fig. 1. Radiation from an electric dipole.

point P, having spherical polar coordinates (R, θ, ϕ), there are meridional and radial components (E_θ, E_R) of electric field, and an azimuthal magnetic field (H_ϕ). These fields oscillate with the dipole frequency v, and propagate along the radius vector OP. Using the customary complex notation, these fields may be written as the real parts of

$$E_\theta = \frac{k^2}{4\pi\varepsilon\varepsilon_0} \left\{ \left(\frac{1}{kR}\right)^2 - i\left(\frac{1}{kR}\right) - 1 \right\} \frac{p \sin\theta}{R} e^{2\pi i(vt - R/\lambda)},$$

$$E_R = \frac{k^2}{4\pi\varepsilon\varepsilon_0} \left\{ 2\left(\frac{1}{kR}\right)^2 - 2i\left(\frac{1}{kR}\right) \right\} \frac{p \cos\theta}{R} e^{2\pi i(vt - R/\lambda)}, \tag{1}$$

$$H_\phi = \frac{k^2 V}{4\pi} \left\{ -i\left(\frac{1}{kR}\right) - 1 \right\} \frac{p \sin\theta}{R} e^{2\pi i(vt - R/\lambda)},$$

where ε and ε_0 are respectively the dielectric constant of the medium and the value of this quantity ascribed to free space. The propagation constant k is equal to $2\pi/\lambda$, where λ is the wavelength in the medium: alternatively $k = 2\pi n/\lambda_0$, where λ_0 is the wavelength in vacuum, and n is the refractive index of the medium. The velocity of light in the medium is $V = v\lambda$.

For the middle region of the visible spectrum, $\lambda = 0.00055$ mm, so that $(1/kR)$ is less than 0.01 for $R > 0.009$ mm. Thus, even at small distances from the dipole the terms in the brackets involving $(1/kR)$ may be neglected, and the field components may be written

$$E_\theta = -\left(\frac{k^2}{4\pi\varepsilon\varepsilon_0}\right)\frac{p\sin\theta}{R}\,e^{2\pi i(vt - R/\lambda)},$$

$$H_\phi = -\left(\frac{k^2 V}{4\pi}\right)\frac{p\sin\theta}{R}\,e^{2\pi i(vt - R/\lambda)}, \tag{2}$$

$$E_R = 0.$$

This is the so-called radiation field of the dipole, consisting of oscillating electric and magnetic fields transverse to the radius vector OP, which is the direction of propagation. The electric field vector lies in a meridian plane through the axis of the dipole, and the magnetic field vector is perpendicular to this plane. The amplitudes of E_θ and H_ϕ are both maximum for points lying in the equatorial plane of the dipole ($\theta = 90°$), and both decrease to zero for points on the dipole axis ($\theta = 0, 180°$). The radiated wave is thus polarized and inhomogeneous in amplitude.

The instantaneous values of the E- and H-vectors are given by the real parts of the expressions (2), that is by

$$E(t) = E\cos\left\{2\pi\left(vt - \frac{R}{\lambda}\right)\right\},$$

$$H(t) = H\cos\left\{2\pi\left(vt - \frac{R}{\lambda}\right)\right\}, \tag{3}$$

where

$$E = -\left(\frac{k^2}{4\pi\varepsilon\varepsilon_0}\right)\frac{p\sin\theta}{R},$$

$$H = -\left(\frac{k^2 V}{4\pi}\right)\frac{p\sin\theta}{R}. \tag{4}$$

Now the velocity of light in the medium, V, the velocity in vacuum, c, and the dielectric constant ε, and magnetic permeability μ, satisfy the relations

$$V = \frac{1}{\sqrt{(\varepsilon\mu\varepsilon_0\mu_0)}}, \qquad c = \frac{1}{\sqrt{(\varepsilon_0\mu_0)}}, \tag{5}$$

ε_0 and μ_0 being the values of ε and μ ascribed to free space. Thus the refractive index of the medium is given by

$$n = c/V = \sqrt{\varepsilon\mu}. \tag{6}$$

The field amplitudes (4) are related by

$$H = \varepsilon\varepsilon_0 V E = \sqrt{\frac{\varepsilon\varepsilon_0}{\mu\mu_0}}\,E \tag{7}$$

or, using (5) and (6)

$$H = (1/\mu\mu_0 c)nE.\tag{8}$$

The quantity $(1/\mu\mu_0 c)$ in (8) is independent of the medium for non-magnetic substances $(\mu = 1)$, and this will include all cases to be considered in what follows.

The instantaneous energy density in the wave at P is given by

$$U(t) = \varepsilon\varepsilon_0 E^2(t) + \mu\mu_0 H^2(t)$$

or, substituting from (3) and using (7) and (6) with $\mu = 1$,

$$U(t) = \varepsilon_0 n^2 E^2 \cos^2\{2\pi(vt - R/\lambda)\}.\tag{9}$$

Over one period $T = 1/v$, the square of the cosine has an average value of $\frac{1}{2}$, so that the mean energy density is

$$\bar{U} = \tfrac{1}{2}\varepsilon_0 n^2 E^2.\tag{10}$$

On the other hand, the instantaneous flux of energy per unit area at P, normal to OP, is given by the vector product of E_θ with H_ϕ. Since these are at right angles in the plane normal to OP, the energy flux is along the radius vector OP, and it has an instantaneous value

$$W(t) = EH \cos^2\{2\pi(vt - R/\lambda)\}$$

and, substituting from (8)

$$W(t) = \frac{1}{\mu_0 c} nE^2 \cos^2\{2\pi(vt - R/\lambda)\},\tag{11}$$

again with $\mu = 1$. The time-averaged value of the energy flux over one period $T = 1/v$ is

$$\bar{W} = \frac{1}{2\mu_0 c} nE^2$$

or, substituting $\varepsilon_0 c = 1/\mu_0 c$ from (5),

$$\bar{W} = \tfrac{1}{2}\varepsilon_0 cnE^2.\tag{12}$$

Since $V = c/n$, $\bar{W}$ is equal to $V\bar{U}$, so that the mean energy flux (12) may be regarded as the energy density $\bar{U}$ travelling with the velocity V of the wave in the medium.

In a thermal light source, such as a tungsten filament lamp, or a gas discharge lamp, the individual atoms will give rise to dipole fields which only radiate for short times, the separate pulses being emitted at random intervals; the dipole axes also have random orientations, giving unpolarized light. The electromagnetic field at any point P illuminated by the source will thus have a resultant electric vector which varies randomly in direction and in its phase of oscillation. Even if passed through a polarizer, the component of the electric field reaching P will still vary randomly in phase. This is the case of an incoherent source. By contrast, in a laser the emission of photons is stimulated by a standing electromagnetic wave system existing in a resonant cavity, such as a Fabry–Perot interferometer, and under these conditions the electromagnetic field associated with each emitted photon is in phase with the stimulating wave. In consequence the dipole fields associated with the different atoms in the source always vibrate in phase with the field stimulating the emission, and the light leaving the cavity does so in continuous wave trains with, in the ideal case, the same phase at all points of the emitted waves. Lasers are, therefore, said to be coherent light sources.

Etymologically, the word 'coherent' means "sticking together". The phases in an ideal coherent light source are always in step at different points in space and time. In an incoherent light source, on the other hand, the excited atoms emit spontaneously and the phases of the different wave trains from different atoms at any one time, and also those from the same atom at different times, are randomly related to each other. It is in this sense, that is of phase-coherence, that the terms 'coherent' and 'incoherent' are applied to laser and thermal light sources respectively. Only thermal light sources will be considered in the present section.

In what follows it will also be usually assumed that all pencils of light are unpolarized and of small angular aperture, such that the approximation $\sin \theta \approx \theta$ may be made, where θ is the angular radius. In these circumstances, any component of the E-vector may be used to describe the light disturbance at any point, and so an effectively scalar wave may be employed. Moreover, the different dipoles in the source will have random orientations, and thus tend to average out the intensity variations with direction present in the radiation field of a single dipole. The resultant intensity will also tend to average to a constant value with time, the remaining factor being the phase which will fluctuate randomly with time.

The light disturbance from a thermal light source may thus be described by a scalar wave which is composed either of randomly emitted short wave-trains, or alternatively as the superposition of monochromatic waves of constant amplitude but randomly varying phase. For the first representation, let $S_n(t)$ be the form of the nth wave-train. If this is emitted at a time $t = \tau_n$, the total scalar wave at the source will be represented by an expression of the form

$$S(t) = \sum_n S_n(t - \tau_n) \tag{13}$$

and the randomness of the source will appear principally in the randomness of the emission starting times, τ_n, but possibly also because of randomness in the forms of the different wave-trains. In the second representation the disturbance will be described as the superposition of scalar waves of different frequency, v, each of the form

$$S_v(t) = \alpha_v \cos\{2\pi v t + \theta_v(t)\}, \tag{14}$$

where α_v is a real amplitude constant with time, and $\theta_v(t)$ is a randomly varying phase. These descriptions are equivalent in that (14) is the resultant of the Fourier components of the different wave-trains in (13), which average to constant intensity, and therefore constant real amplitude, but which produce randomly varying phase.

In this connection it is important to note that the formal Fourier spectrum of any wave-train will have monochromatic, pure-frequency, components which may be thought to exist mathematically from $t = -\infty$ to $t = +\infty$, but which superpose to give zero disturbance outside the time interval of the actual wave-train. Physically, of course, the effect of any wave-train will only exist from the start of its emission $t = \tau_n$ and will cease shortly after the amplitude of the wave-train has decreased to zero. The photons will always be found only in the region occupied by a given wave-train.

The physical significance of the analysis of a finite wave-train into pure frequency components of infinite extent and duration is two-fold. In the first place, corresponding to each pure frequency will exist photons of given energy, and hence the energy spectrum of the emitted radiation is determined by the squared modulus of the Fourier spectrum of the wave-trains. Secondly, photons of different energy, and therefore the different pure frequency components of the light wave, travel at different velocities in a dispersive medium, so that the propagation of the different frequency components in a wave-train have to be considered separately in dispersive media.

2. Relation between the length of wave-train and the energy spectrum: coherence time and coherence length

Suppose a source oscillates with frequency v_0 and constant amplitude α for a time T lasting from $t = -\frac{1}{2}T$ to $t = +\frac{1}{2}T$. The wave disturbance, shown in fig. 2a, may then be written

$$
\begin{aligned}
S(t) &= \alpha \cos(2\pi v_0 t) \qquad |t| < \tfrac{1}{2}T \\
&= 0 \qquad\qquad\qquad |t| > \tfrac{1}{2}T
\end{aligned}
\tag{15}
$$

and the Fourier spectrum of this wave will be

$$
s(v) = \int_{-\infty}^{+\infty} S(t) e^{-2\pi i v t}\, dt
\tag{16}
$$

or, substituting for $S(t)$ from (15),

$$
s(v) = \frac{\alpha \sin\{\pi T(v - v_0)\}}{2\pi(v - v_0)} + \frac{\alpha \sin\{\pi T(v + v_0)\}}{2\pi(v + v_0)}
$$

and this gives the distribution of amplitudes among the different frequency components of $S(t)$.

It will be useful to note here the simple relation between the complex amplitudes of Fourier components of a wave and the Fourier coefficients when the wave disturbance itself is a real quantity. Thus, from (16), for $S(t)$ real, $s(-v) = s^*(v)$, the $*$ denoting the complex conjugate. The Fourier inversion of (16) is

$$
S(t) = \int_{-\infty}^{+\infty} s(v) e^{+2\pi i v t}\, dv
$$

or, with $s(v) = \frac{1}{2}\alpha(v)\, e^{i\theta(v)}$,

$$S(t) = \int_0^\infty \alpha(v) \cos\{2\pi v t + \theta(v)\} \, dv, \tag{17}$$

representing the disturbance directly as the superposition of waves of amplitude $\alpha(v)$ and phase $\theta(v)$. The complex amplitude of such a wave is $\alpha(v)e^{i\theta(v)}$ and so $2s(v)$,

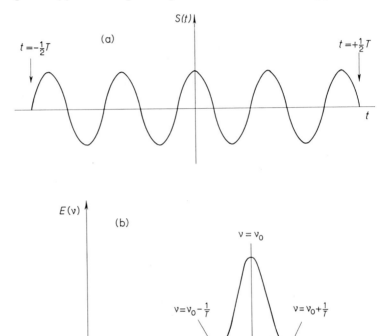

Fig. 2. Energy spectrum of an undamped wave-train of finite duration.

for the positive values of v, gives the complex amplitude of the component of frequency v. Thus only the positive values of v are used; the negative frequency terms merely mirror the positive frequency terms in complex conjugate form. The energy associated with the Fourier component of frequency v is given by

$$E(v) = \{\alpha(v)\}^2 = |2s(v)|^2, \tag{18}$$

where again only the positive values of v are to be considered.

Applying the result (18) to the above Fourier spectrum of (15) the second term is negligible and the first gives for the energy spectrum of $S(t)$,

$$E(v) = \alpha^2 \left\{ \frac{\sin\{\pi T(v - v_0)\}}{\pi(v - v_0)} \right\}^2, \tag{19}$$

the form of which is shown in fig. 2b. Practically the whole of the energy is contained within the frequency range $v_0 \pm 1/T$. The half-width of the energy spectrum is thus related to the duration of emission by the formula,

$$\Delta v = 1/T, \tag{20}$$

so that the half-width of the spectral line is inversely proportional to the emission time.

As the above disturbance leaves the source it travels with a velocity $V = c/n$, where c is the vacuum velocity of light and n is the refractive index of the medium. A wave emitted for a time T thus gives rise to a wave-train of length

$$L = VT \tag{21}$$

Since $V = \lambda v$ and $T = 1/\Delta v$, (21) may be written

$$L = \lambda_0^2/\Delta\lambda, \tag{22}$$

where $\Delta\lambda$ is the half-width of the energy spectrum when considered as a function of wavelength, and $\lambda_0 = V/v_0$ is the wavelength in the medium corresponding to the frequency v_0.

It is largely collisions with other atoms which limits the coherent emission time of any atom. The more frequent the collisions, the shorter the uninterrupted emission times and the broader the spectral line. Conversely the broader the spectral line, the shorter the coherent emission time and the length of the wave-train. The quantities T and L are known respectively as the coherence time and coherence length of the radiation. They are of importance because interference effects of good contrast can only be observed when the optical path differences are appreciably smaller than L.

In addition to collision broadening a spectral line has a natural width resulting from the fact that the atomic dipoles execute damped simple harmonic motion. In place of (15) one now has

$$\begin{aligned} S(t) &= \alpha e^{-\pi\beta t} \cos\left(2\pi v_0 t\right) \qquad & t > 0 \\ &= 0 & t < 0, \end{aligned} \tag{23}$$

where β is a measure of the damping. Substitution of this form in (16) gives

$$s(v) = \frac{\alpha}{4\pi} \left\{ \frac{1}{\frac{1}{2}\beta + i(v - v_0)} + \frac{1}{\frac{1}{2}\beta + i(v + v_0)} \right\} \tag{24}$$

Since $S(t)$ is a real function, the energy spectrum is given by (18) and only the positive values of v are to be considered. For the centre of the visible spectrum $v_0 \approx 0.5 \times 10^{15}$ cps, so that the second term in (24) may be neglected, leaving for the complex amplitude

$$2s(v) = \frac{\alpha}{\pi\beta} \left\{ \frac{1}{1 + i(v - v_0)/\frac{1}{2}\beta} \right\},$$

and the energy spectrum is

$$E(v) = \left(\frac{\alpha}{\pi\beta}\right)^2 \left\{ \frac{1}{1 + \{(v - v_0)/\frac{1}{2}\beta\}^2} \right\}. \tag{25}$$

The form of wave-train (23) and the energy spectrum (25) are shown in figs. 3a and 3b respectively. The energy in the spectrum is very small except in the neighbourhood of $v = v_0$. The half-value width is given by

$$\Delta v = \beta, \tag{26}$$

so the damping coefficient β determines the half-width of the spectral line in the absence of other broadening processes. Also the smaller the value of β, the less the damping and the greater the effective length of the wave-train. As before, therefore, highly monochromatic light is essentially associated with long wave-trains.

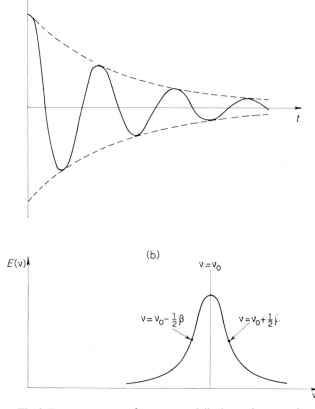

Fig. 3. Energy spectrum of an exponentially damped wave-train.

In most light sources, the above natural width of the energy spectrum is less than 1% of the broadening due to collisions. Of comparable magnitude with the collision broadening is broadening arising from the Doppler effect, when, as in a gas discharge, the emitting atoms are in motion with significant components of velocity in the direction in which light is emitted.

3. The energy spectrum of a randomly spaced sequence of wave-trains

In the previous section only a single wave-train was considered, whereas the light from an incoherent source will consist of a large number of randomly emitted wave-trains. In accordance with (13) above, the light disturbance at any given point P may be written

$$S(t) = \sum_n S_n(t - \tau_n), \tag{27}$$

where $S_n(t)$ gives the form of the nth wave-train and τ_n the arrival time at P of its head. Using (16) the Fourier spectrum of $S(t)$ is found to be

$$s(v) = \sum_n e^{-2\pi i v \tau_n} s_n(v),$$

where $s_n(v)$ is the spectrum of $S_n(t)$. The energy spectrum of (27) is thus given, as in (18), by

$$E(v) = |2 \sum_n e^{-2\pi i v \tau_n} s_n(v)|^2 \tag{28}$$

and only the positive values of v are used. With $2s_n(v) = \alpha_n(v) e^{i\theta_n(v)}$, (28) may be written

$$E(v) = \sum_n \sum_m \alpha_n(v) \alpha_m(v) \cos \{2\pi v(\tau_m - \tau_n) + \theta_n(v) - \theta_m(v)\}$$

or, grouping the terms $m = n$,

$$E(v) = \sum_n \{\alpha_n(v)\}^2 + \sum_n \sum_{\substack{m \\ n \neq m}} \alpha_n(v) \alpha_m(v) \cos \{2\pi v(\tau_m - \tau_n) + \theta_n(v) - \theta_m(v)\}.$$

Since the emission starting times τ_n are random, the cosine terms are as often negative as positive and the double summation vanishes, leaving

$$E(v) = \sum_n \{\alpha_n(v)\}^2 = \sum_n E_n(v), \tag{29}$$

where $E_n(v)$ is the energy spectrum of the nth pulse. To be comparable with (19) and (25), the formula (29) has to be divided by the number of wave-trains, and the energy spectrum is then equal to the mean energy spectrum of the separate wave-trains emitted. This result is clearly only valid for a source emitting a large number of randomly spaced wave-trains. For such sources, however, the mean coherence time and coherence length, being determined by the mean length of wave-train, are still given from the half-width of the energy spectrum by the formulae (20) and (22) respectively. For $E(v)$ in (29) to represent highly monochromatic light the separate wave-trains must be long in order that their energy spectra (29) shall be narrow.

4. The energy spectrum of a regularly spaced sequence of wave-trains. The Fabry-Perot étalon as an optical filter

In the discussion so far the wave disturbance in a light beam has been described by its variation as a function of time at a fixed point in space as the wave passes. An alternative description is to give its spatial form at a fixed instant of time. In the former case the wave function is analysed into a set of temporal frequencies; in the latter it is regarded as a spectrum of spatial frequencies, or wave-numbers. This type of analysis will now be applied to the action of the Fabry–Perot étalon. It demonstrates how from a short wave-train, having a broad energy spectrum, the étalon generates a longer wave-train with a consequent narrower energy spectrum.

Fig. 4a shows a pulse incident normally on the étalon, which consists of a pair of flat parallel plates, each of high reflectivity R and having a transmission coefficient T. Here R and T are the ratios of the reflected and transmitted intensities to the incident intensity. Part of the energy passes straight through the system, giving rise to pulse 1, in fig. 4a, of amplitude $Tf(x)$, where $f(x)$ is the spatial form of the amplitude of the

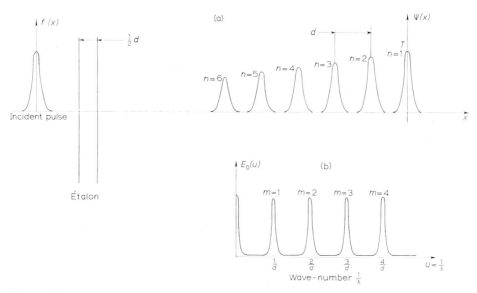

Fig. 4. Fabry–Perot étalon: (a) the generation of a wave-train from a single pulse; (b) the energy spectrum of the impulse response.

incident pulse. Pulse 2 results from the light which is transmitted by the second plate after the incident pulse has been reflected twice in the étalon: it has an amplitude $TRf(x+d)$, being delayed a distance d relative to pulse 1 because of the additional two passes of the étalon space. The nth transmitted pulse will have suffered $2(n-1)$ reflections and has a delay $(n-1)d$, giving an amplitude $TR^{n-1}f\{x+(n-1)d\}$. It will be seen that a single incident pulse $f(x)$ gives rise to a train of pulses equally-spaced by a distance d, which is twice the spacing of the étalon. The transmitted light thus has a spatial distribution of amplitude

$$\psi(x) = \sum_{n=1}^{\infty} TR^{n-1}f\{x+(n-1)d\}, \tag{30}$$

whose Fourier transform is

$$\Psi(u) = \sum_{n=1}^{\infty} TR^{n-1}e^{-2\pi i(n-1)du}F(u), \tag{31}$$

where

$$F(u) = \int_{-\infty}^{+\infty} f(x)e^{2\pi iux}\,dx \tag{32}$$

is the Fourier transform of the incident pulse. Eq. (31) is a simple geometric series which, when summed, gives

$$\Psi(u) = TF(u) \left\{ \frac{1}{1 - Re^{-2\pi idu}} \right\}. \tag{33}$$

The variable $u = 1/\lambda$ is here a spatial frequency, or wave-number. Because both $f(x)$ and $\psi(x)$ are real, the energy spectrum of the transmitted train of pulses is again found using the rule expressed by eq. (18) above. It is thus

$$E(u) = |2\Psi(u)|^2 = \left(\frac{T}{1-R}\right)^2 I(u)E_0(u), \tag{34}$$

where

$$E_0(u) = \frac{1}{1 + \dfrac{4R}{(1-R)^2}\sin^2(\pi du)}, \tag{35}$$

and $I(u) = |2F(u)|^2$ is the energy spectrum of the incident pulse, $f(x)$. If this latter is a pure impulse its energy spectrum is $I(u) = 1$; and, apart from the constant factor $T/(1-R)^2$, the Fabry–Perot function $E_0(u)$ is seen to be the energy spectrum of the so-called impulse response of the system.

The impulse response, illustrated in fig. 4b has peaks at wave-numbers $u = m/d$, that is when $\lambda = \lambda_m = d/m$. Each peak is narrower the larger the value of R; and correspondingly the damping of the successive pulses is also less. Thus a high reflectivity produces long wave-trains and highly monochromatic light at each resonance, $\lambda = \lambda_m$. The energy at each peak is given by

$$E(u_m) = \left(\frac{T}{1-R}\right)^2 I(u_m), \tag{36}$$

the first factor of which is equal to unity if there is no absorption, that is when $T = 1 - R$. The energy transmitted at a wavelength $\lambda = \lambda_m$ is then equal to the energy associated with the spectral component of that wavelength in the incident pulse. If the wavelength λ_m is absent from the spectrum of the incident pulse, there is also no energy at this wavelength in the transmitted light. Thus, although the étalon creates long wave-trains from each pulse, it acts merely as a filter for the photons associated with the incident pulse. Photons are not created by the étalon, and those lost are those absorbed in the reflecting layers. Those photons not transmitted or absorbed are reflected, the narrow peaks in the spectrum of the transmitted light appearing as narrow gaps in the spectrum of the light reflected from the étalon.

When light from an incoherent source falls on a Fabry–Perot étalon, each of the randomly spaced pulses will give rise to a wave-train. The transmitted light then consists of a sequence of randomly spaced long wave-trains, whose energy spectrum will be given by eq. (34), with $I(u)$ replaced by the mean energy spectrum of the incident pulses, in accordance with the results of the preceding section.

Other monochromating devices may be analysed by the method used here, and in each case it is found that the device creates longer wave-trains and filters the appropriate photons from the incident light pulses.

5. Interference between monochromatic light beams of different frequency

Suppose two highly monochromatic light beams intersect at a point P, and have angular frequencies $\omega + \frac{1}{2}\delta\omega$ and $\omega - \frac{1}{2}\delta\omega$ and amplitudes a_1 and a_2. The total disturbance at P at any instant may be written

$$S(t) = a_1 \cos\{(\omega + \tfrac{1}{2}\delta\omega)t + \phi_1\} + a_2 \cos\{(\omega - \tfrac{1}{2}\delta\omega)t + \phi_2\}, \qquad (37)$$

where ϕ_1 and ϕ_2 are the phases at $t = 0$. The instantaneous intensity at P is given by the square of (37), namely

$$I(t) = a^2 \cos^2\{(\omega + \tfrac{1}{2}\delta\omega)t + \phi_1\} + a_2^2 \cos^2\{(\omega - \tfrac{1}{2}\delta\omega)t + \phi_2\} + $$
$$+ 2a_1 a_2 \cos\{(\omega + \tfrac{1}{2}\delta\omega)t + \phi_1\} \cos\{(\omega - \tfrac{1}{2}\delta\omega)t + \phi_2\}. \qquad (38)$$

If the light at P is detected, only the mean intensity over a time T will be recorded. For example a photodetector and amplifier with a band width of 100 megacycles will have an integration time $T = 10^{-8}$ sec, which will include at least 10^6 oscillations of each light beam, since the frequency of these oscillations lies in the range 4.3×10^{14} to 7.5×10^{14} cps for light in the visible part of the spectrum.

The mean intensity observed will be given by

$$I = \frac{1}{T} \int_{-\frac{1}{2}T}^{+\frac{1}{2}T} I(t)\mathrm{d}t,$$

taking the origin of t to be at the mid-point of the integration time T. The first two terms in (38) average to the mean value over one cycle, there being a very large number of cycles in the time T, giving

$$I = \left(\frac{a_1}{\sqrt{2}}\right)^2 + \left(\frac{a_2}{\sqrt{2}}\right)^2 + 2\left(\frac{a_1}{\sqrt{2}}\right)\left(\frac{a_2}{\sqrt{2}}\right)\frac{1}{T}\int_{-\frac{1}{2}T}^{+\frac{1}{2}T}\{\cos(\delta\omega t + \phi_1 - \phi_2)$$
$$+ \cos(2\omega t + \phi_1 + \phi_2)\}\,\mathrm{d}t. \qquad (39)$$

The second term in the remaining integral, being of twice the mean frequency ω, will average to zero over the time T. Eq. (39) may thus be written

$$I = A_1^2 + A_2^2 + 2A_1 A_2 \frac{1}{T}\int_{-\frac{1}{2}T}^{+\frac{1}{2}T}\{\cos\delta\omega t\,\cos(\phi_1 - \phi_2) - \sin\delta\omega t\,\sin(\phi_1 - \phi_2)\}\,\mathrm{d}t, \quad (40)$$

where $A = a/\sqrt{2}$ is the root mean square value of the amplitude.

If the two beams have coherence times T_0 small compared with T, the phase difference $(\phi_1 - \phi_2)$ will suffer random jumps in the time T, and the third term in (40) averages to zero, giving

$$I = I_1 + I_2,\qquad (41)$$

where I_1 and I_2 are the separate intensities in the two light beams. The two disturbances are then incoherent. If the coherence time T_0 is much longer than the integration time T, $(\phi_1 - \phi_2)$ may be regarded as constant, and

$$I = I_1 + I_2 + 2\sqrt{I_1 I_2}\,\cos\,(\phi_1 - \phi_2)\,\frac{\sin\left(\tfrac{1}{2}\delta\omega T\right)}{\tfrac{1}{2}\delta\omega T}\qquad (42)$$

is the mean intensity observed, the third term representing an interference effect and implying some degree of coherence of phase during the time T. When the coherence time T_0 is neither $\ll T$ nor $\gg T$, the resulting intensity is intermediate between (41) and (42).

For the interference term in (42) to have a non-zero value implies restrictions on both Δv_0, the half-width of the energy spectrum of each beam, and also on δv, the difference in their mean frequencies. The coherence time of each beam will be given by $T_0 = 1/\Delta v_0$, and the condition $T_0 \gg T$ thus requires $\Delta v_0 \ll 1/T$, so that

$$\Delta\lambda_0/\lambda = \Delta v_0/v \ll 1/vT\qquad (43)$$

has to be satisfied for interference effects to be detected. For $T = 10^{-7}$ sec and $v = 5 \times 10^{14}$ cps, corresponding to $\lambda = 6000$ Å, the half-width of the light beams must be much less than 0.00012 Å. One of the narrowest thermal light sources is the red line, $\lambda = 6438$ Å, obtained from a low pressure cadmium lamp, for which $\Delta\lambda_0 = 0.0130$ Å; but even this is two orders of magnitude too broad for the phase difference $\phi_1 - \phi_2$ in (42) to remain constant during the time $T = 10^{-7}$ sec.

It is thus only with laser sources that interference may be detected between light beams of different frequency. Moreover, unless the two lasers are tuned to very closely the same frequency, the factor $\sin\,(\tfrac{1}{2}\delta\omega T)/(\tfrac{1}{2}\delta\omega T)$ in (42) will be zero. The permissible frequency difference is such that $\tfrac{1}{2}\delta\omega T < \pi$, so that the condition is

$$\delta v < 1/T,\qquad (44)$$

since $\delta\omega = 2\pi\,\delta v$. The wavelength difference between two lasers must thus be less than 0.0001 Å for interference to be detected with observation times as large as 10^{-7} sec. In consequence extremely fast recording times are needed for experiments of this kind to be successful. It may be noted that δv is the beat frequency between the two mean frequencies.

From what has been said above it will be clear that, with practical detectors, light beams of different frequency from thermal sources will always be incoherent and show no interference effects. The intensities in two such beams thus add directly, as in (41). It will be appreciated that the phrase 'monochromatic light' is used here to mean light having a very narrow range of wavelengths. Even a laser beam has a finite wavelength spread, so that 'strictly monochromatic light' has no physical existence. The pure frequency components in the spectrum of a light beam arise only as useful mathematical concepts in the Fourier analysis of wave-trains. The term 'quasi-monochromatic' is sometimes used to describe monochromatic light.

6. Superposition of light beams (a) from the same source element, and (b) from differents source elements

Fig. 5 shows schematically one arrangement of the Michelson interferometer. Light from a source S, in the focal plane of a lens L_1, is divided into two beams by

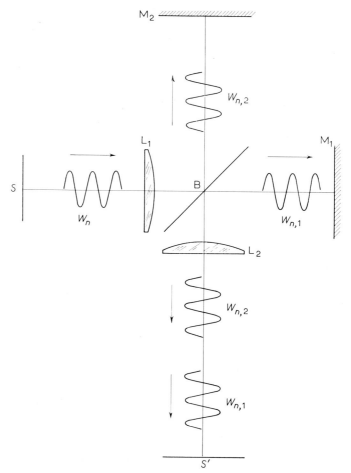

Fig. 5. Wave-trains in the Michelson interferometer.

the beam-splitter B, whence after reflections at mirrors M_1 and M_2, they are brought to focus at S' in the focal plane of the lens L_2. Thus a typical wave-train, W_n, will produce two wave-trains, $W_{n,1}$ and $W_{n,2}$ which will both pass through the point S'.

In the case illustrated in fig. 5, the distance BM_2 is greater than BM_1 by such an amount that the wave-trains $W_{n,1}$ and $W_{n,2}$ do not overlap. From any element of the source at S there will be a very large number of randomly emitted wave-trains arriving at S' at any given instant. However, when the path difference in the two arms of the interferometer is greater than the length of the wave-train, any given wave-train reflected from M_1, such as $W_{n,1}$, will never be present at S' simultaneously with the corresponding wave-train, $W_{n,2}$ reflected from M_2.

Thus, if $S'_{n,1}$ and $S'_{n,2}$ are the disturbances at S' produced by the passage of $W_{n,1}$ and $W_{n,2}$ respectively, the total disturbance in the case considered will be

$$S'(t) = \sum_n S'_{n,1}(t) + \sum_{\substack{m \\ m \neq n}} S'_{m,2}(t), \tag{45}$$

the summations including those wave-trains passing S' at the given time. The condition $m \neq n$ excludes the simultaneous presence of $W_{n,1}$ and $W_{n,2}$ which derive from the same incident wave-train, W_n. The phase of $S'_{n,1}(t)$ will be equal to $\theta_n - kp_1$, where θ_n is the phase of W_n at the source and p_1 is the optical path length from S to S' along arm 1 of the interferometer, with $k = 2\pi/\lambda$. Similarly the phase of $S_{m,2}(t)$ will be given by $\theta_m - kp_2$, where p_2 is the path length from S to S' along arm 2. θ_n is thus the phase of W_n at the source, and

$$\phi_1 = -kp_1, \qquad \phi_2 = -kp_2$$

are instrumental phase-differences. Using $\alpha_{n,1}$ and $\alpha_{m,2}$ for the amplitudes at S', (45) may be written

$$S'(t) = \sum_n \alpha_{n,1} \cos\{2\pi vt + \theta_n + \phi_1\} + \sum_{\substack{m \\ m \neq n}} \alpha_{m,2} \cos\{2\pi vt + \theta_m + \phi_2\},$$

and the instantaneous intensity at S' will be

$$\begin{aligned}
I'(t) = &\sum_n \sum_{n'} \alpha_{n,1} \alpha_{n',1} \cos\{2\pi vt + \theta_n + \phi_1\} \cos\{2\pi vt + \theta_{n'} + \phi_1\} + \\
&+ \sum_m \sum_{m'} \alpha_{m,2} \alpha_{m',2} \cos\{2\pi vt + \theta_m + \phi_2\} \cos\{2\pi vt + \theta_{m'} + \phi_2\} + \\
&+ 2 \sum_{\substack{n \quad m \\ m \neq n}} \alpha_{n,1} \alpha_{m,2} \cos\{2\pi vt + \theta_n + \phi_1\} \cos\{2\pi vt + \theta_m + \phi_2\}.
\end{aligned}$$

If each of these products of cosines is expressed as a sum of cosines and then averaged over a time T as in the previous section, the time-averaged value of $I'(t)$ is found to be

$$\begin{aligned}
I' = &\sum_n \sum_{n'} \alpha_{n,1} \alpha_{n',1} \tfrac{1}{2} \cos(\theta_n - \theta_{n'}) + \\
&+ \sum_m \sum_{m'} \alpha_{m,2} \alpha_{m',2} \tfrac{1}{2} \cos(\theta_m - \theta_{m'}) + \\
&+ 2 \sum_{\substack{n \quad m \\ m \neq n}} \alpha_{n,1} \alpha_{m,2} \tfrac{1}{2} \cos(\theta_m - \theta_n + \phi_2 - \phi_1). \tag{46}
\end{aligned}$$

In the first two summations in (46), the terms other than $n' = n$ and $m' = m$ will average to zero, since, θ_n and $\theta_{n'}$ being random, the cosines will be as often negative as positive. For the same reason the third summation is zero, since $m \neq n$ in the case considered. The remaining terms give

$$I' = \sum_n \tfrac{1}{2}\alpha_{n,1}^2 + \sum_m \tfrac{1}{2}\alpha_{m,2}^2 = I'_1 + I'_2, \tag{47}$$

where I'_1 and I'_2 are the total intensities at S' due to each of the beams from path 1 and path 2 separately.

It follows from (47) that no interference is observed if the path difference between the two superposed beams of light is greater than the length of wave-train, that is, greater than the coherence length of the light emitted by the given element of the source.

If the path difference $(p_2 - p_1)$ is very small compared with the coherence length, the two wave-trains $W_{n,1}$ and $W_{n,2}$ from each incident wave-train W_n are almost exactly superposed in the final space, so that the terms $m = n$ are included in the third summation of (46). The time-averaged intensity is then

$$I' = \sum_n \tfrac{1}{2}\alpha_{n,1}^2 + \sum_m \tfrac{1}{2}\alpha_{m,2}^2 + 2\sum_n \tfrac{1}{2}\alpha_{n,1}\alpha_{n,2} \cos(\phi_2 - \phi_1). \tag{48}$$

$W_{n,1}$ in fig. 5 is transmitted and reflected by the beamsplitter B, and reflected by the mirror M_1. Let ρ_1 be the product of the appropriate transmission and reflection coefficients, and let ρ_2 be the corresponding quantity for $W_{n,2}$. Then

$$\alpha_{n,1} = \sqrt{\rho_1}\,\alpha_n, \qquad \alpha_{n,2} = \sqrt{\rho_2}\,\alpha_n, \tag{49}$$

where α_n is the amplitude of the incident wave-train W_n. In terms of (49), the third term of (48) gives

$$2\{\sum_n \tfrac{1}{2}\alpha_n^2\}\sqrt{\rho_1\rho_2} \cos(\phi_2 - \phi_1),$$

and this, using $I = \sum_n \tfrac{1}{2}\alpha_n^2$ to denote the intensity of the incident beam, may be written

$$2\sqrt{\rho_1 I}\,\sqrt{\rho_2 I} \cos(\phi_2 - \phi_1) = 2\sqrt{I'_1 I'_2} \cos(\phi_2 - \phi_1),$$

where I'_1 and I'_2 are again the intensities produced by the separate beams at S'. Similarly the remaining terms in (48) are equal to I'_1 and I'_2, as in (47). Thus for path differences very small compared with the coherence length,

$$I' = I'_1 + I'_2 + 2\sqrt{I'_1 I'_2} \cos(\phi_2 - \phi_1) \tag{50}$$

or, in terms of the amplitudes $A'_1 = \sqrt{I'_1}$ and $A'_2 = \sqrt{I'_2}$,

$$I' = A'^2_1 + A'^2_2 + 2A'_1 A'_2 \cos(\phi_2 - \phi_1) \tag{51}$$

and interference is thus observed.

If the path difference between the two superposed beams from a single element of the source is neither very much greater, nor very much smaller, than the coherence length, there is only a partial overlap of corresponding wave-trains and a result intermediate between the two above states results. The treatment used here is then not practicable, and the methods of section 7 have to be employed.

It will be noted that the above considerations apply to light from a single element of the source. The criterion for a group of emitting atoms to belong to the same element of the source is merely that the variation in the instrumental phase difference $\phi_2 - \phi_1 = k(p_1 - p_2)$ between them is negligible in comparison with 2π, or alternatively that the variation in $(p_1 - p_2)$ is $\ll \lambda$. The permissible size of such a source element therefore depends on the geometry of the instrumental system.

If one of the mirrors M_1, M_2 in fig. 5 is tilted, light from two separate elements of the source S will be superposed at S'. The resultant intensity will be given by (46), but now all the pulses n come from one element of the source, and the pulses m come from a different element. Because of the random emission times, $(\theta_m - \theta_n)$ is always random, and the third term thus sums to zero. As previously the remaining terms give

$$I' = I'_1 + I'_2 \tag{52}$$

and no interference is observed.

7. The light intensity produced by an extended source having a broad spectral range

The previous sections have shown that two light beams (i) whose frequencies differ by an amount greater than the reciprocal of the integration time of the detector, or (ii) which come from independent source elements, show no interference effects. For practical detector speeds and thermal light sources, therefore, interference is only observed between light beams of the same frequency and from the same source element. These results suggest that the light intensity produced at any point by an extended source may be found by summing the intensities produced at the point by pure monochromatic waves of different frequency assumed to emerge independently from each element of the source. This procedure may be justified as follows.

Let $S_n(t)$ be the form of a typical pulse, or wave-train, emitted by the element at S of a source. In terms of its Fourier transform, $s_n(v)$, it may be written

$$S_n(t) = \int_{-\infty}^{+\infty} s_n(v) e^{2\pi i v t} \, dv. \tag{53}$$

If this pulse is emitted at $t = \tau_n$, the disturbance it produces at the source will be

$$S_n(t - \tau_n) = \int_{-\infty}^{+\infty} s_n(v) e^{-2\pi i v \tau_n} e^{2\pi i v t} \, dv. \tag{54}$$

Fig. 6 shows Young's experiment schematically, in which such a pulse, S_n, which propagates from S as a thin expanding spherical shell, passes through two small apertures P_1 and P_2, which in turn produce diffracted pulses. $S_{n,1}$ and $S_{n,2}$ are two such diffracted pulses proceeding to a point P. By the principle of superposition the disturbance produced at P by the pulse (54) is the same as the sum of the disturbances produced at P by the monochromatic components of the pulse.

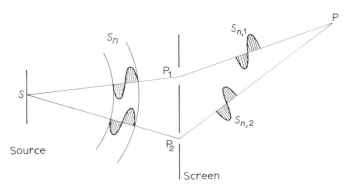

Fig. 6. Wave pulses in Young's experiment.

Suppose, therefore, that a pure monochromatic wave of frequency v, with unit amplitude and zero phase at S, produces complex amplitudes $U_{n,1}(v)$ and $U_{n,2}(v)$ at P, arising from light from P_1 and P_2 respectively. Then each pulse S_n, such as (54), from the source produces at P an effect

$$S_n'(t) = \sum_q \int_{-\infty}^{+\infty} s_n(v)e^{-2\pi i v \tau_n} U_{n,q}(v)e^{2\pi i v t}\,dv, \tag{55}$$

where $\sum_q$ will have $q = 1, 2$ in the case illustrated in fig. 6. If there were N apertures in the screen, each incident pulse would give rise to N pulses at P, and the summation in (55) would include $q = 1, 2, \ldots, N$. The total disturbance at P will be

$$S'(t) = \sum_n \sum_q \int_{-\infty}^{+\infty} s_n(v)e^{-2\pi i v \tau_n} U_{n,q}(v)e^{2\pi i v t}\,dv, \tag{56}$$

which will result in a time-averaged intensity at P given by

$$I' = \frac{1}{T}\int_{-\frac{1}{2}T}^{+\frac{1}{2}T}\sum_n \sum_{n'} \sum_q \sum_{q'} \int\!\!\int_{-\infty}^{+\infty} s_n(v)s_{n'}^*(v')\,U_{n,q}(v)\,U_{n',q'}^*(v')e^{-2\pi i(v\tau_n - v'\tau_{n'})} \times$$
$$\times e^{2\pi i(v-v')t}\,dv\,dv'\,dt, \tag{57}$$

the integrand of the integration with respect to t being the squared modulus of (56).

The integration with respect to t gives

$$\frac{1}{T}\int_{-\frac{1}{2}T}^{+\frac{1}{2}T} e^{2\pi i(v-v')t}\,dt = \frac{\sin(\pi\mu T)}{\pi\mu T},$$

where $\mu = v-v'$. Putting $v' = v-\mu$, (57) now becomes

$$I' = \sum_n \sum_{n'} \sum_q \sum_{q'} \int\!\!\int_{-\infty}^{+\infty} s_n(v)s_{n'}^*(v-\mu)\,U_{n,q}(v)\,U_{n',q'}^*(v-\mu)e^{-2\pi i[v(\tau_n-\tau_{n'})+\mu\tau_{n'}]}\frac{\sin(\pi\mu T)}{\pi\mu T}\,dv\,d\mu. \tag{58}$$

T, the integration time of the detector, will not be less than, say, 10^{-7} sec; and consequently the effective range of μ in (58) will be of the order of 10^7 cps. For the visible spectrum v lies in the range $(6\pm 1.5)\times 10^{14}$ cps; and for $v = 6\times 10^{14}$ cps, a change in frequency $\mu = 10^7$ cps corresponds to a change in wavelength $\delta\lambda = -c\mu/v^2 = 0.001$Å. The factors in (58) will not change appreciably for such small wavelength changes, and so (58) may be written

$$I' = \sum_n \sum_{n'} \sum_q \sum_{q'} \int_{-\infty}^{+\infty} s_n(v) s_{n'}^*(v) U_{n,q}(v) U_{n',q'}^*(v) e^{-2\pi i v(\tau_n - \tau_{n'})} \int_{-\infty}^{+\infty} \frac{\sin(\pi\mu T)}{\pi\mu T} d\mu dv. \quad (59)$$

Making the approximation $s_n^*(v-\mu) = s_n^*(v)$ assumes, of course, that the light comes from a thermal source, which will have a spectral bandwidth orders of magnitude greater than 10^7 cps and not from a laser where the spectral bandwidth could be much smaller than 10^7 cps.

Integrating with respect to μ, (59) becomes

$$I' = \int_{-\infty}^{+\infty} \sum_n \sum_{n'} \sum_q \sum_{q'} \frac{1}{T} s_n(v) s_{n'}^*(v) U_{n,q}(v) U_{n',q'}^*(v) e^{-2\pi i v(\tau_n - \tau_{n'})} dv, \quad (60)$$

in which n and n' refer to any two pulses leaving the source, each of which may produce a group of pulses which travel by different paths q and q' to the point P. If the terms in (60) are written as cosines, the randomness of τ_n and $\tau_{n'}$, results in the terms $n' \neq n$ summing to zero, the remainder giving

$$I' = \int_{-\infty}^{+\infty} \sum_n \frac{1}{T} |s_n(v)|^2 \sum_q \sum_{q'} U_{n,q}(v) U_{n,q'}^*(v) dv.$$

The inner sum is simply the squared modulus of $\sum_q U_{n,q}(v)$, and so

$$I' = \int_0^\infty \sum_n \left\{ \frac{2}{T} |s_n(v)|^2 | \sum_q U_{n,q}(v)|^2 \right\} dv, \quad (61)$$

the limits being changed since $|s_n(-v)| = |s_n(v)|$, $S_n(t)$ being real.

In (61), n refers to any pulse reaching P. Of these pulses a number s will come from any given element S of the source. For each such sub-group of pulses $U_{n,q}(v)$ will have the same value. Let this be denoted by $U_{s,q}(v)$. Eq. (61) may then be written

$$I' = \int_0^\infty \sum_S \left\{ \frac{1}{T} \sum_s 2|s_s(v)|^2 | \sum_q U_{s,q}(v)|^2 \right\} dv, \quad (62)$$

where Σ_s denotes summation over pulses from a given element S of the source, and Σ_S denotes summation over the different elements of the source. Now $|2s_s(v)|$ is the amplitude, and $2|s_s(v)|^2$ the square of the root mean square amplitude of the given pulse. Thus $\Sigma_s 2|s_s(v)|^2$ is the flow of energy in the frequency v from the source element S, and

$$E_s(v) = \frac{1}{T} \sum_s 2|s_s(v)|^2$$

is the mean power from S for the frequency v. This is because the number of terms included in Σ_s will be proportional to the integration time T. Using this in (62) gives

$$I' = \int_0^\infty \sum_S \{E_s(v)|\sum_q U_{s,q}(v)|^2\} \, dv, \tag{63}$$

which is the formula sought.

In (63), $|\Sigma_q U_{s,q}(v)|^2$ is the intensity which is produced at P by a pure monochromatic wave of frequency v originating in the source with unit amplitude and zero phase. Thus, if the element S of the source is assumed to emit monochromatic waves of zero phase but root-mean-square amplitude $\sqrt{E_s(v)}$, (63) may be written

$$I'(v) = \sum_S |\sum_q U_{s,q}(v)|^2, \tag{64}$$

$$I' = \int_0^\infty I'(v) \, dv. \tag{65}$$

Eq. (64) expresses the intensity at P of light of frequency v as the superposition of the intensities produced by monochromatic waves of amplitude $\sqrt{E_s(v)}$ emitted incoherently by the different elements of the source: in (65) these intensities are integrated over the different frequencies in the light emitted by the source.

The above results may be summarized in the following rules:

i) Light beams of the same frequency coming from the same element of the source are perfectly coherent.

ii) Light beams of the same frequency coming from different elements of the source may be considered to be completely incoherent.

iii) Light beams of different frequency are incoherent.

In applications it has only to be remembered that the above rules apply only to the time-averaged intensities recorded by practical detectors when used to detect light from thermal sources. They thus apply when the integrating time of the detector is much greater than the coherence time of the source, and when the different elements of the source are mutually incoherent.

8. The theory of partial coherence

If monochromatic light from an extended thermal source S reaches two points P_1 and P_2, directly or by way of some optical system, each element of the source will produce light disturbances at the two points which are coherent. But this light will be incoherent with light reaching P_1 and P_2 from other elements of the source. The resultant disturbances at P_1 and P_2 will thus show some partial correlation of phase, and are said to be partially coherent. A degree of coherence may be defined which is a measure of the degree to which the phases at P_1 and P_2 are correlated.

The situation is illustrated schematically in fig. 7, where light from P_1 and P_2 proceeds further to a point P, again either directly or by way of some optical system. If the resultant disturbances at P_1 and P_2 are coherent, the amplitudes produced at the point P by light from P_1 and P_2 are added and squared to give the intensity,

I_p, at P. When P_1 and P_2 are incoherent the separate intensities are added to give I_p. These, it will be shown, are special cases of a general formula.

The complex amplitudes of light of given frequency produced at P_1 and P_2 by an element of the source, dS, will be proportional to $\sqrt{dS}$. Let them be $\sqrt{dS}\,U_1$ and $\sqrt{dS}\,U_2$ respectively, and let f_1, f_2 be the complex amplitudes at P resulting from

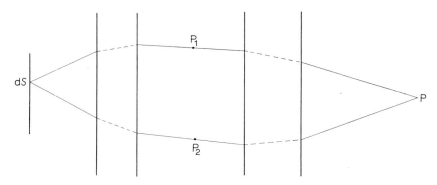

Fig. 7. The spatial coherence between two points.

disturbances of unit amplitude and zero phase at P_1 and P_2. The complex amplitudes at P produced by the source element dS, will then be $(f_1 U_1 + f_2 U_2)\sqrt{dS}$, and this results in an intensity

$$dI_p = |f_1 U_1 + f_2 U_2|^2 \, dS.$$

Since light from different elements of the source is incoherent, the intensities produced by the different elements of the source add, giving

$$I_p = \int\int_S |f_1 U_1 + f_2 U_2|^2 \, dS \tag{66}$$

for the total intensity at P. The integration extends over the whole source S. Expanding the bracket in (66), and noting that

$$I_1 = \int\int_S |U_1|^2 \, dS \qquad I_2 = \int\int_S |U_2|^2 \, dS$$

are the intensities at P_1 and P_2 due to the whole source,

$$I_p = |f_1|^2 I_1 + |f_2|^2 I_2 + 2 \operatorname{Re} \left\{ \int\int_S U_1^* U_2 f_1 f_2 \, dS \right\},$$

Re denoting that the real part is to be taken. This may be written

$$I_p = |f_1|^2 I_1 + |f_2|^2 I_2 + 2\sqrt{I_1 I_2} \operatorname{Re} \{ \Gamma_{21} f_1^* f_2 \}, \tag{67}$$

where

$$\Gamma_{21} = \frac{1}{\sqrt{(I_1 I_2)}} \int\int_S U_1^* U_2 \, dS \tag{68}$$

defines the degree of coherence of the disturbance at P_2 relative to that at P_1. By means of (67) the intensity at P may be found knowing merely the intensities at P_1 and P_2 and the complex degree of coherence Γ_{21}. The quantities f_1 and f_2 specify the optical properties of the paths P_1P and P_2P.

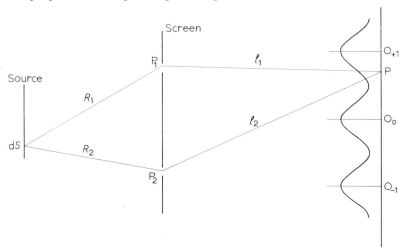

Fig. 8. Young's experiment with finite source size.

The significance of (67) and (68) is most easily understood in terms of Young's interference experiment. The source, fig. (8), subtends only a small angle at the screen. Thus any element dS of a source of uniform intensity will produce complex amplitudes with

$$U_1 = A e^{i\theta_1} \qquad U_2 = A e^{i\theta_2}$$

and the intensities produced by the whole source are

$$I_1 = I_2 = A^2 \iint_S dS = A^2 S,$$

where S is the area of the source. θ_1 and θ_2 are the phases at P_1 and P_2, equal to $-kR_1$ and $-kR_2$, where R_1 and R_2 are the distances of P_1 and P_2 from dS. Using the above values in (68) gives

$$\Gamma_{21} = \frac{1}{S} \iint_S e^{i(\theta_2 - \theta_1)} dS.$$

If the source is very small, or if P_1 and P_2 are very close together, $\theta_2 - \theta_1$ may be taken to be constant and

$$\Gamma_{21} = e^{i(\theta_2 - \theta_1)}. \tag{69}$$

On the other hand for a very large source, or for P_1 and P_2 very far apart, $\theta_2 - \theta_1 = k(R_1 - R_2)$ will be of large variation and

$$\Gamma_{21} = 0. \tag{70}$$

Thus Γ_{21} is determined by the degree to which the phase difference between P_2 and P_1 varies for light from different points of the source. When this variation is $\ll 2\pi$, $|\Gamma_{21}| = 1$ as in (69) and P_2 and P_1 are coherent with a phase difference $\arg \Gamma_{21}$. When the variation is $\gg 2\pi$, $|\Gamma_{21}| = 0$ as in (70) and P_2 and P_1 are incoherent.

In the general case let

$$\Gamma_{21} = V_{21}e^{i\beta_{21}} \tag{71}$$

and write in (67)

$$f_1 = \alpha_1 e^{-ikl_1}, \qquad f_2 = \alpha_2 e^{-ikl_2}, \tag{72}$$

where α_1 and α_2 are the real amplitudes produced at P by unit amplitudes at P_1 and P_2. Using (71) and (72) in (67) gives

$$I_p = I_1' + I_2' + 2V_{21}\sqrt{I_1'I_2'} \cos\left[\frac{2\pi}{\lambda}(l_1 - l_2) + \beta_{21}\right], \tag{73}$$

where $I_1' = \alpha_1^2 I_1$ and $I_2' = \alpha_2^2 I_2$ are the separate intensities produced at P. When $V_{21} = |\Gamma_{21}| = 0$, these intensities simply add. There is no interference, and P_2 and P_1 are incoherent. If $V_{21} = |\Gamma_{21}| = 1$, the amplitudes at P add taking account of the added phase difference β_{21}. In this case P_2 and P_1 are perfectly coherent, with P_2 having a phase β_{21} in advance of P_1. When $1 > V_{21} > 0$, the light is partially coherent, the partial correlation of phase being centred around the phase difference β_{21}. A simple application of Schwarz' inequality to (68) shows that $|\Gamma_{21}| \leq 1$, so that the point Γ_{21} always lies inside or on the unit circle on the Argand diagram.

As P, in fig. 8, is moved across the fringe plane $(l_1 - l_2)$ varies producing maxima and minima of intensity given by

$$I_{\substack{\max \\ \min}} = I_1' + I_2' \pm 2V_{21}\sqrt{I_1'I_2'}.$$

The contrast, or visibility of the fringes is defined by

$$V = \frac{I_{\max} - I_{\min}}{I_{\max} + I_{\min}},$$

so that

$$V = V_{21}\frac{2\sqrt{I_1'I_2'}}{I_1' + I_2'}.$$

For perfectly coherent light, $V_{21} = 1$, and the visibility is then a maximum given by

$$V_{\max} = \frac{2\sqrt{I_1'I_2'}}{I_1' + I_2'}.$$

Thus $V_{21} = |\Gamma_{21}|$ determines the degree to which interference can be produced when the light from P_2 is superposed on that from P_1. The maxima in the fringes occur at points O_m, where

$$\frac{2\pi}{\lambda}(l_1 - l_2) + \beta_{21} = 2\pi m,$$

with $m = 0, \pm 1, \pm 2, \ldots$; if $\beta_{21} \neq 0$, the fringes will be laterally shifted.

The quantity Γ_{21} in (68) specifies the coherence between the disturbances of a given frequency at any two points in the total light beam. It thus describes the spatial coherence in the beam. At any given point there will be a given coherence time for the total light disturbance, depending on the width of the energy spectrum. It is often useful to use the term temporal coherence in this latter case.

The influence of the finite source size on Young's fringes may equally well be treated by noting that each element, S, of the source produces a fringe pattern whose zero-order fringe O_0 will be at the point where the optical paths SP_1O_0 and SP_2O_0 are equal. These different fringe patterns are displaced relative to each other, and their summed intensity gives the same result as that obtained using the spatial coherence between P_2 and P_1. The advantage of using the theory of partial coherence is that the treatment is usually much simpler, and can be applied even where the explicit calculation of the intensity distributions due to the different source elements is too difficult to be of practical use.

The formula (73) applies only to light of a given frequency v, or wave-number $u = 1/\lambda$. If the source has a broad spectral range, the total intensity at any point has to be found by integrating the monochromatic intensity at the point over the range of frequency, or wave-number, in question. In this connection it may be remarked that the theory of coherence may be made to rest on the fact that the time averaged intensity produced by causing a signal $V_1(t)$ to interfere with a second, and 'delayed', signal $V_2(t+\tau)$ may be written

$$I = \langle |V_1(t) + V_2(t+\tau)|^2 \rangle,$$

where $\langle \rangle$ denotes the time average. This expression, when expanded gives

$$I = \langle |V_1(t)|^2 \rangle + \langle |V_2(t)|^2 \rangle + 2 \operatorname{Re} \langle V_1^*(t) V_2(t+\tau) \rangle,$$

the first two terms representing the total intensities of the separate signals, and the mean value in the third term being usually designated the 'mutual intensity' of the two signals. The mutual intensity is the so-called cross-correlation between the two signals. It clearly depends on both the spatial and temporal coherence of the two signals. When based on the methods used for treating stationary random processes, the averaging time T is allowed to tend to infinity. The treatment used here makes the role of the short integrating time more explicit at each point in the argument, and is simpler to assimilate to experimental practice.

9. The spatial coherence over an illuminated plane: the Van Cittert-Zernike theorem

In fig. 9a, S is a source, and P_1 and P_2 are two points in a plane illuminated by S. R_1 and R_2 are the distances of P_1 and P_2 from an element dS_0 of the source at (X, Y), whose monochromatic intensity for the wavelength in question is $\gamma_0(X, Y)$. The complex amplitudes produced by dS_0 at P_1 and P_2 are

$$U_1 = \frac{\sqrt{\gamma_0(X, Y)}}{R_1} e^{-ikR_1} \qquad U_2 = \frac{\sqrt{\gamma_0(X, Y)}}{R_2} e^{-ikR_2}$$

which, used in (68) give

$$\Gamma_{21} = \frac{1}{\sqrt{I_1 I_2}} \iint_S \frac{\gamma_0(X, Y)}{R_1 R_2} e^{ik(R_1 - R_2)} dS_0 \qquad (74)$$

for the degree of coherence between the vibrations at P_2 and P_1. I_2 and I_1 are the total intensities at these points. The form of (74) is identical with the formula for the

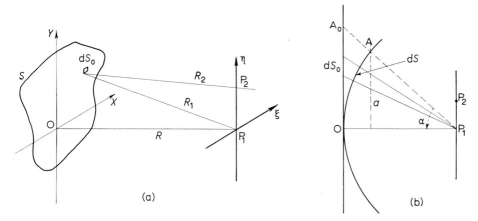

Fig. 9. Spatial coherence produced by a source.

complex amplitude in the diffraction pattern at P_2 formed by an aperture having an amplitude distribution equal to $\gamma_0(X, Y)$, that is to the distribution of intensity over the source S. This result constitutes the Van Cittert–Zernike theorem.

In the paraxial approximation only the first powers in (X, Y) and (ξ, η) are retained, where (ξ, η) are the coordinates of P_2 relative to P_1. To this order of accuracy with $OP_1 = R$,

$$\frac{1}{R_1 R_2} \approx \frac{1}{R^2}$$

$$R_1 - R_2 = \frac{X\xi + Y\eta}{R},$$

$$I_1 = I_2 = \frac{1}{R^2} \iint_S \gamma_0(X, Y) dS_0.$$

Then, writing

$$\gamma(X, Y) = \frac{\gamma_0(X, Y)}{\iint_S \gamma_0(X, Y) dS_0}$$

for the normalized intensity distribution over the source, (74) gives

$$\Gamma(\xi, \eta) = \int\int_S \gamma(X, Y) \exp\left(2\pi i \frac{X\xi + Y\eta}{R}\right) dX dY, \tag{75}$$

where $\Gamma(\xi, \eta) = \Gamma_{21}$. According to (75) the degree of coherence over the illuminated plane is determined by the Fourier transform of the distribution of intensity in the source.

The above paraxial approximation is often inadequate. Suppose, for example, that S is very small, so that $\gamma(X, Y)$ has to be represented by a delta function, $\delta(X, Y)$. Eq. (74) then gives

$$\Gamma(\xi, \eta) = \int\int_S \delta(X, Y) \exp\left(2\pi i \frac{X\xi + Y\eta}{R}\right) dX dY = 1$$

showing, correctly, that P_2 and P_1 are perfectly coherent. However, with $\Gamma'_{21} = 1$, the phase difference between P_2 and P_1 is $\beta_{21} = 0$, whereas in practice they will be illuminated by a spherical wave emitted from O, and giving a phase difference $-k(\xi^2 + \eta^2)/2R$ between P_2 and P_1, which is, of course, neglected in the paraxial approximation. A more detailed treatment shows that the degree of coherence between the points P_2 and P_1 may be written

$$\Gamma(u, v) = e^{-i\varepsilon} \int\int_S \gamma(x, y) e^{2\pi i(ux + vy)} dx y, \tag{76}$$

where (x, y) and (u, v) are suitably normalized forms of the coordinates (X, Y) and (ξ, η), and

$$\varepsilon = k\left(\frac{\xi^2 + \eta^2}{2R}\right).$$

With the definitions following below, (76) holds outside the paraxial region.

In fig. 9b, the reference sphere OA has its centre at P_1 and is of radius R. A_0 is a typical point on the periphery of the source. A_0 projects into the point A on the reference sphere. Let a be the distance of A from OP_1, then $\sin \alpha = a/R$, where α is the angle shown. The actual source, assumed to obey Lambert's law, is now considered to be projected onto the reference sphere, so that an element of the source dS_0 gives rise to dS, and the distribution of intensity in the projected source is given by

$$\gamma(X, Y) dS = \gamma_0(X_0, Y_0) dS_0.$$

It may then be shown that the degree of coherence given by a source $\gamma(X, Y)$ lying on the reference sphere is the same as that given by the actual source. For the new source the coordinates of dS are (X, Y), and the normalized forms of these are

$$x = X/a, \qquad y = Y/a. \tag{77}$$

If now the notation $\gamma_0(x, y)$ is used for the intensity distribution $\gamma(X, Y)$, over the reference sphere the normalized source distribution over the reference sphere is defined by

$$\gamma(x, y) = \frac{\gamma_0(x, y)}{\iint_S \gamma_0(x, y)\,dx\,dy}.$$ (78)

Corresponding to (77), the normalized forms of (ξ, η), the coordinates of P_2, are

$$u = \frac{n \sin \alpha}{\lambda}\,\xi, \qquad v = \frac{n \sin \alpha}{\lambda}\,\eta,$$ (79)

where λ is the vacuum wavelength and n the refractive index of the medium.

The formula (76) is valid outside the paraxial region. It has a form in which $\Gamma(u, v)$ is exactly the Fourier transform of $\gamma(x, y)$ apart from the phase factor $e^{-i\varepsilon}$. If P_2 lies on a sphere of centre O, and not in the plane through P_1, the quantity ε is zero. The use of the projection of the source on the reference sphere and the associated coordinates also fortunately accords perfectly with the treatment of the diffraction theory of image formation. In most practical cases, of course, the angular substance of the source at P_1 is small enough for the distribution of intensity over the reference sphere to be regarded as the same as that over the actual source.

10. Calculation of the spatial coherence: applications

Suppose the source to be circular, and of angular radius α as seen from P_1. For uniform intensity, $\gamma_0(x, y) = 1$ and (78) then gives

$$\gamma(x, y) = 1/\pi,$$

which in (76) yields

$$\Gamma(u, v) = \frac{e^{-i\varepsilon}}{\pi} \iint_{x^2+y^2 \le 1} e^{2\pi i(ux+vy)}\,dx\,dy.$$

Transforming (u, v) and (x, y) to polar coordinates (p, ψ) and (r, ϕ), this integrates to give

$$\Gamma(p) = e^{-i\varepsilon} \frac{2J_1(2\pi p)}{2\pi p}.$$ (80)

If $2\pi(\xi^2+\eta^2)2R \ll \lambda$, the phase factor may be ignored, and the remaining terms are the same as the complex amplitude in the Airy disc pattern associated with an aperture of the same configuration as the source.

The degree of coherence is first zero when $2\pi p = 3.83$, giving $p = 0.61$ or

$$d = 0.61\lambda/n \sin \alpha,$$ (81)

where $d = \sqrt{\xi^2+\eta^2}$ is the actual separation P_1P_2. Good coherence will be obtained when $2\pi p \le 1$, for which $2J_1(2\pi p)/2\pi p \ge 0.88$. Thus

$$d \le \frac{0.16\lambda}{n \sin \alpha}, \qquad \sin \alpha \le \frac{0.16\lambda}{nd},$$ (82)

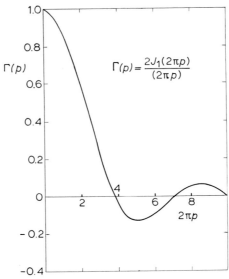

Fig. 10. $\Gamma(p)$ for a circular source.

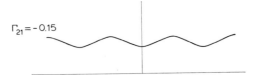

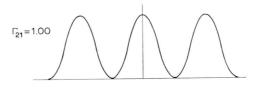

Fig. 11. Form of fringes for different degrees of coherence.

give the conditions on the separation $d = P_1 P_2$, or on the source size α, for good coherence. The form of $\Gamma(p)$, omitting the factor $e^{-i\epsilon}$, is shown in fig. 10. For a fixed separation $P_1 P_2$, as in Young's experiment, the visibility of the fringes decreases with increasing source size. It is zero, giving uniform intensity when $2\pi p = 3.83$, and for $2\pi p > 3.83$ the coherence becomes negative. This implies that $\beta_{21} = \pm\pi$, and the fringes appear displaced so that the positions of the maxima and minima are interchanged. Alternatively this may be regarded as a condition of negative visibility, or revers alof contrast. It is easy to demonstrate this behaviour experimentally. The intensity distributions in the fringes for different values of Γ_{21} are shown in fig. 11.

If the mirrors in the Michelson stellar interferometer define the points P_1 and P_2, and the star to be observed is the circular source, the formula (80) gives the visibility of the fringes seen. These are of zero contrast and thus disappear at the zeroes of $J_1(2\pi p)$.

If the source is a rectangular slit of length k times the width, the angle α may be taken to be that subtended at P_1 by half the width of the source. Then, with $\gamma_0(x, y) = 1$, $\gamma(x, y) = 1/4k$; and, omitting the phase factor in (80),

$$\Gamma(u, v) = \frac{1}{4k} \int_{-1}^{+1} e^{2\pi i u x} \, dx \int_{-k}^{+k} e^{2\pi i v y} \, dy,$$

giving

$$\Gamma(u, v) = \frac{\sin(2\pi u)}{2\pi u} \frac{\sin(2\pi k v)}{2\pi k v}, \tag{83}$$

which is again the form of amplitude distribution in the corresponding Fraunhofer diffraction pattern. When $k \gg 1$, the separation of P_1 and P_2 parallel to the slit-length must be very much smaller than their separation at right angles to the slit-length. Suppose, for example, that $P_1 P_2 = d$, and that $P_1 P_2$ is inclined at an angle θ to the u-axis. Then

$$u = \frac{n \sin \alpha}{\lambda} d \cos \theta, \qquad v = \frac{n \sin \alpha}{\lambda} d \sin \theta$$

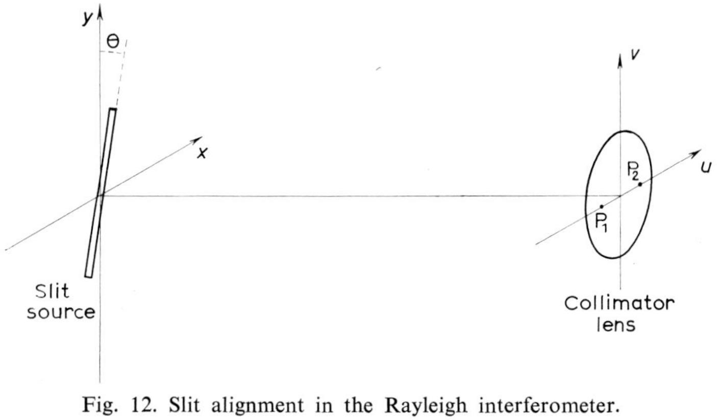

Fig. 12. Slit alignment in the Rayleigh interferometer.

and, if the decrease in coherence is not to be attributed more to the second of the two factors in (83), $kv \leqq u$ and so $\tan \theta \leqq 1/k$. In the Rayleigh gas interferometer light passing through the points P_1 and P_2 shown in fig. 12 interferes after passing through an evacuated and a gas-filled tube. If k is the length/width ratio of the slit source, and this is misaligned by an angle θ as shown, the tolerance on θ is given by $\tan \theta \leqq 1/k$. The tolerance on the width of the source is then given by

$$\frac{\sin (2\pi u)}{2\pi u} \leqq 0.90$$

giving, with $u = (nd/\lambda) \sin \alpha,$

$$\sin \alpha \leqq 0.12 \, \lambda/d. \tag{84}$$

The product of the two factors in (79) will then give $\Gamma(u, v) \geqq 0.80$.

11. Spatial coherence in 2-beam interferometers: fringe localization; tolerances

Two cases have to be distinguished, according to whether Fizeau or Haidinger fringes are being observed. In the former case interference takes place between two wavefronts, and the separate disturbances may be found assuming propagation of the waves according to geometrical optics. Haidinger fringes are observed when two superposed images of the source are formed in the fringe plane, and interference then takes place between two overlapping diffraction images of each point in the source. It is found convenient to use a different procedure in the two cases. For Fizeau fringes tolerances on the source size are obtained. Haidinger fringes are seen with an extended source, and tolerances on alignment of the interferometer are considered.

Fig. 13 shows schematically the general arrangement of a 2-beam interferometer, in which light from a small source proceeds by way of the two arms (1) and (2) to

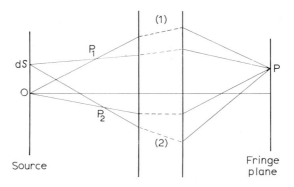

Fig. 13. Spatial coherence in a two beam interferometer.

interfere in the plane where fringes are to be observed. To study the visibility of Fizeau fringes in the neighbourhood of a point P, the conjugate object points P_1 and P_2 in the source space are found, such that P is the image of P_1 formed by light traversing arm (1), and P_2 is similarly the object point which is imaged at P along arm (2). In a practical case P_1 and P_2 may well be virtual object points, but the analysis given below holds in all cases. If P_1 and P_2 are formed at or near the source itself, Haidinger fringes are formed and the treatment given later has to be used.

Since P is the image of P_1, and P_2, the optical path lengths

$$[P_1 \ldots P]_1 = p_1 \qquad [P_2 \ldots P]_2 = p_2 \tag{85}$$

are constant for all rays from the small source*. Let α_1, α_2 be the amplitude attenuations between P_1, P_2 and P, and put

$$f_1 = \alpha_1 e^{-ikp_1} \qquad f_2 = \alpha_2 e^{-ikp_2}.$$

If now an element dS of the source produces complex amplitudes U_1 and U_2 at P_1 and P_2, the disturbances at P produced by dS will be

$$U_1' = f_1 U_1 = \alpha_1 e^{-ikp_1} U_1, \qquad U_2' = f_2 U_2 = \alpha_2 e^{-ikp_2} U_2,$$

giving, for the two light disturbances which interfere at P, a degree of coherence

$$\Gamma_{21}' = \frac{1}{\sqrt{(I_1' I_2')}} \int \int_S \alpha_1 \alpha_2 e^{ik(p_1 - p_2)} U_1^* U_2 \, dS,$$

or, since $I_1' = \alpha_1^2 I_1$ and $I_2' = \alpha_2^2 I_2$,

$$\Gamma_{21}' = e^{ik(p_1 - p_2)} \Gamma_{21}, \tag{86}$$

where Γ_{21} is the degree of coherence between the points P_1 and P_2 in the source space.

In deriving (86) it has been assumed that α_1 and α_2 are constant, which in practice merely requires that light from all points of the source which reaches P_1 and P_2 also proceeds to P. If this is not so, the integration over S in obtaining Γ_{21} must be limited to those parts of S which can be 'seen' from P along one or other of the two arms of the interferometer. Subject to this condition the visibility of the fringes at P is given by the modulus of the coherence Γ_{21} between P_1 and P_2. If these points coincide, there will be perfect contrast, but the contrast will be smaller the more widely separated P_1 and P_2 are in relation to the size of the source. For an ideal point source $\Gamma_{21} = 1$ for all positions of P_1 and P_2, giving perfect contrast for all fringe planes. For larger source sizes the coherence will be very small when P_1 and P_2 are not almost coincident. Good contrast is then only obtained in the fringe planes for which P_1 and P_2 are very close together. The fringes are then said to be localized. In general Fizeau fringes are more sharply localized the larger the source.

If R_1 and R_2 are the distances of P_1 and P_2 from dS, the general formula (74) gives

$$\Gamma_{21} = \frac{1}{\sqrt{(I_1 I_2)}} \int \int_S \gamma_0(X, Y) \frac{e^{ik(R_1 - R_2)}}{R_1 R_2} \, dS, \tag{87}$$

* Stigmatic imaging is assumed, since for a small source only low-aperture pencils will be involved.

where $\gamma_0(X, Y)$ is the source distribution. Let $\bar{R}_1 = OP_1$ and $\bar{R}_2 = OP_2$ be the distances of P_1 and P_2 from the mid-point O of the source, then

$$\frac{1}{R_1} \approx \frac{1}{\bar{R}_1} \qquad I_1 = \iint_S \frac{\gamma_0(X, Y)}{R_1^2} \, dS \approx \frac{1}{\bar{R}_1^2} \iint_S \gamma_0(X, Y) dS,$$

so that

$$\frac{1}{\sqrt{(I_1 I_2)}} \frac{1}{\bar{R}_1 \bar{R}_2} = \left\{ \iint_S \gamma_0(X, Y) dS \right\}^{-1},$$

and writing

$$\gamma(X, Y) = \frac{\gamma_0(X, Y)}{\iint_S \gamma_0(X, Y) dS} \tag{88}$$

for the normalized source distribution, (87) becomes

$$\Gamma_{21} = \iint_S \gamma(X, Y) e^{ik(R_1 - R_2)} \, dS. \tag{89}$$

If, in addition to $\bar{R}_1$, $\bar{R}_2$, the direction cosines (α_1, β_1) and (α_2, β_2) of OP_1 and OP_2 are known, the exponent in (89) may be written

$$k(R_1 - R_2) = k(\bar{R}_1 - \bar{R}_2) + \chi, \tag{90}$$

where, neglecting squares of (α, β) and of (X, Y) the coordinates of dS,

$$\chi = \tfrac{1}{2}k \left(\frac{1}{\bar{R}_1} - \frac{1}{\bar{R}_2} \right) (X^2 + Y^2) + k\{(\alpha_2 - \alpha_1)X + (\beta_2 - \beta_1)Y\}; \tag{91}$$

substituting (90) in (89), (86) becomes

$$\Gamma'_{21} = e^{ik\{(\bar{R}_1 + p_1) - (\bar{R}_2 + p_2)\}} \iint_S \gamma(X, Y) e^{i\chi} dS, \tag{92}$$

in which $(\bar{R}_1 + p_1) - (\bar{R}_2 + p_2)$ is now simply the path difference between the two rays from O which interfere at P.

Consider a uniform source, with $\gamma_0(X, Y) = 1$. The normalized source function (88) is then $\gamma(X, Y) = 1/S$, and the integral in (92) may be written

$$e^{i\bar{\chi}} \frac{1}{S} \iint_S e^{i(\chi - \bar{\chi})} dS, \tag{93}$$

where

$$\bar{\chi} = \frac{1}{S} \iint_S \chi \, dS$$

is the mean value of χ. When the range of variation of $(\chi - \bar{\chi})$ is small, the integrand of (93) may be expanded and powers of $(\chi - \bar{\chi})$ may be higher than the square neglected. Eq. (93) is then easily evaluated, and gives in (92)

$$\Gamma'_{21} = e^{ik\{(\bar{R}_1+p_1)-(\bar{R}_2+p_2)\}} e^{i\bar{\chi}}(1-\tfrac{1}{2}\Omega), \tag{94}$$

where

$$\Omega = \frac{1}{S}\int\int_S \chi^2 \, dS - \left\{\frac{1}{S}\int\int_S \chi \, dS\right\}^2 \tag{95}$$

is the variance of the phase-difference χ. The result (94) holds with good approximation when $V'_{21} = |\Gamma'_{21}| > 0.7$. If the criterion

$$V'_{21} = 1 - \tfrac{1}{2}\Omega \geq 0.80 \tag{96}$$

is imposed, the tolerance on the source size is given by

$$\Omega \leq 0.40. \tag{97}$$

For a circular source (X, Y) are written in polar coordinates (r, ϕ), and (91) then gives, with $k = 2\pi/\lambda$

$$\chi = \frac{2\pi}{\lambda}\{Ar^2 + Br\cos(\phi - \varepsilon)\}, \tag{98}$$

where

$$A = \frac{1}{2}\left(\frac{1}{\bar{R}_1} - \frac{1}{\bar{R}_2}\right), \qquad B = \sqrt{\{(\alpha_2 - \alpha_1)^2 + (\beta_2 - \beta_1)^2\}}, \tag{99}$$

and $\tan \varepsilon = (\beta_2 - \beta_1)/(\alpha_2 - \alpha_1)$. If the source is of radius σ, $S = \pi\sigma^2$ and (95) takes the form

$$\Omega = \frac{1}{\pi\sigma^2}\int_0^\sigma\int_0^{2\pi} \chi^2 r \, dr \, d\phi - \left\{\frac{1}{\pi\sigma^2}\int_0^\sigma\int_0^{2\pi} \chi r \, dr \, d\phi\right\}^2.$$

Using χ from (98), this gives for (95) and (97) the forms

$$\Omega = (\pi/\lambda)^2\{\tfrac{1}{3}A^2\sigma^4 + B^2\sigma^2\} \leq 0.4. \tag{100}$$

From the instrumental geometry A and B may be found for any particular case, and (100) then gives the maximum size of source giving a contrast ≥ 0.80 in the fringes.

Fig. 14 shows the Fizeau interferoscope, in which a small source S in the focal plane of a lens C illuminates an air wedge between two surfaces T_1 and T_2. The reflected light is directed by a glass plate G to the observer's eye, which is focused on the image of a point such as Q, as seen through C. To find the points P_1, P_2, the images Q'_1, Q'_2 of Q in the reflecting surfaces T_1, T_2 are found, and then P_1, P_2 are the object points in the source space of C conjugate to Q'_1, Q'_2. These latter points are at distances $(D-d)$ and $(D-d-2t)$ respectively from the front focus of C, where D is the height of Γ_1 above this focus. Applying Newton's conjugate relation for the lens C, whose focal length is F, leads to the values

$$\bar{R}_1 = \frac{F^2}{D-d}, \qquad \bar{R}_2 = \frac{F^2}{D-d-2t},$$

where, in the latter, the oblique distance OP_2 has been replaced by its projection on the axis. These formulae used in (99) give

$$A = t/F^2, \tag{101}$$

where t is the axial separation of T_1 and T_2.

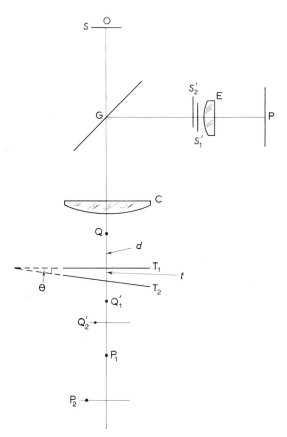

Fig. 14. Fizeau interferoscope: fringe visibility.

The point P_1 lies on the axis, so that $\alpha_1 = \beta_1 = 0$. The distance of Q_2' from the axis is $2(d+t)\theta$, and using the magnification between O_2' and P_2, the angle between OP_2 and the axis is found to be $2(d+t)\theta/F$. Using this for the value of α_2, and putting $\beta_2 = 0$, (99) gives

$$B = \frac{2(d+t)\theta}{F}. \tag{102}$$

Substituting this value and (101) in (100),

$$\Omega = \left(\frac{\pi}{\lambda}\right)^2 \left\{ \frac{t}{3} \left(\frac{\sigma}{F}\right)^4 + 4\theta^2(d+t)^2 \left(\frac{\sigma}{F}\right)^2 \right\} \leq 0.40, \tag{103}$$

and Ω has its smallest value when $d = -t$. The fringes then have maximum contrast, and are thus localized at the surface T_2. When the observer is focused on this plane, the tolerance criterion (103) leads to

$$\sigma/F \leq \sqrt{0.35\lambda/t} \tag{104}$$

for the angular radius that the source subtends at the lens C.

The condition $d = -t$ can only be satisfied exactly at one point of surface T_2. If this latter is, for example, a sphere, there will be non-zero values for $(d+t)$ and θ at some points of T. It is then a simple matter to find the maximum value of $\theta(d+t)$, and to include the second term of (103) in the tolerance criterion.

In fig. 14 two images of the source, S_1' and S_2', are formed at E. When $\theta \neq 0$ these images are relatively displaced as shown. Normally the permissible values of the source size and of θ are so small that both images lie wholly inside the observer's pupil. If this were not so, the integration over S would have to be limited to the region of the source S corresponding to those parts of either S_1' or S_2' which do lie within the pupil at E. It is for this reason that fringes of satisfactory contrast may be seen even with a large source when t and θ are small, the observer's pupil limiting the area of the source from which light reflected at a given point on the air wedge may enter the eye, so that the fringes seen are those formed by only a restricted region of the source.

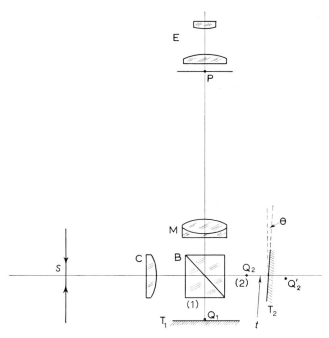

Fig. 15. Interference microscope: effect of source size.

The tolerance formula (103) may be applied to a variety of other practically important 2-beam interferometers, provided suitable meanings are given to t, d and θ.

Fig. 15 shows a simple form of interference microscope. P is a point in the focal plane of the eyepiece E, the instrument being focused on a test surface T_1. Light from a source S, in the focal plane of a lens C, of focal length F, falls on T_1 and on a reference optical flat T_2, the reflected beams forming an interference pattern in the image plane P. In the figure, Q_1 and Q_2 are conjugate to P. Since Q_1 lies on T_1, d is zero. The quantities t and θ are those shown in the diagram. In this case the tolerance, for a given source size, gives the permissible value of t, and thus indicates the precision needed in the axial setting of the reference mirror T_2.

Fig. 16a shows the scheme of the Michelson interferometer. Used with a small source S, the eye is placed at the source image S', and is focused on the points Q_1, Q_2. The quantities d and $d+t$ are shown in the diagram, and F is the focal length of the collimator C. In the Twyman–Green lens testing interferometer, the mirror T_2 is replaced by the lens under test L and a spherical mirror M, as shown in fig. 16b. Rays incident on L are focused at G, and are reflected at normal incidence by M. This combination of L and M is equivalent, so far as Gaussian optics are concerned, to a mirror T_2^*, placed at a distance $\{(F_0-r)^2/r-\varDelta\}$ from the pole of M. Here F_0 is the equivalent focal length of L; $\varDelta$ is the distance HH' from the first to the second principal planes of L; and r is the radius of curvature of M. Alternatively the position of the equivalent plane mirror T_2^* may be specified by its distance $F_0(F_0-r)/r$ from the first principal plane, H, of the lens L. The value of $(d+t)$ is as shown. If the centre of curvature G of the mirror M is moved off-axis, the plane of T_2^* appears to be tilted by the same angle, which then plays the role of the angle θ in (103).

In each of the above cases, the source S will usually be an illuminated small aperture. With a condensor system of aperture much larger than that of the pencils accepted from S by the collimator lens C, the aperture S will behave as an incoherent source. In other cases S may show some degree of coherence, but the formula (103) still ensures 0.80 as the lower limit for the fringe visibility.

In fig. 16a the finite thickness of the beam-splitter B has not been shown, and the customary compensating plate has also been omitted. They have no effect on the spatial coherence, and may thus be ignored, in treating tolerances on source size. They do affect the chromatic coherence, which arises from the finite spectral width of the source.

When arranged to view Haidinger fringes, the Michelson interferometer (fig. 16a) is used with a large source S and fringes are observed in the image plane, S', of the source. In the interferometer space the image of S is at infinity. It is for this reason that the fringes seen are often referred to as 'fringes at infinity'. The points P_1 and P_2 conjugate to any point P of the fringe plane both lie in the source plane S, and a different procedure from that used above is adopted. Each point of the source gives rise to two diffraction patterns at S', which overlap and interfere, provided θ is small. Thus the axial point, O, of the source is imaged geometrically at points O_1', O_2' as shown in the diagram, where $O_1' O_2' = F'\theta$, F' being the focal length of the lens D. The diffraction image centred on O_1' is formed by the wave reflected from T_1, and that

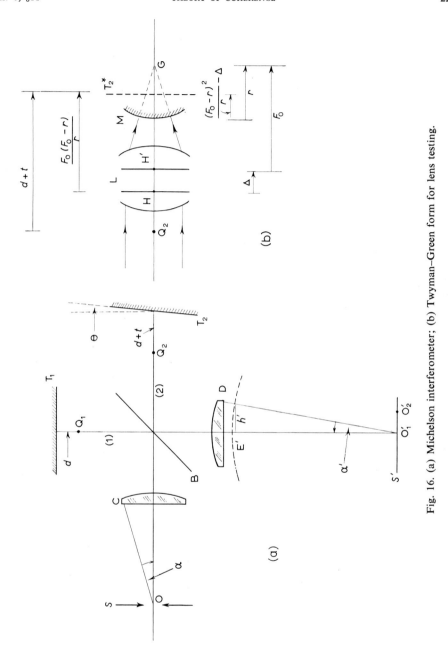

Fig. 16. (a) Michelson interferometer; (b) Twyman–Green form for lens testing.

centred on O_2' is formed by the wave reflected from T_2. The light in each of these two diffraction images is coherent with that in the other, but incoherent with any other light reaching S'. The problem is thus that of interference between two diffraction images, rather than between two wavefronts as in Fizeau fringes.

In the general case the analysis can be somewhat involved, but fortunately the two cases that usually occur in practice may be treated simply. The first is when the source is very small compared with the resolving power of the interferometer forming the two images of the source. This arises in the Michelson stellar interferometer, when the diffraction image of the star is crossed by fringes whose visibility is given by the degree of coherence between the light beams reaching the two outer mirrors. The coherence for a single star of uniform intensity is then given by formula (80) as discussed above.

The second case is when the source is of extent large compared with the resolving power, which arises when Haidinger fringes are observed with an extended source as in the present case. Suppose, for example, that the source S, fig. 16a, subtends an angle $\bar{\alpha}$ at the lens C. The coherence between any pair of points at the aperture of C, distance ρ' apart, is then only appreciable for

$$\rho' \leq 0.61 \lambda / n \sin \bar{\alpha} \tag{105}$$

in accordance with (81) above. Even for $\sin \bar{\alpha} = 0.05$, assuming $n = 1$, $\lambda = 0.0005$ mm, the value of ρ' has to be ≤ 0.03 mm; and, if the aperture of C is of radius, say 20 mm, the ratio of the coherence area to that of the whole aperture is $(0.03/20)^2 = 2.25 \times 10^{-6}$. To good approximation, therefore, the lens aperture may be regarded as incoherently illuminated. In a similar way each of the two beams, namely those reflected from T_1 and T_2 respectively, illuminates the aperture of lens D incoherently. Thus, in either of the two images in the plane S', so far as the coherence between O'_1 and any other point is concerned, this plane may be assumed to be illuminated by an incoherent source lying in the reference sphere at the pupil E' of D and centred on O'_1. For the image formed by light reflected from T_1, for example, the degree of coherence between the points O'_1, O'_2 is, by (80) above,

$$V_{21} \doteq 2J_1(2\pi p)/2\pi p, \tag{106}$$

where $p = (n'\rho'/\lambda) \sin \alpha$, with $\rho' = O'_1 O'_2$.

If O'_2 is the axial point of the image formed by light reflected from T_2, the distance $\rho' = F'\theta$, where θ is the angular misalignment of T_2. In this case the light at the axial point of image 2 interferes with light at the point O'_2 of image 1. Now there is perfect phase-correlation between the disturbances at the axial points of the two images because they are formed by identical beams, apart from a constant phase difference when $t \neq 0$. Thus the phase-correlation between the disturbances interfering at O'_2 is exactly the same as that between the disturbances in image 1 at the points O'_1 and O'_2. The degree of coherence is thus given by (106), with $\rho' = F'\theta$. For $V_{21} \geq 0.88$, the tolerance formula (82) may be used, giving

$$F'\theta \leq 0.16 \lambda / n' \sin \alpha',$$

or, with $F' \sin \alpha' = h'$, the radius of aperture of D,

$$\theta \leq 0.16 \lambda / n' h', \tag{107}$$

where n', the refractive index of the image space, will normally be unity. For $\lambda =$

0.0005 mm and $h' = 20$ mm, (107) gives a tolerance $\theta \leqq 0.40 \times 10^{-5}$, that is $\leqq 0.8$ seconds of arc. The coherence is zero for $F'\theta = 0.61\lambda/n' \sin \alpha'$, which corresponds to a value $\theta = 3.2$ seconds of arc.

It is important to note that the spatial coherence between the disturbances interfering in the image plane S' is determined solely by the angular error θ of the mirror. It is independent of the path difference t in the interferometer. With a practical source, of finite spectral width, the phase-coherence will decrease with increasing t, because the path difference $2t$ will give rise to different phase differences, equal to $(2\pi/\lambda) 2t$, for the different wavelengths present in the source. If these phase differences have a range $\geqq 2\pi$, the maxima produced by any one wavelength will occur at the minima produced by some other wavelength, and the resulting fringes have small or zero contrast. This aspect of coherence is dealt with below under the heading of 'temporal coherence'.

12. Temporal coherence: tolerances on path difference: Michelson-Fourier spectroscopy

The treatment of spatial coherence given above dealt with a single pure frequency component of the radiation, and the results apply directly to practical cases only when the path differences are very small compared with the coherence length of the radiation. When this condition is not satisfied, it is necessary to integrate the intensity distributions over the appropriate frequency range. In practice it is usually more convenient to use the wave-number $\sigma = 1/\lambda = v/c$ in place of the frequency, and this is adopted in what follows. The formula for the total intensity so found serves to introduce a factor which specifies the temporal coherence between two interfering beams.

If the spatial coherence between two points P_1 and P_2 is perfect for all frequencies, the light falling on these points may be regarded as the superposition of mutually incoherent waves of different frequency. The two points thus receive coherent light for any given frequency, but this light is incoherent with that of any other frequency. There is thus a state of partial coherence resulting from the finite spectral width of the source. This is termed the chromatic, or temporal, coherence. Thus spatial coherence is associated with the finite spatial extent of the source, and temporal coherence with the finite spectral range of the source. In the general case these two coherence factors appear combined in a quantity, the total coherence, which proves of practical use only where it can be expressed as the product of two factors, one expressing the spatial, and the other the temporal, coherence.

Suppose, for example, light beams from points P_1, P_2 to superpose at a point P. If, for a given wave-number σ, the separate intensities produced at P are $I_1'(\sigma)$ and $I_2'(\sigma)$, the resultant intensity at P for light of this wave-number is

$$I'(\sigma) = I_1'(\sigma) + I_2'(\sigma) + 2\sqrt{\{I_1'(\sigma)I_2'(\sigma)\}} \operatorname{Re} \{\Gamma_{21}(\sigma)e^{2\pi i\sigma p(\sigma)}\} \tag{108}$$

as shown in (71). $\Gamma_{21}(\sigma)$ is the spatial coherence between P_2 and P_1 for the light of wave-number σ, and $p(\sigma)$ is the optical path difference $[P_1 \ldots P] - [P_2 \ldots P]$ for light of this wave-number. Integrating (108) over the range $\sigma = 0$ to $\sigma = \infty$ gives for the total intensity at P

$$I' = I'_1 + I'_2 + 2\sqrt{(I'_1 I'_2)} \operatorname{Re} \{J_{21}\}, \tag{109}$$

where

$$J_{21} = \frac{1}{\sqrt{(I'_1 I'_2)}} \int_0^\infty \sqrt{\{I'_1(\sigma) I'_2(\sigma)\}} \Gamma_{21}(\sigma) e^{2\pi i \sigma p(\sigma)} \, d\sigma. \tag{110}$$

In (110) the quantity $p(\sigma)$ is only the path difference between $[P_1 \ldots P]$ and $[P_2 \ldots P]$. In general, however, the optical path lengths from points in the source to P_1 and P_2 will differ, and the spatial coherence Γ_{21} will then have a non-zero argument of the form

$$\beta_{21} = 2\pi\sigma p_{21}(\sigma) \tag{111}$$

where the quantity $p_{21}(\sigma)$, which is determined in any given case by the form of Γ_{21}, defines an effective mean path difference between points in the source and P_1 and P_2. If $p_{21}(\sigma)$, as defined by (111), is assumed to be included in $p(\sigma)$ in (110), this latter is written

$$J_{21} = \frac{1}{\sqrt{(I'_1 I'_2)}} \int_0^\infty \sqrt{\{I'_1(\sigma) I'_2(\sigma)\}} V_{21}(\sigma) e^{2\pi i \sigma p(\sigma)} \, d\sigma, \tag{112}$$

where $p(\sigma)$ now represents a mean total path difference from the source to P for light traversing the two paths, by way of P_2 and P_1 respectively.

In place of the intensities in (112), the relative spectral distributions

$$E'_1(\sigma) = \frac{I'_1(\sigma)}{\displaystyle\int_0^\infty I'_1(\sigma) \, d\sigma} = \frac{I'_1(\sigma)}{I'_1},$$

$$E'_2(\sigma) = \frac{I'_2(\sigma)}{\displaystyle\int_0^\infty I'_2(\sigma) \, d\sigma} = \frac{I'_2(\sigma)}{I'_2}, \tag{113}$$

may be employed. The quantities in (113) can be used to define the geometric mean energy distribution

$$E(\sigma) = \sqrt{\{E'_1(\sigma) E'_2(\sigma)\}} = \sqrt{\frac{\{I'_1(\sigma) I'_2(\sigma)\}}{I'_1 I'_2}} \tag{114}$$

of the two light beams arriving at P. (112) is now written

$$J_{21} = \int_0^\infty E(\sigma) V_{21}(\sigma) e^{2\pi i \sigma p(\sigma)} \, d\sigma. \tag{115}$$

If the two paths from the source to P have the same uniform transmissions, the quantities $E'_1(\sigma)$ and $E'_2(\sigma)$ are each equal to $E(\sigma)$, which is then the spectral distribution in the source. In what follows this will be assumed to be so. The formulae (109) and (115) provide the basis for treating the theory of interferometers using extended sources of finite spectral width. Comparing (109) with (65), J_{21} is seen to play the role of a total coherence factor.

An important application of (109) and (115) is in finding the dependence on path difference of the visibility of interference fringes observed with a source of small, but finite, spectral width. In such a case the spatial coherence between two points P_1 and P_2 is practically independent of wave-number. For example, in the case of a circular source (80) above gives

$$V_{21}(\sigma) = \left| \frac{2J_1(2\pi u)}{2\pi u} \right|,$$

which depends on wave-number only through the occurrence of $1/\lambda = \sigma$ in the quantity $u = (n \sin \alpha/\lambda)(P_1 P_2)$. Since, even for a very wide spectral line, the variation in σ will be less than $\sigma_0/1000$, where σ_0 is the mean wave-number, the variation of $V_{21}(\sigma)$ with σ is negligible. In this case, (115) may be written

$$J_{21} = V_{21} \int_0^\infty E(\sigma) e^{2\pi i \sigma p(\sigma)} d\sigma, \tag{116}$$

where $V_{21} = V_{21}(\sigma_0)$. If, further, it is assumed that the path difference arises solely in non-dispersive media, $p(\sigma)$ is also independent of σ, and writing $p = p(\sigma_0)$, (116) becomes

$$J_{21} = V_{21} \int_0^\infty E(\sigma) e^{2\pi i \sigma p} d\sigma. \tag{117}$$

Since the visible region of the spectrum corresponds only to the range $\sigma = 1.43 \times 10^4$ to $\sigma = 2.5 \times 10^4$ cm^{-1}, it is also convenient to regard $\sigma = \sigma_0$ as the wave-number origin, and to write (117) in the form

$$J_{21} = e^{2\pi i \sigma_0 p} V_{21} \int_{-\infty}^{+\infty} E(\sigma - \sigma_0) e^{2\pi i(\sigma - \sigma_0)p} d(\sigma - \sigma_0),$$

that is

$$J_{21} = e^{2\pi i \sigma_0 p} V_{21} K(p), \tag{118}$$

where

$$K(p) = \int_{-\infty}^{+\infty} E(s) e^{2\pi i s p} ds, \tag{119}$$

with $s = \sigma - \sigma_0$. According to (118), the total coherence is now the product of the spatial coherence V_{21} and a temporal coherence factor $K(p)$, which is the Fourier transform of the relative energy distribution in the source. It should be noted that p is here the total path difference from the source to the point P where the two beams interfere.

If $K(p)$ in (118) is written in terms of its modulus and argument,

$$K(p) = W(p) e^{i\delta(p)}, \tag{120}$$

(109) takes the form

$$I' = I'_1 + I'_2 + 2\sqrt{I'_1 I'_2}\, V_{21}\, W(p) \cos\left[2\pi\sigma_0 p + \delta(p)\right], \tag{121}$$

and the visibility of fringes formed near P is given by

$$V = \frac{2\sqrt{I'_1 I'_2}}{I'_1 + I'_2}\, V_{21}\, W(p),$$

or, when $I'_2 = I'_1$,

$$V = V_{21}\, W(p). \tag{122}$$

For zero path difference, that is $p = 0$, by (119) $W(p) = K(p) = 1$; but, for increasing values of p, $W(p)$ will decrease at a rate which is greater the larger the spectral width of the source.

As an example, let the profile of the spectral line be Gaussian, so that

$$E(\sigma - \sigma_0) = \frac{1}{\delta\sigma}\, e^{-\pi\{(\sigma-\sigma_0)/\delta\sigma\}^2}, \tag{123}$$

where σ_0 is the mean wave-number, and $\delta\sigma$ is a measure of the half-value width. More exactly, $\delta\sigma$ is the width of the line profile at the points where the intensity has dropped to a value $e^{-\frac{1}{4}\pi} = 0.45$ times its value at the centre of the line. The factor $1/\delta\sigma$ is included to make the integrated value of $E(\sigma - \sigma_0)$ equal to unity, in accordance with (113) above. With $s = (\sigma - \sigma_0)$, the Fourier transform of (123) gives $K(p)$, namely

$$K(p) = e^{-\pi(\delta\sigma p)^2}. \tag{124}$$

For this case $\delta(p) = 0$, and $W(p) = K(p)$. If a tolerance $W(p) \geq 0.90$ is placed on the reduction in fringe visibility arising from the finite width, $\delta\sigma$, of the source, the optical path difference must be small enough to satisfy

$$|p| \leq 0.18/\delta\sigma = 0.18\lambda_0^2/\delta\lambda, \tag{125}$$

where $\delta\lambda$ is the numerical value of the wavelength difference corresponding to $\delta\sigma$. It will be recalled that $\lambda_0^2/\delta\lambda$ is the coherence length (22).

The above considerations form the basis of Michelson's method for the study of spectral lines, and for its modern variant known usually as Fourier spectroscopy. The source to be studied is used with the Michelson interferometer to form Haidinger fringes; and, in the original form of the method, the visibility of the fringes at the centre of the ring pattern is determined as a function of path difference. For this arrangement $V_{21} = 1$, provided the mirrors are adjusted very precisely; and, by (122), the fringe visibility is then equal to $W(p)$. For a Gaussian profile, $W(p)$ is given by (124) with $\delta\sigma = \delta\lambda/\lambda_0^2$. The calculated forms of $E(\sigma - \sigma_0)$ and $W(p)$ are shown in fig. 17a for the cadmium red line, using values $\lambda_0 = 6438$ Å and $\delta\lambda = 0.013$ Å.

The sodium doublet has two components, at $\lambda_1 = 5890$ Å and $\lambda_2 = 5896$ Å respectively. If each component is assumed to have a Gaussian shape of the same width $\delta\sigma$, the relative distribution of intensity has the form

$$E(\sigma-\sigma_1) = \frac{1}{(1+r)\delta\sigma}\left[e^{-\pi\{(\sigma-\sigma_1)/\delta\sigma\}^2}+re^{-\pi\{(\sigma-\sigma_2)/\delta\sigma\}^2}\right], \qquad (126)$$

where r is the ratio of the peak intensities in the two components. With $s = \sigma-\sigma_1$, (119) gives

$$K(p) = \frac{e^{-\pi(\delta\sigma p)^2}}{1+r}\{1+re^{2\pi i(\sigma_2-\sigma_1)p}\},$$

whose modulus is

$$W(p) = e^{-\pi(\delta\sigma p)^2}\left\{1-\frac{4r}{(1+r)^2}\sin^2\pi(\sigma_2-\sigma_1)p\right\}^{\frac{1}{2}}, \qquad (127)$$

which again gives the fringe visibility as a function of path difference p. The calculated forms of $E(\sigma-\sigma_1)$ and $W(p)$ are shown in fig. 17b, assuming the values $\delta\lambda = 0.62$ Å and $r = 0.5$. The visibility decreases, but varies periodically with period $p = 1/(\sigma_2-\sigma_1) = 0.58$ cm.

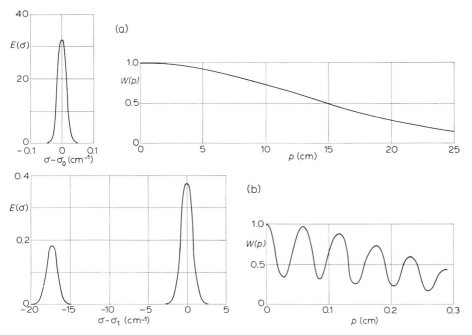

Fig. 17. Variation of visibility with path difference: (a) Cd red line (Cd: 6438 Å; $\delta\lambda = 0.013$ Å) and (b) the Na doublet (calculated) (Na: 5890 Å, 5896 Å; $\delta\lambda = 0.62$ Å; $r = 0.5$).

The curves of fig. 17 have been calculated to agree with those found experimentally. In fact, Michelson derived the values of $\delta\lambda$ and the separation $\lambda_2-\lambda_1$ from measurements of the visibility. The theory of this, first given by Rayleigh, follows from (119), from which the Fourier inversion theorem gives

$$E(\sigma-\sigma_0) = \int_{-\infty}^{+\infty} K(p)e^{-2\pi(\sigma-\sigma_0)p}dp. \tag{128}$$

If now $\delta(p)$ is assumed to be zero or π, which is the case for a symmetrical profile, $K(p) = W(p)$; it being then assumed that $W(p)$ is negative when $\delta(p)=\pi$, corresponding in practice to reversal of contrast in the fringes. In general, however, the form of $E(\sigma-\sigma_0)$ based on using the values of $W(p)$ in (128) is not unique, unless the fringe displacements are also determined, say by comparison with those for a symmetrical line, and used to find the values of $\delta(p)$.

The above difficulty is avoided in Michelson–Fourier spectroscopy. A similar arrangement is used, but an aperture is now placed at the centre of the fringe pattern. This aperture is made small enough for the path difference not to vary appreciably for the different points over its area. The spatial coherence is $V_{21} = 1$, given accurate adjustment of the mirrors. The variation of total light flux passing through the small aperture is measured as the path difference p is varied. Assuming $I_1' = I_2' = I$, in (109) and using J_{21} from (117), gives

$$I' = 2I + 2I \int_0^\infty E(\sigma) \cos 2\pi\sigma p\, d\sigma$$

for the light intensity detected. The varying component of the signal from the detector thus gives

$$B(p) = 2 \int_0^\infty E(\sigma) \cos 2\pi\sigma p\, d\sigma, \tag{129}$$

which is the Fourier cosine transform of $E(\sigma)$. Inversion of (129) gives

$$E(\sigma) = 2 \int_0^\infty B(p) \cos 2\pi\sigma p\, dp \tag{130}$$

for the distribution of energy in the spectrum of the source. In practice (129) is evaluated by means of either a digital or an analogue computer. In its modern form the method may be used for the analysis of complex spectra of large spectral range. In particular, it has been widely applied to the study of infra-red spectra.

It has so far been assumed that the path difference between the interfering beams occurs entirely in a non-dispersive medium. An important practical case is when the two paths also contain different thicknesses of a dispersive material such as glass. The optical path difference is then a function of the wave-number. For a small spectral range centred on σ_0, it is permissible to write

$$p(\sigma) = p_0 + (\sigma-\sigma_0)\left(\frac{dp}{d\sigma}\right)_{\sigma_0}, \tag{131}$$

and the formula (116) then becomes

$$J_{21} = V_{21} \int_0^\infty E(\sigma)e^{2\pi i\sigma\{p_0+\beta(\sigma-\sigma_0)\}}\, d\sigma,$$

where $\beta = (dp/d\sigma)_{\sigma_0}$. Again using $s = \sigma - \sigma_0$, this formula is

$$J_{21} = V_{21} e^{2\pi i \sigma_0 p_0} \int_{-\infty}^{+\infty} E(s) e^{2\pi i [s(p_0 + \sigma_0 \beta) + \beta s^2]} ds.$$

In place of (119), it is then necessary to use

$$K(p_0) = \int_{-\infty}^{+\infty} E(s) e^{2\pi i \beta s^2} e^{2\pi i (p_0 + \sigma_0 \beta) s} ds, \tag{132}$$

and the temporal coherence is no longer simply the Fourier transform of the spectral distribution $E(s)$. For the Gaussian profile (123), the formula (132) gives

$$K(p_0) = \alpha \int_{-\infty}^{+\infty} e^{-\pi \alpha^2 s^2} e^{2\pi i \beta s^2} e^{2\pi i (p_0 + \sigma_0 \beta) s} ds,$$

where $\alpha = 1/\delta\sigma$. This integral can be evaluated to give

$$K(p_0) = \frac{\alpha}{\sqrt{(\alpha^2 - 2i\beta)}} \exp\left[-\pi \left\{ \frac{(p_0 + \sigma_0 \beta)^2}{\alpha^2 - 2i\beta} \right\} \right],$$

whose modulus is

$$W(p_0) = \frac{1}{\sqrt[4]{\{1 + (2\beta/\alpha^2)^2\}}} \exp\left[-\pi \left\{ \frac{(p_0 + \sigma_0 \beta)^2/\alpha^2}{1 + (2\beta/\alpha^2)^2} \right\} \right]. \tag{133}$$

Now $\beta/\alpha^2 = (dp/d\sigma)_{\sigma_0} \delta\sigma^2 = \delta p \, \delta\sigma$, where δp is difference between the path difference for light of wave-number $\sigma_0 + \frac{1}{2}\delta\sigma$ and the path difference for light of wave-number $\sigma_0 - \frac{1}{2}\delta\sigma$. Thus (133) may be written

$$W(p_0) = \frac{1}{\sqrt[4]{\{1 + (2\delta p \, \delta\sigma)^2\}}} \exp\left[-\pi \left\{ \frac{(p_0 \delta\sigma + \sigma_0 \delta p)^2}{1 + (2\delta p \, \delta\sigma)^2} \right\} \right], \tag{134}$$

giving the degree of temporal coherence in terms of the half-value width $\delta\sigma$ and the increment in path difference between $\sigma_0 - \frac{1}{2}\delta\sigma$ and $\sigma_0 + \frac{1}{2}\delta\sigma$, when the path difference for the mean wave-number σ_0 is equal to p_0.

From (134), it is seen that the visibility is a maximum, for given $\delta\sigma$ and δp, when

$$p_0 = -\frac{\sigma_0 \delta p}{\delta\sigma} = \frac{\lambda_0 \delta p}{\delta\lambda}, \tag{135}$$

which implies that

$$2\pi \left(\frac{p_0 + \frac{1}{2}\delta p}{\lambda_0 + \frac{1}{2}\delta\lambda} \right) = 2\pi \left(\frac{p_0 - \frac{1}{2}\delta p}{\lambda_0 - \frac{1}{2}\delta\lambda} \right), \tag{136}$$

that is, that the phase difference is the same for the wave-numbers $\sigma_0 \pm \frac{1}{2}\delta\sigma$. The variation of phase difference with wave-number is then stationary at $\sigma = \sigma_0$. The degree of temporal coherence for this case is

$$W_{max} = \frac{1}{\sqrt[4]{\{1 + (2\delta p \, \delta\sigma)^2\}}}, \tag{137}$$

which is shown in fig. 18a as a function of $\delta p \, \delta \sigma$. The variation of $W(p_0)$ as a function of $(p_0 \delta \sigma + \sigma_0 \delta p)$ is shown in fig. 18b for different values of $\delta p \, \delta \sigma$.

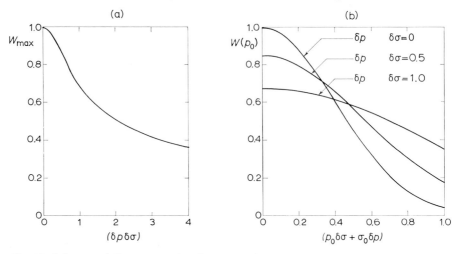

Fig. 18. Influence of dispersive path difference on fringe visibility: Gaussian spectral profile.
σ_0 = mean wave-number; $\delta \sigma$ = half-value width;
p_0 = path difference for $\sigma = \sigma_0$; δp = difference in p for $\sigma = \sigma \pm \tfrac{1}{2} \delta \sigma$.

When $V_{21} = 1$, $W(p_0)$ gives the fringe visibility. If the condition $W_{\text{max}} \geqq 0.80$ is used as a tolerance criterion, the permissible difference in path difference is given by

$$|\delta p| \leqq \frac{0.60}{\delta \sigma} = \frac{0.60 \lambda_0^2}{\delta \lambda} , \qquad (138)$$

it being assumed that the path difference for the mean wave-number is adjusted to the value (135). The tolerance (138) is rather larger than might be expected. This is because the optical path difference in the dispersive medium is numerically larger for the shorter wavelengths. With a path difference in air of opposite sign, the numerical value of the total path difference can thus be made to be greater for the longer wavelength, as seen in (136), giving a phase-difference stationary with wave-number at $\sigma = \sigma_0$ when p_0 satisfies (136).

The formula (138) may be used to estimate the tolerance on difference in glass thickness in the two arms of an interferometer used with white light. Taking $\lambda_0 = 5000$ Å, $\delta \lambda = 2000$ Å and $\delta p = t \delta n$, (138) gives $|t \delta n| \leqq 1.5 \lambda_0 = 0.75 \times 10^{-4}$ cm. Assuming $\delta n = 0.012$, the thickness tolerance is $|t| \leqq 0.006$ cm for crown glass. In practice a rather more severe tolerance would be imposed to allow for possible contrast reduction arising from imperfect spatial coherence.

13. Coherence with multiple beams

In the 3-slit interferometer three beams of light deriving from points P_1, P_2 and P_3 superpose at a common point P. Using the method described in section 8 above, the total intensity at P for a monochromatic component of the light from the source S is given by

$$I_p = \iint_S |f_1 U_1 + f_2 U_2 + f_3 U_3| \, dS, \tag{139}$$

where the complex numbers f_1, f_2 and f_3 are complex transmissions for the paths $P_1 P$, $P_2 P$ and $P_3 P$. Expanding the square, (139) can be written

$$I_p = |f_1|^2 I_1 + |f_2|^2 I_2 + |f_3|^2 I_3 + $$
$$+ 2\sqrt{I_1 I_2} \, \text{Re} \{\Gamma_{21} f_1^* f_2\} + 2\sqrt{I_2 I_3} \, \text{Re} \{\Gamma_{32} f_2^* f_3\} + 2\sqrt{I_3 I_1} \, \text{Re} \{\Gamma_{13} f_3^* f_1\}, \tag{140}$$

where I_1, I_2 and I_3 are the separate intensities at P_1, P_2 and P_3; and Γ_{21}, Γ_{32} and Γ_{13} are the degrees of spatial coherence of the three points taken in pairs.

A corresponding formula can clearly be obtained for any finite number of interfering beams. However, the procedure becomes too unwieldy when a larger number of beams is involved. In the case of image formation when the object is illuminated with partially coherent light, an infinite number of beams contribute to the disturbance at any point in the image plane. The present method is then inapplicable, and the concept of an effective source is introduced. This reduces the problem to the superposition of the separate intensities in the images formed by a mutually incoherent set of coherent illuminating waves.

The formula (140) applies only to one monochromatic component of the light. The same procedure can be used as in section 12 to find the total intensity in terms of the total coherence factors J_{21}, J_{32} and J_{13}, but it is usually simpler to consider practical cases in terms of the superposition of the intensity distributions of the different wavelengths in the source. When all paths differences are much less than the coherence length of the radiation, formula (140) applies as it stands.

CHAPTER 7

USE OF SPHERES IN OPTICS

A. C. S. VAN HEEL†

(Technological University, Delft)

CONTENTS

1. Introduction

Spheres of glass can be made with utmost precision and without too much trouble, provided the diameter of the sphere is not prescribed within narrow limits. It has appeared worthwhile to examine the possibilities of spheres as optical instruments, and here an account of some of these will be given.

First regarding the sphere as an instrument to form an image, we restrict ourselves to the case of parallel incident light and a narrow field of view. Two aberrations are to be considered, spherical aberration and chromatic aberration.

2. Spherical aberration

Comparing the spherical aberration of spheres with different refractive indices n and with a radius r, and limiting ourselves to the aberrations of first and second order (that is of the third and fifth degree), we can write for the lateral aberration in the focal plane:

$$x' = \tfrac{1}{2}m_4 \frac{8(n-1)^3}{n^3} \frac{h^3}{r^3} + \tfrac{3}{8}M_6 \frac{32(n-1)^5}{n^5} \frac{h^5}{r^5}, \tag{1}$$

where h is the incident height at the first surface. Further:

$$m_4 = \frac{n(n^2-3n+1)}{8(n-1)^3} r, \tag{2}$$

$$M_6 = - \frac{n(-3n^4+13n^3-19n^2+13n-3)}{32(n-1)^5} r. \tag{3}$$

This makes the lateral aberration in the focal plane:

$$x' = \frac{1}{2} \frac{n^2-3n+1}{n^2} \frac{h^3}{r^2} - \frac{3}{8} \frac{-3n^4+13n^3-19n^2+13n-3}{n^4} \frac{h^5}{r^4}. \tag{4}$$

The deviation of the emergent wave front from a sphere, expressed as a function of the incident height, is:

$$N = - \frac{(n-1)(n^2-3n+1)}{4n^3} \frac{h^4}{r^3} + \frac{(n-1)(-3n^4+13n^3-19n^2+13n-3)}{8n^4} \frac{h^6}{r^5}. \tag{5}$$

For a focal length $+1$ the radius r_0 is:

$$r_0 = 2(n-1)/n. \tag{6}$$

From these formulae it follows for instance that for a sphere with a refractive index 1.5 and a diameter of $2r = 1.4$ mm, N has a value of 0.000763 mm for $h = 0.27$. The focal length being 1.05 mm, the numerical aperture has a value of about 0.26. With a slightly other focussing than the paraxial focal plane the maximum deviation of the emergent wave front from a sphere can be considerably reduced, so that it is not more than $\tfrac{1}{4}$ of the wave length of 0.00056 mm.

Thus it appears that the small spheres of Van Leeuwenhoek could indeed yield a considerable resolving power. A sphere as described above having a magnification of more than 200 times, viz. 250/1.05, can reveal details of $\lambda/0.25$, that is about two microns.

According to VAN CITTERT [1932] the microscope of Van Leeuwenhoek, now in the possession of the Utrecht University, has a magnification of 270 times and it can resolve details down to somewhat more than one micron. Whether Van Leeuwenhoek used coherent or even dark ground illumination, as suggested by DOBELL [1932], is not known, but possible; his observations seem to prove that one micron was his limit of resolution.

Whether Van Leeuwenhoek's lenses were spheres or nearly spheres, is of no importance for this discussion, as the values of m_4 and M_6 vary only slightly for different forms in the neighbourhood of a sphere.

These remarks resume some of the results of the thesis of WALTHER [1959], where many details of the optics of spheres are discussed.

We can furthermore add that in this case the chromatic aberrations are small enough to be neglected, and that the burden of spherical aberration lies with primary aberration. In the given example the value of 0.000 764 mm of the wave aberration N is composed of a part 0.000 717 from primary spherical aberration (term with h^4) and 0.000 046 from the term with h^6. The higher order terms can be neglected.

3. Spherical aberration of higher orders

The lateral spherical aberration t in the focal plane of a sphere can be expanded in a power series in h^2, h being the incident height:

$$t = -a_3 h^3 - a_5 h^5 - a_7 h^7 - a_9 h^9 - a_{11} h^{11} + \ldots \ldots \tag{7}$$

The coefficients of this series have been evaluated after the method of BUCHDAHL [1954] by G. J. Beernink of Delft (private communication) and are given in table 1.

TABLE 1

n	r		R	l'	
1.4	$\frac{4}{7}$	$= 0.571\,429$	1.750 000	$+\frac{3}{7} =$	$+0.428\,571$
1.5	$\frac{2}{3}$	$= 0.666\,667$	1.500 000	$+\frac{1}{3} =$	$+0.333\,333$
1.6	$\frac{3}{4}$	$= 0.750\,000$	1.333 333	$+\frac{1}{4} =$	$+0.250\,000$
1.7	$\frac{14}{17}$	$= 0.823\,529$	1.214 286	$+\frac{3}{17} =$	$+0.176\,471$
1.8	$\frac{8}{9}$	$= 0.888\,889$	1.125 000	$+\frac{1}{9} =$	$+0.111\,111$

n	a_3	a_5	a_7	a_9	a_{11}
1.4	$+0.968\,75$	$+1.929\,20$	$+4.486\,80$	$+11.277\,27$	$+29.677\,95$
1.5	$+0.625\,00$	$+0.914\,06$	$+1.586\,91$	$+2.995\,15$	$+5.928\,04$
1.6	$+0.430\,56$	$+0.496\,82$	$+0.692\,02$	$+1.053\,97$	$+1.685\,80$
1.7	$+0.308\,67$	$+0.293\,11$	$+0.342\,09$	$+0.439\,54$	$+0.594\,54$
1.8	$+0.226\,56$	$+0.181\,00$	$+0.181\,33$	$+0.201.85$	$+0.237\,59$

The numbers refer to the case of a focal length $+1$; r is the radius and $R = r^{-1}$ the curvature of the sphere, l' is the back focal length.

For a special case the importance of the different orders can be seen from table 2.

TABLE 2

$n = 1.5$, $h = 0.25$	
$-t_3 = 0.009\ 765\ 6 = 0.906\ 9t$	
$-t_5 = 0.000\ 892\ 7 = 0.082\ 9t$	
$-t_7 = 0.000\ 096\ 9 = 0.009\ 1t$	
$-t_9 = 0.000\ 011\ 4 = 0.000\ 8t$	
$-t_{11} = 0.000\ 001\ 4 = 0.000\ 1t$	

Integration gives $N = \Sigma_4^{10} N_i$, cf. table 3.

TABLE 3

$N_4 = 0.000\ 610\ 35 = 0.937\ 72N$	
$N_6 = 0.000\ 037\ 19 = 0.057\ 14N$	
$N_8 = 0.000\ 003\ 03 = 0.004\ 65N$	
$N_{10} = 0.000\ 000\ 29 = 0.000\ 44N$	
$N_{12} = 0.000\ 000\ 03 = 0.000\ 05N$	

For $n = 1.5$ the difference between the series for t up to the 11th degree and the total lateral aberration is 0.2% for $h = 0.4$, 2.5% for $h = 0.5$ and 23% for $h = 0.6$. The contribution of the 11th degree to the total aberration is 0.5% for $h = 0.4$, 2.2% for $h = 0.5$ and 5.8% for $h = 0.6$.

4. Form of the caustic curve

Though we do not yet see any practical use of it, we give in figs. 1a, 1b and 1c the form of the caustic curve for the sphere in air, when the incident light is parallel.

With the origin at the centre of the sphere and the x-axis parallel to the incident light, we have for the coordinates of the points of the caustic curve:

$$x = A \cos 2(i-i') + \sin i \sin 2(i-i'),$$
$$y = -A \sin 2(i-i') + \sin i \cos 2(i-i'), \qquad (8)$$
$$A = n \cos i \cos i'/2(n \cos i' - \cos i).$$

where i is the angle of incidence and i' follows from Snell's law; the radius is 1. In fig. 1b only half of the curve has been drawn, as the complete curve would make the figure less clear.

5. Correction for spherical aberration of the sphere with a parallel glass plate

With the introduction of lasers as light sources an interesting application of optical spheres presents itself. On account of the coherence of the laser light, it can be used

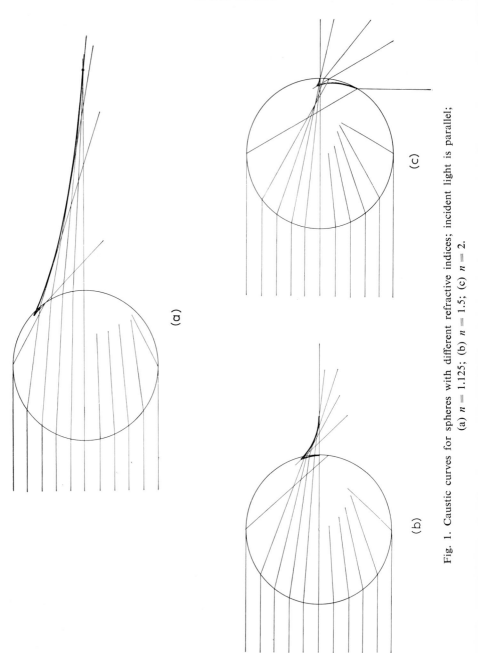

Fig. 1. Caustic curves for spheres with different refractive indices; incident light is parallel;
(a) $n = 1.125$; (b) $n = 1.5$; (c) $n = 2$.

to give interference patterns even when the light path of two interference pencils is far from equal.

One way to achieve this seems worthwhile to describe, as it gives another example of the use of spheres. Fig. 2 gives the set-up. Light from a helium-neon gas-laser, emitting the wave length 632.8 nm in a nearly parallel pencil, is concentrated in a point P, lying at the centre of curvature of a mirror M which is to be tested on its spherical form. At C a cube with a semi-reflecting diagonal mirror first transmits the light from left to right and reflects the pencil returning from M to the eye E. The second pencil is produced by reflection at the hypotenuse surface and at the surface A.

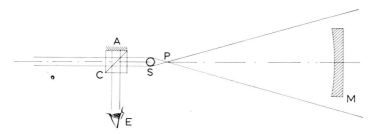

Fig. 2. Interferometric testing of concave mirror with light from a laser.

Instead of a conventional lens system an optical sphere S is made use of to converge the light to the point P. Chromatic aberration plays no part, as the light is mono-chromatic. The spherical aberration must give rise to wave aberrations less than $\frac{1}{4}\lambda$ in the focal plane (to be reduced by a slight change of focus to values well below $\frac{1}{10}\lambda$.

With the given formulae we find that for $n = 1.6$ the radius of the sphere should be about 21 mm. The focal length then being 28 mm, the aperture is $2h/f = 5/28 = 1/5.5$. Thus for mirrors with this aperture in their centre of curvature the device is quite adequate. This means that spherical concave mirrors, whose aperture at the focus is 1/2.7 can be tested in this way. That lenses with an aperture up to 1/5.5 in connec-tion with a plane mirror can be tested in the same way need only be mentioned.

Advantages of this set-up are the relative simple optical parts and the fact that mirrors up to any diameter can be tested. Moreover, centration of the different parts is easily attained.

Not content with the aperture number of 5.5, J. D. de Veer and the author looked out for additional means to improve the aperture of the aberration-free emergent pencil. It appeared that a plane-parallel plate of glass after the sphere can correct primary spherical aberration, leaving an amount of higher order aberrations that is sufficiently small to go to an aperture-number of 1.8. At the same time the diameter of the sphere can be reduced. The distance of sphere and plate is irrelevant. Squaring the plate to the incident pencil is the only additional adjustment.

As an example we describe a special case; see fig. 3. The diameter of the sphere is 7.922 mm, its refractive index 1.656 01, the thickness of the plate is 9.617 mm; its refractive index is 1.498 68. The focal length of the system is 5 mm; $m_4 = 0$; $M_6 = 0.5323$. For an incident height of 1.4 mm the lateral spherical aberration in the (virtual) focal plane is 0.000 538 mm and the wave aberration 0.000 160 mm ($\approx \frac{1}{4}\lambda$). The aperture is $2h/f' = 1/1.79$.

Though this is not the place to dwell upon further improvements, we cannot refrain from mentioning that replacement of the sphere by a concave spherical mirror (with a radius of 8 mm) enlarges the aberration free aperture to 1/1. The corresponding numerical aperture is 0.88. Mirrors of any diameter with an aperture of 1/0.5 in their

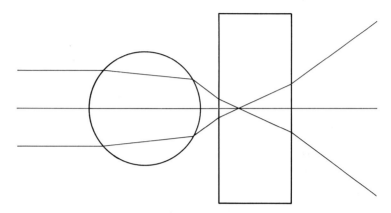

Fig. 3. Correction of spherical aberration of a sphere by means of a plane-parallel plate.

focus can be studied with such an apparatus. Again m_4 is annihilated by an appropriate thickness of a plane-parallel plate. With a refractive index of 1.656 01 this thickness amounts to 2.606 mm. The wave aberration is 0.000 12 mm in the focal plane. With a very slight change of focus it is reduced to $\lambda/20$.

The reader is warned, that for purposes like microscope object lenses, the combination of a sphere and an appropriate plane-parallel plate has, for that use, the serious drawbacks of large chromatic aberration and of a virtual focus.

6. Rainbow

There are some practical applications of the rainbow. At least, the optical principles underlying the formation of the rainbow can be put to practical uses. We will not

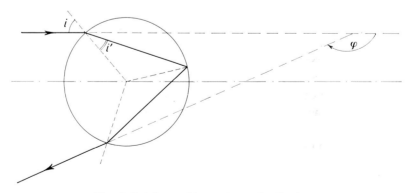

Fig. 4. Rainbow with one internal reflection.

dwell upon these, referring the reader to the literature of the subject (DESCARTES [1637], NEWTON [1704], AIRY [1838], STOKES [1850], MASCART [1889], BOYER [1959]). Let us resume here only the facts connected with our subject.

On a sphere with a refractive index n in air and a radius r falls a parallel pencil of monochromatic light with wave length λ. Fig. 4 represents the case of one internal reflection. The deviation φ of the emergent ray is given by:

$$\varphi = 2i - 4i' + \pi.$$

For more than one internal reflection we have:

$$\varphi = 2i - 2pi' + (p-1)\pi, \tag{9}$$

where the number of internal reflections is $p-1$.

The value of φ depends on the incident height h. When h increases from zero to r, the deviation φ passes through a minimum value φ_0 found by differentiation of φ and applying Snell's law. The angle of incidence corresponding to the ray with minimum deviation follows from the relation:

$$\sin^2 i_0 = (p^2 - n^2)/(p^2 - 1), \tag{10}$$

from which we have:

$$h_0 = r \sin i_0, \tag{11}$$

and

$$\sin i_0' = n^{-1} \sin i_0, \tag{12}$$

so that φ_0, the minimum deviation, is:

$$\varphi_0 = 2i_0 - 2pi_0' + (p-1)\pi. \tag{13}$$

The emergent wave front in the neighbourhood of the ray with minimum deviation can be represented by the formula:

$$y = Hx^3/3r^2, \tag{14}$$

where the origin of coordinates is the point of inflexion of the wave front, the x-axis being along the tangent in the origin and the y-axis coinciding with the emergent ray with minimum deviation (fig. 5). The parameter H is given by:

$$H = \frac{(p^2-1)^2}{p^2(n^2-1)} \left(\frac{p^2-n^2}{n^2-1}\right)^{\frac{1}{2}} \tag{15}$$

This form of wave front gives rise to a beautiful diffraction pattern, consisting of alternately bright and dark (black) bands. The shape of the curve which represents the intensity as a function of v, is shown in fig. 6. It is exactly the same for all cases and for any number of internal reflections the only difference being a contraction or dilatation along the y-axis. Here

$$v = (\varphi - \varphi_0)(48/H)^{\frac{1}{3}}(r/\lambda)^{\frac{2}{3}}.$$

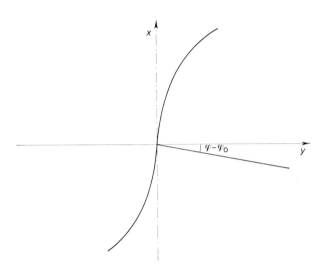

Fig. 5. Form of emergent wave front.

Determination of the angular distance between the maxima and the minima gives the scale. When φ_m is the direction of a maximum or a minimum, $\varphi_m - \varphi_0 = Pv$, where v is given for the first few bands in table 4.

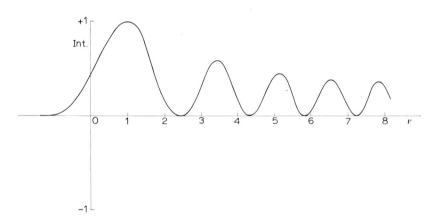

Fig. 6. Light distribution in the diffraction pattern.

The value of P follows from:

$$P = 2.062\,65 \times 10^5 (H/48)^{\frac{1}{3}} (\lambda/r)^{\frac{2}{3}} \text{ seconds of arc.} \tag{16}$$

By means of this table the value φ_0 is readily found; this gives the direction of the emergent ray with minimum deviation, as it follows from the elementary theory sketched above (formula 13). The boundary of fine diffraction bands enables us to determine this direction with great precision.

TABLE 4

Number	Maxima	Minima
1	1.084 5	2.495 5
2	3.466 9	4.363 1
3	5.144 6	5.892 2
4	6.578 2	7.243 6
5	7.868 5	8.478 8
6	9.059 9	9.630 0
7	10.177 4	10.716 1
8	11.236 4	11.749 6
9	12 247 5	12.739 5
10	13.218 5	13.692 4

For a sphere with a radius of 24 mm and $n = 1.5199$ for the green mercury line we have in the case of two internal reflections ($k = 2, p = 3$):

$$\varphi_0 = 270° \; 32', \qquad H = 12.27, \qquad p = 105.1.$$

The value of $\varphi - \varphi_0$ is, in seconds of arc, given in table 5.

TABLE 5

Number	Maxima	Minima
1	114.0	262.3
2	364.4	458.6
3	540.7	619.3
4	691.4	761.3

The fact that the minimum deviation with two internal reflections is about 270° for this refractive index has been used to produce an 'optical plane', perpendicular to the direction of the incident pencil. This proved feasible for distances from 1 to 10 m with a precision of 2 seconds of arc. At larger distances the brightness of the diffraction pattern is too small.

The spacing of the diffraction bands is proportional to $r^{-\frac{2}{3}}$. Therefore the enlargement of the sphere is not very efficient to make the structure of the pattern finer.

7. White rainbow

DE VEER [1962] has described the production of a 'half-optical-plane', where instead of refraction in a sphere reflection at a concave half-sphere is made use of. When a light point is situated at a distance $0.682497r$ from the centre, r being the radius of the spherical mirror, the angle φ as indicated in fig. 7 is 90° and in this direction the deviation is a minimum for $k = 2$ reflections. There a 'rainbow' is formed, lying on a plane surface. The explanation runs along the same lines as with the refracting spheres.

There is however this difference that dispersion does not play a part. The first maximum is white, the first minimum is black. The following maxima and minima assume slowly some colour with increasing number, which is attributable to the occurrence

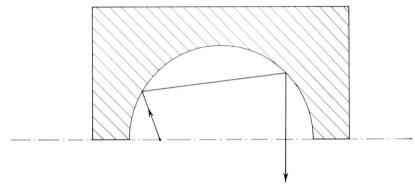

Fig. 7. Formation of white rainbow.

of the wave length λ in the formula (20) for P, applying also in this case. Instead of (19) we have now the following relation for H:

$$H = \frac{(4k^2 - 1)^2}{8k^2(1 - a^2)} \left(\frac{4a^2k^2 - 1}{1 - a^2}\right)^{\frac{1}{2}}, \tag{17}$$

which amounts to 45.7.

The diffraction pattern is less fine than with a sphere of the same radius, but the 'sphere' in this case is of air and can be made considerably larger. With a concave half-spherical mirror with $r = 50.18$ mm the value of P is 100 seconds of arc for the wave length of the green mercury line.

For the way to place the small hole in the right place, its illumination and for other ways to realize a white rainbow we refer the reader to DE VEER [1962].

8. Focussing of collimators and telescopes

Keeping in mind that glass spheres are comparatively easy to make with considerable precision, we want to call attention to other uses, one of which is the focussing of telescopes and of collimators.

In fig. 8 C represents a collimator and T a telescope. Monochromatic light illuminates the slit S at the front focus of the lens L. A sphere M, placed in the parallel pencil of light emerging from L, produces with two internal reflections, a 'rainbow', a diffraction pattern as described above. If the sphere has a refractive index of about 1.52, the deviation is 270°. The pattern is observed with the telescope, focussed for infinity. Wherever the sphere is placed within the pencil, the pattern is visible in the telescope, provided, of course, that the emergent rays B are incident on the object glass O.

By shifting M back and forth in the pencil P (up and down in fig. 8), the focussing of the collimator is tested. When, indeed, S is not exactly in the focal plane of M the pencil P is either divergent or convergent. The direction of B then is not constant and the diffraction pattern is not stationary. As a change of direction of 2 seconds of arc is easily detected, this test is a sharp one.

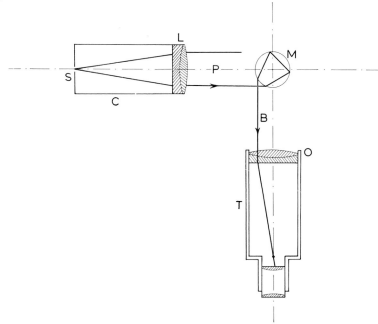

Fig. 8. Focussing of collimator C and telescope T by means of a glass sphere M.

Taking as an example a collimating lens with a diameter of 5 cm and a focal length of 40 cm, we can calculate how good the test is. The deviation from flatness is about $\frac{1}{2}\lambda$, that is not very far from interferometric precision.

Aberrations in L of this amount are as easily detected.

In order to reduce light losses, the two regions of the surface of the sphere, where the internal reflections take place, are aluminized.

Focussing of the telescope is performed in the same way, now shifting M back and forth before T.

It has to be remarked that focussing of C and T is done independently from one another.

9. Determination of the refractive index of a glass sample

One of the neatest practical applications of the diffraction patterns produced by the spheres is the determination of the refractive index. We will show that the precision of the results and the ease to obtain them are strong recommendations of this method, devised, studied and tested by WALTHER [1959], from whose thesis also the contents of the preceding sections are taken.

What is wanted is a theodolite and a collimator. The sample, of which the refractive index n is to be determined, should be made into a good sphere. The set-up is represented in fig. 9. We assume that the collimator and the telescope are both focussed for infinity. The theodolite must be placed in such a position that the telescope object glass can receive the light from the 'rainbows' formed by the sphere with one and with two internal reflections.

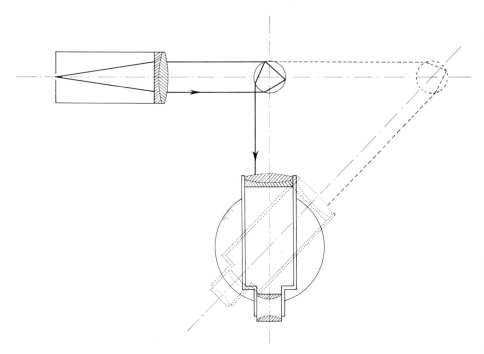

Fig. 9. Determination of the refractive index of a glass sphere.

The diffraction bands are observed and from the angular readings the reading for the minimum deviations for $k = 1$ and $k = 2$ are calculated in the way indicated in § 6. Let these be φ_{01} and φ_{02}. The angle between these directions is: $\alpha = \varphi_{01} + \varphi_{02} - 2\pi$, as φ_{01} and φ_{02} are measured in clockwise and anticlockwise directions respectively. The angle α is a function of n only. It might be expressed explicitly in n, but this gives rise to an unwieldy equation of very high degree. A practical solution is to calculate α for a few values of n and to interpolate. The necessary formulae are:

$$\sin i_{01} = [\tfrac{1}{3}(4-n^2)]^{\frac{1}{2}}, \qquad \sin i_{02} = [\tfrac{1}{8}(9-n^2)]^{\frac{1}{2}},$$
$$\sin i'_{01} = n^{-1} \sin i_{01}, \qquad \sin i'_{02} = n^{-1} \sin i_{02}, \qquad (18)$$
$$\varphi_{01} = 2i_{01} - 4i'_{01} + \pi, \qquad \varphi_{02} = 2i_{02} - 6i'_{02} + 2\pi.$$

With high values of n (larger than 1.7), the deviation in the case of one internal reflection is approaching 180°; for $n = 2$ it is 180°. For these values it is preferable to make the observations with two and three internal reflections.

In any case the parts of the sphere where the reflections occur should be aluminized.

Discussion of the errors shows that with a theodolite of which the readings can be trusted to 2 seconds of arc, the error in n for a sphere with a diameter of 30 mm is only 2×10^{-6}. Even for smaller spheres of say 10 and 4 mm diameter the error is small, viz. 4×10^{-6} and 8×10^{-6} respectively.

When a theodolite is used which gives readings to half a minute, the errors are much larger of course. Still it is to be noted that for diameters of 30, 10 and 4 mm they compare favourably with the usual refractometers, viz. errors of 3×10^{-5}, 6×10^{-5} and 12×10^{-5}.

It goes without saying that these numbers only refer to samples of which the material is homogeneous within these limits.

For utmost precision a correction must be applied for the fact that the slit S has finite height; with a reasonably narrow slit a correction for finite slit width is not necessary.

The diffraction bands are curved, except when the deviation is 90° or 270°, when they are straight. In all other cases a correction must be made for the overlapping of the curves, produced by the different points of the slit. Walther has shown that for a deviation φ the correction is:

$$\sigma = \tfrac{1}{6}\delta^2/\mathrm{tg}\,\varphi, \tag{19}$$

where δ is the height of the slit divided by the focal length of the collimating lens L. It must be added to the acute angle between the direction of observation and the direction of the pencil produced by the collimator.

With a few words it can be made clear why the use of spheres is greatly to be preferred to the classical method, determining the refractive index with a prism. This discussion is made by WALTHER [1959] in the following words:

'The question arises whether it has advantages to use this new method of determining refractive indices instead of the common measurement with a prism and a spectrometer. First of all it is more accurate. With a prism it is very difficult to obtain a precision better than one unit in the fifth decimal place. The change of the minimum deviation for a 60 degrees prism with a refractive index of about 1.5 is only 0.3″ when the index is changed by one unit in the sixth decimal place. In the experiment described above the change of α would be 0.9″ and the change in β would amount to 0.5″. This difference is not purely accidental. In the case of a prism only the difference on the angle of incidence and the angle of refraction occurs in the measurements. When we use the sphere, however, different multiples of i and i' enter into the formula which determines the deviation. This requires too that the angle i must have a significance in itself without direct recourse to Snell's law. This significance, a functional dependence between the refractive index and the angle of incidence alone, is given by eq. (10). In this respect the measurement with the sphere is comparable with the use of Brewster's angle (a relation between the refractive index and a specific angle of incidence because of the total linear polarization) and more or less to Abbe's refractometer (a similar relation, this time brought about by the condition of total reflection).

Another point of interest is that the sphere is much more easily made than a prism. Two planes of a prism must be perfectly plane; this can only be accomplished by an experienced polisher. The manufacturing of spheres requires a certain amount of skill but it is not nearly as difficult, mainly because of the radius of the sphere not being prescribed.

There are more advantages: we use a theodolite instead of a spectrometer. The latter is about eight times as expensive as the former. And in using a spectrometer the prism must be placed right on top of the axis, the most delicate part of the instrument. This is a serious drawback when e.g. we want to measure the effect of the temperature on the refractive index. The sphere can be placed at a fairly great distance of the collimator and the theodolite.

Moreover the arrangement with a sphere is easier to handle; no careful adjustments of the specimen required, like putting the refracting edge of the prism parallel to the axis of the spectrometer. Some people prefer making settings on the diffraction pattern to carrying out measurements with the slit image. Finally there is not trouble with parallax.

One disadvantage must be mentioned, however: the brightness of the image that must be observed is rather poor. The mercury e and g line can be used very well, also the sodium D line. But we found it difficult to carry out measurements with the hydrogen C and F lines. Those lines are essential when the dispersion of the glass is wanted. A provisional set-up with cylindrical lenses showed that this difficulty can be overcome; one should use an eye piece of which the magnification in the vertical plane is about three times as small as in the horizontal plane. This is feasible, but we will refrain from discussing the technical details of this provision.'

Other fields of application have been studied; we will finish here, however, our account of the subject.

References

AIRY, G. B., 1838, Trans. Cambridge Phil. Soc. **6**, pt. 3, p. 379.
AIRY, G. B., 1848, Trans. Cambridge Phil. Soc. **8**, pt. 5, p. 593.
BOYER, C. B., 1959, The rainbow (London).
BUCHDAHL, H. A., 1954, Optical aberration coefficients (New York).
DESCARTES, R., 1637, Les météores (Leyde).
DE VEER, J. D., 1962, Testing the straightness of lines and the flatness of surfaces, part 2, *in*: Proc. Conf. Opt. Instr., 1961 (Chapman and Hall, London) p. 394.
DOBELL, C., 1932, Anthony van Leeuwenhoek and his "Little Animals" (Amsterdam).
MASCART, M. E., 1889, Traité d'optique (Paris).
NEWTON, I., 1704, Opticks (London).
STOKES, G. G., 1850, Trans. Cambridge Phil. Soc. **9**, pt. 1, p. 166.
VAN CITTERT, P. H., 1932–1933, The van Leeuwenhoek microscope in possession of the University of Utrecht. Koninkl. Ned. Akad. Wetenschap., Proc. **36**.
WALTHER, A., 1959, Optical applications of solid glass spheres, Thesis, Delft.

CHAPTER 8

THE PRODUCTION OF OPTICAL PARTS

GEORG FRANKE

Wetzlar and Giessen, Germany

CONTENTS

F. Twyman 1876–1959

1. Introduction

Glass possesses a unique physical constitution. Tammann considered it a 'supercooled liquid' in which the constitution of the characteristic fluid state is maintained, even when cooled. The viscosity of glass rises without a definite temperature of solidification. Nevertheless, the arrangement of the ions is fundamentally the same in glasses as in crystals. In quartz (SiO_2) every silicon cation is surrounded by four oxygen anions, forming a tetrahedron with the ions in the corners. Every oxygen ion is bound to the silicon cation by only one valence, the other valence being free to participate in the next tetrahedron. Thus every oxygen ion belongs to two tetrahedra, and the ratio between silica cations and oxygen ions is therefore 1 : 2, in accordance with the formula for quartz, SiO_2.

The arrangement of the tetrahedra in a crystal is also regular, forming a periodic lattice. In the molten states of both glass and quartz, the individual tetrahedra are displaced in relation to each other, and the lattice is therefore distorted (fig. 1).

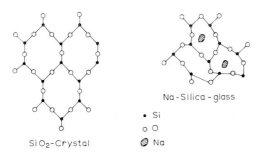

Na - Silica - glass

• Si
○ O
⊘ Na

SiO_2-Crystal

Fig. 1. The constitution of a quartz crystal and of glass.

A network of ions is formed, but with a disturbed periodicity. Silicon is the most stable glass-former, but there are others with similar structures. The best-known glass-formers are SiO_2, GeO_2, B_2O_3, P_2O_5, and some others. In addition to these classical glass-formers, some mixtures of ingredients that cannot form a glass by themselves, become a glass when melted together. For example, a 0.6 mol of TeO_2 and a 0.07 mol of Al_2O_3 form a glass of special optical properties.

It is possible to insert alkalines, earth-alkalines, and metal oxides into the meshes in the networks of the glass-formers. These ingredients alter the refractive index and colour dispersion of the glass. We then obtain solid solutions of alkalines or metal oxides in the glass.

From the point of view of the lens designer or manufacturing optician, the optical properties of glass are far more important than the mechanical, chemical, and physical properties. The lens designer selects glasses primarily according to the requirement for correcting optical aberrations, and the glass producer tries to provide glasses of specially desirable optical properties. On the other hand, of course, when it is possible to choose between glasses with the same or similar optical specifications, one prefers to use those glasses having the best mechanical and chemical characteristics.

The resistance of the glass to chemical corrosion is important because the atmosphere contains not only carbon dioxide and traces of sulphuric acid, but other corrosive gasses as well. In addition, occasional touching of the lens surface cannot be avoided, and by these finger contacts a minute quantity of perspiration is deposited on the surface. With some varieties of glass this will later result in the formation of spots, and antireflection surface coating becomes difficult. These are primarily the barium silica glasses that corrode with every contact with human perspiration. On the other hand, these glasses possess high refractive indices and low colour dispersion, thus offering special advantages for the correction of an optical system. In recent years, these sensitive glasses have been replaced by new types having the same or similar positions in the chart of refractive index and colour dispersion, in which the silicon oxide has been replaced by borium phosphate. These glasses are much less sensitive to spotting.

Certain other glasses, the low dispersion flints, necessary for a higher degree of colour correction, contain up to 30 % sodium oxide or potassium oxide. This lowers their resistance to humid air, and the surfaces are soon corroded, especially in tropical zones. It is readily understandable that such sensitive glasses require working techniques different from those employed with more stable glasses.

Although glass blocks are delivered with diamond-scribed markings to identify the refractive index and other optical properties, as measured by the producer, glass destined for quantity production should be tested before it is used. This can be done, for example, with an Abbe refractometer. A novel way of obtaining the refractive indices of a sample, having some decided advantages over the classical methods, is described in chapter 7 under the head of rainbow optics.

In some cases, additional quality-control may also be advisable. Inner tensions become visible between two crossed polarizers, and striae in a Schlieren instrument. Both methods require two polished surfaces.

In the actual manufacture of lenses and prisms, that is, once the optical design has been fixed, we are no longer interested in the optical properties of the glass, but only in its mechanical and chemical behaviour. The primary consideration is the physical hardness of the material. The normal technical definitions of hardness, as given by the standardized Vickers, Brinell or Rockwell figures, are of minor importance in glasses, at least in so far as grinding is concerned. This is because of the special state of glass in which the process of grinding is different from that of metals. The Auerbach test provides a much more appropriate method for defining the hardness of glasses. In this method, a small spherical ball is pressed against the surface until the limit of elastic deformation is exceeded, and a permanent plastic deformation begins, or a crack is formed in the brittle material.

Even better is a practical method first used for natural stones, and later applied to glasses. In this method, a piece of plane glass is pressed with a load of 600 g/cm^2 on a disc grinding with loose emery. After a distance of 608 m, the loss of glass thickness is measured in μm. The reciprocal of this number is the grinding-hardness value for the glass. Actual figures vary between approximately 140 for a soft glass of dense flint, and about 500 for a hard glass such as a zinc crown. This method has amply proved its worth for the calculation of working times in optical workshops.

In addition to this test for grinding hardness, another definition is in use which better meets the conditions of grinding or milling with bound grain. This is the scratch-hardness test measured by drawing a diamond point with a pyramidal angle of 120° over the glass surface under a load of 20 g. The width of the scratch thus produced is measured, and again the reciprocal is used as an expression of the hardness. No mathematical correlation exists between the grinding-hardness and scratch-hardness tests, although, of course, a glass that is hard on one scale is also hard on the other.

2. Production techniques

More than in any other technical branch, the production of high quality optical parts depends largely upon the skill and experience of the craftsmen. The principal methods were given to us by Newton, who described his methods for making lenses and astronomical mirrors, as well as by Van Leeuwenhoek, who explained his microscopial lens-grinding methods. In the course of time, the optical industry has gained much practical experience, and many optical plants have developed production methods which are sometimes hoarded as secrets. Production techniques are, however, fundamentally the same in all optical workshops. A comparison of the literature will, on the other hand, often reveal remarkable differences in the advice given by practical opticians. Frequently, a method recommended by one expert is strongly disparaged by another, both experts giving excellent reasons for their opinions.

Single elements for prototypes and experimental purposes are made by hand, craft skills and proper routines counting for far more than the occasional use of machinery. The paths to such small-scale production have been well beaten, and the methods employed are more or less identical. In mass-production, the planning is most important, and it must be emphasized that lenses for such different instruments as photographic cameras, astronomical telescopes, microscopes, and field glasses require (or permit) different production methods for obtaining maximum manufacturing efficiency and economy. These different production methods derive from such variables as the changing ratios in diameters, powers, and precision required by the various types of optical instruments. The extensive use of automatic machinery is justified only if the number of units to be produced is sufficiently high.

The production of such ordinary optical parts as lenses and prisms can be divided into the following separate steps:
1. *Generating the rough form,*
2. *Milling, or rough-grinding the surface to the approximate curvature required,*
3. *Trueing the surfaces,*
4. *Smoothing,*
5. *Polishing,*
6. *Centring, or edging and chamfering the border.*

To avoid confusion, let us first define our terms. We will define *milling* as the process of grinding with *bound grain*. The workpiece is either still, or makes only slow movements, whilst the tool is turning at a very high speed. By *trueing* we mean the grinding to the correct curvature, but with an abrasive of *finer grain* than is used to obtain the rough form. *Smoothing* is a *fine grinding* to impart a silky glaze. The surface curvature should in no way be affected by this step. *Polishing* gives the surface its *final finish* prior to the application of an antireflection coating.

Before describing the individual steps in lens and prism making in detail, let us first discuss the methods used for working glass. The initial form-giving process can be effected either by processing with abrasives, or by moulding the heated glass while it is still in the viscous state. In the final polishing process, conditions are very complicated, being a combination of chemical, physical and abrasive phenomena.

Optical glass is delivered to the lens maker in the form of cast blocks, plates or bars, or as roughly preformed 'pressings' in the approximate shape of the intended lens or prism. The mass-production of optical parts from blocks requires many operations starting with the cutting of the blocks into smaller pieces, and the rounding of these pieces by milling or rough-grinding. This means that a large portion of the delivered block is simply pulverized and wasted. In addition, glass blocks frequently contain impurities and inhomogeneities such as bubbles, striae and small streaks which must be removed by cutting these portions away from the main block. From the standpoint of maximum utilization of purchased material, the use of preformed optical pressings is therefore more economical. Such moulded parts involve a minimum loss of material, an important consideration for glasses which contain expensive ingredients. Such preformed parts also minimize the number of necessary manufacturing operations, thereby adding another important economy factor.

Not all types of optical glasses are suitable for moulding, however, some tending to crystallization under the force of the solidifying temperature that destroys the glass state. Heating and pressing have some influence on the refractive index, but this can easily be taken into consideration. Aside from this alteration of the refractive index, the homogeneity of the lens is even higher in the case of pressings when the pieces are cooled slowly to permit the tensions to equalize. The use of pressings does, however, require special tools for every type of lens or prism to be worked. This method is therefore advisable only for the mass-production of very large series. The decision to start either from preformed moulded parts, or from conventional glass blocks, demands a most scrupulous prior calculation.

When mass-production is not the case, or when preformed pressings are not available, the initial rough form must be achieved by means of abrasive methods. These methods have been investigated by many authors, using both optical and electronic microscopes. Two possibilities present themselves: The traditional grinding with loose grain, or the more modern method of milling with bound grain. To balance the advantages and disadvantages of the two methods we must compare the very different attacks against the surface made by the loose- and bound-grain methods.

In grinding with loose grain, the emery is suspended in a liquid and brought into a convex or concave tool of the appropriate curvature, the glass workpiece being shift-ed in every possible direction against the tool. The more or less round specks of loose grains are rolled over the surface, their sharp edges pressing into the glass to break away mussel-shaped glass fragments, or 'flakes'. Cracks appear in the neighbourhood of each grain, extending to a depth of perhaps some tenths of a millimetre. The trace of an individual abrasive grain is a chain of such local disturbances, the glass surface being quite literally split open (see fig. 2.). The effect is directly proportional to both the rate of movement and the pressure exerted.

Fig. 2. The trace of a single grain of emery on a glass surface.

1. Rough grinding has the sole purpose of removing material very rapidly. It is accomplished with coarse grain having diameters between 200 and 500 μm, and leaves a cleft and fissured surface. Therefore, at the end of the rough-grinding process both the glass workpiece and the grinding tool must be washed thoroughly to remove all traces of the original rough abrasive.

2. Medium grinding is performed with grain diameters of 30 to 80 μm, and is the 'trueing', or form-giving process by which the spherical form of the required curvature is first achieved. Lenses are given the correct thickness with a small amount of surplus material for the fine grinding and polishing.

3. Fine grinding, or smoothing, produces a silky-smooth surface that is ready for final polishing, and is accomplished with grain sizes of 5 to 20 μm.

Figs. 3 and 4 illustrate progressive stages in the grinding of two kinds of glass, a soft one, SF6, and a hard one, BK7, these designations being from the catalogue of Schott & Gen. In studying the profiles, bear in mind that the vertical magnification is much higher than the horizontal magnification. In actual fact, even the steepest slopes of the diagrams are shallow cavities whose diameters greatly exceed their depths.

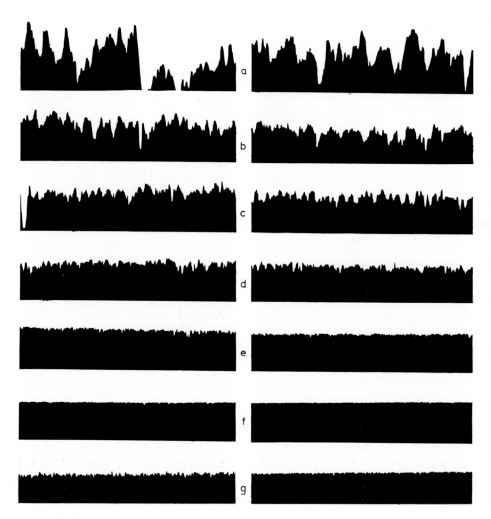

Fig. 3 (left). The different steps of grinding a soft glass (SF6, double extra dense flint). Horizontal magnification (a–g): 15×; vertical magnification (a–f): 225×, (g): 750×.

Fig. 4 (right). As fig. 3, but for a hard glass (BK7, borosilicate crown).

Cracks extending into the glass body cannot be measured with a contact pin, since the pin is far too coarse for the cracks. The different steps, and the grain sizes used, are given in the following table:

Steps	Process	Grain sizes (μm)	Normally used sizes (μm)
1	Roughing	150–460	270–390
2		70–240	120–180
3	Trueing	30–120	57–86
4		15–60	25–38
5	Smoothing	5–27	12–17
6		2.5–12.5	5–7.5

It is inevitable in the different steps that a small grain will sometimes cause an outbreaking of relatively great dimensions. Finer grinding can be seen to produce a surface that only in the average shows mountains and valleys smaller than in the preceding step. This phenomenon illustrates what is meant by describing grinding with loose grain as a process out of control. The profiles illustrated in figs. 3 and 4 cannot be taken as evidence against such occasional flaking since they represent only a short arbitrary section of the surface, recording only a small part of the whole.

The most commonly used abrasive materials today are *emery* (Al_2O_3), *carborundum* (SiC), and *boroncarbide* (B_4C), all very hard synthetic materials. In some shops the grains sizes are even today expressed in terms of minutes, e.g., as '2, 10, 30 or 240 minute grain'. In this case, the separation of the grain sizes is made by decanting it and measuring the time after which the fluid containing the smaller grains is separated from the sediment. Fresh abrasive is delivered by the producers in selected grades, and can be used without any additional treatment. In use, however, the grain changes in size, being broken into particles of different diameters. To regenerate such abrasive,

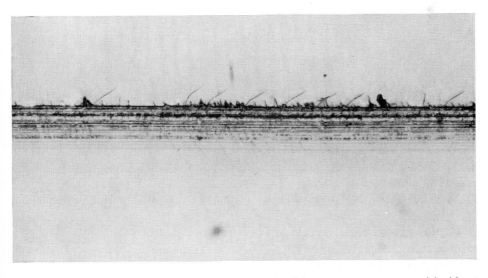

Fig. 5. Drawing a diamond edge across the surface under light pressure removes material without cracking.

it must be purified by a fractional decanting process. The chemical apparatus industry has developed screens down to a few thousandths of a millimetre, but these have not yet been introduced for the separation of emery and other abrasives.

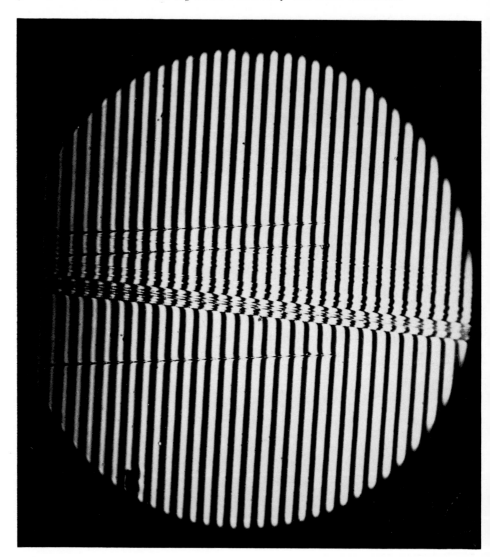

Fig. 6. The fringes in a micro-interferometer show the deformation alongside the scratch-line.

In grinding with bound grain (e.g., a carborundum wheel) it is always the same edge of each individual grain that comes in contact with the surface. The edges of the grains are soon worn down and the grains must be replaced with new ones. Grinding stones differ with respect to granularity and binding. Natural emery stones have today been abandoned because of insufficient homogeneity. Ceramic grinding stones make for finer grinding, and are better with respect to form resistance than plastic grinding stones. The self-renovation of the grain is, however, faster with plastic grinding stones, and such emery stones are therefore very appropriate for rough-grinding operations. The most efficient grinding stones are made of iron and carry a layer of sintered diamond bort. These offer the longest working lives, and hold their forms best.

The control of abrasion is far better with bound- than with loose-grain methods. The edge, say of a single diamond splinter, ploughs across the surface producing a straight furrow, the glass particles being scraped away (fig. 5). The interference photo-micrograph, fig. 6, reveals the raised borders of the furrow, and shows that a plastic deformation is connected with this ploughing. A series of transitional states between a reversible trace and a deep cleft occurs according to the variables of glass qualities, movement velocity, and pressure exerted on the diamond edge. A constant scratching of the surface with only occasional flakes can be achieved by varying these conditions. The mussel-shaped outbreakings occur if the pressure is excessive, and if the flanks of the diamond splinters (instead of only their points) are brought into contact with the workpiece (fig. 7). By controlling the grinding load and speed either a smooth or a

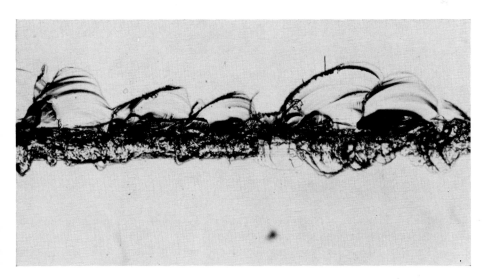

Fig. 7. Heavy pressure leads to outbreakings and cracks.

rough abrasion can be achieved. Some cracks can be observed along the scratch-line, but even these do not penetrate the glass body nearly so deeply as is the case when grinding with loose grain, since the forces in bound-grain grinding remain parallel to the surface.

Impregnated diamond tools are suitable for fine grinding as well as for rapid rough-ing, depending mainly on the feed of the work, although, of course, they are available with different grain sizes (GEORG [1948/49]). The principal difference between the two grinding methods lies in the direction of the forces. In loose-grain grinding, the grain is pressed normal to the surface, and enters the surface to cause a breaking-out of glass particles. The forces in bound-grain grinding are strictly tangential to the surface, the grain remaining completely external. Grinding can, therefore, be clearly defined as an abrading away of unwanted material.

Figs. 8 and 9 illustrate the difference between the two grinding methods. Both are photomicrographs of a surface after smoothing and ready for polishing. Fig. 8 shows a surface ground with loose grain, while the surface in fig. 9 shows the effect of grind-

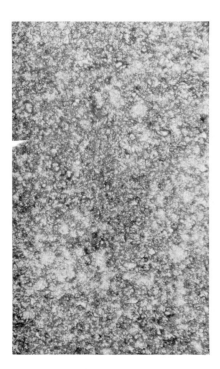 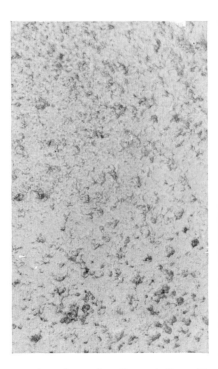

Fig. 8 and 9. Grinding with loose grain (left) causes a more irregular surface than grinding with bound grain (right).

ing the same type of glass with a diamond tool. The structure of the surface in fig. 8 indicates that loose-grain grinding produces a surface with deeper flakes than the diamond-ground surface in fig. 9, and that the former will require very much more final polishing than the smoother, diamond-ground surface.

So many different influences are inter-related in polishing that a clear definition of this process is most difficult. Polishing must generate a glossy glass surface whose unevenness must be no more than 0.1 μm, or even better, down to 0.01 μm. For a long time it was believed that abrasion was the main polishing effect, as in grinding, and that only the finer grain used in polishing accounted for the glossiness of the final surface. It is, of course, obvious that some abrasion does occur during polishing, since the thickness of the glass is measurably reduced. But the process of abrasion that occurs during polishing is very different from the purely mechanical abrasion associated with grinding.

It appears to be clear today that abrasion is of only secondary importance in polishing, and that it cannot account for the formation of a glossy surface. Only in the first stages of polishing, with the attendant breaking-down of the highest protruding peaks, can polishing be considered in any way comparable to grinding with bound grain. The polishing tool consists of a solid metal body covered by a relatively soft material such as cloth, felt, pitch, wax, or a plastic substance. The polishing powder is extremely fine, having diameters of only a few μm. This grain is pressed into the pitch, or other soft material, and held firmly in place. Sometimes the grain is even added directly to the heated pitch.

The polishing process has been investigated by many authorities, again using both optical and electronic microscopical observations. These researchers have shown that a plastic smearing over the surface levels the unevenness in polishing. This has led to the general assumption that melting processes play some part in polishing.

The great importance of melting phenomena in the polishing of metallic surfaces was stated by BOWDEN and RIDDLER [1937]. They found that a polishing effect on metallic surfaces could only be expected if the melting point of the polishing material is higher than that of the metal, even when the relation of hardness is reversed. But these results were not confirmed with glass because this material is quite different from metals.

Of the many theories offered to explain glass polishing, perhaps the best known is that of KLEMM and SMEKAL [1941], which has also been adopted and modified by BRÜCHE and POPPA [1955, 1956, 1957] and POPPA [1957]. This theory regards glass polishing mainly as a thermo-plastic effect spreading out over the whole surface, with only minor (initial) abrasion. In polishing, the temperatures of both the tool and the workpiece rise, but since temperature is itself a statistical concept, it can be doubted whether the concept of temperature is sufficient to justify its application in the interpretation of molecular effects. The energy required to separate a particle from the mass can, of course, be expressed as a certain amount of heat. But it is not possible to state a well-defined volume to which this amount of heat shall be referred for calculating a temperature.

This theory has thus to be supplemented by the concept of a complicated chemical process, as was done by GREBENSCHTSCHIKOW [1935]. and KALLER [1957, 1959]. In this, chemical processes work together between the glass, the water, the polishing material and the pitch or felt of the polishing tool. The alkalines, primarily of sodium or potassium, are dissolved by the water and replaced by hydrogen. In this manner, a layer of silica-gel (SiOH) is generated over the surface of the glass, protecting it against further attack by the water. The speed with which this layer is formed, and its thickness, depend on the composition of the glass and the pH value of the water.

The silica-gel can in turn react directly with carboxyl groups of the felt, or resinous acids of the pitch. Kaller demonstrated this by successfully polishing certain kinds of glass without a polishing material, using only pitch or felt. On the other hand, he

demonstrated that it was impossible to obtain a polished surface from a cotton polisher. This shows that the older, purely mechanical theories of polishing cannot be
true. But it is also true that the main work of removing the silica-gel layer is done by
the polishing material.

For this purpose, certain ferrous oxides ('rouge') or cerium oxide are generally
used, the latter being more effective. Contrary to the general opinion, Kaller stated
that the effectiveness of a polishing material is not given by its hardness alone, but by
its brittleness and chemical activity as well. The grain is broken down in the polishing
process, and the fresh fractures develop a high level of activity. In any case, the silica-
gel is pushed aside, and fresh glass is laid open for the attack of the water. Finally,
the remaining layer of silica-gel covers the whole surface uniformly. This theory leaves
many an open question, however, especially concerning the polishing of glasses that do
not contain halogens, or even silica, since such glasses and crystals can be polished
just as well as the classical glasses, and by the same methods, even though the theory
does not apply to them.

The practical course of the polishing process can be described as follows: Shortly
after the start of polishing, the peaks of the rough surface are broken down (figs.
10a and 10b). At this stage the surface shows low elevations, with many cavities and

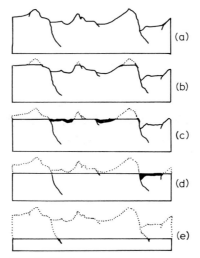

Fig. 10. Ideal polishing would remove
material below the level of the valleys.

cracks extending into the glass. In the next stage, small glossy areas are generated,
expanding increasingly (figs. 10c and 10d) until they grow together to cover the whole
surface. Individual depths still remain, and waste from the grinding process is deposited in them. These deposits can easily be removed since they do not adhere very
firmly to the bases of the cavities. But, as these cavities become progressively smaller,
there is a tendency of smearing them over with silica-gel. A glossy surface is thus
generated which hides beneath its skin all the impurities and cracks that remain.

In this stage the surface appears nearly perfect, but cleaning can cause the cavities to be broken open, revealing the sub-surface imperfections. The polishing process is for this reason not yet completed.

In the course of further polishing, the closed-over cavities are levelled down with the sound surface. A satisfactory polish can, however, be achieved only when the glass surface is removed below the level of the cavities (fig. 10e). This last stage occupies most of the time in the polishing process, becoming progressively slower as the state of polish advances. Figs. 11 and 12 illustrate different grades of polish seen through an optical microscope. The surface was ground with a fine loose grain, following the normal procedures used in optical workshops. In fig. 11 the polishing

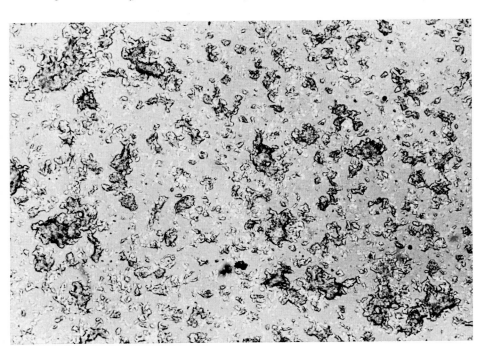

Fig. 11. The appearance of a surface polishing for 10 min (340×).

time was 10 minutes; this was extended to 20 minutes in fig. 12. The state of polish achieved after 45 minutes is shown in fig. 13; only a few surface imperfections can now be seen. Figs. 14 and 15 show a surface under the higher magnification of an electron-microscope. In fig. 14 the polishing was done with pitch. Three flakes are still open, shortly before closing over. Other flakes are daubed over already and only their contours can be seen. In fig. 15 the polishing was done with felt alone, without polishing powder. Here the abrasion is much more intensive and the flakes contain only a small quantity of silica-gel.

The silica-gel skin can be removed by treating the surface with hydrofluoric acid. The result of such treatment is shown in fig. 16: The old surface failures, mainly cracks, are once more visible. It must be noted that the situation is different if the grinding and smoothing of the surface prior to polishing was done with diamond tools, with a

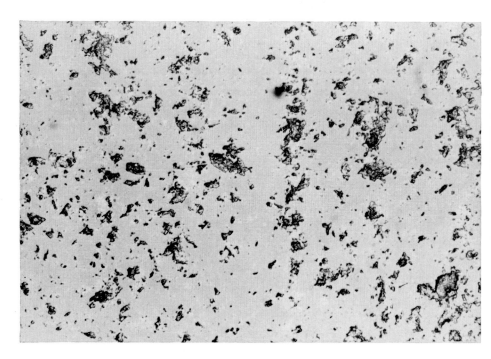

Fig. 12. The appearance of a surface after polishing for 20 min (340×).

low feed in the last state of smoothing. In this case only very few imperfections are revealed after removal of the polish skin. In addition, the time required to achieve the polish is much shorter than with surfaces smoothed by a loose-grain process.

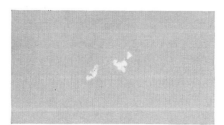

Fig. 13.   The appearance of a surface after
polishing for 45 min.

3. Lens making

We now turn to a description of lens making. We shall describe prism making separately, even though many of the problems are the same, because the nearly

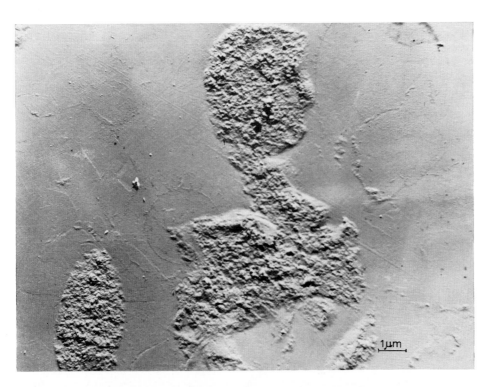

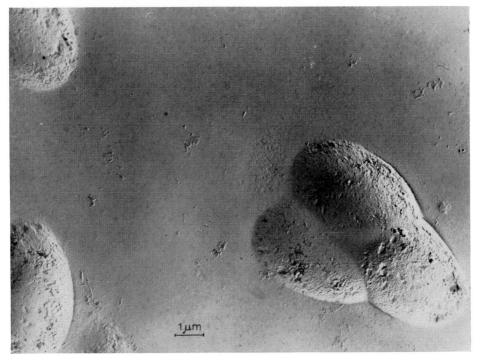

Figs. 14 and 15. Electron photomicrographs of surfaces polished with pitch (above) and with felt (below) omitting the polishing powder.

always plane surfaces of prisms require different individual steps and tools. This presentation has the advantage of paralleling the separation of prism and lens making into different departments in most optical plants.

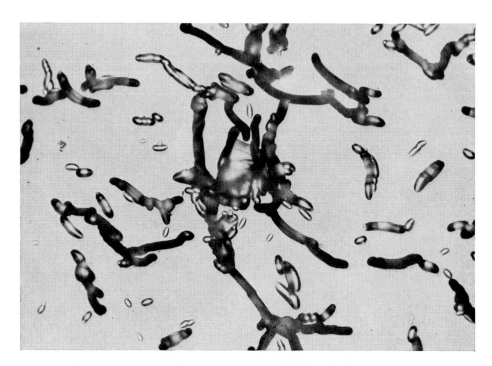

Fig. 16. Surface at 840× after removal of polishing skin with fluoric acid.

3.1. OBTAINING THE ROUGH LENS FORM

The moulding process

Glass for the production of moulded lens-blanks is used in the form of guts or rectangular pieces cut from a plate. The weight of the individual pieces must be checked carefully to obtain consistent lens-blanks. The pieces of glass are heated in a furnace to the softening temperature (Littleton point), and the pasty pieces are dropped into the heated parts of the mould. Air-pressure is used for small-diameter lenses, hydraulic pressure for larger lens and prism pressings (fig. 17). After moulding, the lenses are brought into an annealing oven to equalize the tensions. The slow reduction of temperature is regulated automatically, according to a specific program for the type of glass and the form of the moulded piece. This cooling occupies days, or even weeks.

The surfaces of moulded lens-blanks are rough, and require grinding. The blank-thickness is therefore some one to two millimetres larger than the final value. To obtain a glossy pressed surface, the steel mould must be highly polished, and free from even the slightest amount of dust. During pressing, surface dust is vapourized, producing small holes in the glass surface. The surface is covered by such impurities and has a scaly structure. Glossy mouldings are therefore suitable for only the crudest optical purposes, such as illumination lenses for spot-, flood-, and signal-lights.

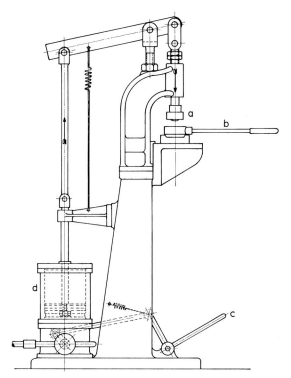

Fig. 17. A moulding press, (a) moulding form, (b) blank holder, (c) pedal, (d) cylinder.

Glossy moulding makes it easy to produce spheric lenses for condenser illumination systems, and surfaces generated by this kind of firepolishing are noticeably harder than those obtained by artificial polishing methods. The danger of such lenses bursting due to the heat in an illumination system is less, because they have no scratches or other cavities hidden below the surface polish skin.

Block cutting

Glass delivered in the form of large blocks must be divided into plates of appropriate thickness before production can begin. This cutting was formerly accomplished with discs of soft iron, or even copper, and loose sand or emery, and was more a grinding than a sawing operation. Impregnated diamond wheels are preferred today. Methods for producing such diamond saws are contained in the literature, but this cannot be recommended since the economical production of high-quality diamond tools capable of a long cutting life requires extensive manufacturing experience, and very excellent diamond impregnated discs are today supplied by specialist manufacturers in the field.

These discs are driven with a speed of 10 to 20 m/sec. The feed is given by attachable weights which press the glass block against the saw blade. The feed required

Fig. 18. Sawing.

depends upon the hardness of the glass, and is regulated for an average rate of 10 cm²/min, lighter feeds giving a smoother cut. The disc is cooled with water, or better with oil, to obtain a smoother cutting action. In some applications several diamond wheels are combined in a frame-saw arrangement to deliver several plates simultaneously.

The working life of a diamond wheel is given by the area cut and, of course, by the glass hardness. On the average, an area of 1500 cm² can be cut for every cm of circumference. Cut plates can be used directly only if the cutting face is extremely smooth. Most cuts are rather irregular, and require some subsequent grinding to impart a uniform initial working surface. This grinding can be done without the complicated procedure of making plane plates described later on. The square pieces are ground from both sides simultaneously (fig. 19). For the production of lenses of very high precision, the plates are sometimes polished for a further quality inspection. Pieces containing striae or veils must be removed. Bubbles and dead metal are not so important, but they must be held below a limit given by the lens purpose. Large bubbles and inclusions make a piece of glass unuseable. This checking does not entail excessive effort if a method for grinding and polishing both sides simultaneously is employed. Such a method will be discribed later.

Fig. 19. Lapping.

Rounding

The plates must be cut into square pieces. Diamond cutters should not be used for ground glass, as they are soon ruined, and a steel roller is preferable for this purpose. Plates thicker than about 10 mm tend to break outside the stroke and should be cut with a slitting wheel. For economical rounding, a number of the square pieces are heated and cemented together as a rectangular stack, with metal tool-pieces at either end. The cemented stack of lens-blanks is then milled to form a cylinder whose diameter is slightly larger than that of the finished lenses (figs. 20 and 21). Modern rounding machines permit the pre-setting of this diameter. Plates for large-diameter lenses must be rounded individually. Such discs may be obtained by trepanning them out of a large plate with a tubular diamond tool or a round pot with diamond bort sintered onto its borders. In some instances, glass is supplied in cylindrical bars of the required diameters, permitting the discs to be sawn off as required.

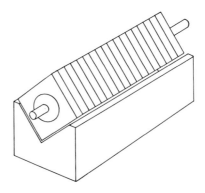

Fig. 20. The stacking of rectangular pieces.

Fig. 21. A rounding machine.

Roughing the curvature

Rough grinding with loose emery has long been abandoned since it is now generally recognized that milling with bound grain is far more economical. The working scheme of milling machines appropriate to this purpose is shown in fig. 22.

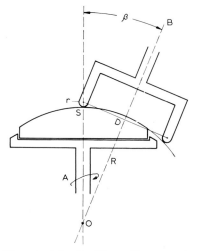

Fig. 22. The principle of milling with a pot-shaped tool.

The lens is on top of the axis A, and rotates only once or twice during the milling. The cylindrical diamond tool has the form of a pot, whose rim has radius of curvature r, and turns rapidly around its axis, B. Its working line is a circle of the diameter D, and it is most important that this working line touches the lens at its vertex, S. The radius of curvature R of the lens is given by the angle β between the two axes A and B, according to the relationship:

$$R = \frac{D}{2 \sin \beta} \pm r.$$

The negative sign refers to convex surfaces, the positive to concave surfaces.

The tool is fixed on a cross support, and the adjustment is made as carefully as possible, using a model. The final position is then preset for automatic operation of the machine. The lens is held in its casing by tongs, or a pneumatic device, enabling a single operator to supervise a number of machines (fig. 23). During the first turn of the machine the tool cuts deeply, and afterwards with a low feed. Lenses so produced exhibit a silky glaze. This system is obviously not self-centring, and one is therefore dependent upon the precision of the bearings. The spherical form cannot generally be guaranteed, and it is therefore sometimes recommended that a further smoothing be made with loose grain to secure the exact spherical shape.

The advantages of this method of milling are that many different radii of curvature can be produced with the same tool, and that once the tool is accurately adjusted the procedure is extremely fast. When the angle of the two axes is set at zero the machine can be employed for trepanning round discs from glass plates. Of course, in this application the diameter of the discs depends on the inner diameter of the tool. Machines built to permit a horizontal positioning of the axis A are also very useful

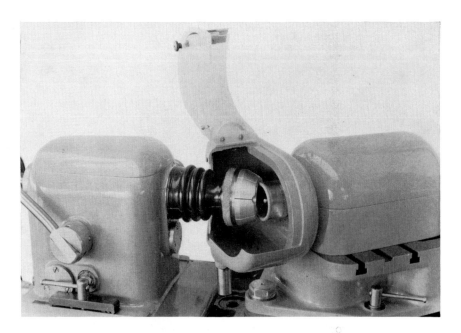

Fig. 23. Milling machine for spherical surfaces.

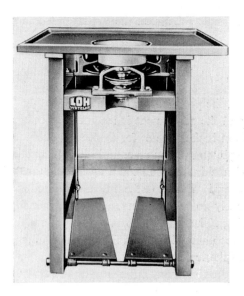

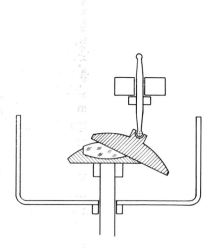

Fig. 24. A trueing machine.   Fig. 25. A double pedal grinding machine.

for the production of convex and concave grinding tools. For this application the diamond can be replaced by a steel tool.

3.2. TRUEING AND SMOOTHING

It is quite possible to grind concave and convex surfaces by hand, with the aid of a still concave or convex tool. Emery is mixed with water to form a paste that is smeared between the tool and the lens, and the lens is moved to and fro with light hand pressure, so that all areas of the tool make contact with all areas of the lens. It is, however, more convenient to drive the tool by means of a foot-tredle of motor, with the lens mounted at the end of a dowel or other handgrip. Even today, single lenses are often ground in this manner, especially when prototypes or masters are to be made, when the curvature exceeds a hemisphere, or when the diameter is unusually small. The vertical axis of the machine is threaded to accept the tool, and a cage or pan is arranged around the spindle to collect emery thrown off during the working (fig. 24).

Fig. 26. A double eccentric arrangement.

In a further refinement, the movement of the lens is also automatic. Fig. 25 shows a machine in which the lens is mounted of top of a vertical axis. A concave tool rests on the lens, and is held in its centre by a ball-and-socket universal joint. The movement of the tool is effected by one or two eccentric arms that shift the tool to and fro over the lens surface (fig. 26). This movement acts only on the ball joint, and the rotation of the tool is effected by friction through the turning of the work piece. The aim is to bring all areas of the tool in contact with all areas of the surface so that the workpiece is evenly abraded. This cannot be achieved perfectly. The movement of single points of the tool have been investigated frequently. The curve described by every point of the tool on the surface is a complicated cycloid of a high geometrical degree. Its form depends on the eccentric mechanism, on the ratio of the rotation speeds of the workpiece and the eccentric, and on the degree of eccentricity. Some special cases are shown in figs. 27, 28 and 29. These curves were obtained by putting

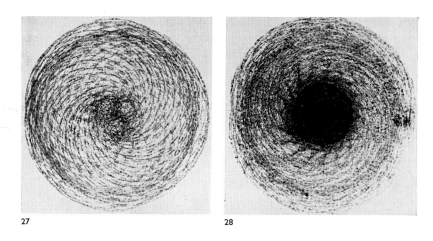

27   28

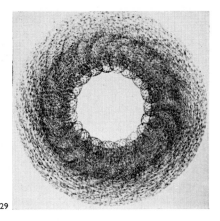

29

Figs. 27, 28 and 29. Pencil-point traces show the effect of grinding with eccentric ratios of 1:1.4, 1:1, and 1:3, respectively.

a pencil into the tool and allowing it to mark its path on a plane plate of glass. The machine had a double eccentric mechanism, and the ratio of the two eccentrics was varied. In fig. 27 this ratio was 1 : 1.4. If it is made to be 1 : 1 we obtain a stronger abrasion at the centre than at the border, see fig. 28. Contrary to this, a ratio of 1 : 3

in the eccentric positions leads to increased abrasion at the borders (fig. 29). The operator has to adjust the degree of eccentricity according to his experience. Too much eccentricity will generate faster grinding at the borders. This means that in grinding a convex surface there is a tendency for the radius of curvature to become too short, and for concave surfaces too long.

The system is wholly self-centring, since the universal ball-and-socket joint is movable in all directions, and the whole surface of the tool always rests upon the whole surface of the workpiece. This self-centring is in no way dependent on the accuracy of the bearings. The feed can be varied by means of weights placed upon the eccentric lever. In grinding spherical surfaces, however, the pressure of the weights changes with the position of the ball-joint. For this reason, in many modern grinding machines the weights are replaced by adjustable springs which assure that the tool is always pressed normal to the workpiece. Modern machines also contain an automatic emery feed, so that the emery-laden water is sprayed onto the workpiece, or so that the tool dips periodically into the emery paste at its deepest point of movement.

Fig. 30. A multiplex grinding machine.

In another design, the movement of the tool is effected by pure oscillations rather than by an eccentric mechanism. Such machines are generally built as multiplex grinders with a series of spindles united in a row, as shown in fig. 30. The operation of such a machine is supervised by a worker who keeps the spindles supplied with emery paste, and who checks the lenses from time to time, adjusting the degree of spring pressure and/or eccentricity as the grinding progresses. In the trueing process he must carefully check the tool, correcting it when worn at the centre or border.

A general rule adopted in most optical workshops is to let the concave surface – tool or workpiece – be always arranged above the convex piece. During rotation, the emery floats slowly down to the borders, providing greater grinding action where this is most needed, since more material must be removed from the border than from the center. Contrary to this almost universal custom, F. Twyman, in his famous book *Prism and Lens Making*, recommends that the tool should always be located below the workpiece. The reason given is that in this position wearing of the tool can be controlled and compensated easily by altering the pressure and stroke.

The tool radius differs from that of the workpiece by the average diameter of the grain. In trueing this average grain diameter lies between 25 and 80 μm, and in smoothing between 5 and 25 μm. If, for example, the tool used for roughing a convex form were provided with the grain for trueing, it would attack only the centre of the lens, ruining the spherical form already achieved (fig. 31). Different tools must therefore

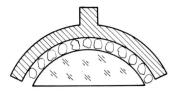 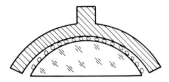

Fig. 31. Since the tool must attack the workpiece at the border, its radius of curvature must be selected in relation to the diameter of the grain.

be used for successive grinding stages, and the optical shop must keep a complete set of tools for each radius of curvature in stock.

Smoothing serves only to prepare the surface for final polishing. There is, however, a fundamental difference between trueing and smoothing. In point of fact, a grain may occasionally produce a new and deeper pitting of the surface because the elementary process is out of control in grinding with loose grain.

Experiments have been carried out to accomplish both trueing and smoothing with a tool whose surface is impregnated with sintered diamond bort. The results are excellent, and quite encouraging. There is no appreciable wearing of the tool whose working life is practically unlimited. In addition, such tools require no correction. A heavy feed and a high turning speed can be chosen for rough grinding, and smoothing can be accomplished by lowering the feed to the minimum required to maintain working contact. Surfaces so ground are much more uniform than those produced by grinding with loose grain. Because of this, the polishing time can be reduced to a fraction of the normal working period. Production carried out with diamond tools can therefore compete economically with normal methods, and it can be confidently expected that the extensive use of diamond tools will initiate a revolution in lens and prism making. On the other hand, it must not be concealed that the fabrication of these diamond tools requires the solution to some difficult problems. For one thing, the necessarily high sintering temperatures cause the body of the tool to warp, and this loss of form precision has to be corrected. Here, hardness is actually a disadvantage since diamond tools require higher form accuracy than normal ones. This is because ordinary tools regenerate their spherical form during working, while diamond tools transfer their form to the workpiece because of their greater hardness.

3.3. POLISHING

A smoothed surface exhibits an average roughness of 7 μm left by the last working tool, and less if the grinding and smoothing was carried out with diamond tools. Loose grain produces a less regular surface, particularly when a few larger grains come into play, forming flakes or pits between the hills and valleys. An ideal polishing would smooth the peaks down to the level of the deepest valleys. But, as previously described, a skin of silica-gel is formed over the whole glass surface, covering the peaks and valleys at the conclusion of the polishing process.

Polishing is carried out with pitch, cloth, or felt. Felt is used only for lenses not destined to produce the highest image quality because this thick and yielding material does not maintain the form previously achieved by the smoothing stage, having an undesirable tendency to remove an excessive amount of border material. Felt polishing does, however, work very quickly, particularly when the load is high. Cloth polishing does not affect the form as much as felt because it is thinner and has a more uniform consistency. Ferrous oxides ('rouges') were formerly used as polishing powders, but in modern practice cerium oxide, and the oxides of various rare-earth elements are preferred because they shorten the polishing time very considerably.

The best polish is obtained with pitch. To make a pitch tool a concave or convex cast-iron head is given a coating of about 2 mm and is reversed into a warmed counter-form having the exact curvature of the lens surface. The finished tool is then given some rough scratches on its polishing surface. These grooves have three functions: they give the polishing powder a grip, prevent the tool from pasting at the lenses, and give room for the pitch to expand in, as it becomes warm in working. The composition of the pitch must be adapted to the kind of glass to be polished, and to the ambient room temperature, if the workroom is not fully airconditioned, as it should be in a modern optical works. The softening-point of the pitch, and its viscosity, vary with the proportion of the components used. The normal components are pure wood pitch, beeswax, and colophonium. Today, the chemical industry offers synthetic materials as a substitute for pitch. In the first line, a diphenyl chlorate proved successful in shortening the polishing time and lengthening the life of the polisher.

In some cases, the polishing powder is added directly to the pitch, instead of being smeared between the tool and the workpiece during polishing. Being the final step in lens manufacture, as regards the surface, polishing must result in an absolutely glossy surface that has the correct curvature. If the surface is destined to be the second surface of a lens, the thickness must lie between extremely narrow tolerances set forth by the lens designer. During polishing, the optician must constantly check the quality of the surface, i.e., the curvature and the degree of polish. This last point is checked by inspecting the surface before a broad and very bright light-source. A greyish appearance indicates that the surface has not yet received sufficient polishing. The inspection must reveal no scratches or pitting.

Lens curvature is tested with a thick glass or quartz testplate having the precise counter-curvature in the utmost spherical form, and a plane rear surface. The lens surface to be tested and the test-plate curvature are cleaned with extreme care, and then brought together in tight contact. The accuracy of the lens surface can now be judged in terms of the Newton rings produced, the matching of the two surfaces being expressed as the number of such rings and their circular shape (fig. 32). If the lens is

Fig. 32. Test-plate in contact with lens surface, showing Newton rings.

removed from its holder, other interference methods involving no physical contact can be used, thereby reducing the danger of injuring the surface to a minimum. Frequently, as one side of the lens is finished, it is given a coat of protective paint in order to guard against mechanical or chemical damage.

3.4. BLOCK METHODS

Up to this point we have discussed the manufacture of a single lens. But it is easy to realize that a number of lenses can more practically be worked simultaneously during milling, trueing and polishing operations. To achieve this higher manufacturing efficiency, the lenses need to be mounted on a carrier in such a way that all of their surfaces are areas of the same sphere forming a block (fig. 33). The number of lenses

Fig. 33. The block method is indispensible for mass-production of lenses.

that can be made together in this manner depends on the ratio of the lens diameter to the radius of curvature to be ground, as well as on the type of production machinery available in the optical shop. The approximate number of lenses that can be arranged on the block can be shown with a nomograph. But the most economical number of lenses that are to be worked simultaneously must be calculated for each case in respect to the cost of making the block and the working time saved, especially in the polishing stage.

Two patterns can be used for arranging the lenses on a concave or convex carrier. The first places one lens in the centre, surrounded by rings of six, twelve, and so forth (fig. 34). The other pattern has no lenses in the centre, but starts instead with a central ring of three lenses. The next ring can take nine, and the following 15 lenses (fig. 35). The latter pattern is preferable if the grinding is to be carried out with a diamond pot-tool, the adjustment of the pattern being somewhat less critical than with the first pattern.

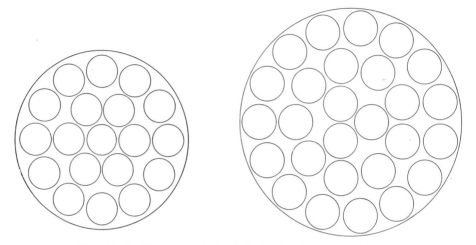

Figs. 34, 35. The two methods of distributing lenses on a block.

There is some objection to filling the carrier or block with lenses up to a hemisphere. However, the pressure of the load on the grinding head varies during the shifting from the centre to the border, and abrasion is therefore less in the equatorial than the polar areas. In this case, a block near to a hemisphere cannot be overly recommended. When the grinding pressure is generated by springs, as is the case in certain kinds of modern machines, as previously noted, the attack of the grain will be nearly uniform over the whole surface of the lens carrier. Eventually, the extensive use of diamond tools in spherical form may upset the currently valid calculation in favour of the loose grain method. With the shortening of the polishing time, some of the advantages of the block method are lost. At present, the modern use of diamond tools is still in its infancy, and grinding with loose grain remains in vogue. We have, therefore, to describe the making of blocks.

Fig. 36. A pitch mallet.

Two types of blocks are in general use today, differing principally in the methods applied in fixing the lenses to the carrier. The first type is the pitch-mallet block in which a lump of pitch placed on the rear surface of the lens is used to affix it to the carrier (fig. 36). The lenses are arranged in a concave fixing tool when convex surfaces are to be ground, and on a convex fixing tool for concave surfaces. The lenses must have a little space between them, and the radius of curvature of the fixing tools has

to be either longer or shorter than the final surface, depending upon the amount
of material that must be removed. This becomes evident from fig. 37. The radius of

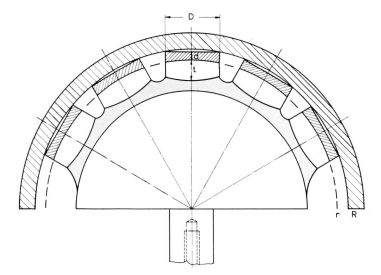

Fig. 37. Adjusting the blanks with an auxiliary tool.

Fig. 38. Making a block with annular pitch mallets.

the curve to be made is r. The blanks may have a plane surface. The hatched parts of the lenses have to be ground away, the thickness of this surplus being d. The radius of the fixing tool, R, is given by the distance between the spherical centre and the edge of the blanks, D, according to the formula: $R = \sqrt{[(r+d)^2 + (\frac{1}{2}D)^2]}$. This calculation of the correct curvature for the fixing tool is part of the preparatory work plan.

The block is warmed and placed on the pitch mallets. After sinking into the softened pitch, the block is cooled and the whole assembly is lifted out of the fixing tool (fig. 38).

The other type is the spot-block, a very complicated device that has to be made by a skilled toolmaker. Once in hand, however, the spot-block is much easier to work with than the pitch-mallet method. Because they are costly, spot-blocks are economical only for large-scale series production. In spot-block carriers (fig. 39) the lenses are

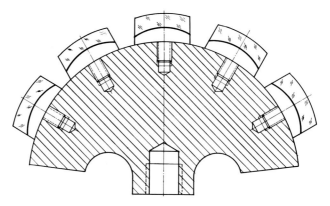

Fig. 39. A spot-block with interchangeable seats.

seated in individual holders that are screwed into the body of the block. These metal holders, or 'seats', are adapted in shape and size to the curvature of the rear surface of the lens, and the lenses are fixed into their seats by means of round pieces of resin-impregnated tissue.

The seats are usually screwed onto the carrier. This facilitates the making of the block, but seats milled directly into the body of the carrier are more precise. Some reference points have to be provided on the block in order to check the thickness of the lenses during working. The uniformity of the lens thicknesses depends upon the accuracy of the spot-block itself, as well as on the accuracy of the seats and of the lens fastening.

Many forms of spot-blocks are used in different optical plants, their design depending more on the special experience of the individual workshop supervisors than on any other factor. Fig. 39 shows such a block in which the support is screwed into the carrier body and the lens is fastened to the support on its whole surface by means of a resin-impregnated tissue disc. In fig. 40 the lens support is cut directly into the body of the spot-block, and the lens lies in this seat resting against a small circle close to the border. The central part of the seat is a little deeper in order to accept the fastening wax. The wax layer has to be thin, especially for negative shapes having little physical thickness. This is because the shrinking and stiffening of the wax sets up forces which can distort the shape of thin lenses. For this reason, this sort of mounting should be

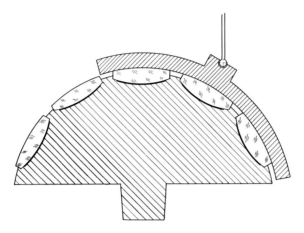

Fig. 40. A spot-block with seats engraved into the carrier.

restricted to lenses whose physical thickness is equal to at least 10 % of their diameters. The holder for the body of the spot-block is slightly conical in form in order to facilitate the centring of the block in the machine. Spot-blocks of this type afford the best accuracy in respect to maintaining precision lens thicknesses.

3.5. CENTRING

The optical axis of a lens is given by the straight line running through the centres of curvature of the two surfaces. (see fig. 41). The edge of the lens needs to be centred in

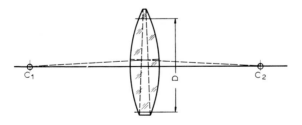

41. Centring a lens.

relation to the optical axis by the grinding of a concentrically cylindrical or conical surface. This process is sometimes combined with chamfering, the milling of sharp edges to prevent chipping.

The optical axis can be either optically or mechanically located. In the optical method, the heated lens is fixed onto the edge of a rotary tubular spindle, with pitch. The bearings of the spindle are manufactured with a very high degree of precision, and the observation of an illuminated target (i.e., cross-hairs) permits the optician to judge the adjustment. It is very important that the rear face of the lens be in good contact with the edge of the centring tube, and that this edge be precisely at right angles to the optical axis. The correct position occurs when the reflected target image comes to a complete rest during rotation of the lens. The tube is cooled cautiously until the pitch becomes rigid, and the physical border is then ground with a carborundum or diamond tool (fig. 42).

Fig. 42. Centring a lens on a rotating spindle.

The adjustment of the lens on the centring tube is a time-consuming operation. The tubes are therefore made to be interchangeable so that they can be easily removed from, and inserted into the edge-grinding machine. The fine adjustment of the lens on the tube can then be made away from the edge-grinder, on a special centring device. The interchangeable spindles are inserted into the machine only for grinding the edge. This method calls for a very high degree of precision in the centring tubes in order to avoid cumulative or systematic errors. In critical cases, the adjustment is made on a tube fixed in the edging machine, and the image of the illuminated cross-hairs is examined with a special autocollimation microscope.

The second, or mechanical method of centring employs two tubes which are centred as well as possible. These tubes are made from hardened tool-steel, and are ground on the machine itself. When the lens is inserted between the two ends, the tubes are pressed together by either spring or pneumatic pressure. This pressure automatically shifts the lens into the correct position, permitting the grinding of the edge without disturbing the position of the lens (fig. 43).

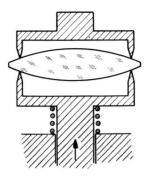

Fig. 43. Mechanical centring.

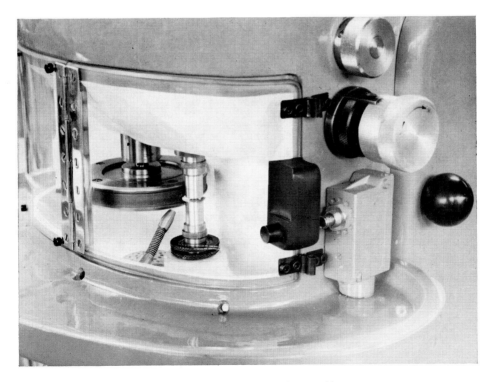

Fig. 44. An automatic centring machine.

This mechanical method can be applied with reasonable accuracy only when the angle between the surface and the plane at right-angles to the axis at the contact-line is at least 14°. If this angle is smaller, accurate centring cannot be guaranteed, although, of course, such machines can be employed for rounding-off lenses or plane discs. Fig. 44 shows an automatic centring machine of this type that takes each lens from the plate pneumatically, delivers it to the diamond tool, and then returns the centred and edged lens to the plate. On the average, some 90 % of lenses produced in a typical optical works are suitable for mechanical centring methods. Economically, however, these methods require the in-plant manufacture of special tools, and the feasibility of its application therefore depends upon the quantities of the same lens that are to be produced. Another objection to the use of mechanical methods is the danger of damaging the polished surfaces. When all operative factors are considered it is obvious that optical centring methods afford the highest precision.

After centring, the lens has sharp edges that are susceptible to chipping, especially with concave surfaces. The lenses must therefore be chamfered. As stated previously, this can generally be accomplished along with the centring and edging, using a carborundum wheel or a diamond tool. The method of chamfering with loose grain is today obsolete since it is undesirable for polished surfaces to come into contact with any loose grain. If the chamfering cannot, for any reason, be combined with the centring, it can safely be accomplished in a later stage through the use of a concave diamond tool having a curvature appropriate for the lens in question. A chamfering angle of 45° is customary, although this can be varied in accordance with other requirements. To obtain the radius of curvature, R, for the concave tool, in terms of the diameter, D, of the lens, the formula $R = 0.7D$ is used. The lens is held pneumatically against a pierced handle, and pressed gently against the diamond tool (fig. 45).

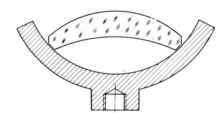

Fig. 45. Chamfering is done separately with a diamond tool.

In making single lenses, e.g., microscope lenses, it is sometimes possible to postpone the polishing until after the centring. This is quite reasonable because in this sequence of operations the vulnerable surface is not exposed to any other working processes, save the application of an anti-reflection coating. In this sequence, the lenses have to be decemented from the block, and later from the centring tool, and must be thoroughly cleaned for inspection of surface quality, as well as for the test-plate. For this purpose alcohol or methylated spirits are normally used since nearly all cements are soluble in this medium. Paraffin, beeswax, and pitch are easily dissolved in carbon tetrachloride. This liquid is, however, used only very reluctantly because of its adverse effects on the workers' health, and the use of trichloroethylene is therefore recommended.

3.6. THE PRODUCTION OF SPHERES

Lenses that exceed a hemisphere are often used in optical systems, such as high-aperture microscope objectives. In this case they are extremely small, sometimes hardly more than 1 mm in diameter, but in condenser systems diameters of up to about 20 mm are reached. Previously, such spheres had to be manufactured on an individual basis, and their production was all the more difficult due to the extraordinarily high precision required in microscopy.

A more simple way to produce such lenses than by applying the traditional way of grinding spherical lenses is to start by producing a complete sphere. This can be done with high accuracy, and the second surface (which may be plane or spherical) is then ground onto the sphere. There are several methods known for making good spheres. If they are very small, they can be made by heating lumps of glass of the right weight until they transform to spheres by the action of surface tension. Following another proposal, cubic pieces are placed into a drum along with emery, and the drum is rotated, or 'tumbled' until the cubes have been worn down to spheres. The rough spheres are then ground between two parallel high-speed grinding discs, a cage preventing the spheres from banging into each other. Polishing is carried out with a similar mechanical arrangement.

3.7. TOOL MAKING

Concave or convex grinding tools are turned on a lathe equipped with ball-bearing supports, conventional machines being able to produce curvatures of up to about one

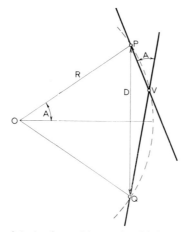

Fig. 46. Principle of device for making tools with large radii of curvature.

metre in diameter. Care must be exercised to make certain that the centre of the support is exactly in the axis of the spindle. If this is not the case, toric forms will be generated. The length of the bench must be in proportion to the length of the radii, and to maintain accurate centring of the two axes, the bench must be very substantial.

Another method is sometimes employed for cutting long radii with a short-bed lathe, as shown in fig. 46. If the two sides of fixed angle A slide over two fixed points P and Q at the distance D, the vertex V of this angle describes a circle. The radius R of this circle can be found easily by considering the angle as a peripheral angle belonging to the angle $2A$ at the centre O. We then have the relationship:

$$R = \frac{D}{2 \sin A}.$$

By varying the angle A, any radius between the minimum given by the tool and infinity can be achieved. This principle is employed in some supports for the production of optical tools, the steel cutting tool moving along a rule and pressed against the workpiece by a spring.

It is, however, difficult to give this system the mechanical precision needed for the production of optical tools. Furthermore, for long radii the angle A needs to be very small, thus leading to a loss of accuracy because the value for sin A is in the denominator of the fraction. Modern technology has fortunately provided the optical industry with universal copying machines of very high precision. In these machines the cutting edge is usually controlled by an hydraulic system, according to a master model. This master can be made with the aid of a pair of compasses, cutting it out of a piece of sheet metal. A positive and a negative piece must be made, the two being ground together until the required curvature is achieved. The copying machine then reproduces the curvature of the model in the workpiece.

Although optical tools must have the correct spherical form, a very smooth surface is not required. This is generated automatically in working. At the same time, however, the form of the tool is lost through use, and it is up to the optical worker to keep the tool in form, especially those used for trueing and smoothing. This is done by frequently testing lens surfaces generated by the tool for curve conformity. Small discrepancies can be corrected by altering the eccentricity and the load on the level, as described in the section on grinding methods. When these machine adjustments are no longer effective, the shape of the form must itself be corrected. The best method is to remove some metal from the tool by scratching with a carborundum stone. If the lenses exhibit a curvature that is too shallow (i.e. a longer radius) some material has to be removed from the central area of the tool, and a radius that is too short means that border material must be removed. Such corrections are necessary only in the last stages of grinding, trueing and smoothing.

4. Plane plates

The machinery needed for the production of plane plates is in principle very similar to that required for the grinding and further working of spherical curvatures. It must, however, be recognized that the precision of parallelism is mainly dependent on the diameter of the tools, and that for plane surfaces the size of the machine is itself an important factor. This entails no disadvantage, since larger tools in any case make for more economical series production, and there is normally no limit on the diameter of the tools. On the other hand, these larger tools occupy more work-area, and it is therefore customary to produce plane optics in a separate workshop or working area.

The rough plates are embedded in pitch for the grinding and polishing of the first side. To work the second side, the plates are cemented, finished-side-down, onto a thick disc of plane glass. Spiral or crossed grooves cut into the plate facilitate cement adhesion. After the engraving of these grooves, the glass work-disc must be polished to the best degree possible. It is sometimes recommended in the literature that for good flatness three discs should be worked together, using each to grind the others. But, as we have previously seen, polishing cannot be accomplished with glass-to-glass contact. The three-disc method can, therefore, be used only for grinding and testing, and not for the final polishing operation. To Twyman belongs the credit for first introducing the interferometer method for testing in workshops on a large scale. Today, even the testing of very large optical parts is carried out more simply by means of the interferometer than by the three-disc method.

The cementing of the plates is done with soft pitch, or even better, with wax. This is because the disc can become deformed if the cementing medium is too hard. The grooves take up the superfluous cement thereby making for better contact be-tween the flat workpiece and the raised portions of the base disc. Good contact is essential for ensuring the parallelism of the two sides of the worked plates. Parallelism can be checked by measuring the thickness of the plates at different points, the accura-cy of this test being in direct proportion to the distance between the chosen measuring points. The diameter of the base disc is therefore quite large.

In addition to parallelism, the flatness of the surface must also be tested since there is a tendency to spherical errors. To minimize this difficulty, the work-disc should be filled with workpieces, arranging them in an approximate circle, or series of concentric circles. If necessary, auxiliary pieces of scrap glass are used to fill out the circular form (fig. 47).

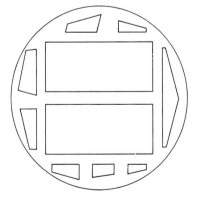

Fig. 47. In grinding plane surfaces, auxiliary pieces of scrap glass
improve the plane-parallelism of the surfaces.

In addition to this traditional method of making plane-parallel plates, a new method is today being adopted in many works. This is the lapping of the plates by simultaneously working both sides. The plates are placed on an annular pitch polisher, and another polisher is placed over them. The workpieces are held in a cage that permits them to rotate according to the forces acting on them, but prevents any contact between them. The two polishers are put on a grinding machine working through an eccentric. The lower polisher is attached to the vertical spindle, while the upper spindle is driven by the eccentric. It is turned either automatically, as in grinding spheres, or is driven by planetary gears. The amplitude of the eccentric movement must lead the polisher far enough to make all areas of both polishers work in the same way, in order to ensure that both are worn equally. This lapping method yields a very high degree of precision in respect to plate thickness and parallelism.

Temperature is the principal problem encountered in polishing with large machines. This depends upon the speed of the spindle, the load placed on the tool and, of course, on the natures of the polisher, polishing medium and glass. Heat developed by polishing friction causes deformations in the worked plates, and a change in the viscosity of the pitch. In this respect, the provision of the polishers with a network of engraved grooves has proved most advantageous. A primary consideration in obtaining a polish of high accuracy is that the material should be stressed as little as possible.

5. Prism making

Prisms are given their initial rough form by sawing and milling in a device that fixes the angles between the planes. The planes can be ground with the workpiece held firmly in a plaster block. The roughly formed prisms are placed face-down on a plate, and the fluid plaster is poured over them. After the plaster has hardened, this plate is inverted and the plane surfaces to be worked are laid open by lightly engraving the empty spaces between individual prisms with a sharp knife or razor blade. The plaster must now receive a shellac coating to protect it against water

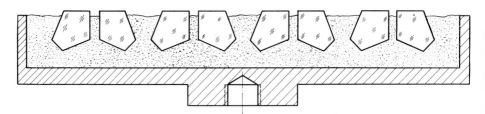

Fig. 48. A plaster block for prism making.

during grinding (fig. 48). This plaster-block method has, however, been abandoned in most modern plants because the hardening of the plaster introduces different stresses on the embedded prisms. These forces turn the prism workpieces slightly away from their intended positions and the angular relationships are therefore incorrect.

Modern prism manufacture is accomplished by mounting the prisms on metal holders using a thin cement. The plane surfaces of these holders are grooved so that the prism does not rest on the whole surface (fig. 49). This trick is important for easier cleaning of the surfaces before the prisms are mounted, as well as to facilitate their removal after the surfacing. If the holding devices are made from metals such as steel or brass they can be screwed onto the baseplate.

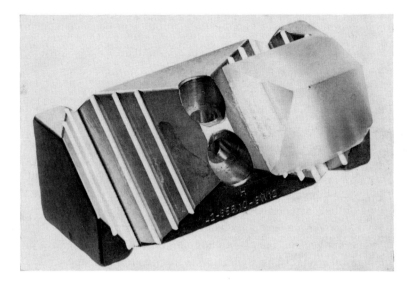

Fig. 49. A jig for prisms.

For the highest degree of angular accuracy, however, the holding devices are made of glass. In this case the setting and adjusting of the prisms can be controlled by observing the Newton fringes. The baseplate is also made of glass, thus permitting the individual holders to be cemented in their working positions free from Newton fringes. Such precision is demanded for the production of roof-prisms in which the 90° angle must sometimes be controlled to an accuracy of only a few seconds of arc in order to avoid double contours in the instruments. It should be clear that the adjustment and cementing of prisms in the working device is a more than usually complicated process that demands a high order of skill and precision.

In a reflecting prism, at least three surfaces are used optically: two for the entrance and exit pupils, and one for the reflection. These surfaces must not only form the correct angles from one to the next, but the third in respect to the first as well (see fig. 50). This means, in other words, that the *three* planes must be at right angles to the base plane. A deviation from this condition is called pyramidal error, as a consequence of which we obtain not only an incorrectly aligned optical axis but, in addition, a rotation of the image around the axis. The tolerance for this condition is, of course, much higher in a reflecting prism than in a roof-prism.

After the cement has been dissolved, the finished surface is given a protective coating to avoid damage during further treatment. The ridge of a roof-prism must sometimes be made as sharp as possible. In this case, after the first plane of the roof is finished, an auxiliary piece of glass of the same type is cemented against the finished surface. The other plane is then ground and polished together with the auxiliary protective piece. After cautiously dissolving the cement, the ridge is very sharp and extremely vulnerable, requiring extreme care in further handling.

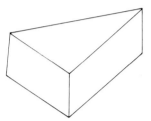

Fig. 50. Pyramidal error.

6. Proof plates

Proof plates are fundamental tools in the production of lenses, providing a fast and accurate workshop method for testing surface curvatures, the difference between the curvature of the lens and the proof plate being revealed as the deviation of the surface from a perfect sphere. Errors in the radius of curvature cause Newton rings between the lens surface and the proof plate, this deviation being seen as an elliptical pattern of Newton rings. In this case the surface has a toric form, the amount of deformation being proportional to the number of visible rings. If the surface curvature is symmetrical to the axis, but non-spherical (e.g., egg-shaped), the Newton rings exhibit irregular diameters. In a perfect sphere, these diameters have a ratio number that is the square root of a whole number.

The material of the proof plate is well annealed crown glass or fused quartz. Both materials are desirably hard, but the latter offers the added advantage of a lower sensitivity to temperature variations. The rear surfaces are always plane, and the thickness is usually about one third of the diameter. Proof plates are always made in concave/convex pairs. Their production begins with normal tools on which they are ground to a close approximation of the required curvature. The fine grinding, and subsequent steps, are always carried out by hand, one piece being worked against the other. The alteration of the curvature is given by a simple rule: Since one piece is on the turning spindle, and the other is above it, being moved to and fro, the border is always abraded more than the centre. Following this principle, the correct curvature can quite easily be realized.

During this hand procedure, the curvature must periodically be checked with a spherometer. The polishing tool is made with the help of the finely ground surfaces themselves. The need is less for high surface perfection than for maximum spherical accuracy. After polishing, the final curvature is measured as precisely as possible, a deviation from the required value of 0.1 % being generally considered satisfactory.

7. The measurement of curvature

The curvature of a lens surface can be compared with that of an appropriate test surface, and the differences in the radii can be evaluated by the number of Newton rings. Precise measurement of the test surfaces have to be made very accurately, using optical or mechanical methods.

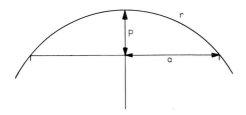

Fig. 51. The principle of spherometry.

Mechanical measurement of surface curvature requires the use of a spherometer, the principle for which is shown in fig. 51. If a circle is marked on a sphere, the relationship between the diameter of the circle $2a$, the radius of the sphere r, and the depth p, is given by

$$r = \tfrac{1}{2}(a^2/p+p).$$

In the instrument illustrated in fig. 52 the circle is represented by a steel ring whose upper surface has been lapped plane to a very high standard. The outer edge of this

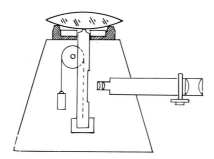

Fig. 52. A spherometer.

ring is used for the measurement of concave surfaces, the inner edge for convex surfaces. The two diameters must be known very precisely, being used in the formula as a square. A movable contact pin is pressed against the surface by a light weight. Its position can be observed through a microscope and read off on a calibrated scale to which the pin is connected. By first placing a plane surface, and then a spherical one on the ring, its depth can be measured and the curvature of the spherical surface calculated by using the formula given above. The accuracy of the value obtained by this procedure depends essentially on the magnitude of the ratio a^2/p. For this reason, the diameter of the ring should be only slightly smaller than the diameter of the lens to be tested. Errors will result if the ring is not perfectly circular, or if the edges are either dull or damaged.

The use of the spherometer should therefore be limited to the laboratory, rather than the workshop. Simplified versions of this instrument are available for workshop use although, of course, they do not yield the same order of accuracy. These workshop spherometers operate on the principle of three points defining a surface, or even with only two points, and are usually calibrated directly in curvature values. For best accuracy, two corresponding surfaces of the same curvatures, one convex and the other concave, are measured by placing them on the spherometer ring in succession. The sum of the two depths $p = p_1 + p_2$ is read on the instrument, and the radius of curvature has to be evaluated. One must, however, consider that in this method the concave surface was touched by the outer edge of the ring, and the convex curvature by the inner edge. Two different values of the edge radii will therefore appear in the formula for the radius of the curvature. Thus:

$$r = \frac{a_1^2 + a_2^2}{2p} + \tfrac{1}{4}p + c,$$

where c is usually negligibly small. Actually, the gain in measuring accuracy is not high enough to justify this method.

In many cases, a higher degree of precision in curvature measurement is required than can be achieved by means of even an exceptionally good mechanical sphero-meter. An extremely high order of curvature measuring precision can be obtained optically, by means of improved autocollimation methods that provide an accuracy for r of approximately 10^{-5}. When cross-hairs are projected onto a spherical surface by means of an autocollimation microscope, an image can be obtained at only two positions on the sphere (see fig. 53). In the first position A the rays fall normal to the

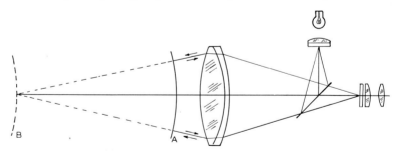

Fig. 53. Measuring of curvature by autocollimation.

surface, and are themselves reflected. In the other position B the image is formed on the vertex of the surface, the rays being reflected symmetrically. The distance between these two positions is the radius of curvature.

For long radii, a telescope with a special head is employed. This focuses the rays to a point by means of an objective, and magnifies their convergence by means of a system of prisms, as shown in fig. 54. To obtain a more stringent adjustment than can be obtained solely by judging the sharpness of the cross-hairs, a reticule consisting of three equidistant lines is employed. The correct setting is obtained when the two

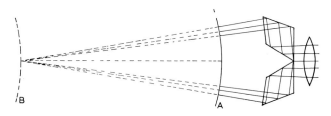

Fig. 54. Measuring-head for long radii.

three-line images are brought into coincidence. The sensitivity of an observer is, however, much higher in judging a symmetrical arrangement of lines than in judging coincidence. It is therefore better to make two successive adjustments, selecting the two possible symmetrical positions of the two sets of lines, as is shown in fig. 55. The two images are here drawn with a small difference in height, in order to make them

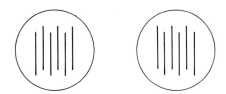

Fig. 55. The two position for symmetry adjustment.

more distinguishable. The arithmetical mean of the two distances read off a scale gives the final value. This adjustment must be made for the two positions on the surface, as previously described.

8. Cementing lenses

Before the anti-reflection treatment of glass surfaces was known, a principal aim of the lens designer was to limit the number of air-glass interfaces to the smallest possible number. If the curvatures of adjacent lenses within the system curve toward each other, and can be made equal in radius, but opposite in sign, the two lenses can be cemented together. Because of anti-reflection coatings, or 'blooming', this is not as urgent today as it was formerly. In fact, by dispensing with cementing new possibilities for superior correction with the same number of lenses can often be obtained. On the other hand, cementing is sometimes necessary to avoid excessively high angles of incidence, and offers many other advantages. These include the fact that minor surface irregularities can sometimes be permitted since their influence is suppressed by cementing, and the savings that can be effected by having to provide a mechanical mount for one lens instead of for two. For these, and other reasons, the cementing of lenses is still part of the ordinary routine in modern optical plants.

Prior to cementing, the lenses must be cleaned very carefully, using alcohol or ether and a camel's hair brush. A wiper consisting of a small piece of chamois leather stuck on a peg may also prove useful. The lenses are laid together and checked by inspecting the coloured Newton rings to be sure that both surfaces are suitable for cementing. They are then placed on a heated plate, the concave surface to be cemented facing upward. The upper lens is lifted, and a drop of Canada balsam (or other adhesive) is applied to the surface (fig. 56). The two lenses are then pressed together lightly,

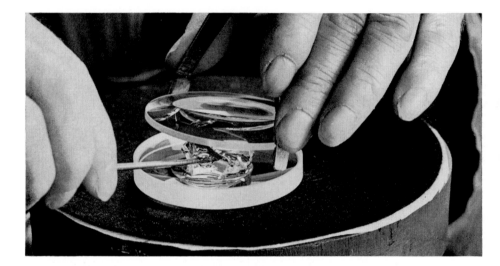

Fig. 56. Cementing lenses.

with a slow turning motion to squeeze out all air-bubbles and superfluous adhesive. A very careful inspection must be made to be certain that no air-bubbles or particles of dust are present, especially if the cemented achromat is intended for use in an ocular. Balsam layers should not exceed a thickness of approximately 0.02 mm.

Canada balsam is available in three hardness grades. The hardest type has a melting point of 78 °C, and is the most commonly used. Medium balsam melts at 60 C°, and the soft grade at 50 °C. The heat used for cementing must therefore be chosen for the type of balsam being used. The softer grades are used only when three lenses have to be cemented together, the first cementing being done with a balsam having a higher melting point than that used for subsequent cementing. After cementing, the lenses must be held at the cementing temperature for a short time to permit the tensions to equalize before they are slowly cooled.

The principal problem in cementing is the centring of the pair. When the diameters of the two lenses are exactly equal, two straight edges at right-angles to each other will be a help, and as long as the pair remains warm, they can be shifted into the correct position. If the diameters are different the centring must be performed on a simplified centring device. This consists of a vertical axis set in high-precision bearings that rests on the top of a short tube turned only by hand.

The cemented pair is placed on the end of this tube, and the centring adjustment is made by observing the reflected image of a small illuminated target (fig. 57). The

Fig. 57. Centring during the cementing of lenses.

mechanical centring method previously described can also be used in cementing, provided that the radii of curvature are sufficiently short to permit the shifting of the lenses into the correct position.

The chemical industry has recently developed, and is today offering, several cements for optical usage which belong to the family of epoxy resins. Although these cements are fluid at room temperature, it is preferable to apply them when warmed. After the lenses have been cemented and centred, they are baked for several hours, according to the specific instructions given for each type of epoxy resin. These new cements withstand temperature variations over a range of -40 to $+80$ °C, without detaching, as would be the case with Canada balsam. Epoxy resins are also exceptionally strong and shock-resistant, the bonds being often stronger than the glass itself. In addition, they can be obtained with special UV-absorbing properties which can be of benefit to the correction. In working with these materials, special care has to be exercised to prevent the lenses from shifting between cementing and polymerization.

9. Aspherical lenses

Every lens designer is familiar with the possibilities given by the use of aspherical lens surfaces. Such surfaces are symmetrical to the axis, but their generating meridional section is not part of a circle. The meridional curve may be a conic section, i.e. a curve of the second order, or even of a higher order. The only condition for the usefulness of aspherical surfaces in optics is that the curvature from the vertex to the border must change continuously. In special cases, the deformation of the surface is made by hand for lowering zonal aberrations. In this way corrections are given to Newtonian telescope mirrors and lenses.

Searchlight mirrors usually have both a high aperture and a large diameter. They therefore require an aspherical correction to achieve satisfactory quality. If the imaging is accomplished by the front surface alone, a purely parabolic concave form is the best. In this case, however, the reflecting surface is exposed to atmospheric attack. For this reason it is usually the rear surface which carries the reflective coating. This means that the surface has to compensate for aberrations introduced by the front surface that is used twice, and the rear surface must have a much more complicated aspherical shape. In some cases both surfaces are aspherical.

Such searchlight mirrors cannot be mass-produced. But, on the other hand, they are seldom required in sufficient quantities to justify the provision of special production tools. The rough form is instead created by permitting the heated disc to sag into an iron mould. Trueing is accomplished with a flexible strip of steel carrying the grinders and supported from the other side by adjustable rollers. This is moved to and fro over the rotating mirror surface. The form has to be checked frequently and requires periodic corrections which are made by changing the adjustment of the rollers. A tool in the form of a tripod is used for polishing to a glossy surface.

This method does not, of course, lend itself to large-scale series production but the manufacture of aspherical illumination lenses, as well as aspherical ophthalmic lenses for persons operated on for cataracts, must be done in large quantities if at all. The deviation of the meridional generatrix from a true circle is highest in illumination lenses, although in this application there is no particular need for great surface accuracy. Aspherical illumination lenses are therefore usually cast in a glossy mould. In ophthalmic lenses, on the contrary, the aspherical deviation from a perfect sphere remains mostly below 0.3 mm at the border. In this application, high precision is required to make sensible the use of an aspherical curvature.

Zeiss pioneered the mass-production of aspherical lenses, beginning with illumination lenses. With the experience gained in this field, many aspherical ophthalmic lenses, and even some objectives with aspherical surfaces were produced. The accuracy achieved can be measured by attempting to generate a spherical curvature on a machine intended for aspherical surfaces. The results of such tests have been quite satisfactory, and a very high percentage of the spherical surfaces so produced exhibited a deviation of only three Newton rings.

The rough working of aspherical lenses is performed with a diamond tool in a

machine that copies the surface of a master profile. In this part of the process, the
final form is approached to within about 0.05 mm. The lenses are then put into a
second machine for smoothing to the final form (see fig. 58). The principal part of
this machine is its aluminium or brass grinding disc *12* which yields a fine grinding
with loose grain. The relatively soft metal takes the grain into its surface to work,
in effect, very similar to a tool grinding with bound grain.

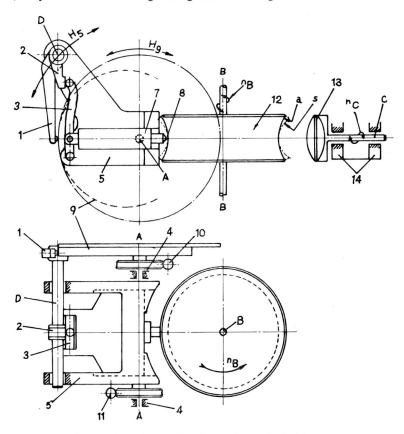

Fig. 58. The Zeiss machine for trueing aspherical lenses.

This grinding disc rotates around a vertical axis, working with its periphery which
bears the generating curve for the aspherical surface. The lenses *13* are pressed
against this curve by air, oil, or spring pressure. The lenses rotate about their own
axis, making contact with the whole of the generating meridional curve. Contrary
to the general rule in grinding spherical surfaces by areal osculation, this method provides purely linear contact. It can be assumed that this linear contact accounts for the
superiority of this design over all aspherical grinding methods that employ point
abrasion.

A zig-zag slit cut into the circumference of the grinding disc is another important
factor. The form of this slit can be seen in fig. 59 on the unrolled periphery of the

grinding disc. In grinding any convex surface, more material must be removed from the borders than from the central region. Ordinarily, this is taken care of by the fact that the higher edge-velocity of the tool automatically increases abrasion at the border. In this case, however, because the axis of rotation of the tool is at right-angles to the axis of the workpiece, grinding is more-or-less completely uniform over the whole lens surface. We must, therefore, find a means of reducing the grinding efficiency in the centre.

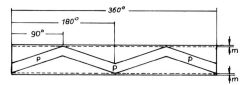

Fig. 59. Zig-zag in grinding disc circumference.

Exactly this effect is achieved by diminishing the circumference of the grinding disc in its middle section by means of the zig-zag slits. In addition, emery admitted through these slits disperses uniformly over the whole mantle line. Several lenses are worked simultaneously, neighbouring lenses rotating in opposite directions. This is because the relative velocities of the grinding disc and the lenses are different at the upper and lower parts of the form, in one part adding, and in the other subtracting. If all the lenses turned in the same direction, the disc would be worn differently in its upper and lower regions. By causing the lenses to rotate in opposite directions this is effectively avoided.

The grinding disc must be corrected for the right profile at frequent intervals, a diamond tool being brought against the disc to renew the mantle line. The design of

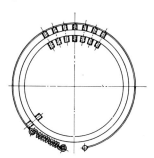

Fig. 60. Flexible metal strip determines the aspherical form.

this trueing mechanism, following the description by Twyman (based on an official report) can be seen in the left part of fig. 58. The radius in the vertex of curvature of the aspherical surface is set by the point A. The master aspherical cam 9 is mounted on a continuation of the shaft supporting the trueing mechanism, and represents an enlargement of the required aspherical curve, depending on the gear-ratio. The trueing mechanism 5 swings about the axis AA' in the indicated direction H5, and can be moved to either side. This is driven by gear *11* which is shown in the drawing as a worm-gear drive but, on the machine itself appears to be a pulley-and-weight system.

Lever *1* slides by means of a ball-joint over cam *9*, a flexible metal strip (see fig. 60) which may be set to the desired curvature by means of adjusting screws. Lever *2* is mounted on the same shaft as lever *1*, and moves lever *3* which, in turn, imparts the slope of the aspherical curve to the diamond tool *8* through the tool-holder *7*. This movement of the diamond cuts the mirror image of the desired surface into the tool *12*. The radius of the spherical lens is indicated by *s*, and the aspherical curve produced by the tool *12* is indicated by *a*. The lens is not removed from the adapter until the polishing.

Polishing must be carried out with an elastic medium over which a polishing cloth is stretched. As previously mentioned, the grinding is very similar to working with bound grain, giving a sufficiently fine surface to result in a relatively short polishing time. This is very important since the polisher has no definite form, and a long period of polishing would adversely affect the accuracy of the ground surface.

These machines were in operation until they were destroyed in 1945. In a more highly developed form, even elements for photographic lenses could be made quite satisfactorily on a machine of this type.

Schmidt plates are deformed plane plates and have relatively large diameters. They are primarily used in telescopes and other astronomical instruments, as well as in some television sets. Schmidt made his plates by placing flat discs over a pot which was then evacuated to bend the plates by vacuum pressure. The surface was then ground even and polished. After releasing the vacuum, the plate exhibits zonal deformations. To obtain a plate of the desired form Schmidt had to calculate the bending of the plate by applying the theory of elasticity. In addition to this difficulty, not every desired deformation could be produced by this method. However, other methods have been developed, most of which use a flexible material for both grinding and polishing. It would appear that these techniques are still in the experimental state, and not ready for quantity production.

10. Toric surfaces

A toric surface is generated when a circle is turned around an axis which does not coincide with the diameter of the circle (fig. 61). We have therefore to distinguish

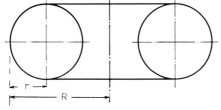

Fig. 61. Axial cross section of a toric surface. *r* radius of the forming curvature
R radius of the rotation curvature.

between the forming curvature given by the radius of the circle itself, and the rotation curvature given by the same radius plus or minus the distance between the turning axis and the centre of the circle. Thus the radius of rotation can be either shorter or longer than the forming radius. A toric lens surface gives different refracting powers in the two main directions, according to the two curvatures. For optical purposes only a segment of the toric body is used that is cut parallel to the rotation axis and has two convex main curvatures. Toric lenses, i.e. lenses with at least one toric surface, are used primarily for ophthalmic glasses, when astigmatism must be corrected. It is also advantageous in instrument design to use a toric surface to compensate for astigmatism. In illuminating systems the filament of the light source can sometimes be better adapted to the aperture of the imaging system using toric lenses. Finally, a collecting mirror inclined to the optical axis can be made free from astigmatism employing a toric mirror surface.

The method of producing toric surfaces follows, the generating principle. A block is formed by affixing the blanks on a wheel that turns around its axis (fig. 62). The plane

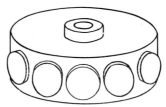

Fig. 62. A carrier for the production of toric lenses.

grinding tool is swung around an axis through the centre of the generating circle touching the workpiece only in one point. This method does not yield the highest precision of the surface, but generally the utmost accuracy is not demanded in toric lenses.

In this part only a concise description of the methods for the production of optical elements could be given. For further details reference is made to the following books: ORFORD [1940], SCHADE [1955], TWYMAN [1957]. ZSCHOMMLER [1963].

References

BOWDEN and RIDLER, 1936, Cited by TWYMAN [1957, p. 57].
BRÜCHE, E. und H. POPPA, 1955, Glastech. Ber. **28**, 232.
BRÜCHE, E. und H. POPPA, 1956, Glastech. Ber. **29**, 183.
BRÜCHE, E. und H. POPPA, 1957, Glastech. Ber. **30**, 163.
GEORG, K., 1948/49, Glastech. Ber. **22**, 296.
GREBENSCHTISCHIKOV, I. W., 1935, Sozial. Aufbau und Wissenschaft, pp. 22–33.
KALLER, A., 1957, Jenaer Jahrbuch, pp. 145-167.
KALLER, A., 1959, Jenaer Jahrbuch, pp. 181-210.
KLEMM, W. and A. SMEKAL, 1941, Naturwissenschaften **29**, 688.
ORFORD, H., 1940, Lens work for amateurs (London).
POPPA, H., 1957, Glastech. Ber. **30**, 387.
SCHADE, H., 1955, Arbeitsverfahren der Feinoptik (Deutscher Ingenieurverlag, Düsseldorf).
TWYMAN, F., 1957, Prism and lens making (Hilger and Watts, Ltd., London).
ZSCHOMMLER, W., 1963, Feinoptik – Glasbearbeitung (C. Hanser Verlag, München).

MODERN LIGHT SOURCES

A. A. KRUITHOF

Technical University, Eindhoven

CONTENTS

Contents continued overleaf

Contents, continued

1. Light sources

In this chapter 'light source' or 'source of radiation' denotes a device producing electromagnetic radiation, the frequency of which lies in or near the region of visible radiation. Sources of infrared and ultraviolet radiations will be dealt with in addition to those for visible radiation or light sources in the narrowest sense, because in principle the action of all three types of source is the same. The former two radiations have lower and higher frequencies respectively, and consequently longer and shorter wave-lengths than visible light. If in the following, one of the three kinds of radiation sources has to be indicated separately, we shall speak of a source of visible light, of infrared or of ultraviolet radiation.

Sources of radiation may be classified in many different ways. Obviously, the luminance and the corresponding quantity for invisible radiation, i.e. the radiance, are of great importance for the application of the sources in conjunction with optical instruments. The value of the radiance is closely connected with the mechanism producing the radiation in the source. In the first instance we shall therefore group the light sources according to these mechanisms. The groups can be arranged as follows:
(a) solids at high temperatures,
(b) gases at high temperatures,
(c) gases, directly excited by electrons,
(d) luminescent materials,
(e) lasers,
(f) light sources, not included in (a) to (e).

2. Subdivision of the chapter

The subject-matter of this chapter will be dealt with in 11 sections.

In §3 the relationship between radiation and light will be treated. It will appear that the concepts concerning radiation are directly connected with well-known physical quantities. For light, on the contrary, new concepts have to be introduced to take account of the properties of the human eye.

In §4, definitions will be given for the most important quantities belonging to radiation, as well as for the corresponding ones pertaining to light. The usual symbols for these quantities and the units by which they are expressed will also be given.

A few general physical laws about the production of radiation will be discussed in §5. It will appear that in the strictest sense, most of these laws cannot be applied to real sources of radiation. Nevertheless, they often indicate surprisingly well what may be expected of a given source.

In the last six sections of this chapter the principal properties and examples of the groups of light sources mentioned in §1 under (a) to (f) will be given. In each group, the sources with a constant radiant flux as a function of time will be discussed first. After that, the periodical, the flashing and the periodically flashing sources will follow, in so far as they are generally used.

3. Radiation and light

The name radiation is used for electromagnetic waves, which are characterized by their frequency v, expressed in Hz (hertz=cycles per second). $\lambda v = c$ is the relation between the velocity of light c, the frequency v, and the wave-length λ, expressed in m, μm, nm or Å (1 Ångström unit $= 10^{-10}$ m). In vacuum, $c = 2.998 \times 10^8$ m·s^{-1}, so that λ can be calculated when v is given and vice versa. In air, the velocity of light differs so little from its value in vacuum that for most purposes the same wave-lengths may be used. In this chapter we shall roughly restrict the discussion to radiations for which 3×10^{12} Hz $< v < 3 \times 10^{16}$ Hz, and consequently 100μm $> \lambda > 10$ nm. Frequencies smaller than 3×10^{12} Hz are in the field of microwave technique, those greater than 3×10^{16} Hz in the field of X-rays.

A further important characteristic of radiation is the radiant flux, i.e. the power P expressed in watts transmitted by the radiation, while passing any given surface which may be a flat or a curved surface somewhere in space, or the surface of an object. In this case the radiant flux directed outwards is the total power emitted by the object in the frequency range under consideration; the flux directed inwards is the power it receives. We shall deal with sources of radiation, so that we shall be mainly interested by the flux directed outwards.

3.1. SPECTRAL ENERGY-DISTRIBUTIONS

In general the radiant flux will depend on the frequency v, and consequently also on the wave-length λ. We are now confronted with two cases:
(a) It is found that power is sent out only in the immediate proximity of some discrete frequencies (wave-lengths); this is called a line spectrum;
(b) power is sent out throughout an entire region of frequencies (wave-lengths); this is called a continuous spectral energy-distribution or a continuous spectrum.

In order to represent a line spectrum with the frequency marked along the horizontal axis, it would be possible to draw a vertical line at each frequency v_n where energy is emitted. The length of the line could represent the emitted power P_n. However, we prefer drawing rectangles with a fixed base width Δv, the area being equal to the emitted power P_n. This procedure has been used in fig. 1a with $\Delta v = 2 \times 10^{13}$ Hz for the line spectrum of a 40 W low pressure mercury–argon discharge in a $1\frac{1}{2}$ inch tube (inner diameter 36 mm) of 4 foot (120 cm) length. The quantity plotted in the vertical direction is $P_n(\Delta v)^{-1}$; it is expressed in W·Hz^{-1} = W·s. The unit of the vertical scale is 10^{-14} W·s = 0.2 W per 2×10^{13} Hz.

In order to represent a continuous spectral energy-distribution with the frequency marked along the horizontal axis, the power in watts emitted by the source in the frequency band between v and $v + dv$ is written as $P_v dv$. The quantity P_v, introduced in this way, is called the spectral concentration of radiant flux in terms of frequency; it is expressed in W·Hz^{-1} = W·s. In fig. 2a, P_v is plotted in the vertical direction for a 40 W incandescent lamp ($T_c = 2850$°K, see § 6). The unit of the vertical scale is 10^{-14} W·s.

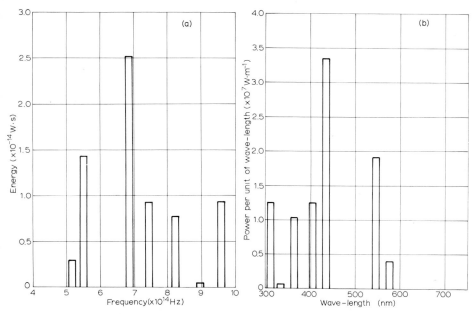

Fig. 1. Line spectrum of a 40W low pressure mercury–argon discharge. (a) Plotted with $\Delta\nu = 2 \times 10^{13}$ Hz. (b) Plotted with $\Delta\lambda = 15$ nm.

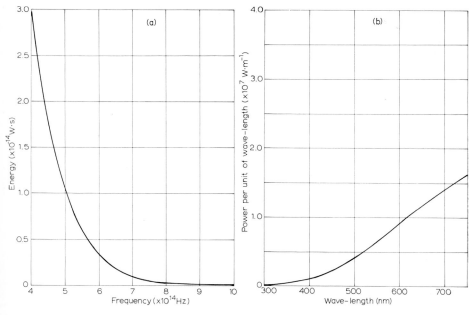

Fig. 2. Spectral energy-distribution for a 40W incandescent lamp. (a) Frequency ν on the horizontal axis. (b) Wave-length λ on the horizontal axis.

Both quantities, $P_n(\Delta v)^{-1}$ and P_v, plotted in figs. 1a and 2a respectively, are measured in W·s. If now in these figures 1 W·s is represented by the same length and also the units of the horizontal scales are equal, 1 W of radiant flux is represented by the same area in both figures. The advantage of this becomes clear as soon as a light source emitting spectral lines as well as a continuous spectrum is concerned. The two figures can then be combined, as it has been done in fig. 3a for a 40 W 'daylight-colour' fluorescent lamp. For the mercury lines $\Delta v = 2 \times 10^{13}$ Hz. The unit of the vertical scale is 10^{14} W·s $= 0.2$ W per 2×10^{13} Hz.

A comparison of the area representing a given spectral line with that below the curve for the continuous spectrum immediately shows the ratio of the radiant fluxes concerned.

Line spectra and continuous spectra can be represented with the wave-length as well as the frequency marked along the horizontal axis. For that purpose, in the procedure outlined in the preceding paragraphs frequency v is replaced by wave-length λ. The fixed base width of the rectangles representing spectral lines is now $\Delta\lambda$; the corresponding quantity plotted in the vertical direction $P_n(\Delta\lambda)^{-1}$, expressed in W·m^{-1}. The power emitted in a wave-length band between λ and $\lambda + d\lambda$ of a continuous spectrum is written as $P_\lambda d\lambda$. P_λ is the spectral concentration of radiant flux (in terms of wave-length)*; it is expressed in W·m^{-1} and plotted in the vertical direction. In fig. 1b

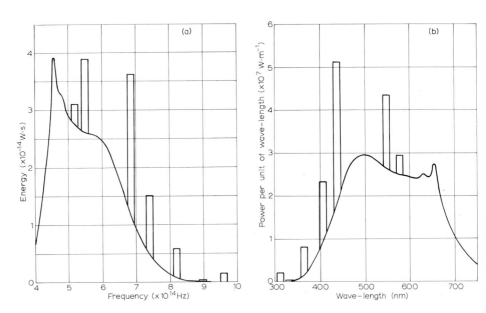

Fig. 3. Spectral energy-distribution for a 40 W 'Daylight' fluorescent lamp. (a) Frequency v on the horizontal axis, for the mercury lines $\Delta v = 2 \times 10^{13}$ Hz. (b) Wave-length λ on the horizontal axis, for the mercury lines $\Delta\lambda = 15$ nm.

---

* The expression in brackets will be omitted in the following if confusion with the spectral concentration of radiant flux in terms of frequency is unlikely.

the line spectrum of the 40 W low pressure mercury–argon discharge has been plotted with $\Delta\lambda = 15$ nm. The unit of the vertical scale is 10^7 W·m$^{-1} = 0.15$ W per 15 nm. In fig. 2b, P_λ is given for the incandescent lamp. The unit of the vertical scale is 10^7 W·m^{-1}. For a source emitting spectral lines as well as a continuous spectrum, the figures can be combined. This has been done in fig. 3b for the 40 W 'Daylight' fluorescent lamp. For the mercury lines $\Delta\lambda = 15$ nm. The unit of the vertical scale is 10^7 W·m$^{-1} = 0.15$ W per 15 nm.

In the figures representing a line spectrum, both $\Delta\nu$ and $\Delta\lambda$ have a fixed value. Therefore, the heights of the rectangles representing the value of P_n in corresponding points of these figures connected by the relation $\lambda\nu = c$, have a fixed ratio. In figs. 1a and 1b this ratio is 1. In contrast to this there is no fixed ratio between P_ν and P_λ at corresponding points of figures representing a continuous spectrum. Still, there is a connection between the quantities mentioned, because $\lambda = c/\nu$. Corresponding frequency- and wave-length bands dν and dλ satisfy the relation $d\lambda = -(c/\nu^2)d\nu$. If the power emitted in the bands is equal, $P_\nu d\nu = -P_\lambda d\lambda$, from which it follows that $P_\nu d\nu = (c/\nu^2)P_\lambda d\nu$ or $(\nu^2/c)P_\nu = P_\lambda$ and $P_\nu = (\lambda^2/c)P_\lambda$. As this condition is fulfilled in figs. 2a and 2b, the areas below corresponding parts of the curves in both figures are equal.

According to PLANCK [1900], radiation is always emitted in quanta, each carrying the energy $h\nu$. By plotting radiant flux as a function of frequency, figures are obtained from which the number of quanta, emitted per unit of time, can directly be derived. To characterize light sources, however, figures are usually drawn in which the wave-length is marked along the horizontal axis. Further on we shall stick to this use.

3.2. RADIANT FLUX AND LUMINOUS FLUX

In the human eye radiation may cause the impression of light. The eye is not equally responsive to all wave-lengths. In principle, the ratio between the luminous efficiencies V_{λ_1} and V_{λ_2} for two wave-lengths λ_1 and λ_2 is determined in the following way. Each of two pieces of the retina, which are of the same size and situated next to each other, is evenly illuminated by radiation of one of these wave-lengths. After that the radiant fluxes $P_{\lambda_1}d\lambda$ and $P_{\lambda_2}d\lambda$ are varied, untill both surfaces look 'equally bright' and the ratio $V_{\lambda_1}/V_{\lambda_2}$ is found from

$$\frac{V_{\lambda_1}}{V_{\lambda_2}} = \frac{P_{\lambda_2}d\lambda}{P_{\lambda_1}d\lambda} = \frac{P_{\lambda_2}}{P_{\lambda_1}}.$$

When measured with relatively high fluxes, like the values which occur in daylight, the decision whether both surfaces are equally bright or not becomes more difficult as λ_1 and λ_2 are further removed from each other as a result of the colour difference. In such a case the comparison is made easier for the observer by showing both illuminated surfaces at the same place of the retina, not at the same time but alternating in a rapid succession. The observer no longer sees the difference in colours, and decides only upon equal or different brightness. If the brightnesses are different, the field of vision flickers; if they are equal it remains quiet. In two different regions of radiant flux, both roughly covering a range of 1 to 10^4, reproducible values for V_λ are found for every observer, provided that appropriate conditions are fulfilled. These conditions mainly relate to the surrounding field of view and to the state of adaptation of the retina. One curve, marked V_λ, holds for larger values of the flux, like those occurring in daylight, the other one, V'_λ, for small values like those occurring at night, with moon- or starlight. The former case is called photopic vision, the latter scotopic vision. In the region in between, bridging a range of about 1 to 300, both curves gradually pass into each other. When many observers are tested, it is found that the curves V_λ and V'_λ are very well reproduced by most of them. In 1924, the C.I.E.* accepted an average curve for V_λ (fig. 4) and in 1951 a curve for V'_λ (see also fig. 4);

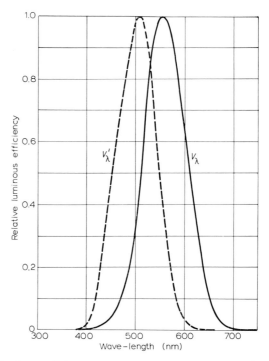

Fig. 4. Relative luminous efficiency curves; V_λ for photopic vision, V'_λ for scotopic vision.

both normalized in such a way that their maximum values are 1. For V_λ this maximum is found at $\lambda = 555$ nm; for V'_λ at about $\lambda = 510$ nm. It will depend on the value of the radiant flux to be observed, whether curve V_λ or curve V'_λ has to be used. The phenomena in the field in between are extremely complicated; we shall not take them into consideration.

Two important laws hold good for the human eye in the regions of photopic and

* C.I.E.: Commission Internationale de l'Eclairage; International Commission on Illumination.

of scotopic vision, as well as for the photoelectric cell and the photographic plate. The first law is the transitivity of equality of brightness; if two patches of light A and B are equally bright and also the patches B and C, then A and C are equally bright too. The second is the so-called summation law, which can be applied to mixtures of radiation of all visible wave-lengths. The summation law can be worded as follows. If two equally bright mixtures of radiation, M_1 and M_2, are given and a part αM_2 of M_2 is replaced by another mixture M_3, which is equally bright as αM_2, then the new mixture $(1-\alpha)M_2+M_3$ is still equally bright as M_1. Formulated in this way, the law seems rather evident, but many processes may be pointed out for which it does not hold good. These two laws have the far-reaching consequence that the judgement on brightness by the eye can be replaced by measurements with a photoelectric cell. The cell has to satisfy the condition that its relative sensitivity varies with the wave-length in the same way as V_λ or V'_λ according as photopic or scotopic vision is concerned.

Let us first take into consideration the region of photopic vision. If $\int P_{1\lambda}V_\lambda d\lambda = \int P_{2\lambda}V_\lambda d\lambda$ holds good for two radiant fluxes $\int P_{1\lambda}d\lambda$ and $\int P_{2\lambda}d\lambda$ reaching the eye in the same way, they will be experienced as being equally bright. Moreover, a larger value of the integral corresponds with a larger brightness. The conclusion is that, under the given conditions, the value of the integral can be used to characterize the effect of a radiant flux in terms of light. Consequently, the definition is given that the luminous flux Φ, belonging to a given radiant flux $P=\int P_\lambda d\lambda$ is equal to $\Phi = K_m \int P_\lambda V_\lambda d\lambda$. For the spectral concentration of luminous flux Φ_λ it follows that $\Phi_\lambda = K_m P_\lambda V_\lambda$. For Φ the lumen (lm) is used as a unit. This unit shall be further considered in the following section. It will appear that the value of K_m is about 680 lm·W^{-1}. From here on we shall characterize sources of visible light by quantities derived from the lumen.

A luminous flux Φ' is also defined in the region of scotopic vision. $\Phi' = K'_m \int P_\lambda V'_\lambda d\lambda$ and $\Phi'_\lambda = K'_m P_\lambda V'_\lambda$. This luminous flux is explicitly called the scotopic luminous flux. For Φ' the scotopic lumen is used as a unit. The value of K'_m amounts to about 1740 scotopic lm·W^{-1}.

In the region of photopic vision a beam of light shows colour in addition to brightness. The characterizations of colour and brightness are similar. For the complete characterization of colour, however, three sensitivity curves are needed, while in the case of brightness one is sufficient. In 1931 three suitable curves $\bar{x}_\lambda$, $\bar{y}_\lambda$, and $\bar{z}_\lambda$ were normalized by the C.I.E. As the summation law holds for colour vision too, the functioning of the eye can be represented in this respect with the aid of three photoelectric cells, the sensitivity curves of which have the forms of $\bar{x}_\lambda$, $\bar{y}_\lambda$ and $\bar{z}_\lambda$.

4. Quantities, definitions, symbols, units

Starting from the concepts of radiant flux and luminous flux defined in the preceding section, new quantities can now be introduced. We shall give the definitions for photopic vision, where the photopic relative luminous efficiency curve V_λ (fig. 4) and the value $K_m = 680$ lm·W^{-1} apply.

In these definitions, the geometrical notion 'solid angle of a cone' is used, i.e. the area cut by a cone from a sphere with radius 1, of which the centre coincides with the apex of the cone. The unit is the steradian (sr).

The definitions given here are based on the definitions given by the C.I.E. in the International Lighting Vocabulary [1957]. As a rule they are given for radiation; the alterations which have to be introduced in order to apply them to light are placed in brackets. Sometimes, however, the differences are very great and in those cases on the left-hand side of the page the definition is given for radiation, and on the right-hand side that for light.

Radiant power or radiant flux

Symbols: P, Φ_e, F_e.

Units: watt (W).

Power, emitted, transferred or received in the form of radiation.

$P = \int P_\lambda \, d\lambda$,

λ = wave-length,

P_λ = spectral concentration of radiant power,

V_λ = photopic relative luminous efficiency,

K_m = maximum value of photopic luminous efficiency.

Luminous flux

Φ, F.

lumen (lm).

The quantity, characteristic for radiant flux, which expresses its capacity to produce a luminous sensation, evaluated according to relative luminous efficiency.

$\Phi = K_m \int P_\lambda V_\lambda \, d\lambda$.

Quantity of radiant energy

Symbols: Q_e.

Units: joule (J).

Quantity of light

Q.

lumen second (lm·s),

lumen hour (lm·h).

The product of radiant power (luminous flux) and the time during which the radiation is maintained.

$Q_e = \int P \, dt$.

$Q = \int \Phi \, dt$.

Radiant intensity (of a source in a given direction)

Symbols: I_e.

Units: watt per steradian (W·sr^{-1}).

Luminous intensity (of a source in a given direction)

I.

candela (cd).

The amount of the radiant power (luminous flux) emitted by a source or by an element of source in an infinitesimal cone containing the given direction, divided by the solid angle of that cone.

$$I_e = \frac{dP}{d\omega_1}.$$

$$I = \frac{d\Phi}{d\omega_1}.$$

$d\omega_1$ = solid angle of the infinitesimal cone, having its top at the surface of the source.

A special definition of the unit for radiant intensity is superfluous as this notion is derived in the way we have sketched from radiant power, a well-defined physical quantity.

The magnitude of the candela is such that the luminous intensity of a full radiator (see §5) having an area $A\,\text{m}^2$, at the temperature of solidification of platinum, is $6 \times 10^5\,A\,\text{cd}$.

From this definition of the unit of luminous intensity, stated by the 9th General Conference on Weights and Measures (1948), the approximate value $680\,\text{lm·W}^{-1}$ is calculated for the factor K_m.

Radiant intensity per unit area (radiance) (at a point of a surface and in a given direction)

Symbols: L_e.
Units: watt per square metre per steradian $(\text{W·m}^{-2}\text{·sr}^{-1})$, watt per square foot per steradian $(\text{W·ft}^{-2}\text{·sr}^{-1})$.
$1\,\text{W·m}^{-2}\text{·sr}^{-1} = 0.0929\,\text{W·ft}^{-2}\text{·sr}^{-1}$.

Luminance (at a point of a surface and in a given direction)

L, B.
candela per square metre or nit (cd·m^{-2}), stilb (sb), apostilb (asb), lambert, footlambert.

$$1\,\text{cd·m}^{-2} = 1\,\text{nit}.$$
$$= 10^{-4}\,\text{sb}.$$
$$= \pi\,\text{asb}.$$
$$= \pi 10^{-4}\,\text{lambert}.$$
$$= 1/3.426\ \text{footlambert}.$$

The amount of the radiant intensity (luminous intensity) in the given direction of an infinitesimal element of the surface, containing the point under consideration, divided by the area of the orthogonal projection of this element on a plane perpendicular to the given direction.

$$L_\text{e} = \frac{\text{d}^2 P}{\cos \varepsilon_1 \text{d}A_1 \text{d}\omega_1}.$$

$$L = \frac{\text{d}^2 \Phi}{\cos \varepsilon_1 \text{d}A_1 \text{d}\omega_1}.$$

$\varepsilon_1 =$ angle between the surface element and the plane perpendicular to the given direction.
$\text{d}A_1 =$ area of the infinitesimal element.

Radiant emittance (from a point of a surface)
Symbols: M_e.
Units: watt per square metre (W·m^{-2}), watt per square foot (W·ft^{-2}).
$1\,\text{W·m}^{-2} = 0.0929\ \text{W·ft}^{-2}$.

Luminous emittance (from a point of a surface)
M.
lumen per square metre (lm·m^{-2}), lumen per square foot (lm·ft^{-2}).
$1\,\text{lm·m}^{-2} = 0.0929\ \text{lm·ft}^{-2}$.

The amount of the radiant power (luminous flux) emitted by an infinitesimal element of a surface containing the point under consideration, divided by the area of the element.

$$M_e = \frac{\mathrm{d}P}{\mathrm{d}A_1} . \qquad\qquad\qquad M = \frac{\mathrm{d}\Phi}{\mathrm{d}A_1} .$$

Irradiance (at a point of a surface)	*Illumination (at a point of a surface)*
Symbols: E_e.	E.
Units: watt per square metre ($\mathrm{W \cdot m^{-2}}$),	lumen per square metre ($\mathrm{lm \cdot m^{-2}}$),
watt per square foot ($\mathrm{W \cdot ft^{-2}}$)	lux (lx), phot, footcandle,
$1\,\mathrm{W \cdot m^{-2}} = 0.0929\,\mathrm{W \cdot ft^{-2}}$.	lumen per square foot ($\mathrm{lm \cdot ft^{-2}}$)

$$1\,\mathrm{lx} = 1\,\mathrm{lm \cdot m^{-2}}.$$
$$= 10^{-4}\,\mathrm{phot}.$$
$$= 0.0929\ \mathrm{footcandle}.$$
$$= 0.0929\,\mathrm{lm \cdot ft^{-2}}.$$

The amount of the radiant power (luminous flux) incident on an infinitesimal element of surface, containing the point under consideration, divided by the area of that element.

$$E_e = \frac{\mathrm{d}P}{\mathrm{d}A_2} . \qquad\qquad\qquad E = \frac{\mathrm{d}\Phi}{\mathrm{d}A_2} .$$

$\mathrm{d}A_2 =$ infinitesimal element of surface where radiation (light) is incident.

Spectral reflection factor; spectral reflectance.
Spectral transmission factor; spectral transmittance.
Spectral absorption factor; spectral absorption.
Symbols: ϱ_λ, τ_λ, α_λ respectively.
Units: these quantities are dimensionless numbers.
The ratios of the spectral concentration of the reflected, the transmitted and absorbed radiant powers (luminous fluxes) to that of the incident power (luminous flux) for a given wave-length.

$$\varrho_\lambda = \frac{P_{r,\lambda}}{P_{0,\lambda}} , \qquad\qquad \varrho_\lambda = \frac{\Phi_{r,\lambda}}{\Phi_{0,\lambda}} = \frac{K_m P_{r,\lambda} V_\lambda}{K_m P_{0,\lambda} V_\lambda} = \frac{P_{r,\lambda}}{P_{0,\lambda}} ,$$

$$\tau_\lambda = \frac{P_{t,\lambda}}{P_{0,\lambda}} , \qquad\qquad \tau_\lambda = \frac{\Phi_{t,\lambda}}{\Phi_{0,\lambda}} = \frac{K_m P_{t,\lambda} V_\lambda}{K_m P_{0,\lambda} V_\lambda} = \frac{P_{t,\lambda}}{P_{0,\lambda}} ,$$

$$\alpha_\lambda = \frac{P_{a,\lambda}}{P_{0,\lambda}} . \qquad\qquad \alpha_\lambda = \frac{\Phi_{a,\lambda}}{\Phi_{0,\lambda}} = \frac{K_m P_{a,\lambda} V_\lambda}{K_m P_{0,\lambda} V_\lambda} = \frac{P_{a,\lambda}}{P_{0,\lambda}} .$$

The subscripts r, t, a and 0 stand for reflected, transmitted, absorbed and incident radiant fluxes (luminous fluxes) respectively. Generally, the three quantities ϱ, τ and α will depend on the direction with respect to the normal on the surface in question.

A physical law, originating from Abbe states that the radiance (or luminance) of the image obtained with the aid of an optical instrument consisting of mirrors, lenses etc. is always smaller than that of the light source itself. Abbe's law lends particular importance to the property 'radiance (or luminance) of a light source'. In the limiting case of negligible losses by reflections at refracting surfaces, by absorption, by the production of diffracted stray light on account of imperfect polish, by non-perfect reflection at mirrors or by the presence of aberrations, radiance (luminance) undergoes no change. For completeness it should be added that in the case where the object space and the image space have a different refractive index n, Abbe's law has the form: L_e/n^2 is invariant; for light: L/n^2 is invariant. This again is true in the limiting case of no losses.

5. Some general laws about radiation

A number of relations between the quantities defined in §4 are direct consequences of the definitions given in that section. Moreover, the radiant flux in a wave-length region $d\lambda$, $P_{0,\lambda}d\lambda$, is equal to the sum of the reflected, the transmitted and the absorbed radiant fluxes $P_{r,\lambda}d\lambda$, $P_{t,\lambda}d\lambda$ and $P_{a,\lambda}d\lambda$ respectively, so that the following relation holds:

$$\varrho_\lambda + \tau_\lambda + \alpha_\lambda = \frac{P_{r,\lambda}d\lambda + P_{t,\lambda}d\lambda + P_{a,\lambda}d\lambda}{P_{0,\lambda}d\lambda} = 1.$$

5.1. THE LAMBERT RADIATOR

The radiance $L_{e,\lambda}d\lambda$ of a surface element dA_1 of a radiating source in the wave-length band $d\lambda$ will generally depend on the direction with respect to the normal of the element, which is determined by the angle ε_1 with this normal. With many radiators this dependence is not strongly marked. A radiator is called a diffuse radiator or a Lambert radiator, if $L_{e,\lambda}$ is not at all dependent on the direction. In that case $I_{e,\lambda} = L_{e,\lambda} \cos \varepsilon_1 =$

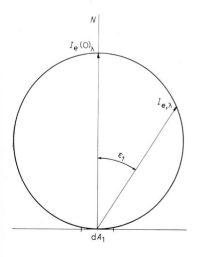

Fig. 5. Lambert radiator (diffuse radiator).
dA_1 = surface element of radiator.
N = normal to dA_1.
$I_{e,\lambda}$ = spectral concentration of radiant intensity.
ε_1 = angle between the directions of $I_{e,\lambda}$ and N.
$I_e(0)_\lambda$ = spectral concentration of radiant intensity in the direction of N.

$I_e(0)_\lambda \cos \varepsilon_1$ (see fig. 5), in which $I_e(0)_\lambda = L_{e,\lambda}$ is the value of $I_{e,\lambda}$ for $\varepsilon_1 = 0$. For Lambert radiators the relation $M_{e,\lambda} = \pi I_e(0)_\lambda = \pi L_{e,\lambda}$ applies. The two relations discussed do not only hold for the radiation in the wave-length region $d\lambda$, but also for the corresponding quantities relating to total radiation or light.

5.2. THE BLACK-BODY RADIATOR, KIRCHHOFF'S LAW

If we leave lightning, aurora borealis and fire-flies out of consideration, the oldest sources of radiation known to man have been glowing objects, like the sun, the stars, or solid particles of carbon in the flames of a fire or in a candle flame. Later on, the incandescent gaslight and the electrical incandescent lamp, which are also radiation sources of this type, arrived. For an idealized solid body, the radiative properties can be marked very precisely if it is assumed that the body absorbs all radiation falling on to it, so that $\alpha_\lambda = 1$ for all the wave-lengths. That is why this object is called a black body. Now $\varrho_\lambda + \tau_\lambda + \alpha_\lambda = 1$ so that for the black body $\varrho_\lambda = \tau_\lambda = 0$; it does neither reflect nor transmit radiation. Moreover, it is a Lambert radiator. The study of the radiation of a black body is of great importance. As is worked out in §6 the black body is realized by an enclosure, in the wall of which a small aperture allows an (infinitesimal) quantity of radiation to escape. PLANCK [1900] made the assumptions that for each frequency v occurring as radiation in the cavity, there are resonators in the wall and – quite new for that time – that these resonators can only have energy contents which are multiples of an energy quantum hv. Here h is a universal constant, so that the magnitudes of the energy quanta are proportional to their frequencies.

Planck applied Boltzmann statistics to the resonators, according to which at a temperature $T°K$ the number of resonators N having an energy content nhv, is $N_0 e^{-nhv/kT}$, if N_0 is the number of resonators with zero energy. The average energy content of a resonator $E(T)_v$ is then

$$E(T)_v = \frac{\sum\limits_{n=0}^{\infty} N_0 nhv e^{-nhv/kT}}{\sum\limits_{n=0}^{\infty} N_0 e^{-nhv/kT}} = \frac{hv}{e^{hv/kT}-1}.$$

Planck derived the frequency distribution of the radiant emittance $M_e(T, 1)_v$ of the black body at an absolute temperature T from this result. The outcome was

$$M_e(T, 1)_v = \frac{2\pi hv}{c^2} \frac{1}{e^{hv/kT}-1},$$

from which it follows that the wave-length distribution of radiance $L_e(T, 1)_\lambda$ of the black body at the absolute temperature T is

$$L_e(T, 1)_\lambda = \frac{2hc^2}{\lambda^5(e^{hc/k\lambda T}-1)} = \frac{2C_1}{\lambda^5(e^{C_2/\lambda T}-1)}$$

where $C_1 = hc^2$ and $C_2 = hc/k$. Although, according to modern principles, Planck did not use the right form of statistics in his derivation, the result is correct. A modern derivation of Planck's radiation formula will be found in any textbook on statistical mechanics, for example in DAVIDSON [1962].

With the values for h, c and k given by COHEN and DUMOND [1964] it is found that $C_1 = 5.955 \times 10^{-17} \mathrm{W \cdot m^2}$ and $C_2 = 1.438 \times 10^{-2} \mathrm{m ^\circ K}$. This value for C_2 was already adopted in 1948 for practical use by the General Conference on Weights and Measures. The C.I.E. [1957] gives $C_1 = 5.953 \times 10^{-17}$ $\mathrm{W \cdot m^2}$.

In fig. 6 the curves $L_e(T, 1)_\lambda$ are drawn for the temperatures $T = 1895 °\mathrm{K}$, $2850 °\mathrm{K}$, $3995 °\mathrm{K}$ and $6500 °\mathrm{K}$, which are found in the candle flame, the electric incandescent lamp, the positive crater of the carbon arc and the sun respectively. Each of these curves shows a maximum at a wave-length λ_{max}, which is calculated from $\lambda_{max} T = 2.898 \times 10^{-3} \mathrm{m ^\circ K}$. This relation, Wien's displacement law, is a direct consequence of Planck's radiation formula.

When $M_e(T, 1)_\lambda$ is integrated for all wave-lengths, the total emittance $M_e(T, 1)$ is

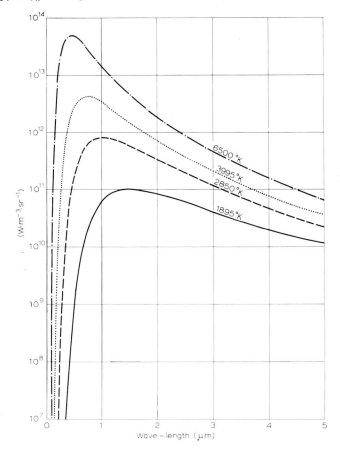

Fig. 6. Spectral energy-distribution curves for the full radiator. 1895 °K, 2850 °K, 3995 °K and 6500 °K = temperatures of the radiator. $L_e(T, 1)_\lambda$, the spectral concentration of radiance for the full radiator, is marked along the vertical axis.

obtained for the black body at the absolute temperature T:

$$M_e(T, 1) = \frac{2\pi^5(kT)^4}{15h^3c^2} = \pi\sigma T^4.$$

The value of σ is $1.805 \times 10^{-8}\,\text{W·m}^{-2\cdot\circ}\text{K}^{-4}$. The C.I.E. [1957] gives

$$\sigma = 1.809 \times 10^{-8}\,\text{W·m}^{-2\cdot\circ}\text{K}.$$

For an object that is not black, the ratio of its radiant intensity to that of a black body at the same temperature and at the same wave-length, is called the emissivity (symbols e_v or e_λ). Generally, the emissivity will depend on the direction.

In a state of temperature equilibrium any object must emit as much radiation as it absorbs. From this condition Kirchhoff derived that the emissivity is equal to the spectral absorption factor, so $e_\lambda = \alpha_\lambda$. Then it follows that for an arbitrary object at an absolute temperature T the radiance $L_e(T, \alpha)_\lambda$ is given by

$$L_e(T, \alpha)_\lambda = \frac{2\alpha_\lambda C_1}{\lambda^5(e^{C_2/\lambda T} - 1)}.$$

As generally $\alpha_\lambda < 1$, the radiation of a black body for each wave-length is greater than that of an arbitrary radiator of the same temperature. Therefore, a black body is also called a full radiator.

The velocity of light has a finite value, so that radiation emitted from the wall at one side of an enclosure towards the opposite wall will be inside the cavity for some finite time. Thus there will always be energy of radiation inside an enclosure the walls of which have temperature T. The energy per unit of volume is called the energy density $\varrho(T)$. For a frequency band $\mathrm{d}v$, the energy density is

$$\varrho(T)_v \mathrm{d}v = \frac{8\pi h v^3}{c^3(e^{hv/kT} - 1)}\,\mathrm{d}v,$$

for a wave-length band $\mathrm{d}\lambda$

$$\varrho(T)_\lambda \mathrm{d}\lambda = \frac{8\pi hc}{\lambda^5(e^{hc/k\lambda T} - 1)}\,\mathrm{d}\lambda = \frac{8\pi C_1}{c\lambda^5(e^{C_2/\lambda T} - 1)}\,\mathrm{d}\lambda.$$

Temperature equilibrium can only exist if the energy density is constant everywhere in the cavity. Further the energy does not depend on the nature of the wall, providing that the latter does not transmit radiation.

5.3. RADIATION AND ATOMS

If there is a gaseous element in an enclosure, then, according to atomic physics, the various atoms of that element may be found in different states, characterized by quantum numbers and with energy contents $E_0 \leqq E_1 \leqq \ldots E_n \leqq \ldots \leqq E_m$. The state with the lowest energy content E_0 is called the ground state of the atom, those with higher energies are the excited states. At room temperature – and even at temperatures of a few thousand degrees – the vast majority of the atoms will be found in the ground state. It may happen that groups of g_i different states have the same energy content E_i, in which case g_i is called the statistical weight of the energy level E_i.

If an atom makes a transition from a state with energy E_m into a state having a lower energy E_n a spectral line with frequency $v = (E_m - E_n)/h$ is emitted; in the case of the inverse transition, the same spectral line is absorbed. The spectral lines for which the state with lower energy E_n is the ground state with energy E_0, will be absorbed very strongly by the gas near room temperature. These lines are called the resonance lines of the element.

Einstein defined the probabilities controlling the atomic transitions as follows; suppose that per unit of volume N_m and N_n atoms are found in states having energies E_m and E_n respectively. Further there may be the radiation energy density $\varrho_v dv$ between the frequencies v and $v + dv$. Then the following occurs:

(a) Per second $A_{mn} N_m$ atoms per unit of volume pass from E_m to E_n, and the power $A_{mn} N_m (E_m - E_n)$ is added to the radiation field. A_{mn}, the probability per unit of time that an atom makes this spontaneous jump, is called the transition probability.

(b) As a consequence of the presence of the radiation field, moreover $B_{mn} \varrho_v N_m$ atoms per unit of volume pass per second from E_m to E_n, and the power $B_{mn} \varrho_v N_m (E_m - E_n)$ is added to the radiation field. B_{mn} is called the coefficient of induced emission.

(c) Per second $B_{nm} \varrho_n N_n$ atoms per unit of volume make the upward bound from E_n to E_m and the power $B_{nm} \varrho_v N_n (E_m - E_n)$ is absorbed from the radiation field. B_{nm} is called Einstein's absorption coefficient.

If the situation is stationary for the numbers of atoms with energies E_m and E_n as well as for the energy in the radiation field, the relation $A_{mn} N_m + B_{mn} \varrho_v N_m = B_{nm} \varrho_v N_n$ must hold or

$$\varrho_v = \frac{A_{mn} N_m}{B_{nm} N_n - B_{mn} N_m}.$$

In a cavity at the temperature T with walls which do not transmit radiation, the situation certainly is stationary. For such a cavity we know

$$\varrho_v = \varrho(T)_v = \frac{8\pi h v^3}{c^3(e^{hv/kT} - 1)},$$

while according to Boltzmann statistics

$$\frac{N_m}{g_m} = \frac{N_n}{g_n} e^{-(E_m - E_n)/kT} = \frac{N_n}{g_n} e^{-hv/kT}.$$

Consequently

$$\frac{8\pi h v^3}{c^3(e^{hv/kT} - 1)} = \frac{g_m A_{mn}}{g_n B_{nm} e^{hv/kT} - g_m B_{mn}}$$

has to be satisfied for all temperatures. That is possible on the condition that A_{mn}, B_{mn} and B_{nm} satisfy $g_n B_{nm} = g_m B_{mn}$ and $A_{mn} = 8\pi h v^3 B_{mn}/c^3$.

In the preceding paragraphs, the fact that a spectral line occupies a certain width of frequency or wave-length was not taken into account. If necessary, instead of

A_{mn}, B_{mn} and B_{nm} the corresponding quantities per frequency band dv, $A_{mnv}dv$, $B_{mnv}dv$ and $B_{mnv}dv$ respectively may be introduced. Because of the principle of detailed balancing, the relations derived for A_{mn}, B_{mn} and B_{nm} also apply for A_{mnv}; B_{mnv} and B_{nmv}.

About the induced emission it has to be mentioned that in this process the direction of the emitted quantum coincides exactly with that of the quantum causing the emission. Moreover, the two quanta are entirely coherent. These properties are used in the laser, a source of radiation which shall be dealt with in §10.

6. Solids at high temperatures

The radiance and luminance of a full radiator at a known temperature can be calculated with the aid of the Planck method, as is evident from the preceding section. At low temperatures the radiation is weak, especially for the shorter wave-lengths. For two reasons, however, the radiance rapidly increases at rising temperatures:
(a) the total emittance is proportional to T^4,
(b) according to Wien's displacement law, the wave-length of the maximum spectral concentration of radiance is inversely proportional to T.

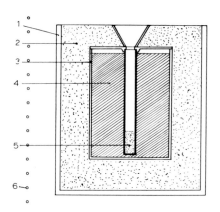

Fig. 7. Black-body radiator for the temperature of solidifying platinum.
1, porcelain crucible.
2, thoria powder.
3, thoria crucible.
4, platinum ingot.
5, sight tube one-third full of thoria powder.
6, induction heater coil.

Starting from the relatively low temperature of solidifying gold (1336°K), which is found with the gas thermometer, higher temperatures may be established by means of relative measurements of radiance which are much simpler than absolute measurements. In order to approach the black body in the way mentioned in the preceding section for these measurements a deep cylindrical cavity is used, which is closed at one end. The cavity wall does not transmit radiation. Radiation falling into the cavity will be reflected repeatedly. At each reflection, part of it will be absorbed, and the part leaving the cavity after many reflections is quite small. If the wall of the cavity is maintained at a uniform temperature, the opening radiates nearly like a full radiator. An up-to-date design of such a black body, constructed by SANDERS and JONES [1962] for the temperature of solidifying platinum (2042°K), is drawn in fig. 7. Many other constructions for the black body have been devised. It appears that the accuracy of the measurements is satisfactory only when solidifying metals are used to obtain constant and uniform temperatures. These instruments can only be managed with difficulty. They are used as primary standards for basic measurements.

For working-standards, practically always incandescent solids are used, without making a black body out of them. If it is desirable to know the radiance of such a radiator, Kirchhoff's law has to be applied, so that the true temperature T as well as the absorption factor $\alpha_\lambda = e_\lambda$ must be known.

Usually more attention is given to the relative variation of the radiance of a radiator with the wave-length, than to its absolute value. In the region of visible radiation, for many solids α_λ varies so regularly that a temperature T_c can be found for which the radiance of a full radiator is practically proportional to that of the radiator considered. The temperature T_c, which may be higher than T for one material and lower for the other, is called the colour temperature of the radiator.

Moreover, the notion luminance temperature (for a given reference wave-length) is introduced as being the temperature T_l of a full radiator for which its luminance at a reference wave-length has the same spectral concentration as for the radiator in question. In practice, particularly in pyrometry, the reference wave-length is as a rule 655 nm.

In the years 1881 till about 1906, radiators were used of carbon, a mixture of zirconia and yttriumoxide (Nernst radiator), osmium, tantalum, and tungsten successively. The most important of these materials, tungsten, is still in use; sporadically carbon and tantalum carbide are applied. The Nernst radiator and a radiator of silicon carbide (Globar) are used to produce infrared radiation (cf. §6.3).

6.1. TUNGSTEN LAMPS

Tungsten is the metal with the highest melting point while it has a low vapour pressure. As a result of these two properties, it is pre-eminently suitable as a material for producing radiation by incandescence. The radiative properties of tungsten have been examined in detail. Measurements of the emissivity have been performed by amongst others: HAMAKER [1934, 1936], DE VOS [1953] and LARRABEE [1959]. Tungsten oxidizes in air at high temperatures; consequently the transmittance for the radiation under consideration of a bulb, a glass window or a fused-silica window, must always be taken into account, if this material is used. As a radiator, usually a tungsten strip, a straight wire, a coiled wire or even a coiled coil is used.

With tungsten-strip lamps it is important that only the central part of the strip which has a uniform temperature, radiates in the forward direction. With modern lamps as depicted in fig. 8, this uniformity has been achieved within $\approx 10°K$. Fig. 9 gives as an example the spectral concentration of radiance for such a strip lamp with $T = 2700°K$ (i.e. $T_c = 2745°K$; $T_l = 2405°K$; $L = 5 \times 10^6 \, cd \cdot m^{-2}$). For a specific gasfilled strip lamp the curve, giving the luminance temperature T_l of the strip as a function of the current i, is in principle determined by comparing it with a primary

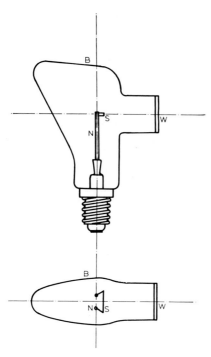

Fig. 8. Tungsten-strip lamp.
S = tungsten strip.
N = supports.
B = bulb $\Big\}$ glass or fused silica.
W = window

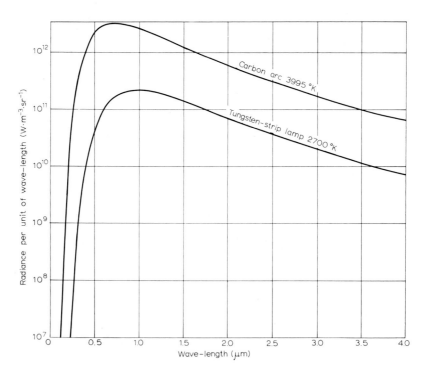

Fig. 9. Spectral energy-distributions for working-standards.

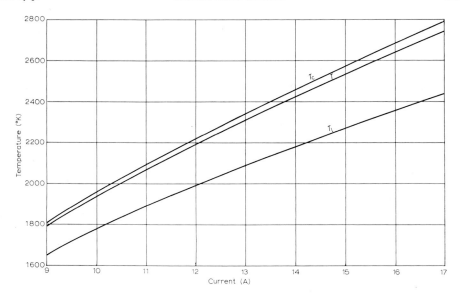

Fig. 10. Temperatures for tungsten-strip lamp. T = temperature of the strip.
T_1 = luminance temperature. T_c = colour temperature.

radiation standard. This curve, the calibration curve, is slightly different for individual lamps of the same construction; an example is given in fig. 10. From T_1 the true temperature T, the spectral energy distribution, the colour temperature T_c and the luminance L can be calculated with the aid of the known values of the emissivity mentioned; these temperatures are also given in fig. 10. If carefully used, strip lamps are very reliable working-standards for radiance in the wave-length region of $\lambda = 230$ nm to $\lambda = 4\,\mu$m, where the emissivity of tungsten is known and where fused silica transmits the radiation adequately.

If a narrow and rather long light source is needed, it may be advantageous if the radiator is a straight tungsten wire. An example is the lamp used for the reproduction of sound of a cinema sound track. The emission properties are the same as those for strip lamps. Further, limited application of straight wires is found in small-wattage general-purpose vacuum lamps for 110 or 220 V ($T_c \approx 2500\,°$K).

In light sources like general-purpose incandescent lamps ($T_c \approx 2850\,°$K for the gas-filled type), projection lamps ($T_c \approx 3250\,°$K) and lamps for photographic purposes ($T_c = 3000\,°$K to $3400\,°$K), coiled tungsten wires are used as radiators. With these a higher emissivity is found between the windings of the coil than on the outside of each winding because the cavity in the spiral somewhat resembles the black body. The radiance (luminance) of the coil will not be uniform, and if this kind of radiator is used for measurements, then the radiations of windings and interspaces must be mixed thoroughly.

It will be clear that the short thick spiral of lamps for low voltage and high current can stand for a longer time the deleterious effects of evaporation of the tungsten material during its use as a radiator, or alternatively a higher temperature, than the longer spirals of thinner wire in lamps for high voltage and of the same power consumption.

In an improved variety of the projection lamp for 8 and 16mm film projectors, low voltage spirals (for 6, 12 or 24V) are used. Also, the bulb is composed of a part of a sphere and of an ellipsoid, which are both internally coated with a reflecting layer. The radiator, which often has the shape of a flattened coil, is in the centre of the sphere and at the same time in one of the foci of the ellipsoid. The light reflected by the ellipsoid goes through a window in the spherical mirror, and forms an enlarged real image of the coil in the other focus of the ellipsoid, outside the lamp (see fig. 11).

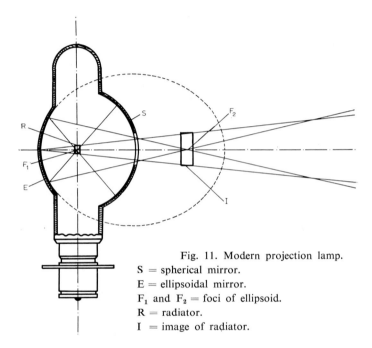

Fig. 11. Modern projection lamp.
S = spherical mirror.
E = ellipsoidal mirror.
F_1 and F_2 = foci of ellipsoid.
R = radiator.
I = image of radiator.

A considerable part of the light radiated by the spiral in the forward direction also comes in the image after it has first been reflected by the sphere and after that by the ellipsoid. In the projector the enlarged image of the coil is used to illuminate the film; in other cases it may be used to illuminate a small rectangle (about 8×6mm) very strongly. Cold light mirrors are sometimes used in the lamp to restrict the radiated heat in the image of the coil.

As an incandescent radiator slowly evaporates at its working temperature vapour is deposited on the wall of the bulb, which consequently blackens. If, however, the temperature of the wall is sufficiently high and a small quantity of iodine is present in the bulb, this will react with the tungsten; a volatile iodide is formed. The iodide disintegrates at the incandescent radiator. The tungsten is deposited on the radiator instead of on the wall, so that the latter remains clear. Based on this principle the quartz–iodine lamp was developed, which is much smaller than a lamp of the same power consumption without iodine. These lamps have a high luminance ($L=3 \times 10^7$ cd·m^{-2}) and a high colour temperature ($T_c=3400\,°K$); they are used as lamps for photographic purposes e.g. in filmstudios, and as projection lamps in 8 and 16 mm film projectors, and even as motorcar headlamps.

6.2. CARBON AS A RADIATOR

A second material, possessing excellent properties for use as an incandescent radiator is carbon Although the melting point is some $400\,°K$ higher than that of tungsten, the vapour pressure at a given temperature is not as low. At the melting point the vapour pressure amounts to more than one atmosphere as it sublimes without melting at the open air. In §3 it was mentioned that glowing carbon particles cause the light emission in the flame of a candle and in other flames of organic materials being burnt. For the Hefner-candle, one of the first standard light sources, the amyl-acetate flame was used, which burnt under exactly prescribed conditions. In the oldest incandescent lamps, a filament of carbon was used. For special purposes carbon lamps are still applied ($T_c \approx 2200\,°K$).

The hottest spot on the anode of an ordinary carbon arc has a definite temperature for a wide range of currents and electrode diameters. For very pure carbon this temperature amounts to $3995 \pm 20\,°K$. It may be interpreted as the sublimation temperature of carbon.

The emissivity was measured by EULER [1953] between $\lambda=250\,nm$ and $\lambda=1800\,nm$, in which region e_λ varies only from 0.71 to 0.79. Consequently in this wave-length region the carbon arc is a source of known radiance (see fig. 9) and luminance ($\approx 1.85 \times 10^8$ cd·m^{-2}), which may be used for many purposes.

6.3. COMPOUND RADIATORS

Round the year 1930, many experiments were made with incandescent tantalum carbide filaments. The melting point of this material is very high, ($4150 \pm 150\,°K$) and it was expected that it would be suitable for higher temperatures than tungsten. From these experiments it appeared that this is not the case, because the filaments quickly decarbonize, as a result of which the melting point decreases. PEEK [1956] described a lamp in which the tantalum carbide radiator, having the shape of a toadstool, was heated by means of a high-frequency induction current. The disk of the toadstool had a diameter of about 8 mm ($\frac{5}{16}$ inch) and a thickness of about 2 mm ($\frac{5}{64}$ inch); it was placed in argon of 2 atm pressure. Owing to its great thickness and to the high gas pressure, the disk decarbonized relatively slowly, even at a temperature of e.g. $3500\,°K$. At this temperature the front of the disk was a very uniform light source of high luminance ($L=4 \times 10^7$ cd·m^{-2}, $T_1=3150\,°K$, $T_c=3650\,°K$), which is used among other things to reprint colour films and to copy colour negatives. Only for such very special purposes it is worth-while to use a high-frequency generator having a power consumption of more than 1.5 kW to operate a light source producing a luminous flux of roughly 650 0lm.

A light source of small dimensions and with great brightness, is the so-called concentrated arc. In a tungsten cylinder a cylindrical hole is drilled in axial direction. The hole is filled with zirconia. An arc discharge, for instance in argon, for which the zirconia serves as the cathode and a metal ring as the anode, brings the oxide at a temperature of about 3600 °K. In the direction of the axis of the hole a high luminance is obtained (4 to 9×10^7 cd·m^{-2}). The luminance increases as the lamp becomes smaller and consumes less power. There are types from 2 W up to 100 W. For power consumption higher than 100 W, the arc is generally burnt in air. The smallest lamp may for instance be used to give very sharp silhouettes.

To generate infrared radiation, considerably lower temperatures may be used than for visible light or ultraviolet radiation. However, the radiator must be able to stand these temperatures in air, because glass and fused silica at wave-lengths of 2.5 and 4 μm respectively begin to absorb radiation very strongly. As sources for infrared spectrophotometer the so-called Nernst radiators are used, as well as bars of silicon carbide (Globar material).

The Nernst radiator is a sintered bar, mainly consisting of zirconia mixed with about 10 % yttriumoxide. At high temperature this mixture conducts electricity. Nernst radiators are used at temperatures near 2000 °K. Complications are that:
(a) the bars can only stand a small number of cycles of heating and cooling;
(b) they must be made conductive by external heating;
(c) the current must be limited, for instance with a resistor connected in series with the bar.

If silicon carbide is used these complications do not occur but the temperature has to be lower. A bar having a diameter of 4.75 mm ($\frac{3}{16}$ inch) and a length of 5 cm (2 inch) is brought at about 1375 °K. The power consumed is ca. 200 W ($i = 5$ A). The maximum of the spectral concentration of radiance lies then just above $\lambda = 2 \mu$m, and the radiation source may well be used for measurements up to $\lambda = 40 \mu$m.

6.4. FLASH-LIGHT SOURCES

Light sources giving short light flashes are used for photography and also to obtain strong radiation in the far ultraviolet.

In photographic flash-lamps, a certain quantity of metal, e.g. zirconium, is burnt in pure oxygen. The extent of the blackening of the negative is determined by the quantity of light, produced in the time during which the shutter is open (10–50 ms). The duration of the chemical reaction is roughly adapted to the shutter time. The total quantity of light produced by the lamp ($Q = 5000$ to 100000 lm·s) is determined by the quantity of metal burnt. If the shutter time is considerably shorter than the duration of the reaction, it has to be taken into account that only a small part of the light produced is really used. The lens aperture must then be chosen correspondingly larger. The greater part of the light is produced by the incandescent metal, the rest in the gas phase as a result of the chemical reaction. Fig. 12 gives the spectral energy-distribution curve for a flash-lamp with a zirconium filling ($T_c = 3900$ °K). Flash-lamps for taking pictures with a daylight-colour film have a blue filter which is applied as a lacquer on the lamp bulb. By this filter T_c is increased to about 5000°K. Fig. 12 also gives the energy distribution curve of this blue flash-lamp.

Strong radiation in the far ultraviolet may be generated by suddenly heating a metal wire by means of a very large electric current. The wire evaporates and, during a very short period of time, gives the desired radiation.

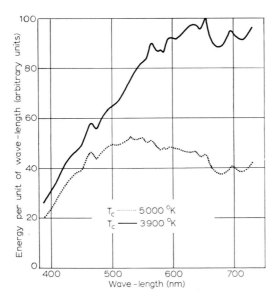

Fig. 12. Spectral energy-distributions for flash-lamps with zirconium filling. Full line: clear glass bulb ($T_c \approx 3900°K$), dotted line: with blue filter ($T_c \approx 5000°K$).

7. Gases at high temperatures

Gases at high temperatures emit radiation, the intensity of which is mainly determined by the temperature as well as by the pressure of the gas and the properties of its atoms. First of all, the question arises whether there is thermal equilibrium in the gas. One would expect that this cannot be the case, because the temperature of the gas is not even uniform, the walls of the vessel being colder than the gas itself. However, upon closer examination it appears that at a given point in the gas the deviations from the thermal equilibrium are not serious, even if the energy flow lasts only for some microseconds (current-pulse, shock wave). A condition for this so-called local thermal equilibrium is that the gas pressure is not too low and amounts at least to a few times ten Torr (see also §8).

Owing to the local thermal equilibrium at temperature $T°K$, and according to Boltzmann's distribution law the number of atoms N_m per unit volume in the state with energy E_m amounts to

$$N_m = N_0 \frac{g_m}{g_0} e^{-(E_m - E_0)/kT}.$$

Per unit of time, $n_{m \rightarrow n}$ of these atoms pass into the state with energy $E_n < E_m$

$$n_{m \rightarrow n} = A_{mn} N_0 \frac{g_m}{g_0} e^{-(E_m - E_0)/kT}$$

The power liberated per unit of volume at frequency $v = (E_m - E_n)/h$, i.e. at wave-length $\lambda = hc/(E_m - E_n)$ is

$$P_{mn} = hv A_{mn} N_0 \frac{g_m}{g_0} e^{-(E_m - E_0)/kT}.$$

This amount of power is actually radiated providing that the radiation is not notice-ably absorbed by the gas. This condition holds good for spectral lines for which P_{mn} is just measurable with a reasonable accuracy. From the relation found and from the measured value of P_{mn}, with known value of A_{mn} on the one hand T may be determined or, on the other hand, with known T the value of A_{mn}. A large number of values of A_{mn} for various elements have thus been interrelated by CORLISS and BOZMANN [1962]. As for a few lines the values of A_{mn} were known from other measurements or from theoretical calculations, these authors could give absolute values for the transi-tion probabilities.

A more direct method to find the temperature of the hot gas is based on Kirchhoff's law discussed in §5. However, when applying this law, the difference between a solid and a gas has to be taken into account; for the gas $\varrho = 0$, so $e = \alpha = 1 - \tau$. Somewhere in a spectral line a wave-length λ is chosen where the gas shows an appreciable absorp-tion, and τ_λ is measured. Also the spectral concentration of radiance $L_e(\alpha)_\lambda$ of the gas for that wave-length λ is compared with that of the full radiator, $L_e(T, 1)_\lambda$, for various temperatures T. As soon as $L_e(\alpha)_\lambda = (1 - \tau_\lambda) L_e(T, 1)_\lambda$, T is the temperature of the gas.

If a full radiator of variable temperature T is available, the comparison of radiances can be carried out without establishing α_λ explicitly. For this purpose the full radiator is placed behind the gaseous radiator. In a spectral line at wave-length λ the transmis-sion factor of the gas is $\tau_\lambda < 1$ and the radiance amounts to $L_e(\alpha)_\lambda + \tau_\lambda L_e(T, 1)_\lambda$. At either side of and close to the line, $\tau_\lambda = 1$ and the radiance is $L_e(T, 1)_\lambda$. T is adjusted till the line disappears in its background. Then so

$$L_e(\alpha)_\lambda + \tau_\lambda L_e(T, 1)_\lambda = L_e(T, 1)_\lambda$$

or

$$L_e(\alpha)_\lambda = (1 - \tau_\lambda) L_e(T, 1)_\lambda,$$

that T is the temperature of the gas (see BUNDY and STRONG [1954]).
Both methods discussed start from the supposition that the hot gas has a uniform temperature. In reality this is not the case, so that with these methods a kind of effective temperature is determined. By applying refined methods, the maximum temperature and the temperature distribution in the gas can be found, as well as the effective temperature (see ELENBAAS [1951]).

For a strong spectral line the shape as a function of λ generally is dented in the

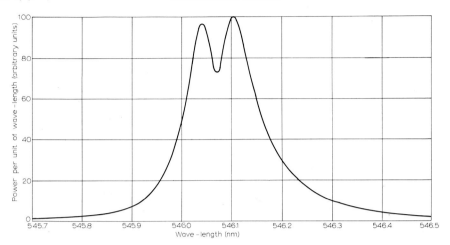

Fig. 13. Self-reversal of mercury line at $\lambda = 546.1$ nm in a discharge of about 1 atm mercury vapour pressure.

middle (see fig. 13), because from the centre of the luminous column to the outside, the gas consists of layers of lower and lower temperature. In the middle of the line so much more of the originally higher flux is absorbed by the colder outer layers that less radiation remains than from the lower flux radiated for wave-lengths at some distance from the middle. This phenomenon is called self-reversal of the spectral line.

In gas discharges at high pressures and with large current densities extraordinarily high concentrations of ions and electrons are found. Then a continuous spectrum appears, which may be attributed to three phenomena, often occurring simultaneously: the broadening of resonance lines, which can go so far that the wings form if it were a continuous spectrum; the recombination of ions and electrons, and the sudden accelerations and retardations of the electrons during their thermal movement through the Coulomb fields of the ions, causing the so-called Bremsstrahlung.

The gas is brought at high temperature by feeding energy into it, for instance by means of a chemical reaction, an electric current or a shock wave. An example of a chemical reaction is the flame, and of an electric current, the arc discharge. A shock wave develops when suddenly a high gas pressure is admitted at one side of a long tube in which there is a low-pressure gas. Then a very steep pressure front moves through the tube. The pressure front is coupled with a thin layer of gas at high temperature.

In this section the word 'gases' stands for the well-known inert gases: helium, neon, argon, krypton and xenon; molecular gases such as hydrogen, nitrogen, oxygen, carbon dioxide and carbon monoxide, and also for metal vapours like mercury vapour and sodium vapour.

7.1. FLAMES

In first instance flames, as sources of radiation, are used for chemical analysis. A well controlled gas flow carries a mist of dissolved metal salt along with it, and the gas is burnt in the flame. The emitted spectrum is searched for spectral lines of elements, which may be present in the dispersed liquid. Because the temperature of the flames seldom exceeds 3000 °K, the method is particularly suitable to find elements having a low ionization potential, like the alkali metals. The apparatus may be calibrated, after which it can be used for the quantitative determination of the elements found (see DEAN [1960]). Further, the flames are used to establish the transition probabilities A_{mn} mentioned in §5. For this purpose the temperature of the gas-flame is determined by one of the methods discussed in this section, after which A_{mn} follows from the measured value of L_e for the spectral line under consideration.

7.2. ARC DISCHARGES *

An electric discharge takes place between a negative electrode, the cathode, and a positive one, the anode. Near the electrodes the character of the discharge deviates from that in the middle, named the column. Because there is a local thermal equilibrium at the gas pressures discussed here, this is called a thermally excited column. With many sources of radiation used in practice, the length of the column is much greater than its width (long columns); with other sources length and width are about the same (short columns).

The composition of the column-gas is simplest if the discharge contains one inert gas only. Mostly xenon is used, because with this inert gas the column produces more light than with any other. Moreover, the light of the xenon column very much resembles daylight, and consequently renders colours very naturally.

TABLE 1

Xenon arc lamps with long luminous columns

Data**	Units	I	II	III	IV	V	VI
l	10^{-3}m	50	75	110	600	750	1500
b	10^{-3}m	1.8	2.6	5.2	17	24	24
V_N(dc)	V	110	—	220	—	—	—
ac		+	+	+	+	+	+
V_B	V	90	125	165	135	140	270
i	A	11.1	22.3	36.5	45	75	75
P	W	1000	2500	6000	6000	10000	20000
Φ	10^3lm	23.5	77	205	140	250	500
η	lm·W^{-1}	23.5	30.8	34.2	23	25	25
I	10^3cd	2	6.5	17.3	—	—	—
L	10^3cd·m^{-2}	23	33	30	1.4	1.4	1.4
dt		fs	fs	fs	fs	fs	fs
env		fs, gl	fs, gl	fs, gl	—	—	—
w		+	+	+	—	—	—

* See also: Note 1 added in proof (p. 381).
** The symbols are defined in the appendix at the end of the chapter.

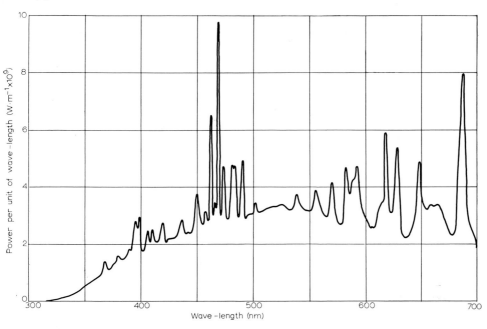

Fig. 14. Spectral energy-distribution for a 10 kW xenon discharge lamp with long column.

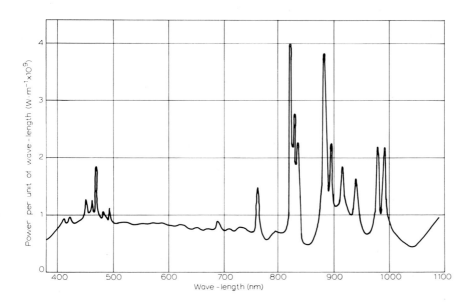

Fig. 15. Spectral energy-distribution for a 1600 W xenon discharge lamp with short column.

TABLE 2

Xenon arc lamps with short luminous columns

Data*	Units	I	II	III	IV	V	VI	VII
l	10^{-3} m	2.2	1.8	1.7	2.5	3.3	4.2	6.0
b	10^{-3} m	1.7	0.8	1.4	1.7	2.3	2.7	3.2
$b_{\frac{1}{2}}$	10^{-3} m	0.7	0.5	0.8	0.7	0.8	1.4	1.5
V_N (dc)	V	—	65	60	70	70	70	85
ac		+	—	—	—	—	—	—
V_B	V	20	17.5	14	19.5	21.5	25.5	30
i	A	8	8.5	18	23	42	63	83
P	W	150	150	250	450	900	1600	2500
Φ	10^3 lm	3.2	3.0	4.3	13	30.5	60	100
η	lm·W^{-1}	21.3	20.0	17.2	29	34	38	40
I	10^3 cd	0.33	0.28	0.50	1.9	4.1	7.4	11.7
L	10^6 cd·m^{-2}	90	200	210	450	550	650	610
dt		fs	fs	fs	fs	fs	fs	fs

* The symbols are defined in the appendix at the end of the chapter.

In xenon lamps with long columns, the gas pressure is about 100 Torr when the lamps are cold, but after the discharge has been started, the pressure increases to about 1 atm. A few data on these lamps are mentioned in table 1; the spectral energy-distribution of one of these types is given in fig. 14. The lamps are used for the comparison of colours and for the lighting of streets, squares and large halls.

In lamps with short columns the gas pressure is 8 to 10 atm; in operation the pressure mounts to about the fivefold value. Consequently, efficient safety measures

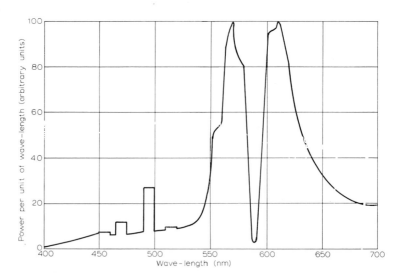

Fig. 16. Spectral energy-distribution for a high pressure sodium discharge lamp.

have to be taken. Data of these lamps are given in table 2; in fig. 15 an example is given oı the spectral energy-distribution. They are used in optical instruments, for cinema projection and other similar purposes.

In case the radiation of metal vapours is wanted, a little inert gas is added in order to make starting of the discharge more easy. In normal operation the tube is so hot that the metal evaporates and all the radiation is produced by the metal vapour.

Experiments were made with the univalent alkali metals in high pressure discharges with long columns. In the sodium discharge the greater part of the radiation has to be ascribed to the strongly broadened yellow resonance lines ($\lambda = 589.0$ and 589.6 nm), as appears from the spectral energy-distribution published in ELECTRICAL REVIEW [1963] and reproduced in fig. 16. NELSON [1964] reports a 400 W lamp producing about 40 000 lm. The sodium vapour pressure is near 200 Torr. A very densely sintered alumina was used for the wall of the vessel, because fused silica blackens quickly if exposed to the discharge in alkali vapour. It is to be expected that, as a consequence of the lower ionization energy, the continuum will grow relatively stronger as a heavier alkali metal is used. According to MOHLER [1939] in the high pressure cesium discharge the continuum may even dominate.

The radiation of high pressure mercury lamps slowly changes with increasing vapour pressure. For lamps having a long column, three pressure regions will be distinguished in the following, viz.:
(a) from 200 Torr to 3 atm,
(b) from 3 atm to 15 atm,
(c) above 15 atm.

At vapour pressures between 200 Torr and 3 atm, the resonance line at $\lambda = 253.7$ nm is markedly broadened; the line also shows self-reversal; the continuum is still weak. The lamps are mainly used for medical purposes (vapour pressure ≈ 1 atm; power

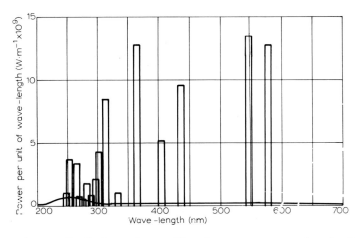

Fig. 17. Spectral energy-distribution and spectral lines for a mercury vapour lamp for the production of phototypes. Vapour pressure ≈ 1 atm. Power consumption 2 kW, arc length 550 mm, fused-silica tube and outer bulb. $\Delta\lambda$ for the mercury lines is 10 nm.

TABLE 3

Mercury arc lamps with long luminous columns
Vapour pressures 200 Torr to 3 atm

Data*	Units	I	II	III	IV	V	VI	VII	VIII	IX	X
l	10^{-3} m	100	144	417	1217	1354	550	400	590	1370	1370
V_N(dc)	V	–	–	–	–	–	–	–	–	–	–
ac		+	+	+	+	+	+	+	+	+	+
V_B	V	120	130	190	550	550	550	550	550	1250	1800
i	A	2.25	3.7	4.2	4.2	5.5	4.2	2.9	4.2	2.9	3.2
P	W	250	450	700	2000	2500	2000	1200	2000	3000	5000
Φ	10^3 lm	9	18.5	–	–	–	–	–	–	–	–
η	lm·W^{-1}	36	41	–	–	–	–	–	–	–	–
dt		gl	gl	fs†	fs†	fs†	fs	fs	fs	fs	fs
env		gl	gl	–	–	–	–	gl	gl	gl	gl

* The symbols are defined in the appendix at the end of the chapter.

† These lamps are available with a wall of fused silica and also with a wall of a special kind of fused silica, transmitting only radiation for which $\lambda > 200$ nm. Such lamps do not produce ozone from atmospheric oxygen.

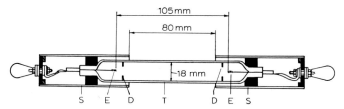

Fig. 18. Krefft's ultraviolet standard lamp. T=fused silica discharge tube. E=electrode. D=glass diaphragm. S=metal shield.

consumption 250 to 500 W) and for the production of phototypes (vapour pressure ≈ 1 atm; length up to 1.5 m; power consumption up to 3 kW. Fig. 17 gives the spectral energy-distribution for a 2 kW fused-silica lamp with an outer bulb of the same material. If a glass outer bulb is used, the part of the spectrum for $\lambda < 320$ nm is absorbed. Table 3 gives data about some lamps of this kind.

The ultraviolet standard lamp developed by KREFFT et al. [1937] is also a radiator of this type. The lamp is sketched in fig. 18; it is made from fused silica according to very strict specifications. The radiation of the lamp is then closely determined by its power consumption which is adjusted to 250 W (dc). The lamp can be used as a radiation standard in the ultraviolet. The distribution of the irradiance on a plane at a 1 m distance from the lamp among the lines as well as in the continuum as a

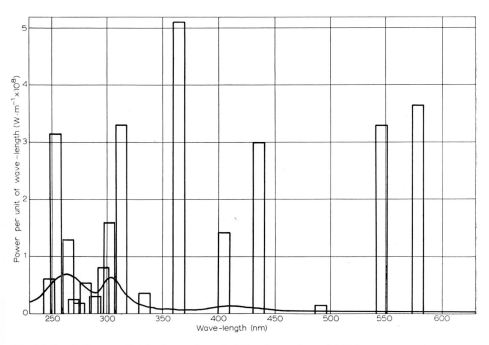

Fig. 19. Spectral energy-distribution and spectral lines for an air-cooled high pressure mercury vapour lamp. Power consumption of the lamp 125 W, mercury vapourpressure about 10 atm, $\Delta\lambda$ for the mercury lines is 10 nm.

TABLE 4

Irradiance produced by Krefft's ultraviolet standard lamp on a plane at 1 m distance from the axis of the lamp

Mercury lines

λ (nm)	E_e (10^{-2} W·m^{-2})	ΣE_e (10^{-2} W·m^{-2})	λ (nm)	E_e (10^{-2} W·m^{-2})	ΣE_e (10^{-2} W·m^{-2})
230.2	1.1		404.7	26.7	
232.3	0.5		407.8	4.0	
235.2	1.7		435.8	50.5	
237.8	2.0		491.6	0.7	
240.0	2.4	15	546.1	62.8	
244.6	0.5		577.0	51.4	197
246.4	0.6		579.1		
248.2	6.6		623.4	0.1	
248.3			671.6	0.08	
253.7	−5.2		690.7	0.6	
257.6	1.1		708.2	0.2	
260.3	0.4		709.2	0.08	
264.0	0.4		772.9		
265.2	16.2	47	816.3	0.06	0.6
265.4	3.1		819.7	0.1	
269.9	2.7		875.8		
275.3			878.4	0.1	
276.0			898.8		
280.4	7.1		899.1	0.1	
289.4	4.1		941.9	0.09	
292.5	1.1		944.3		
296.7	10.7		1014.0	23.8	
302.2	19.9		1128.7	9.5	
302.7		142	1188.7	4.8	64
312.6	46.9		1207.0		
313.2			1357.0	14.3	
334.1	5.1		1367.3		
365.0	69.7		1395.1		
366.3			1691.8		
390.6	0.6		1693.9	11.9	
			1710.8		

Continuum

λ (nm)	$E_{e\lambda}$ (10^{6} W·m^{-3})	$\int E_{e\lambda}\,d\lambda$ (10^{-2} W·m^{-2})	λ (nm)	$E_{e\lambda}$ (10^{6} W·m^{-3})	$\int E_{e\lambda}\,d\lambda$ (10^{-2} W·m^{-2})
200	0.0		400	0.7	
205	0.0		450	0.5	
210	0.3	18	500	0.4	21
215	1.9		550	0.5	
220	4.2		580	0.5	
225	5.6		600	0.4	
230	5.9		700	0.4	
235	5.4		800	0.4	
240	4.9		900	0.3	
245	4.4		1000	0.3	
250	3.8		1500	0.3	
253.4	150.8	36	2000	0.4	31.5
255	77.7		2500	0.6	
260	16.7				146
265	8.5				
270	4.3	17			
275	3.0				
280	2.6				
285	2.5				
290	2.6				
295	2.7				
300	2.9				
310	3.3				
320	3.6	16			
330	3.7				
340	3.2				
350	2.5				
360	1.8				
370	1.2				
380	0.9	6.5			
390	0.7				

Legend to table 4

E_e = irradiance for mercury lines on a plane at 1 m distance from the lamp.
$E_{e\lambda}$ = spectral concentration of irradiance for the continuum.
$\int E_{e\lambda} d\lambda$ = irradiance for the continuum in a spectral band between the two wave-lengths joined by
            the brace.
The line $\lambda = 253.7$ nm shows self-reversal. Therefore it is given with a negative value which is sub-
tracted from the concerned value for $\int E_{e\lambda} d\lambda$, obtained from a smoothly drawn curve. Above
$\lambda = 1000$ nm, $E_{e\lambda}$ contains an appreciable amount of radiation produced by the fused-silica discharge
tube. The value given for $\int E_{e\lambda} d\lambda$ is Rössler's best estimate for the radiation of the discharge in this
wave-length region (RÖSSLER [1952]).

function of wave-length is quoted in table 4 from a paper by RÖSSLER [1952]. In this
paper the total radiant flux $\Phi_e = 67.6$ W and the total luminous flux $\Phi = 8500$ lm of the
lamp are given, too.

For vapour pressures of about 3 to 15 atm, the resonance line is strongly broadened;
the continuum contains roughly as much radiant power as the lines. The discharge
tube usually is made of fused silica. Fig. 19 gives the spectral energy-distribution for
a 125 W lamp. Mostly the lamps are fitted with a fused silica or glass outer bulb. In
the latter case the radiation with $\lambda < 320$ nm is absorbed. On the inner side of the
outer bulb a phosphor such as magnesium arsenate or magnesium fluoro-germanate
may be applied, as a result of which part of the violet and ultraviolet radiation is

TABLE 5

Mercury arc lamps with long luminous columns
Vapour pressures 3–15 atm

Data*	Units	I	II	III	IV	V	VI	VII	VIII	IX
l	10^{-3} m	16	25	30	35	58	72	100	125	200
b	10^{-3} m	—	3.5	—	2.4	3.5	6.2	—	—	17
V_N(dc)	V	—	—	—	—	—	—	—	—	—
ac		+	+	+	+	+	+	+	+	+
V_B	V	95	115	130	125	135	140	140	145	150
i	A	0.6	0.8	0.9	1.15	2.0	3.2	5.6	7.5	14
P	W	50	80	100	125	250	400	700	1000	2000
Φ	10^3 lm	1.6	3.0	3.5	5.2	11	20	37	52	120
η	lm·W^{-1}	31	38	35	42	44	50	53	52	60
L	10^6 cd·m^{-2}	—	3.5	—	6.4	5.5	4.5	—	—	3.5
dt		fs	fs	fs	fs	fs	fs	fs	fs	fs
env		gl	gl	gl†	gl†	gl	gl	gl	gl	gl

* The symbols are defined in the appendix at the end of the chapter.
† The 100 W and 125 W discharge tubes are available with clear glass envelopes and also with envelopes
made of Wood's glass transmitting mainly radiation near $\lambda = 365$ nm and no light. A special 125 W
type of lamp ($l = 30$ mm) is made, which is used without an envelope.

If the inner wall of the envelope is provided with a layer of fluorescent material, all the data but
one are as given in the table. In this case the luminance for the 50 W lamp amounts to $\approx 8 \times 10^4$ cd·m^{-2},
for the 80 W and 125 W lamps to $\approx 10^5$ cd·m^{-2} and for the larger lamps to $\approx 1.5 \times 10^5$ cd·m^{-2}.

converted into deep red light. The total light emitted by the lamp will now have a more agreeable colour, while also the reproduction of colours is improved. For lamps of this category, the power absorbed lies between ≈ 50 and 2000 W. Table 5 gives information on frequently used types. The lamps are used for general lighting purposes and, because of their rich content of near-ultraviolet radiation for the excitation of fluorescence in microscopic objects (e.g. in the fluorescent antibody technique). In this case appropriate filters, passing the near-ultraviolet and stopping the visible light, have to be applied.

At vapour pressures higher than 15 atm the lines are entirely dominated by the continuum. Experiments have been made with pressures up to 300 atm, but in practice the pressure in lamps is not much higher than 100 atm. In by far the most cases water-cooling is applied, and only occasionally forced air cooling. The discharge tube is thin (inner diameter e.g. 2 mm i.e. $\frac{5}{64}$ inch), so that the current density is large. Owing to this as well as to the high mercury pressure, a high luminance is achieved, which may equal the luminance of the sun. Table 6 gives some information on three examples; fig. 20 gives a spectral energy-distribution and fig. 21 shows how according to ELENBAAS [1951] this distribution changes as a function of the vapour pressure.

Many attempts have been made to supplement the mercury spectrum with red spectral lines, for instance of cadmium or zinc, in order to improve the colour of the light and the reproduction of colours (see ELENBAAS [1935], [1948]). In this respect marked improvements have recently been achieved. It appeared that the same transport process which keeps the wall in the quartz–iodine incandescent lamp free from

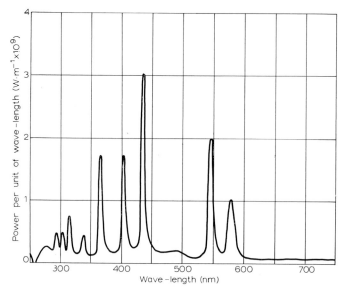

Fig. 20. Spectral energy-distribution for a water-cooled super-high pressure mercury vapour lamp. Power consumption of the lamp 1000 W, mercury vapour pressure about 100 atm. The mercury lines are broadened to such an extent that they can be given in their actual widths.

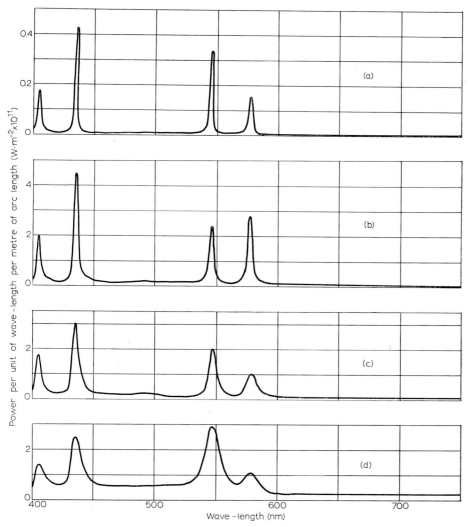

Fig. 21. Spectral energy-distributions for mercury vapour lamps of various pressures, after ELENBAAS [1951].

(a) Tube diameter $=4.2$ mm; $i=0.4$ A; $Pm^{-1}= 4000$ W·m^{-1}; $p= 25$ atm.
(b) Tube diameter $=4.5$ mm; $i=5.8$ A; $Pm^{-1}=72000$ W·m^{-1}; $p= 30$ atm.
(c) Tube diameter $=2$ mm; $i=1.2$ A; $Pm^{-1}=50000$ W·m^{-1}; $p=100$ atm.
(d) Tube diameter $=1$ mm; $i=1.1$ A; $Pm^{-1}=71000$ W·m^{-1}; $p=150$ atm.

tungsten, may be used in the mercury discharge to bring various elements e.g. sodium, thallium, indium etc. into the discharge path and to keep them there. A particular advantage with alkali metals is that the fused-silica wall of the discharge tube is not chemically affected, while the other metals are simply prevented from depositing on the walls. The radiation of the discharges contains far more lines than if the tubes were filled with mercury alone, as appears from figs. 22 to 25; the colour of the light can

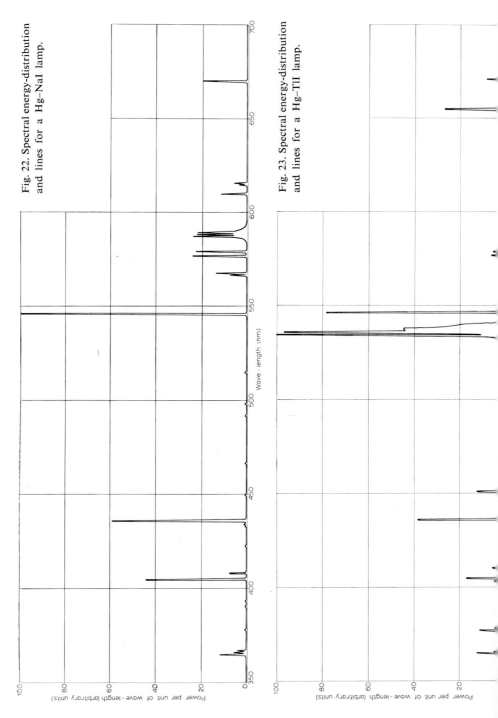

Fig. 22. Spectral energy-distribution and lines for a Hg–NaI lamp.

Fig. 23. Spectral energy-distribution and lines for a Hg–TlI lamp.

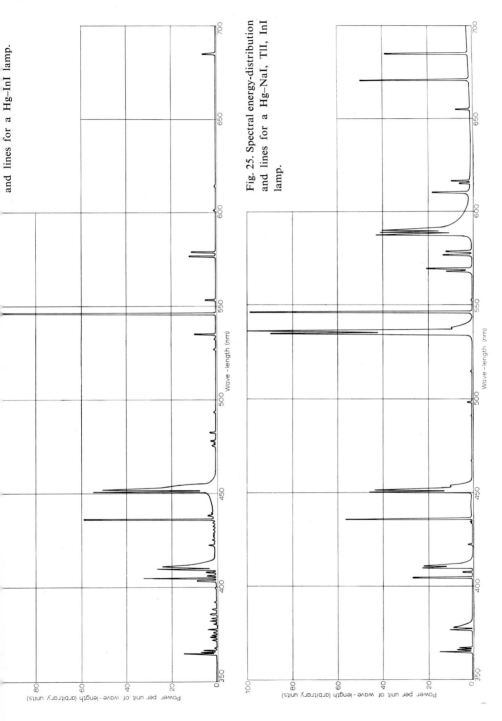

and lines for a Hg–InI lamp.

Fig. 25. Spectral energy-distribution and lines for a Hg–NaI, TlI, InI lamp.

TABLE 6

Mercury lamps with long luminous columns
Vapour pressures near 100 atm

Data*	Units	I	II	III
l	10^{-3} m	12.5	25	12.5
b	10^{-3} m	1.0	0.9	1.1
V_N(dc)	V	—	—	950
ac		+	+	—
V_B	V	450	750	500
i	A	1.4	1.5	2
P	W	500	900	1000
Φ	10^3 lm	30	50	60
η	lm·W^{-1}	60	56	60
L	10^6 cd·m^{-2}	250	220	450
dt		fs	fs	fs
w		+	—	+

*The symbols are defined in the appendix at the end of the chapter.

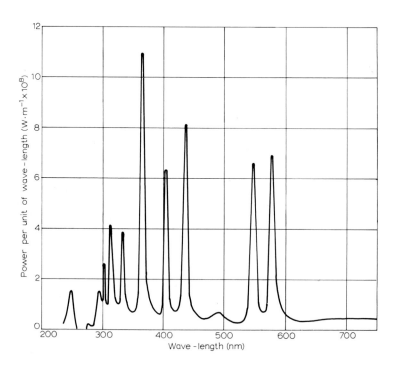

Fig. 26. Spectral energy-distribution for a 200 W mercury discharge lamp with short column.

be made whiter and the reproduction of colours is much more natural, while as
REILING [1964] states at the same time the luminous efficiency is higher. It is possible
to make lamps producing more than 100 lm·W^{-1}; for practical applications lamps
giving ≈ 80 lm·W^{-1} are the most suitable. By applying the deep red phosphor magnesium fluoro-germanate – as mentioned before – on the inner wall of the outer bulb,
sometimes an extra quantity of red light is added. The power absorption is some
hundreds of watts (e.g. 400 W); the lamps are used for the lighting of factories, streets
and squares. It is to be expected that the number of types of these lamps will be
strongly expanded.

Mercury lamps are made with short arcs, just like inert gas lamps. When these
lamps are cold, the pressure of the rare gas, added for starting, is low, but in operation
the pressure of the mercury vapour amounts to some tens of atmospheres, so that
safety measurements will be needed. Table 7 gives information on a few examples;
fig. 26 shows a spectral energy-distribution. The lamps are used for instance in optical
instruments if a small light source of very high luminance is required and the reproduction of colours does not matter too much.

The composition of the gas in the discharge is again more complicated if an arc
discharge is formed between two metal electrodes in air. Both the cathode and the
anode become hot, and the column of the discharge contains metal vapour, oxygen
and nitrogen. The discharges are mainly used for research on the spectra of the
elements of which the electrodes are made.

For research on the arc discharge having a very large power absorption, the column
is intensely cooled, for instance by burning it in a thin canal of mutually insulated
short brass tubes (see SHUMAKER [1961]) or in the centre of a whirling gas or water

TABLE 7

Mercury arc lamps with short luminous columns

Data*	Units	I	II	III	IV	V	VI
l	10^{-3} m	2.8	0.25	2.0	2.2	4.1	4.2
b	10^{-3} m	1.5	0.6	1.4	1.4	2.3	3.7
$b_{\frac{1}{2}}$	10^{-3} m	0.7	0.25	0.6	0.6	1.1	2.5
V_N(dc)	V	–	60	–	120	160	–
ac		+	–	+	+	+	+
V_B	V	50	20	66	55	75	70
i	A	1.7	5	2.7	3.5	6.5	14
P	W	75	100	150	200	500	1000
Φ	10^3 lm	2.6	2.0	7	10	28	50
η	lm·W^{-1}	35	20	47	50	56	50
I	10^3 cd	0.27	0.26	0.7	1.0	2.8	5.5
L	10^6 cd·m^{-2}	65	1700	250	330	300	350
dt		fs	fs	fs	fs	fs	fs
env		gl	–	–	–	–	fs

* The symbols are defined in the appendix at the end of the chapter.

column, according to PFENDER and BEZ [1962] and to MAECKER [1951] respectively.

Finally, carbon arcs with a hole drilled in the cathode are used. This hole is filled with a metal salt or a mixture of metal salts; the gas in the column contains in addition to nitrogen, oxygen and carbon, as well as their various combinations, also metals, metal oxides etc. In spite of the complicated composition of the gas in the arc, the light source is used for the analysis of the composition of the salt mixture in the cathode. With small concentrations of a metal in this mixture, the radiances of its spectral lines are proportional to the concentration. The apparatus can now be calibrated with known concentrations, and consequently a quantitative analysis of quantities of the order of parts per million can be made (see NACHTRIEB [1950]). Carbon arcs with metal salts in the electrodes are also used as very intense light sources. With salts of the rare earth metals, e.g. cerium, the luminance of the arc column is much higher than that of the anode, the brightest of the electrodes. If the current in these arcs is increased to many hundreds of amperes the luminance of the column can increase up to $1.2 \times 10^9 \, cd \cdot m^{-2}$. These arcs are used as light sources in spot lights. Arcs of smaller power consumption are used in cinema projectors.

7.3. FLASH-LIGHT SOURCES

In the introduction of this section it was already mentioned that transient emission of radiation can be excited by means of an electric current pulse, which is usually obtained by discharging a capacitor, or by means of a shock wave.

Inert gases and molecular gases are generally used as bearers of the capacitor discharge; metal vapours are less suitable because it is difficult to make the vapour pressure have the right value before each flash.

The energy $W = \frac{1}{2} CV^2$, stored in a capacitor with capacitance C and charged to a voltage V, is mainly dissipated in the discharge; the quantity of light Q produced is found from $Q = \eta W \, lm \cdot s$. Here $\eta \, lm \cdot W^{-1}$ denotes the luminous efficiency of the discharge.

It is obvious that for the same value of W, a smaller capacitor which consequently must be loaded to a higher voltage, gives a shorter flash than a larger capacitor loaded to a lower voltage. For inert gases the duration of the flash is generally longer than for molecular gases. With very short flashes it is possible that a considerable energy loss occurs in the lead-in wires of the tube, which manifests itself in an apparent decrease of η.

Discharge flash-lamps, filled with inert gases, are usually equipped with an ignition electrode on the outside of the tube, which electrode may consist of a conducting strip or of a transparent conducting layer. The voltage of the capacitor is chosen within a certain range, so that the lamp cannot ignite spontaneously, and the ignition is caused at the time desired by a voltage surge, e.g. of 8 kV, at the ignition electrode.

The duration of the flash generally lies between 3 and 1000 μs. By connecting a resistor in series with the discharge, its duration may be lengthened, at the cost of extra losses in the resistor of course. The lamps are made for loads of 25 to 10^5 J per flash. They are used for example in photography and for optical pumping of lasers (see §10).

The highest values of the luminous efficiency, $\eta = 40$ to 50 lm·W^{-1}, and the best adaptation of the spectral energy-distribution to that of daylight is found with xenon, so that this is the most suitable filling gas for application in photography. A comprehensive article on these lamps was written by MEYER [1961]. For general photographic use, the duration of the flash should not be much shorter than 1 ms, because for shorter exposures the sensitivity of the photographic emulsion decreases. Consequently large electrolytic capacitors and voltages of $\approx 500 \text{V}$ are mainly used for this purpose. Further, for amateur photographers, the dimensions of the lamp will be made small in order to illuminate the object to be photographed economically and evenly with a small reflector. Therefore, many forms of lamps are made, such as I, O, U, Ω and spiral-shaped ones. For reporters, the dimensions may be somewhat

TABLE 8

Discharge- or electronic flash lamps

Data*	Units	I	II	III	IV	V	VI	VII
l	10^{-3} m	44	65	70	63	110	500	205
V_c	V	500	500	500	500	500–2500	2700	2700
W	J	40	60	140	200	300	800	1000
W_{max}	J	50	100	165	235	500	1100	1500
Q	10^3 lm·s	1.9	2.8	6.6	9.4	15	40	46
η	lm·W^{-1}	48	47	47	47	50	50	46
T_c	°K	6400	5800	6500	7100	6600	5800	6900
Sp		I	U	U	Ω	Ω	spiral	Ω
dt		gl	gl	gl	fs	fs	fs	fs

*The symbols are defined in the appendix at the end of the chapter.

larger, and for studio lighting they may even be quite large. Table 8 gives the most important properties of some examples; fig. 27 gives a spectral energy-distribution. For comparison the distribution for daylight according to HERRMANN [1947] is also given.

For laser stimulation, the larger types of discharge flash-lamps are used, starting from about 250 J per flash. Sometimes these lamps are filled with helium.

If flash durations shorter than 1 μs are desired, discharges in air can be used quite well. The spectrum contains lines of nitrogen and oxygen, and also of the material the electrodes are made of. In these spark discharges the temperature is very high, so that the spectral lines of singly or doubly ionized atoms, the so-called spark lines, appear. The use of 'spark' discharges is not restricted to air. The discharge can take place in a closed vessel which may be filled with any other gas. Radiation sources are even used in which the spark strikes between two metal electrodes under water. This

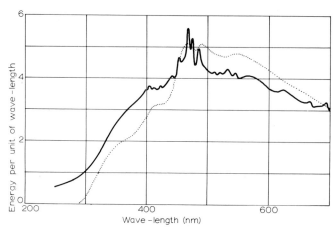

Fig. 27. Solid curve: spectral energy-distribution for a xenon-filled flash lamp ($l=46$mm; $V=500$V; $W=62$J). Broken curve: radiant power of daylight per unit of wavelength in arbitrary units. Unit on the vertical axis $J \cdot m^{-1} \times 10^7$

underwater spark gives the spectral lines of the metal of the electrodes and of the ions of this metal.

By using shock waves for the excitation of radiation temperatures were recently obtained of about $10^5 \,^\circ K$. This is the result of the application of a magnetic field, the direction of which is perpendicular to the plane of a T-shaped discharge tube. In the cross beam of the T a high-current pulse discharge is caused, so that in the leg a shock wave appears. This shock wave is intensified by the magnetic field. A tube of this kind was described by WIESE et al. [1960].

7.4. PERIODICAL FLASH DISCHARGES

The flash discharges discussed might be used for the periodical excitation of light flashes, if they did not get rather warm after every flash as a result of the loading. Therefore they need a period of rest to cool down. If a fixed, not too small repetition frequency v_r is desired, the lamp has to be specially constructed. For lamps giving single flashes, the maximal energy W_{max} per flash was specified; for periodical flash-lamps the maximal average loading $\bar{P}_{max}$ in watts that can be borne should be given. The lamps are among other things applied in stroboscopes and as pulsed lamps for cinema projection.

For the use as a stroboscope lamp it is desirable that v_r is variable over a wide range. The average loading $\bar{P}$ will now also vary and consequently the temperature of the lamp. For such a lamp a filling with an inert gas is more suitable than a filling with metal vapour. An example described by DE BRUIN [1946] is a lamp filled with argon, the duration of each flash being $\approx 10 \,\mu s$; v_r can be varied from 0.5 to 250 Hz. The maximum current amounts to 2000 A, the energy per flash is $W=2$J; the quantity of light per flash $Q=200$ lm·s. In order to make the periodical starting of the discharge easier, a small permanent load is maintained. As a result of this, at $v_r=25$ flashes per sec the total average load is $\bar{P}=75$ W.

With lamps for use in cinema projectors, v_r is a fixed multiple of 24 Hz. Thus, the average loading $\bar{P}$ is fixed, so that in this case metal vapour may be used. Flashing light sources are to be preferred to light sources with a constant light flux, in so far as the former have the advantage that all the light produced can be profitably used, while in one of the dark intervals per $\frac{1}{24}$ s the film is transported to the next picture (see HOEKSTRA and MEYER [1959]). In the mercury vapour lamps used in practice 3×24 current pulses per sec of 2.5 ms length and 15 A height are applied. The value $v_r = 72$ Hz was chosen in order to ensure that the picture does not flicker. Each current pulse has an energy of 11 J, so that $\bar{P} = 800$ W; the lamp is water-cooled. The electrode distance is 17 mm; $\eta = 50$ lm·W^{-1}, so that $\Phi = 40000$ lm. Of these 40000 lm, 5000 to 6000 lm appear on the screen if a well constructed optical system is used. Owing to the high pulse loading, the spectrum of these lamps has a stronger continuum than that of the dc water-cooled mercury lamp (cf. fig. 20, discussed before, and fig. 28), but the strong violet mercury lines at $\lambda = 408$ nm and $\lambda = 436$ nm prevent a correct reproduction of yellow and blue in colour pictures (see KRUITHOF and OUWELTJES [1957]). Recent developments led to a lamp with 14 J per flash and $\bar{P} = 1000$ W, giving a continuum which is relatively still stronger than with $\bar{P} = 800$ W. Owing to the larger power consumption and to further improvements of the optical system, the light flux on the screen is increased about 1.8-fold, so that it is worth while to sacrifice part of it, say

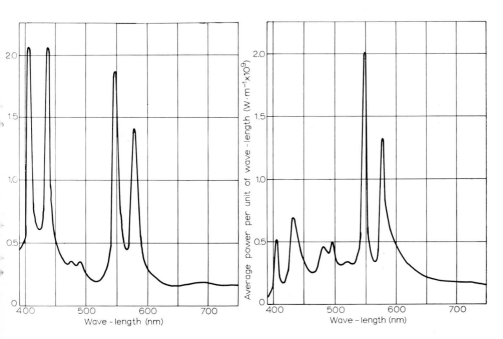

Fig. 28. Spectral energy-distribution for a water-cooled flashing mercury cinema-lamp. 72 flashes per second; 11 J per flash; $\bar{P} = 800$ W.

Fig. 29. Spectral energy-distribution for a water-cooled flashing mercury cinema-lamp with yellow filter. 72 flashes per second; 14 J per flash; $\bar{P} = 1000$ W.

about 20 %, in order to improve the reproduction of colours. Therefore, a pale yellow interference filter is inserted in the light path, which for a considerable part absorbs the mercury lines mentioned before (see fig. 29). The reproduction of colours of the new lamp with filter is now practically as good as that of the carbon arc. The lamp was described by HOEKSTRA [1963].

8. Gases, directly excited by electrons

A radiating gas is a mixture of atoms in the ground state, electrons, ions and excited atoms (see §5), which particles are continually colliding with each other. These collisions can be either elastic or non-elastic. The mass of the electron is thousands of times smaller than that of an atom. Consequently, with an elastic collision between an electron and an atom only an extremely small part of the kinetic energy of the electron is transferred to the atom, so that, as mentioned in §7, a gas pressure of at least a few times ten Torr is needed to establish the local temperature equilibrium between electrons and gas atoms through the interaction of the elastic collisions. With gas pressures lower than approximately 10 Torr the mean energy of the electrons can be much higher than that of the atoms. This high electron energy is attained by means of a gas discharge. The electrons are accelerated by the electric field between the electrodes, and accumulate kinetic energy. At this high energy, in addition to elastic collisions non-elastic collisions occur, as a result of which the gas atoms are directly excited or ionized by the electrons. In order to be able to check how many excitations from the ground state to a certain excited state take place per second, the mean, electron energy, the distribution of this energy about the mean value, and the number of electrons per unit of volume have to be known, as well as the properties of the atoms concerned. The total number of excitations thus calculated is equal to the number of radiation quanta produced per second in the gas if losses of excitation energy due to other causes than radiation are left out of consideration. Some of these quanta can leave the gas freely, other quanta, namely those of the resonance lines (see §5), are repeatedly absorbed in the gas and emitted again. This process has two consequences: (a) After each absorption the resonance quanta remain 'stored' in the absorbing atom for some time. Although this time may be short, all kinds of collision processes are possible, as a result of which the stored excitation energy may be converted into various other kinds of energy, such as ionization energy or heat, and is lost for the radiation. In order to avoid these losses it is necessary to keep the pressure of a radiating inert gas below approximately 1 Torr; with metal vapours this limit is about 0.01 Torr.

(b) The centre of the line is more strongly absorbed than the wings. If the effect is serious, self-reversal occurs, and the line will look as depicted in fig. 13. To suppress the process effectively the pressure of the radiating metal vapour has to be chosen very low, approximately 10^{-4} Torr.

In low pressure gas discharges used as sources of radiation the electrons generally behave as a separate gas, mixed with the main gas. In this case the mean electron energy and the distribution of this energy about the mean value both are characterized by the electron temperature T_e by analogy with the gas temperature T characterizing the mean value and the distribution of the atomic kinetic energy. One of the methods to determine T_e uses the known relationship between this quantity and the energy of the noise induced by a gas discharge in a wave-guide. The method was applied and compared with other methods by among others KNOL [1955], and BEKEFI and BROWN [1961]. Another method, elaborated by Langmuir about 1930, makes use of a probe, i.e. a small metal plate or wire, which is introduced into the discharge. The relationship found between the current to the probe and its potential contains T_e as a parameter. Besides T_e the probe measurements of Langmuir give a value for the number n_e of electrons per unit of volume. For the determination of n_e some other methods are available, one of which makes use of the change occurring in the resonance frequency of a microwave resonance cavity when a gas discharge is ignited in the cavity. The method was submitted to a critical inspection by PERSSON [1957] and applied by among others ANDERSON [1961].

With the aid of probe measurements a detailed investigation of the low pressure discharge in a mixture of argon and mercury vapour was carried out by VERWEIJ [1961]. Furthermore KENTY [1950], and KOEDAM and KRUITHOF [1962] calculated the concentrations of the three principal excited states of the mercury atom in this discharge from the results of absorption measurements on the relevant spectral lines. The concentrations found were so large that, in consequence of the value T_e near $10^4\,°K$ as found by Verweij, it has to be assumed that in the first instance the atoms are brought from the ground state into one of the three states considered, and that mainly from here they are ionized or excited to higher states. These processes of excitation or ionization in two steps, called cumulative processes, are losses of excitation energy as referred to in the first paragraph of this section. Moreover KOEDAM et al. [1963] obtained a general insight in the distribution of the power absorbed by the mercury–argon discharge among the radiation and the various losses. The insight obtained in the matter of the mercury–argon discharge will serve as a starting point to explain roughly the mechanisms of the low pressure gas discharge lamps to be dealt with in the following.

8.1. LOW PRESSURE GAS DISCHARGE LAMPS

Low pressure gas discharge lamps are made to give the radiation of inert gases or of metal vapours. In cases where a metal vapour is used an inert gas is added to carry the discharge current when the lamp is cold and the vapour pressure of the metal is negligible. If the lamp is designed for the production of resonance radiation the consequences of repeated absorption and emission make it necessary, as we have seen, that the pressure of the radiating metal vapour be very low. Another reason to add the inert gas is that the electrons are forced to make large detours by the many collisions with the atoms of this gas and consequently have a greater chance to meet and to excite an atom of the radiating vapour.

It is a matter of course that in general the luminance (radiance) of the low pressure discharge is small, compared to that of the light sources dealt with in §6 and §7. However, there are three interesting applications where they have such great advantages, that this drawback is outweighed.

The first of these applications is the production of light (or radiation) with as high a luminous efficiency as possible. For this purpose the width of the spectral lines produced is of no importance.

For the second application, as a light source for optical pumping (see §10), it is necessary to produce as much radiation as possible in a rather narrow spectral region about the centre of a given spectral line.

The third application is the use of the low pressure discharge for the establishment and the specification of lengths, among other things of the unit of length, for which as narrow as possible spectral lines of a strictly determined frequency and wave-length are required.

8.2. HIGH EFFICIENCY LAMPS †

The appropriate form of discharge for the production of light by means of a low pressure discharge is the positive column. Well-known light sources of this kind are sodium vapour lamps, fluorescent lamps and electric light signs. Examples of other applications are germicidal lamps and ozonizator lamps.

The mechanism of the positive column in the vapour of an alkali metal is much simpler than in mercury vapour as alkali metals do not have metastable states, so that cumulative processes cannot occur. This means that high efficiencies may be expected. In order to get the vapour pressure of a few times 10^{-3} Torr required, the temperature of the coldest spot of the discharge tube of, for example, a sodium lamp has to be between $250\,°C$ and $290\,°C$. Evidently the power employed to maintain this temperature is lost for the excitation of radiation. For many years, a vacuum glass has been used for the heat insulation of the tube. The luminous efficiency of this type of sodium lamp is ≈ 80 lm·W^{-1}. When it was realized that the remaining loss was

TABLE 9

Sodium lamps

Data*	Units	I	II	III	IV	V
V_B	V	80	105	160	160	260
i	A	0.6	0.6	0.6	0.9	0.9
P	W	45	60	85	140	200
Φ	10^3 lm	3.7	5.0	8.4	14	23
		(2.6)	(4.0)	(6.2)	(11)	—
η	lm·W^{-1}	82	83	99	100	115
		(58)	(67)	(73)	(79)	—

† See also: Note 2 added in proof (p. 381).
* The symbols are defined in the appendix at the end of the chapter. In brackets data for lamps of older design.

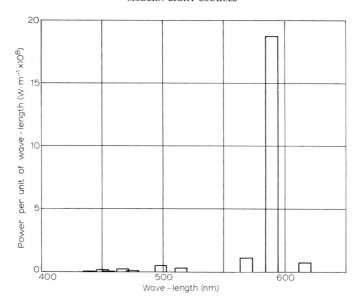

Fig. 30. Spectral energy-distribution for a sodium lamp. Power consumption 140 W, $\Phi = 11\,000$ lm, $\Delta\lambda$ for the lines is 10 nm.

mainly caused by radiation of wave-lengths near 5 μm, a reflector for this radiation was sought which would also transmit the yellow sodium light properly. A coating of electrically conducting tin oxyde appeared to possess these two properties. The result is that sodium lamps are now manufactured having a luminous efficiency larger than 100 lm·W^{-1}. Table 9 gives a survey of a few frequently used types of sodium lamps and their most important properties while fig. 30 gives the spectral energy-distribution for the 140 W type. In principle low pressure lamps with other alkali metals are just as possible as lamps with sodium. An example is the cesium lamp for the excitation of the resonance lines in the infrared at $\lambda = 852$ nm and $\lambda = 894$ nm, described by BEESE [1946].

As was mentioned before, the low pressure positive column discharge in argon-mercury mixtures has been extensively investigated. As we have seen the cumulative processes mean a loss for the atoms excited in the upper level of the strongest reso-nance line at $\lambda = 254$ nm and these atoms are also taken away via the metastable states. Yet the efficiency of the production of the resonane radiation in the discharge is surprisingly high, which appears from the following example: according to KOEDAM et al. [1963], in a discharge tube having an internal diameter of 36 mm, a filling of 3 Torr argon and saturated mercury vapour at 40 °C, in the positive column with a cur-rent of 0.3 A, more than 55 % of the power of 32,5 W fed per metre of column length is converted into radiation at $\lambda = 254$ nm and, moreover, nearly 10 % into resonance radiation at $\lambda = 185$ nm. The radiation at $\lambda = 254$ nm is applied in germicidal lamps. In this case the wall of the tube is generally made of a special kind of glass or fused silica, transmitting the line desired, but absorbing the one at $\lambda = 185$ nm. The latter radiation is not desirable for germicidal lamps because it converts oxygen into ozone. However, this radiation is applied in ozonizator lamps, which therefore are made of ordinary fused silica. In fluorescent lamps the ample production of ultraviolet radiation by the low pressure mercury–argon column is used to excite visible light. For that purpose, the inner wall of the glass discharge tube is coated with a mixture of fluorescent materials. The luminous efficiency of a complete 40 W lamp (length 120 cm = 4 foot; outer diameter ≈ 38 mm $= 1\frac{1}{2}$ inch), in which, as known, at the cathode and at the anode extra losses occur, amounts to ≈ 75 lm·W^{-1}. An important advantage of these lamps is that the spectral composition of the light produced can be widely varied by changing the composition of the mixture of fluorescent materials. Fig. 3 gave the spectral energy-distribution of a 'Daylight' fluorescent lamp; fig. 31 gives that of a 'Warmtint de luxe' lamp and fig. 32 that of a lamp for phototype purposes. Until some ten years ago, the power per metre length that could be advantageously converted into light in a fluorescent lamp was limited to ≈ 40 W because, as a result of repeated absorption and emission, the production of resonance radiation by the low pressure mercury discharge shows a broad maximum at 40 °C. If the lamp is loaded too highly, the temperature of the wall would exceed this favourable value too much. Nowadays the principle of Watt is applied; the wall of the tube is provided with a spot where the temperature does not exceed 40 °C in spite of the higher loading. The means to provide such a cold spot are among other things a small bulge or a part

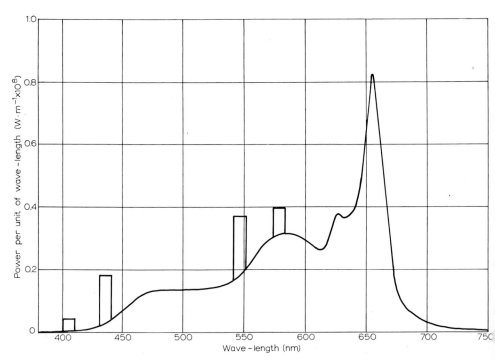

Fig. 31. Spectral energy-distribution for a 'Warmtint de luxe' fluorescent lamp. Power consumption 40 W, $\Phi = 1870$ lm, $\Delta\lambda$ for the mercury lines is 10 nm.

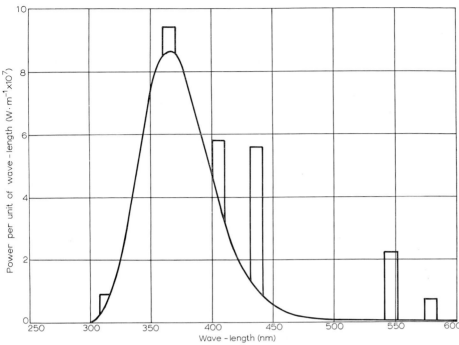

Fig. 32. Spectral energy-distribution for a fluorescent lamp for phototype purposes. Power consumption 40 W, $\Delta\lambda$ for the mercury lines is 10 nm.

TABLE 10

Fluorescent lamps

Data*	Units	I	II	III	IV	V	VI	VII	VIII	IX
l†	10^{-3} m	114	190	266	570	950	1180	1180	1480	1480
b	10^{-3} m	16	16	16	38	38	38	38	38	35
V_N(dc)	V	—	—	—	—	—	—	—	—	—
ac		+	+	+	+	+	+	+	+	+
V_B	V	30	45	58	58	95	103	103	108	100
i	A	0.15	0.155	0.165	0.39	0.30	0.44	0.44	0.70	1.5
P	W	4	6	8	20	25	40	40	65	120
Φ	10^3 lm	0.10	0.24	0.39	1.15	1.7	3.0	2.45	4.58	7.3
η	lm·W^{-1}	25	40	49	58	68	75	61	75	61
L	10^3 cd·m^{-2}	5.6	8.0	9.3	5.5	4.8	6.8	5.6	8.7	14.3

*The symbols are defined in the appendix at the end of the chapter.

l† is the luminous length of the lamp without the caps.

b is the outer tube diameter.

s: direct-start lamps.

For the colour 'Warmtint' the values Φ, η and L are the same as for white; for the colours 'Daylight', 'White de luxe' and 'Warmtint de luxe' they are roughly 30 % smaller.

Special dc lamps are available; they are not mentioned in the table.

of the tube behind the electrodes where no discharge takes place. Table 10 gives the most important data for a number of frequently applied types of fluorescent lamps. These lamps are dealt with extensively by AMICK [1960] and ELENBAAS [1959]. Other well-known applications of the low pressure mercury discharge are the tubes for electric light signs, having a fluorescent coating on the inner wall as fluorescent lamps, while the currents used are between 10 and 200 mA.

Resonance radiation of inert gases, in particular of krypton at $\lambda = 116$ nm and $\lambda = 124$ nm or of xenon at $\lambda = 130$ nm and $\lambda = 147$ nm are applied for the excitation of photochemical processes. OKABE [1964] used an electrodeless high frequency discharge in a tube with a diameter of 13 mm, giving the best output of radiation for either of the two gases at a pressure of ≈ 1 Torr. In both cases the line with the longest wave-length appeared to be the strongest of the two. For the excitation of lines other than the resonance lines of the radiating gas in the low pressure discharge, the gas pressure is usually higher than 1 Torr, so that it is not necessary to add extra gas to facilitate the ignition of the discharge. Examples of sources producing a large radiant flux are tubes for the irradiation of plants. The current in the positive column of the neon discharge used for this purpose may sometimes be as high as 6 A. Intense red light is radiated. Also the red tubes of neon signs are examples of this type of low pressure discharge. These tubes are filled with neon gas having a pressure of ≈ 10 Torr. The current lies between 10 and 200 mA.

8.3. SOURCES FOR OPTICAL PUMPING

As a source of radiation for optical pumping, sometimes the low pressure positive column is applied, but lately more and more the electrodeless high frequency discharge has come into use. The advantages of the latter type of discharge is that the construction of the tube is rather simple. It may, for instance, consist of a hollow flat disk, a cylinder or a sphere of glass or fused silica. In sources of resonance radiation the repeated absorption and emission will have to be avoided by choosing the pressure of the radiating gas at $\approx 10^{-4}$ Torr. BREWER [1961] describes a source for the rubidium resonance radiation, consisting of a spherical discharge vessel without electrodes, having a diameter of 25 mm (1 inch) and filled with one Torr argon and some rubidium, with at the lowest spot of the sphere the tipping-off point. When the tube is in operation this is the coldest place, where the metal condenses. The desired vapour pressure of 8×10^{-5} Torr is attained by loading the lamp with 40 W, so that the temperature of this coldest spot is 90 °C. The production of the radiation takes place in a thin layer close to the inner wall of the sphere. Noticeable self-reversal does not occur; the line width is $\approx 3 \times 10^9$ Hz and the total radiant flux in the two resonance lines of rubidium ($\lambda = 780$ nm and $\lambda = 795$ nm) is estimated at 13 W (i.e. $\frac{1}{3} \times 40$ W). Such a spherical lamp is also suitable for the excitation of the resonance radiation of other alkali metals such as sodium, potassium and cesium. The resonance radiation of mercury has occasionally also been used for optical pumping experiments as well as various helium-4 and helium-3 lines (COLEGROVE et al. [1964]).

8.4. LAMPS FOR THE ESTABLISHMENT OF LENGTHS

To establish lengths use is made of the property of the low pressure discharge, that the electron temperature can be high enough to excite the spectral lines desired, while the temperature of the gas is low. Thus the well-known Doppler broadening of the spectral line is minimized. The frequency spread of this broadening is proportional to the velocities of the atoms along the 'line of sight' and hence increases with the temperature of the gas – which is thus a decisive factor in determining the width of the line. ENGELHARD [1959] developed a light source containing krypton-86 as a radiating gas. A pure isotope with an even mass number was chosen because these isotopes give very narrow spectral lines without any structure. The gas pressure at the very low working temperature of 63 °K, attained by cooling the tube with liquid nitrogen, amounts to 0.03 Torr. The width at half height of the orange krypton line at $\lambda = 605.8$ nm is then 4×10^8 Hz. With the aid of this line according to TERRIEN and HAMON [1962] the length of 1 m can be established with an accuracy of about 2×10^{-9} m. As secondary standards of length, other spectral lines of krypton-86 and lines of cadmium-114 and mercury-198 are used.

9. Electroluminescence

In §§ 6 and 7 it was described that at high temperatures solids as well as gases emit radiation. At low temperatures, gases also emit radiation if an electric current is passed through them, as discussed in §8. Analogous phenomena are found in solids, particularly in crystals. The emission of radiation by a solid at low temperature under the influence of a stationary or alternating electric field, is called electroluminescence. LOSSEW [1923] observed this phenomenon for the first time in silicon carbide; DESTRIAU [1936] discovered it in zinc sulfide. From extensive examinations which mostly were carried out after 1950 it became clear that electroluminescence can be caused by various processes (IVEY [1963]).

In order to be able to explain some of these processes, we start from a result of solid state physics, namely that in a crystal electrons can in principle move freely

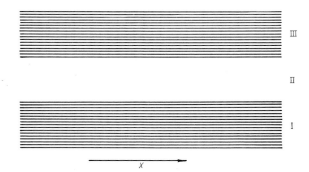

Fig. 33. Energy bands in a crystal. I and III are allowed energy bands, II is the forbidden energy region.

through the lattice, but that there are allowed and forbidden values for the electron energy. As is shown in fig. 33 the allowed energy values group themselves in energy bands between which there are forbidden regions. Each allowed band can contain only a definite number of electrons. If a band is completely filled, then an electric field has no influence on the average movement of the electrons in this band, for instance for each electron moving to the left and which might be turned to the right by the field, another electron, moving to the right, has to go to the left. The uppermost completely filled band is called the valence band. If a crystal contains only completely filled and entirely empty bands, then on an average an electric field will not be able to make electrons move; the crystal is an insulator. However, a certain degree of conduction will appear as soon as a few electrons are in the lowermost empty, but allowed, energy band, which is called the conduction band (see fig. 34a). Conduction may also

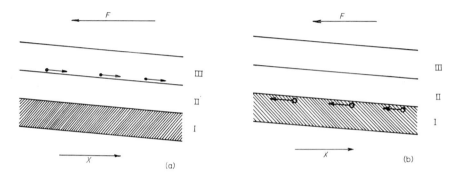

Fig. 34. (a) Electrons in the conduction band, (b) holes in the valence band. I is the valence band, II the forbidden energy region and III the conduction band. ●→ are electrons, and ←○ holes. both moving in the directions of the arrows. F is the electric field.

be expected if there are some unoccupied places in the valence band (see fig. 34b). These empty places, called holes, behave as mobile positive particles. Materials having a limited degree of conduction, caused by the presence of a small number of free electrons or holes, or of both kinds of mobile charge carriers, are called semi-conductors. A semi-conductor is called n-type if it contains free electrons and almost no holes; with holes and almost no free electrons it is called p-type.

9.1. LOSSEW-ELECTROLUMINESCENCE AT p–n JUNCTIONS

The first process which may cause electroluminescence occurs when there is an abrupt transition in a semi-conductor between an n-type part of the crystal and a p-type part. At such a p–n junction, as shown in fig. 35, a space-charge double layer D develops. The junction acts as a rectifier. If, as shown in the figure, a voltage is applied to the junction in the forward direction, the electrons are driven from the n-type part to the p-type part, where by nature many holes are found. At the same time, a current of holes moves to the n-type part, where many electrons are found. At either side of the junction the equilibrium between holes and electrons will be disturbed and

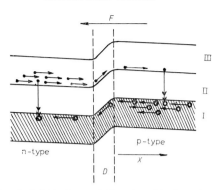

Fig. 35. p–n junction with electric field in forward direction. I is the valence band, II the forbidden energy region and III the conduction band. ●→ are electrons, and ←○ holes, both moving in the directions of the arrows. Double arrows indicate recombination.

holes will be filled by electrons. Energy is released, because the electrons as it were fall down to a lower energy passing the forbidden region. In this case emission of radiation may take place. This kind of electroluminescence is called p–n luminescence. In principle, p–n luminescence may already occur at very low voltage across the junction, so that the efficiency of the radiation production may even be larger than 1. In reality, a high quantum efficiency is only occasionally quoted for gallium arsenide (see KEYES and QUIST [1962]). Other materials showing this kind of electroluminescence in the visible region are for example silicon carbide (LOSSEW [1923]) and gallium phosphide (GRIMMEIS and KOELMANS [1960]). As the emission of light occurs already when the voltage across the crystal is low, applications combined with photo-sensitive elements in so-called opto-electronic devices have been suggested. For this application an important property of p–n luminescence is that the radiation can be modulated with frequencies up to approximately 10^7 Hz. Emission in the infrared is, for instance, shown by germanium and silicium. This emission was for the first time found by HAYNES and BRIGGS [1952].

9.2. DESTRIAU-ELECTROLUMINESCENCE

A second kind of electroluminescence can occur with zinc sulfide and related materials. These materials are luminescent if they contain certain impurities like silver and copper, called activators. The emission of radiation is enhanced by adding co-activators as for example chlorine or aluminium. The luminescence can be excited in a variety of ways, such as exposing the material to ultraviolet radiation or to bombardment with fast electrons. The excitation may either directly transfer an electron from an activator atom to the conduction band or an electron may be lifted from the valence band to the conduction band, leaving a hole in the former which is picked up by an activator atom. The ultimate effect in both cases is that some of the activator atoms are short of an electron and that the conduction band contains free electrons. The luminescence appears as the defect in the activator atom is filled up by a free electron from the conduction band.

Materials like zinc sulfide, which are insulators, are prepared for electroluminescence by adding a small amount of a conducting material. With zinc sulfide itself cuprous sulfide is often used for this purpose, so that zinc sulfide activated with copper and with some extra copper added to form cuprous sulfide constitutes a well-known electroluminescent material. To excite the electroluminescence, the crystal is placed in a strong electric field. ZALM [1956] and FISCHER [1962, 1963], have explained in what way this electric field may make the activators lose an electron and take up another one later on from the conduction band. Both explanations are based on the assumption that there is a concentration of the electric field in certain small regions of the crystal. According to Zalm, the concentration is found in a thin layer of the

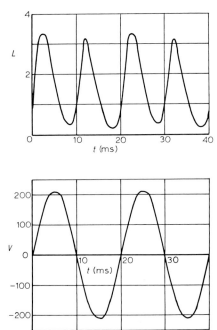

Fig. 36. Luminance of electroluminescent cell as a function of time. V = voltage, L = luminance in arbitrary units, t = time.

crystal at the side of the negative electrode. Here some electrons come into the conduction band by injection from an extremely thin layer of cuprous sulfide, covering the crystal at the outside. These electrons are accelerated by the strong electric field and are then able to deprive activator atoms of their electrons. According to Fischer the field is concentrated inside the crystal at the ends of conducting lines. These conducting lines consist of cuprous sulfide and are found at lattice imperfections, e.g. line-shaped dislocations. As a consequence of the very strong field, a conducting line injects electrons into the crystal at the side of the positive electrode, and holes at the opposite side. The holes may deprive activator atoms of their electrons and after that the electrons injected in the conduction band may cause the emission of radiation.

For practical application using alternating voltage the zinc sulfide crystals are embedded in a dielectric, for which an insulating organic material or an enamel may be used. The dielectric with the embedded crystals is applied as a thin coating between a metal layer and a transparent conducting film, for instance one consisting of conducting tin oxide. It is of great importance that the dielectric constant of the dielectric is high, in order to concentrate as much as possible of the potential difference between the metal and the conducting layer in the crystals. Two kinds of supports may be applied with all dielectrics: a solid metal plate at the back or a glass plate at the luminous side of the element. Moreover, an organic dielectric may be combined with a metal foil; the whole structure is then covered with a layer of plastic, so that a flexible luminous ribbon results.

Fig. 36 gives an example of the dependence of the luminance of an electroluminescent cell on time. The curve was derived from a figure published by ZALM [1956],

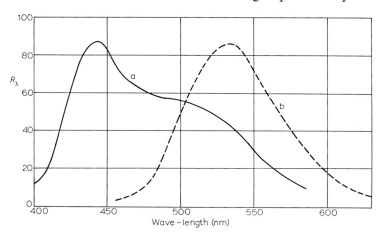

Fig. 37. Spectral energy-distribution of electroluminescent phosphors. Excitation frequency 50 Hz. (a) ZnS–6 × 10⁻⁴ Cu. (b) ZnS–10⁻³ Cu, 8 × 10⁻⁴ Al. R_λ = spectral concentration of radiance in arbitrary units.

for 50 Hz ac voltage having an amplitude of 210 V (150 V r.m.s. value). The two most important characteristics of the curve are that in every cycle of the voltage two light flashes occur, and that, under the prevailing circumstances, these flashes arrive earlier than the maxima of the voltage. The oscillograms of the luminance are not always as simple as shown in fig. 36. It often happens that secundary maxima are found close to the minima between the two main peaks.

For new electroluminescent lamps having an enamel as a dielectric (so-called ceramic lamps) and to be used at 60 Hz, 120 V (r.m.s. value), WEBER [1964] gives luminance values of 1.5 to 5 cd·m⁻² and luminous efficiencies of 0.7 to 1.3 lm·W⁻¹. For lamps having an organic dielectric the values are 17 to 20 cd·m⁻² and 2 to 5 lm·W⁻¹ respectively. The luminance of the lamps used at 50 Hz, 220 V (r.m.s. value) is roughly a factor 2 greater. The luminance can be strongly raised by increasing the frequency to 1000 or 2000 Hz. With still higher frequencies the increase is only small. A consequence of the increased frequency, however, is that the luminance as a function of time of operation decreases much quicker.

Fig. 37 gives the spectral energy-distributions of two phosphors described by ZALM [1956]. The phosphor belonging to curve (a) gives blue light, the other one, belonging to curve (b), gives green light. Electroluminescent cells are applied for scale illumination of measuring instruments and radios, for the illumination of photographic dark rooms and for orientation illumination in dark buildings.

10. Lasers* †

In §5 the coefficients B_{nm} and B_{mn} for absorption and induced emission of radiation, introduced by Einstein, were defined, and it was found that $g_n B_{nm} = g_m B_{mn}$. For simplicity's sake, we shall in the following assume that $g_n = g_m$, so that $B_{nm} = B_{mn}$. Just as in §5, we shall assume that per unit volume the number of atoms in state m, with energy E_m, is N_m, and in state n, with energy $E_n < E_m$, is N_n. If now a parallel beam of radiation, in which p quanta per second pass through a diameter of $O \, \mathrm{m}^2$, is directed through the material, then we say that the flux of quanta through the diameter amounts to p and the radiation density in this beam will be $\varrho_v = phv/c'O$ in which c' is the velocity of light in the material under consideration. Here v is given by $hv = E_m - E_n$ and Δv is the width of the spectral line considered. According to Einstein, $B_{nm} \varrho_v N_n$ quanta per second per unit volume are absorbed from the beam of radiation, and, as a result of induced emission, $B_{mn} \varrho_v N_m$ quanta per second per unit volume are added to it. The latter quanta move in the same direction as the quanta of the beam; and thus, they intensify the radiation in the beam. Quanta produced by spontaneous emission move in all directions; the probability is negligible that their direction should coincide exactly with those of the beam which therefore they do not noticeably intensify. A slice of the beam with length dl has a volume $O \, dl$. In this disk the number of quanta per second decreases by $B_{nm} N_n phvO \, dl/c'O \Delta v$ and increases by $B_{mn} N_m phvO \, dl/c'O \Delta v$, so that

$$\mathrm{d}p = phv B_{mn}(N_m - N_n)\mathrm{d}l/c'\Delta v.$$

If $N_m < N_n$, then p decreases; if $N_m > N_n$, then this quantity increases as:

$$p = p_0 \exp\left[(hv/c'\Delta v)B_{mn}(N_m - N_n)(l - l_0)\right]$$

in which p_0 represents the flux of quanta through the diameter of the beam for $l = l_0$.

If there is a temperature equilibrium, Boltzmann's statistics give $N_m = N_n \exp(-hv/kT)$, so that $N_m < N_n$, because T is positive. If one manages to disturb this temperature equilibrium to such a degree that $N_m > N_n$, then we speak of a 'population inversion' or of a 'negative temperature' for the states m and n. Once a population inversion in a medium has been created, then an incident beam of radiation of frequency v will be amplified after having passed through the medium. If, with the aid of a mirror, the beam is directed again through the medium, it will be amplified again.

---

* See also ch. 14.

† See also: Note 3 added in proof (p. 381).

If use is made of two parallel mirrors, then the radiation can move many times to and fro between these mirrors, and, if the gain in the medium with one vice versa movement is greater than the loss due to the reflections of the two mirrors, the beam will become stronger and stronger. This phenomenon is called the laser effect (*light amplification by stimulated emission of radiation*), analogous to the maser effect (*microwave amplification by stimulated emission of radiation*) already found earlier. If one of the mirrors used transmits a little of the radiation, then a very intense parallel beam of radiation will come out of the laser.

There are many methods to create the necessary population inversion for the laser effect. With all these methods it is advantageous if, for the two energy levels E_m and E_n under consideration, the population of the upper level E_m does not decay too quickly, whereas that of the lower level E_n decays as fast as possible. A few of the most important methods will now be discussed.

The simplest method for producing a population inversion is, without doubt, the direct excitation of level E_m in a gas discharge. This method can be applied to all inert gases. A better method is to use a mixture of two inert gases, e.g. helium with 5–20 % neon. Above level E_m of neon there is a metastable excited state of helium.

TABLE 11

Gases and mixtures of gases showing the laser effect

Gas or mixture	Mech.	Wave-lengths in nm of laser action
He	d.e.	2060
Ne	d.e.	1152· 2102
Ar	d.e.	1694; 2062
Kr	d.e.	2116; 2190
Xe	d.e.	2026; 3507
He–Ne	m.e.	633; 1152; 1161; 1523; 3391; 53486
He–Xe	m.e.	2026; 3507
Ne–O$_2$ Ar–O$_2$	diss.	845
He–CO He–CO$_2$ Ne–CO Ne–CO$_2$	diss.	845; 1069; 1454
He–NO He–NO$_2$ Ne–NO Ne–NO$_2$	diss.	845; 1358; 1454
SF$_6$ He–SF$_6$	diss.	1046; 1063
Ar–Br$_2$	diss.	844.628; 844.638; 844.670; 844.679

Mech. = mechanism causing population inversion.
d.e.   = direct excitation by electrons.
m.e.   = excitation via metastable state of helium.
diss.   = dissociation of the molecule.

TABLE 12

Combinations of host materials (vacuum) and impurities showing
the laser effect if excited by optical pumping

Host mat.	Imp.	Wave-lengths (nm)	Host mat.	Imp.	Wave-lengths (nm)	Host mat.	Imp.	Wave-lengths (nm)
Al_2O_3	Cr	694.3	LaF_3	Nd	1039.9	$CaWO_4$	Pr	1046.8
		700.9			1063.1			
		704.1			1063.3	$CaWO_4$	Tm	1906.0
		692.9						1911
			LaF_3	Pr	598.5			1911.5
Y_2O_3	Nd	1073						1916
		1078	$CaMoO_4$	Nd	1067			
					1067.3	$SrWO_4$	Nd	1057.4
MgF_2	Ni	1624						1060.7
			$SrMoO_4$	Nd	1057.6			1062.7
CaF_2	U	2240			1059			1063
		2510			1061.1			
		2570			1062.7	silicate		
		2610			1064.0	glass	Ho	>1950
					1064.3			
CaF_2	Dy	2360			1065.2	silicate		
						glass	Yb	1015
CaF_2	Er	1617	$PbMoO_4$	Nd	1058.6			
						barium		
CaF_2	Ho	2092	$CaWO_4$	Er	1612	crown		918.0
						glass	Nd	1060
CaF_2	Nd	1045.7	$CaWO_4$	Ho	2046			
					2055.6	vacuum	Cs	3200
CaF_2	Sm	708.2			2059			7180
					2070.7			
CaF_2	Tm	1115.3			2074.0			
BaF_2	U	2556	$CaWO_4$	Nd	914.5			
					1057.6			
BaF_2	Nd	1060			1058.2			
					1063.3			
SrF_2	U	2407			1064.1			
					1065.2			
SrF_2	Nd	1037.0			1065.0			
		1043.7			1066			
					1337.2			
SrF_2	Sm	696.9			1339.2			
					1345			
SrF_2	Tm	1972			1387			

The various laser wave-lengths listed for one combination may appear at different impurity concentrations or temperatures.

In the discharge, relatively many excited helium atoms are produced, and because these are continually colliding with neon atoms, the excitation energy is easily transferred to the neon, as a result of which level E_m is filled and the laser effect is attained.

Besides the two methods just described, there is still another way to attain population inversions in gases and in gas mixtures, namely through the dissociation of molecules like O_2, CO or SF_6.

Table 11 gives a number of gases and gas mixtures in which the laser effect has been attained. It gives, moreover, the mechanisms causing the population inversions, and the wave-lengths at which laser radiation occurs. The data of this and the two following tables were compiled by BIRNBAUM [1964].

Absorption of strong radiation may cause a population inversion. This method is called optical pumping. The material responsible for the laser effect is a vapour of low pressure or distributed impurity atoms in a crystalline or glass-like host material. For the ruby laser for example, a single crystal of alumina is used with chromium as an impurity. The host material with the impurity is exposed to strong radiation of appropriate wave-lengths. As a result of this, the atoms are either immediately excited to the state desired with energy E_m, or a state with energy $E_0 > E_m$ is excited, which may be a state of the atom or of the host material. In the former case, the population inversion occurs immediately, in the latter, the energy difference $E_0 - E_m$ has first to be disposed of. It is often easier to cause a population inversion if the host material is cooled down to $77\,°K$ or $20\,°K$ for example, than at room temperature. Table 12 shows a number of combinations of host materials and impurities in which laser effects were found at the wave-lengths, which are also indicated.

Apart from these, a method is used analogous to the excitation of p–n luminescence. In §9 an explanation was given of how, as a result of an electric current being sent in forward direction through a p–n junction, at either side of this junction high concentrations of electrons in the conduction band and of holes in the valence band occur. Consequently, for the vicinity of the p–n junction, the considerations given above about absorption and amplification of radiation can be applied. As with optical

TABLE 13

Materials in which p–n junctions may show the laser effect

Material	Wave-length in nm of laser action
GaAs	824.0; 837.0; 852.5; 902.0
Ga(As, P)	640–840 ($x=0$–1)
(In, Ga)As	840–3100 ($x=0$–1)
InAs	3112.0; 3150.0
InP	≈ 903; ≈ 910
In(P, As)	1602 ($x=0.49$)
InSb	5180

(A, B) means A_x, B_{1-x}.

pumping, it is often necessary to cool down the p–n junction to 77°K, 20°K, 4.2°K or 1.9°K, to produce the laser effect. Table 13 gives some materials in which p–n junctions can show this effect.

The construction of a laser depends on the medium used and on the mechanism for the excitation of the population inversion. With the aid of a few sketches we shall describe four examples of constructions which are often used.

Fig. 38 shows the construction of a laser, in which the laser effect is excited by means of a gas discharge. The two parallel flat mirrors, as already mentioned, are utilized to isolate the interior of the gas discharge tube from the air.

A second construction for a gas discharge laser is shown in fig. 39. The parallel flat plates, shutting off the tube, are here placed at an angle, known as the Brewster angle, to the axis of the tube. Such a window transmits radiation with almost no loss if this radiation is polarized in a plane perpendicular to the window, and in that plane perpendicularly to the axis of the tube. The mirrors sketched in fig. 39 are concave, while their focal points coincide. In such a mirror system, each ray inter-

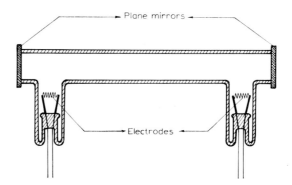

Fig. 38. Gas discharge laser with plane mirrors. The plane mirrors are used to isolate the interior of the tube from the air and to reflect the radiation to and fro through the gas discharge passing between the electrodes.

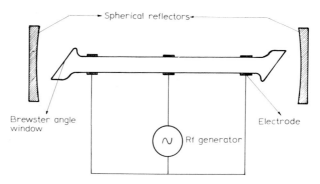

Fig. 39. Gas discharge laser with confocal spherical mirrors. The parallel windows making the Brewster angle with the axis of the tube, shut off the interior of the tube from the air. The mirrors are independent of the gas discharge tube, which is excited by means of a radiofrequency discharge.

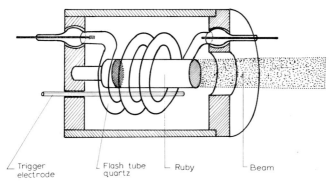

Fig. 40. Laser with optical pumping excitation. The ruby crystal is excited by the radiation due to a condenser discharge through the quartz flash tube which ignites if a voltage surge is given on the trigger electrode.

secting the optical axis and staying in the neighbourhood of that axis after four reflections, returns in itself, just as each ray which is parallel to the axis between two parallel flat mirrors after two reflections. For that reason, a system of confocal concave mirrors can also be used for the construction of a laser, offering the advantage that the adjustment of the concave mirrors is far less critical than of the flat mirrors.

The laser of fig. 40 is stimulated by optical pumping. The radiation required is excited by means of a condensor discharge in a spiral flash tube (see §7). The radiation is concentrated as much as possible in the cylindrical rod, consisting of a single crystal of, for instance, ruby. Both the ends of the rod are flat, cut parallel, and mirrored.

Finally, fig. 41 shows an enlarged and idealized model of a laser with p–n transition. The parallel planes, which have to be perpendicular to the plane of the junction, can be made by cleaving the crystal. In general, it will not even be necessary to mirror these planes in order to achieve the laser effect.

The two parallel mirrors, between which the radiation of a laser is excited, form an interferometer, but they can also be regarded as a resonance cavity for very short

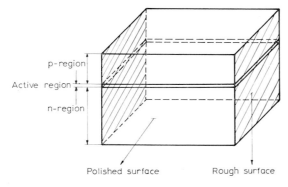

Fig. 41. Laser with p–n junction. The p–n junction is the active region of the laser. The direction of the beam is perpendicular to the polished front and back surfaces. Voltage is put across the crystal in forward direction i.e. the p-region is made positive and the n-region negative.

wave-lengths. As the cavity lengthwise contains a large number of waves, the quality factor Q is very high. As a result of this, the frequency spread of the laser radiation is extremely narrow and it is, as a near approximation, a coherent beam. This approximation is more precise for a cavity with flat mirrors than for one with confocal concave mirrors, and further it is the more accurate the larger the number of waves between the mirrors. That is why in general long gas discharge lasers show best coherence as compared with lasers with crystal or glass rods as well as with p–n lasers.

We shall now discuss the most important consequences of coherence, and mention a few practical applications for which laser radiation is used or is planned to be used. As typical examples of lasers, we choose the helium–neon laser as shown in fig. 39, with mirrors at a distance of 1.3 m, and the ruby laser of fig. 40. According to BENNET [1962], the former type of laser ($\lambda = 1152.3$ nm) can give a continuous output of 20 mW, and according to MAIMAN et al. [1961] the latter laser ($\lambda = 694.3$ nm) gives spiked pulses with spikes of ≈ 1 μs; total duration ≈ 3 ms and total energy ≈ 1 J.

A direct consequence of the great coherence of laser radiation is that interference tests can be carried out over long distances. Whereas with formerly known light sources it was only possible to determine interferometrically the standard length of 1 metre by measuring it in two or three parts, with the laser radiation tests have already been carried out over a distance of 9 metres, and in this the limit has by far not been reached. An ideally coherent beam of radiation has a completely flat wave front, so that the beam does not show any spread. With laser radiation, spreading does occur, but only very slightly. The pencil produced by the He–Ne laser mentioned had a beam divergence angle of 3 min. If the concave mirrors are replaced by flat ones, then this angle is only $\approx \frac{1}{2}$ min. The significance of these figures becomes clear if we realize that in the former case the pencil widens to 0.85 m over a distance of one kilometre, and in the latter only to 0.14 m. For the transmission of signals this beam spread can be further reduced by the use of suitable lens systems, and one of the principal potential applications of laser radiation is therefore the use in telecommunication. It is expected that by this method interplanetary, or even interstellar distances may be bridged.

A second consequence of the small spreading of laser beams is that they have an enormous radiant intensity. For the He–Ne laser with concave mirrors as mentioned before, the radiant intensity amounts to 3.5×10^6 W·sr^{-1}, and as the radiation comes from a spot on the mirror with 1.4 mm diameter, the radiance of this spot will be 2×10^{12} W·sr^{-1}·m^2. These values are larger by a factor 70000 than those for the total radiation of a spherical black body of the same dimensions, at the temperature of the sun, viz. 6500 °K. Thus the laser is the only optical instrument which seems to break through Abbe's Law (see §4). Of course this is not a real violation of the law as the laser essentially does not consist of lenses, mirrors and the like.

With a lens or mirror having a relative aperture of 1:1 and a diameter equal to that of the beam, a coherent beam of radiation can in principle be focussed on a tiny spot of size λ^2 m^2, or in a volume of λ^3 m^3. This would mean an enormous concentration of energy, for example in the case of the ruby laser 2×10^{12} J·m^{-2} or 3×10^{18} J·m^{-3}. In practice, lenses with longer focal lengths are used, so that the energy is less concentrated. Nevertheless, with the focussed radiation of a ruby laser, one can easily melt a hole in a steel safety razor blade. In opthalmology the energy concentration by the ocular lens itself is applied to reattach a loosened retina through coagulation. In matter, non-linear effects appear as a result of the intense concentration of energy, so that, for instance, the double frequency of the laser radiation used can be observed. In order to increase the energy for these experiments on non-linear optics still more – although during a short period only – so-called giant-pulse lasers were constructed. With a certain version of these lasers, called Q-spoiled lasers, the quality factor Q of the resonant cavity is first made low, and then increased suddenly. This is the moment that, according to MCCLUNG and HELLWORTH [1962, 1963], a giant pulse occurs, lasting for instance 3×10^{-8} s and having a power of 15×10^{6} W.

As a result of the high quality factor of the resonance cavity in which the laser radiation is excited, its frequency is determined sharply. The oscillation in the cavity can take place in various modes, each mode corresponding with an extremely narrow spectral line. Experimentally, for the ruby laser line widths smaller than 0.01 nm are found. At $\lambda = 694.3$ nm this line width corresponds to about 6×10^9 Hz. This width is not extremely small; it is determined by the stability of the set-up used. Theoretically it should be possible to achieve lines which are narrower by many orders of magnitude. If we take into account the line width of 0.01 nm, which has now already been definitely established, then the spectral concentration of radiance for the ruby laser is greater by a factor 2×10^{10} than the one of a black body at sun temperature.

As laser wave-lengths and frequencies depend on the dimensions of the resonance cavity, it is not possible to carry out absolute calibrations of lengths with the aid of laser radiation. Investigations are being made to find a version of the laser which can be used for this purpose. However, in principle it is indeed possible to compare lengths very accurately with the aid of laser radiation.

11. Miscellaneous lamps

In this section, the following four kinds of radiating gas discharges will be dealt with:
(a) the cathode region of the glow-discharge,
(b) the hot cathode arc-discharge,
(c) the hydrogen lamp,
(d) spectral lamps.
The cathode region of the glow-discharge is a typical low-pressure discharge, in which the atoms are directly excited by fast electrons. The reason why we deal with this part of the discharge here, separately from the positive column (see §8), is that the cathode region has properties which differ completely from those of the column. The glow-discharge takes place on a metal surface if this is used as a cathode in a gas discharge. If an anode is placed close enough to the cathode it absorbs the electrons formed at the cathode and in the gas and no positive column is formed. Then the discharge is seen as a luminous spot on the cathode. The section of this discharge, producing the main part of the light, is called the negative glow. With many discharges of this

TABLE 14

Colours and normal cathode falls for various gases

Gas	K_1	K_2	V_B
He	red	green	150
Ne	yellow	orange	150
Ar	pink	dark blue	165
Kr		green	215
Xe		olive green	306
Air	pink	blue	269
H_2	brownish red	pale blue	250
N_2	pink	blue	215
O_2	red	yellowish-white	290
Hg	green	green	298

$K_1 =$ colour of the first cathode layer.
$K_2 =$ colour of the negative glow.
$V_B =$ normal cathode fall (Fe cathode).
Colours and values of V_B according to FRANCIS [1956].

type, we see, close to the cathode, a layer of different colour, the first cathode layer. Table 14 gives the colours of the two parts of the discharge for a number of gases. The radiation produced by the cathode region of the glow-discharge mainly consists of spectral lines of the gas in the tube. Because the electrons in the discharge pass through a potential difference of many tens to some hundreds of volts, it is also possible that the lines of the ionized atom can be seen. Sometimes it happens that the cathode is sputtered so strongly that lines of the electrode material appear. A characteristic of the discharge is that at a given gas pressure and for each combination of metal and gas, there is a fixed current density, called the normal current density, provided that the discharge does not completely cover the cathode. If the current is increased, then the discharge extends till the whole cathode is covered. Under these circumstances we speak of a normal discharge. The discharge voltage has a definite value, called the normal cathode fall. Table 14 gives the values of the normal cathode fall for the gases mentioned in this table, when an iron cathode is used. If, after the cathode has been completely covered with the discharge, the current is increased further, then the discharge voltage increases and we speak of an abnormal glow-discharge. The normal current is strongly dependent on the gas pressure; with a low gas pressure p_1 the normal current density is small, with a higher gas pressure p_2 it is higher by a factor $(p_2/p_1)^2$.

As a light source, in most cases, the orange-coloured cathode region of the glow-discharge in neon is used in so-called glow-lamps. These lamps are manufactured for use on direct current or on alternating current. In dc lamps, the forms of cathode and anode nearly always differ. For instance, as a cathode a small flat disc is used, and as an anode a small ring, facing the cathode. If the pressure and current are adjusted in such a way that the whole cathode is covered by the discharge, then we attain an approximately even luminous spot.

In ac lamps, the two electrodes have generally the same form. They are alternatively cathode and anode. If we observe one of the electrodes separately, then we find that, with not too high frequencies, the light is produced when this electrode is the cathode. In the opposite half of the cycle the other electrode is the cathode and lights up. If both electrodes have the form of a semi-circle, and if the current and gas pressure are properly adjusted, we see, apart from the dividing line between the semicircles, the whole circle lighting up. If necessary, a material with a lower normal cathode fall than pure iron is used for the electrodes, like magnesium for instance, so that the lamps ignite and give light on the available mains voltage.

Glow discharges are used for various purposes, for example to indicate that the mains voltage is on, or for orientation lighting.

The arc discharge with a hot cathode can occur is various forms; with a very low current as an anode glow, with a slightly higher current as a ball of fire in the neighbourhood of the cathode, and, with a current larger than the electron emission of the cathode, as a glow, surrounding the whole cathode. The last two forms of discharge are summed up under the name low-voltage arc. In the first sodium lamps, use was made of this low-voltage arc for the production of radiation. Nowadays, the low pressure positive column (dealt with in §8) is used for this purpose, as it has a much higher efficiency.

The hydrogen lamp gives a continuous spectrum and the so-called Balmer-lines. The continuous spectrum lies between $\lambda = 185$ nm and $\lambda = 500$ nm and originates from the hydrogen molecule; the lines are radiated by the hydrogen atom. The wave-lengths of the three strongest Balmer-lines are $\lambda = 656.3$ nm (H_α), $\lambda = 486.1$ nm (H_β) and $\lambda = 434.0$ nm (H_γ).

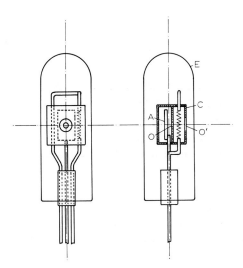

Fig. 42. Hydrogen lamp. C = thermionic cathode, S = screen, O = circular opening or slot where the discharge is concentrated, A = anode, O′ = opening in the cathode screen S so let through the radiation.

Fig. 42 shows how in principle a hydrogen lamp is built up. The lamp contains a hot cathode, the dc discharge is forced to pass through a narrow opening in a screen around the cathode. The concentrated discharge in the opening is the source of the radiation desired. The anode is placed near the opening. The construction of any special lamp is completely adapted to the practical demands of the spectral apparatus in which this lamp is used. Thus, the narrow opening may be circular or it may be a slot. The current of the discharge, too, is adapted to need and use is made of values between 0.24 A and 1.5 A.

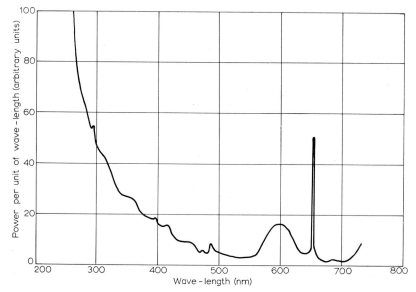

Fig. 43. Spectral energy-distribution for hydrogen lamps.

An example of the spectral energy-distribution of such a hydrogen lamp ($i = 0.3$ A) is given in fig. 43. The line H_α is clearly visible. It is remarkable that the continuum to shorter wave-lengths becomes increasingly stronger. It is possible to increase the radiation in the short-wave region by a factor of 2, by filling the lamp with deuterium instead of hydrogen. Hydrogen lamps are used for investigations on ultraviolet radiation, particularly if measurements are to be carried out with a continuous range of wave-lengths, for instance, of transmission factors, or on the excitation of fluorescence.

The radiating parts of spectral lamps are in general positive column discharges for ac, which in principle can be classified in the various headings of §7 and §8. For the user, however they form one group. For that reason they are all dealt with in this section. The various elements used in manufacturing spectral lamps are listed in table 15. The lamps can be arranged in groups so that in one group they carry the same current. Lamps of such a group can be used with one ballast; they can, one after the other, be placed into one lamp holder, without any change of the circuit.

TABLE 15

Spectral lpmas

Gas or vapour	Type I						Type II					
	$i(A)$	$P(W)$	$l(10^{-3}\,m)$	$b^*(10^{-3}\,m)$	dt	env	$i(A)$	$P(W)$	$l(10^{-3}\,m)$	$b^*(10^{-3}\,m)$	dt	env
He	0.9	45	32	12	gl	gl	1.2	60	15	8	gl	gl
Ne	0.9	25	40	12	gl	gl	1.5	40	20	8	gl	gl
Ar	0.9	15	40	12	gl	gl	—	—	—	—	—	—
Kr	0.9	15	40	12	gl	gl	—	—	—	—	—	—
Xe	0.9	10	40	12	gl	gl	3	90	12	1.8	fs	—
Na	0.9	15	40	12	gl	gl	1.3	25	15	10	gl	gl
K	0.9	10	40	12	gl	gl	1.5	14	15	10	gl	gl
Rb	0.9	15	40	12	gl	gl	1.5	13	20	10	gl	gl
Cs	0.9	10	40	12	gl	gl	1.5	10	15	9	gl	gl*
Zn	0.9	25	30	7	fs	fs, gl	1.5	20	15	8	fs	gl*
Cd	0.9	25	30	7	fs	fs, gl	1.5	18	17	8	fs	gl*
Hg(l)	0.9	15	40	12	fs, gl	fs, gl	0.12	2	12	6	gl	—
Hg(h)	0.9	90	30	2	fs	fs, gl	1.2	55	20	3	fs	gl*
Hg(h)	—	—	—	—	—	—	1.1	50	20	2	fs	gl°
HgCd	—	—	—	—	—	—	1.0	30	20	3	fs	gl*
HgCdZn	0.9	90	30	2	fs	fs, gl	—	—	—	—	—	—
In	0.9	25	25	2	fs	fs	—	—	—	—	—	—
Tl	0.9	20	30	9	fs	fs	1.0	13	8	3	fs	gl

The symbols are defined in the appendix at the end of the chapter.

b^* approximate values.

(l) low pressure.

(h) high pressure.

gl* denotes a special kind of glass, transmitting for $\lambda > 280\,nm$.

gl° the envelope has a hole permitting radiations with $\lambda < 280\,nm$ to be utilized.

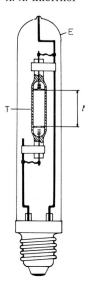

Fig. 44. Spectral lamp.
T = discharge tube,
E = envelope,
l = length of luminous part.

In fig. 44 we see how, with most of the spectral lamps, the discharge tube is surrounded by an envelope, mainly serving for the thermal insulation of the tube. Table 16 gives the most important spectral lines of the elements, which were mentioned in table 15. Furthermore, a rough estimate is given of the strength of the lines. Spectral lamps are used for the calibration of wave-length dials of spectral apparatus, such as spectrographs and monochromators.

Legend to table 16

Wave-lengths in nm. The radiant intensities of the lines have been given roughly for each element on a logarithmic scale in parentheses. The scales for different elements are not interrelated.

scale value	radiant intensity
0	<1
1	1– 3
2	3– 10
3	10– 30
4	30–100

TABLE 16

Wave-lengths of the most important lines of the elements used in spectral lamps, cf. table 15

Helium	638.299 (3)	750.387 (3)	419.313 (3)	*Cadmium*	275.277 (2)	616.076 (2)	603.409 (1)
51.364 (1)	640.225 (3)	763.510 (3)	450.098 (3)	214.504 (2)	275.284 (1)	818.327 (2)	621.287 (2)
70.500 (1)	650.653 (3)	772.376 (2)	452.468 (2)	223.986 (2)	280.348 (1)	819.481 (3)	658.651 (2)
31.961 (1)	653.288 (2)	772.421 (2)	462.428 (3)	226.503 (2)	280.446 (1)		672.328 (2)
38.685 (3)	659.895 (3)	794.817 (2)	467.123 (3)	226.747 (0)	280.542 (1)	*Potassium*	697.329 (2)
96.473 (1)	667.828 (2)	800.616 (3)	469.702 (2)	228.802 (3)	284.783 (0)	344.672 (2)	794.411 (3)
02.619 (2)	671.704 (2)	810.369 (3)	473.415 (3)	228.874 (0)	289.359 (1)	344.770 (2)	807.902 (3)
12.081 (1)	692.947 (3)	811.531 (3)	480.702 (3)	232.928 (2)	292.541 (1)	404.414 (3)	852.110 (3)
14.376 (1)	703.241 (3)	826.452 (3)	491.651 (2)	276.389 (2)	296.728 (2)	404.720 (2)	894.350 (3)
38.793 (1)	717.394 (3)	840.821 (3)	492.315 (2)	277.505 (1)	302.150 (2)	578.260 (1)	
47.148 (2)	724.516 (3)	842.465 (3)	589.499 (2)	283.691 (2)	302.348 (1)	580.196 (1)	*Indium*
71.314 (1)	743.890 (2)	852.144 (3)	616.366 (2)	288.077 (2)	302.750 (1)	581.252 (1)	256.023 (2)
92.193 (1)	748.887 (2)		628.601 (2)	288.123 (1)	312.566 (2)	583.209 (1)	271.026 (3)
01.567 (2)	753.577 (2)	*Krypton*	687.211 (3)	298.063 (3)	313.155 (2)	691.130 (2)	271.393 (2)
04.774 (1)	841.843 (2)	366.533 (2)	764.202 (2)	298.134 (2)	313.183 (2)	693.898 (2)	275.388 (2)
87.562 (3)		367.956 (1)	823.163 (4)	298.189 (1)	334.148 (2)	766.491 (4)	293.262 (2)
67.815 (2)	*Argon*	367.961 (1)	828.012 (4)	308.083 (2)	365.015 (2)	769.898 (2)	303.936 (3)
06.519 (2)	339.281 (2)	377.342 (1)	834.682 (3)	308.268 (1)	365.483 (2)		325.609 (3)
06.570 (1)	339.375 (2)	427.397 (3)	840.919 (3)	313.317 (2)	366.328 (3)	*Rubidium*	325.856 (2)
28.135 (1)	355.431 (2)	428.297 (3)	881.941 (3)	325.030 (2)	390.641 (1)	358.708 (2)	410.177 (3)
	355.597 (2)	431.855 (2)		326.106 (3)	398.398 (1)	359.159 (2)	451.132 (3)
Neon	360.652 (3)	431.958 (3)	*Zinc*	340.365 (2)	404.656 (2)	420.185 (3)	570.975 (2)
36.981 (2)	383.468 (3)	436.264 (2)	213.856 (3)	346.620 (3)	407.781 (1)	421.556 (3)	572.827 (1)
36.991 (3)	394.750 (3)	437.612 (3)	249.148 (2)	346.766 (3)	410.808 (0)	543.153 (2)	684.777 (1)
41.790 (2)	394.898 (3)	445.392 (3)	251.581 (2)	361.051 (3)	433.913 (1)	564.810 (2)	
41.801 (2)	404.442 (3)	446.369 (3)	258.244 (2)	361.287 (3)	434.750 (1)	565.374 (2)	*Thallium*
44.770 (2)	415.859 (3)	450.236 (3)	258.249 (2)	361.445 (1)	435.835 (3)	572.445 (2)	253.818 (2)
47.257 (2)	418.188 (3)	557.029 (3)	260.856 (2)	467.816 (2)	491.604 (1)	572.495 (1)	258.559 (1)
50.122 (2)	419.071 (2)	587.092 (3)	260.864 (2)	479.992 (2)	546.074 (3)	607.075 (2)	266.557 (2)
52.047 (3)	419.103 (3)	642.103 (2)	275.686 (2)	508.582 (3)	576.959 (2)	615.962 (2)	276.787 (2)
59.353 (2)	419.832 (3)	645.629 (2)	277.086 (2)	643.847 (3)	579.065 (2)	620.631 (3)	282.616 (2)
59.364 (2)	420.067 (3)	758.741 (2)	277.098 (2)			629.833 (3)	322.975 (3)
63.366 (2)	425.936 (3)	760.154 (3)	280.087 (2)	*Mercury*	*Sodium*	629.923 (2)	351.924 (3)
40.056 (3)	426.629 (3)	768.525 (3)	280.106 (2)	226.22 (0)	330.232 (2)	727.999 (2)	352.943 (3)
85.249 (3)	427.217 (3)	769.454 (3)	307.206 (2)	237.83 (0)	330.299 (2)	740.817 (2)	377.512 (1)
88.189 (3)	430.010 (3)	785.482 (3)	307.590 (2)	239.94 (0)	449.427 (1)	780.023 (4)	535.046 (3)
94.483 (2)	433.356 (3)	805.950 (3)	328.233 (2)	246.41 (0)	449.772 (1)	794.760 (3)	654.977 (2)
96.547 (2)	434.517 (3)	810.436 (3)	330.259 (3)	248.201 (1)	466.486 (1)		671.369 (2)
02.999 (3)	451.073 (3)	811.290 (3)	330.294 (3)	248.272 (1)	466.860 (2)	*Cesium*	
07.434 (3)	459.610 (3)	819.005 (3)	334.502 (3)	248.383 (1)	498.284 (2)	361.152 (2)	
09.616 (2)	462.844 (3)	826.324 (3)	334.557 (2)	253.652 (3)	514.909 (2)	361.714 (1)	
14.306 (3)	470.232 (3)	829.811 (3)	462.981 (1)	257.486 (0)	515.364 (2)	387.639 (2)	
16.359 (3)	604.323 (2)		468.014 (2)	265.204 (2)	567.018 (2)	388.865 (2)	
21.728 (3)	641.631 (2)	*Xenon*	472.216 (2)	265.368 (2)	567.570 (2)	455.535 (3)	
26.649 (3)	696.543 (2)	395.092 (2)	481.053 (2)	265.512 (2)	588.995 (4)	459.318 (3)	
30.479 (2)	706.722 (2)	396.754 (2)	636.235 (3)	269.885 (1)	589.592 (4)	583.911 (2)	
33.443 (3)	738.398 (2)	407.882 (2)		269.950 (1)	615.423 (2)	601.033 (1)	

APPENDIX

Data, given in the tables on gas discharge lamps

l=length of the discharge between the electrodes.

b=estimated breadth of the luminous part of the discharge, calculated from l, I and L
  or, if I is not given, from l, Φ and L as follows: $b=I/lL$ or $b=\Phi/\pi^2 lL$.

$b_{\frac{1}{2}}$=breadth of that part of the luminous column, where, according to the manufacturer, the luminance exceeds 50 % of its maximum value.

$V_N(dc)$=lowest dc voltage in the circuit with which the discharge is stable. The
  − sign means that no dc lamps of the type in question are known.

ac; the + sign means that ac lamps of this type are known; the − sign means that they
  are not known.

V_c=the voltage to which the condenser is charged for flash lamps.

V_B=lamp voltage.

i=lamp current.

P=power absorption of the lamp.

W=nominal energy per flash.

W_{max}=maximum energy per flash.

Φ=luminous flux.

Q=quantity of light for energy W.

η=luminous efficiency; $\eta=\Phi/P$ or $\eta=Q/W$.

I=luminous intensity, perpendicular to the axis of the discharge.

L=luminance as given by the manufacturer.

T_c=colour temperature.

Sp; shapes to which the data in the columns of the table refer particularly.

dt; fs means that fused silica discharge tubes are available; gl that glass tubes are made.

env; fs means that the discharge tube is protected by a fused silica envelope; gl means
  that it is protected by a glass envelope. The −sign or the whole line missing means
  that the lamp is used without an envelope.

w; the +sign means a water-cooled lamp; the −sign or the whole line missing means
  air-cooled lamps.

Notes added in proof

1. ARC DISCHARGES

Xenon short arc lamps (table 2)

A xenon short arc lamp of 6500 W power consumption was developed.

High pressure sodium lamps

New data on the high pressure sodium lamps were given by MILES and STEVENS [1964], LOUDEN and SCHMIDT [1965], RIGDEN [1965], DE VRIJER [1965], and in Light and Lighting [1966].

High pressure mercury lamps

High pressure mercury vapour lamps and their applications are the subjects of a book, edited by ELENBAAS [1965].

Krefft's ultraviolet standard lamp

ZSCHAECK [1964] carried out measurements on Krefft's ultraviolet standard lamp. He resolved several line groups not resolved by Rössler and his results for the spectral radiant power are a few percent lower.

Mercury halide lamps

Many types of mercury halide lamps ranging from 250 W to 2000 W became available. Data were published by DELRIEU and FAXIL [1964], HOLMES and DE BOER [1964], KÜHL [1964], MARTT et al. [1964], NELSON [1964], WAYMOUTH et al. [1965], and in Light and Lighting [1966].

2. 8.2. HIGH EFFICIENCY LAMPS

Sodium lamps

The trend of the development of high efficiency sodium lamps continued and led to a 200 W lamp producing 30000 lm (VAN BOORT [1965]).

3. 10. LASERS

Continuously new lasers have been developed. Two interesting types are the carbon dioxide–nitrogen laser, giving an extremely high output and the chemically excited laser.

a) *The carbon dioxide–nitrogen laser*

This laser is a gas discharge laser, essentially filled with carbon dioxide and nitrogen. According to WITTEMAN [1966] the mechanism of the laser action is governed by the following four processes:

i) vibrational excitation of the nitrogen molecules by electron impact during the discharge;

ii) vibrational energy transfer from the vibrationally excited nitrogen molecules to the asymmetrical valence vibration of the carbon dioxide molecules;

iii) stimulated transfer of quanta from the asymmetrical valence vibration of the carbon dioxide molecules;

iv) depopulation of the lower laser level of carbon dioxide by thermal relaxation. Addition of helium (PATEL et al. [1965], Bell Lab. Record [1965]) increases the maximum continuous output to more than 100 W, presumably by increasing the electron temperature in the gas discharge at high power load and, consequently, increasing the vibrational excitation of the nitrogen molecule. Addition of water vapour (WITTEMAN [1966]) accelerates the depopulation of the lower laser level, thereby increasing the efficiency of the laser process so that an overall energy-conversion efficiency of $12\frac{1}{2}\%$ is obtained. Lasers of this type can be made in a sealed-off system in which the gas mixture permanently has such a high purity that output and efficiency are maintained. The wavelength of this laser is 10.61 μm.

b) *The chemically excited laser*

A chemical reaction may produce vibrationally excited molecules in large numbers so that a population inversion is the result. This population inversion can be used to obtain laser action. KASPER and PIMENTEL [1965] used the reaction of hydrogen and chlorine gas producing HCl. The radiation produced had a wavelength of 37.7 μm.

References

AMICK, C. L., 1960, Fluorescent lighting manual, 3rd ed. (McGraw-Hill, New York).
ANDERSON, J. M., 1961, Rev. Sci. Instr. **32**, 975.
BEESE, N. C., 1946, J. Opt. Soc. Am. **36**, 555.
BEKEFI, G. and S. C. BROWN, 1961, J. Appl. Phys. **32**, 25.
Bell Lab. Record, 1965, **43**, 464.
BENNETT, Jr., W. R., 1962, Applied Optics, Suppl. on Optical masers (Wiley, New York) p. 24.
BIRNBAUM, G., 1964, Optical masers (Academic Press, New York).
BREWER, R. G., 1961, Rev. Sci. Instr. **32**, 1356.
BUNDY, F. P. and H. M. Strong, 1954, Measurements of flame temperature, pressure and velocity, in: H. S. Taylor, B. Lewis and R. N. Pease, eds., Physical measurements in gas dynamics and combustion, pt. 2 (Princeton Univ. Press, Princeton, N.J.) p. 346.
C.I.E., 1957, International lighting vocabulary, vol 1, 2nd ed. (Bureau Central, Commission Internationale de l'Eclairage, Paris).
COHEN, E. R. and J. W. M. DUMOND, 1964, Present status of our knowledge of the numerical values of the fundamental physical constants, in: W. H. Johnson, ed., Nuclidic masses, Proc. 2nd Intern. Conf. Nuclidic Masses, Vienna, Austria (Springer-Verlag, Wien) p. 152.
COLEGROVE, F. D., L. D. SCHEARER and G. K. WALTERS, 1964, Phys. Rev. **135**, 353.
CORLISS, C. H. and W. R. BOZMAN, 1962, Experimental transition probabilities for spectral lines of seventy elements, Natl. Bur. Std. Monograph 53 (U.S. Printing Office, Washington, D.C.).
DAVIDSON, N., 1962, Statistical mechanics (McGraw-Hill Book Co., New York).
DEAN, J. A., 1960, Flame photometry (McGraw-Hill Book Co., New York).
DE BRUIN, S. L., 1946, Philips Tech. Rev. **8**, 25.
DELRIEU, P. and A. TAXIL, 1964, Bul. Soc. Française Elect. [8]**5**, 50.
DESTRIAU, G., 1936, J. Chem. Phys. **35**, 587.
DE VOS, J. C., 1953, The emissivity of tungsten ribbon, Thesis, Vrije Universiteit, Amsterdam.
DE VRIJER, B., 1965, Elektrotechniek **43**, 512.
Electrical Review, 1963, **172**, 768.
ELENBAAS, W., 1935, Physica **2**, 45.
ELENBAAS, W., 1948, Rev. Opt. **27**, 683.

ELENBAAS, W., 1951, The high pressure mercury vapour dischages, *in:* J. De Boer, H. Brinkman and H. B. G. Casimir, eds., Selected topics in modern physics, vol. 2 (North-Holland Publ. Co., Amsterdam).

ELENBAAS, W., ed., 1959, Fluorescent lamps and lighting (Centrex Publ. Co., Eindhoven).

ELENBAAS, W., ed., 1965, High pressure mercury vapour lamps and their applications (Centrex Publ. Co., Eindhoven).

ENGELHARD, E., 1959, Z. Instrumentenk. **67**, 59.

EULER, J., 1953, Ann. Physik **11**, 203.

FISCHER, A. G., 1962, J. Electrochem. Soc. **109**, 1043.

FISCHER, A. G., 1963, J. Electrochem. Soc. **110**, 733.

FRANCIS, G., 1956, The glow discharge at low pressure, *in:* S. Flügge, ed., Encyclopedia of Physics, vol. 22. Gas discharges II (Springer-Verlag, Berlin) pp. 58. 88.

GRIMMEIS, H. G. and H. KOELMANS, 1960, Philips Res. Rept. **15**, 290.

HAMAKER, H. C., 1934, Reflectivity and emissivity of tungsten, Thesis, Utrecht.

HAMAKER, H. C., 1936, Physica **3**, 561.

HAYNES, J. R. and H. B. BRIGGS, 1952, Phys. Rev. **86**, 647.

HERRMANN, R., 1947, Optik **2**, 384.

HOEKSTRA, P., 1963, Philips Kinotech. **39**, 364.

HOEKSTRA, P. and CH. MEYER, 1959, Philips Tech. Rev. **21**, 121.

HOLMES, T. and J. B. DE BOER, 1964, Public Ltg. **29**, 224.

IVEY, H. F., 1963, Electroluminescence and related effects (Academic Press, New York).

KASPER, J. V. V. and G. C. PIMENTEL, 1964, Phys. Rev. Letters **5**, 231.

KENTY, C., 1950, J. Appl. Phys. **21**, 1309.

KEYES, R. J. and T. M. QUIST, 1962, Proc. IRE **50**, 1822.

KNOL, K. S., 1955, Philips Res. Rept. **6**, 288.

KOEDAM, M. and A. A. KRUITHOF, 1962, Physica **28**, 80.

KOEDAM, M., A. A. KRUITHOF and J. RIEMENS, 1963, Physica **29**, 565.

KREFFT, H., F. RÖSSLER and A. RÜTTENAUER, 1937, Z. Tech. Physik **18**, 20.

KRUITHOF, A. A. and J. L. OUWELTJES, 1957, Philips Tech. Rev. **18**, 249.

KÜHL, B., 1964, Lichttechnik **16**, 68.

LARRABEE, R. D., 1959, J. Opt. Soc. Am. **49**, 619.

Light and Lighting, 1966, **59**, 34.

LOSSEW, O. W., 1923, Telegrafia i Telefonia **18**, 61.

LOUDEN, W. C. and K. SCHMIDT, 1965, Illum. Engng. **55**, 696.

MAECKER, H., 1951, Z. Physik **129**, 108.

MAIMAN, T. H., R. H. HOSKIN, I. J. D'HAENENS, C. K. AZAWA and V. EVTUHOV, 1961, Phys. Rev. **123**, 1151.

MARTT, E. C., A. C. GREEN and L. J. SMIALEK, 1964, Illum. Engng. **59**, 34.

MCCLUNG, F. J. and R. J. HELLSORTH, 1962, J. Appl. Phys. **33**, 826.

MCCLUNG, F. J. and R. J. HELLWORTH, 1963, Proc. IEEE **51**, 46.

MEYER, C. H., 1961, Philips Tech. Rev. **22**, 377.

MILES, E. E. and W. R. STEVENS, 1964, Public Ltd. **29**, 239.

MOHLER, F. L., 1939, J. Opt. Soc. Am. **29**, 152.

NACHTRIEB, N. H., 1950, Principles and practice of spectrochemical analysis (McGraw-Hill Book Co., New York).

NELSON, E. H., 1964, G.E.C. J. Sci Technol. (London) **31**, 92.

OKABE, H., 1964, J. Opt. Soc. Am. **54**, 478.

PATEL, C. K. N., P. K. TIEN and J. H. MCFEE, 1965, Appl. Phys. Letters **7**, 290

PEEK, S. C., 1956, Sylvania Technologist, **9**, 71.

PERSSON, K. B., 1957, Phys. Rev. **106**, 191.

PFENDER, E. and W. BEZ, 1962, Ein wirbelstabilisierter Bogen in reiner Wasserstoffatomsphäre als

Vorionisierungsstrecke für eine stromstarke Impulsentladung, *in*: H. Maecker, ed., Proc. 5th Intern. Conf. Ionization phenomena in gases, Munich, 1961 (North-Holland Publ. Co., Amsterdam).

PLANCK, M., 1900, Verhandl. Deut. Physik. Ges. **2**, 237.

REILING, G. H., 1964, J. Opt. Soc. Am. **54**, 532.

RIGDEN, S. A. R., 1965, G.E.C. J. Sci. Technol. (London) **32**, 37.

RÖSSLER, F., 1952, Ann. Physik [6]**10**, 177.

SANDERS, C. L. and O. C. JONES, 1962, J. Opt. Soc. Am. **52**, 731.

SHUMAKER, J. B., 1961, Rev. Sci. Instr. **32**, 65.

TERRIEN, J. and H. HAMON, 1962, Mesure de la longueur d'onde des radiations étalons secondaires et de la radiation primaire sans perturbation, *in*: Comité Intern. Poids Mesures, Rapports du Comité Cons. pour la définition du mètre, 3ième session, 1962 (Gauthier-Villars, Paris) p. 76.

VAN BOORT, H. J. J., 1965, Elektrotechniek **43**, 509.

VERWEY, W., 1961, Philips Res. Rept. **15**, suppl. 2.

WAYMOUTH, J. F., W. C. GUNGLE, J. M. HARRIS and F. KOURY, 1965, Illum. Engng. **60**, 85.

WEBER, K. H., 1964, Illum. Engng. **54**, 329.

WIESE, W., H. F. BERG and H. R. GRIEM, 1960, Phys. Rev. **120**, 1079.

WITTEMAN, W. J., 1966, IEEE J. Quantum Electronics, in press (special Quantum Electronics Conference issue).

ZALM, P., 1956, Philips Res. Rept. **11**, 353, 417.

ZSCHAECK, H., 1964, Explt. Tech. Physik **12**, 373.

CHAPTER 1

THE CORONAGRAPH

J. DEMARCQ

Institut d'Optique, Paris

AND

J. RÖSCH

*Observatoire du Pic du Midi
et Faculté des Sciences de Paris*

CONTENTS

1. Introduction

1.1. HISTORY

Astronomers have long been worried by the shortness of the observations of the solar corona, restricted to the duration of the total eclipses of the Sun, when the sky does not scatter the solar light any more, thus permitting the corona to become visible. All attempts failed to detect the corona out of the time of an eclipse until LYOT [1939] first succeeded in 1930 to observe it all the year round. He did so by constructing his so-called *coronagraph* (French *coronographe*) in such a way as to eliminate most of the light scattered outside the instrument and by observing in a mountain station in order to reduce, too, the atmospheric scattering. Later on, he built another instrument (the coronometer) with which he could observe the corona in spite of the highly scattering atmosphere and optics. The second instrument (being a very sensitive photoelectric polarimeter) has no special optical features, and will not be described here.

Techniques developed, since 1930, and a better knowledge of the corona, entirely due to the work of Lyot, have led to coronagraphs with new capabilities, without any significant departure from the principles first laid down by Lyot.

This paper will first describe these principles, then the technology of the polishing of the objective which is the masterpiece of the instrument, and lastly some alternative devices which have been used.

1.2. THE GEOMETRICAL PRINCIPLES

Basically, the coronagraph is a telescope in which the solar image is focussed on a metallic disc slightly larger in diameter. However, this 'artificial eclipse' is not enough to make it possible to observe the solar corona, the brightness of which, in the focal plane, is much weaker than the one produced by the spurious light from various origins:

(a) the light scattered by the terrestrial atmosphere in directions close to the Sun; obviously, however perfect the coronagraph can be built, it must only be used in conditions that do not limit its capabilities; therefore the instrument must be mounted at high altitude in case of a location with average or low geographic latitude;

(b) the light scattered or diffracted by the limiting surfaces of the material of the objective; reducing the amount of this spurious light is the main optical problem of the coronagraph, as will be discussed below;

(c) the light diffracted by the edge of the objective, or reflected twice by its limiting surfaces, which Lyot got rid of by using the optical system shown in fig. 1.

The main objective, O_1, forms an image of the Sun, approximately 1970″ in diameter, on a disc, D, the diameter of which is in excess by about 40″ to 60″ so that the lowest parts of the corona which can be observed are about 20″ to 30″ above the solar limb. In order to avoid excessive heating, a metallic mirror (either flat or conical), just in front of the disc, reflects most of the solar light to the walls of the telescope tube, or possibly outside the tube through a suitably positioned open window. The occulting disc must be changed several times in the course of the year, as the apparent diameter of the Sun varies within ± 1.7 per cent because of the ellipticity of the Earth's orbit. The disc is carried at the end of a metallic rod attached at the centre of the field lens O_2, usually a simple plano-convex lens. This lens focusses an image of the main objective, O_1, on to a diaphragm, Δ, the aperture of which is only 0.7 to 0.8 times the diameter of the image of the objective. Thus, most of the diffraction fringe surrounding this image is discarded.

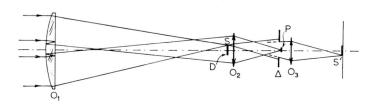

Fig. 1. General scheme of Lyot's coronagraph.

On the other hand, a portion of the incident light, being reflected on the back surface of O_1, then on its front surface, forms an image of the Sun somewhere between O_1 and the disc (one-fifth of the focal length from O_1 if O_1 is a plano-convex single lens). This image is quite small, but the aperture of the beam is large, so that it casts light on to the focal plane well outside the occulting disc, superimposed on the coronal light. From it, the field lens O_2 again forms a solar image close to the plane of the diaphragm Δ; one takes advantage of this fact to fix across the diaphragm a metallic thread provided with a small metallic bead P exactly located on the optical axis of the instrument, which stops the undesired beam.

Next to the diaphragm, a third objective, O_3, forms a real image S' of the corona and of the disc on any auxiliary equipment desired, such as an eyepiece, a photographic slit, a spectrograph slit, etc.

2. Making a coronagraph objective

Whether the objective is a single lens, a doublet, or even a triplet, the problem is twofold: (a) choice of material, and (b) polishing.

Since the first coronagraph objectives were made, many of the basic difficulties have been overcome. Indeed, producing lenses with very faint scattering in the material is no longer a major problem since modern techniques of continuous casting from platinum crucibles have come into use. A better understanding of the polishing process, together with the use of abrasives of improved quality and uniformity of grain size, also helped in solving the difficulties which the pioneers met. Likewise, the refinement in the testing methods brought out by the phase contrast principle have made the work of the optician very much easier, and the success now only depends upon his care taken during the polishing.

2.1. TESTING THE MATERIAL

The glass used for single lens objectives is usually a borosilicate crown. It can be produced free from bubbles and veins. Its hardness is such that it can be worked with limited risk of accidents. Its chemical reaction with the polishing material is weak, so that it can be rubbed for a long time without becoming oxidized.

First, the raw discs or plates are roughly polished as plano-parallel plates and tested by the shadow method suggested by ARNULF [1927] (cf. fig. 2). A very bright

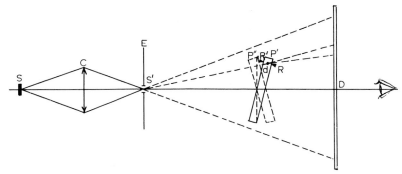

Fig. 2. Shadow method for testing glass (Arnulf).

point source S (mercury lamp HBO 500 or zirconium arc) is imaged by a condensor C on a pinhole S′. The plate being tested, P, stands between S′ and a ground glass D on which the defects are seen by their shadows. An estimate of their extent is obtained by moving the ground glass along the axis of the system. By tilting the plate P from P′ to P″, provided thick pencil marks R, R′ have been affixed on the surfaces, the depths of the defects in the plate appear, so that one can foresee whether or not they will be avoided by a convenient cutting or by reducing the thickness.

This first test permits rejection at low cost of any unsuitable raw material. The next test is performed with the blanks selected by the shadow method. They are ground and polished as bi-convex lenses in order to minimize spherical aberration at magnification 1, the optical power being taken about the same as for the final objective. These lenses are given good conventional pitch polishing, which suffices for the detection of internal defects.

As the brightness of the photosphere is of the order of 10^6 times the brightness of the corona at a few minutes of arc from the solar limb, the total amount of light scattered by the surfaces and the internal defects must be less than 10^{-7} times the total flux received by the objective. LYOT [1946] devised a method equivalent to ZERNIKE's [1942] *phase-contrast* method which can be applied (LYOT and FRANÇON [1948] to the present problem.

Let O_1 be the objective being tested (fig. 3), S a point source (HBO 500 lamp) and S′ its image formed by O_1. A photographic objective O_2 coinciding with S′ forms an image O_1' of O_1. A colour filter E is used in front of S to isolate the green radiation ($\lambda = 0.545\,\mu$) of mercury. Due to the defects on the surfaces or in the material, the outcoming wavefront is not perfectly spherical. A so-called *phase-plate* (metallic coating of suitable thickness produced by vacuum evaporation on polished glass) is inserted in the beam at S′ covering the central part of the image which is pro-

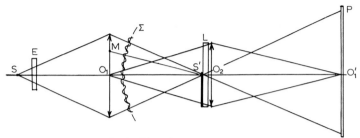

Fig. 3. The phase contrast test.

duced by the reference spherical wavefront. Conversely, the outer parts of the image, which are produced by the differences between the real and reference wavefronts, are not occulted by the phase-plate. Thus, for instance, in O'_1, the image of the centre of the objective, amplitudes arising from the defects are not reduced, whereas the amplitude produced by the spherical wavefront is reduced by a factor $\sqrt{N}$, N being the opacity of the plate. At the same time, the plate shifts the phase by $\frac{1}{2}\pi$ so that the waves from the spherical front and from the defects become in phase. N is chosen such that both amplitudes in O'_1 become comparable. It can be shown that a defect occurring on the spherical wave as a phase difference ψ appears in the image plane P with a contrast $\gamma = 2\psi\sqrt{N}$.

This method will be used both for testing the material and for controlling the quality of the polishing. The main defects (veins, bubbles and impurities) which scatter the light are very sensitively exhibited. The blank being found satisfactory, the residual defects must be located. LYOT and FRANÇON [1948] used a stereoscopic method, by examining in a stereo-comparator a pair of photographs of O_1, O_1 being tilted on the axis SS′ by $\pm 10°$.

To measure the flux diffracted by the defects, the phase-plate is replaced by a small opaque screen to occult the central part of S′. The defects are seen bright on a dark background (strioscopy). Their magnitude is estimated by comparison with some calibrated defects (thread, circular screen with known diameter, etc.) located in the plane of the objective O_1 (FRANÇON [1948], FRANÇON and LYOT [1950]).

2.2. GRINDING

From an equi-convex shape, radius of curvature R, the lens is then ground plano-convex, radius of curvature $R' = \frac{1}{2}R$, the focal lengths remaining about the same. Any rough work such as grinding, bevelling the edges, must be completed before the lens enters the smoothing and polishing shop.

Coming out of the grinding shop where he has left his corresponding working clothes, the optician should take extreme care not to carry with him any residual of the coarse abrasive.

The polishing shop should be a clean room, with light coloured walls and waxed linoleum floor. Dust should be wiped off by means of a slightly wet sponge. No broom should be brought in until the end of the operation. Air filtering, although desirable, is not compulsory. The polishing machine is a conventional one. The basin should be rather large (500 mm) and contain a few millimetres of water, an efficient barrier to dust (fig. 4). The dust particles driven around by the rotation of the vertical shaft

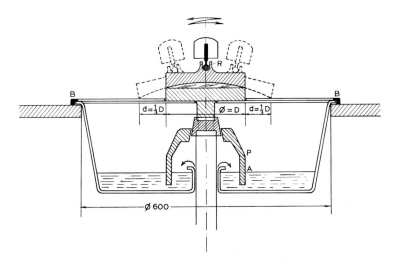

Fig. 4. Polishing machine for coronagraph work.

are stopped in A by a ring P. Any gap between the table and the basin should, for the same reason, be tightened by using some plastic adhesive tape.

The tools carrying the glass and the polisher are coated by sprayed alcohol varnish, in order to fill the small cavities in the metal surface which could retain adhesive grains.

The spherical joint R is slightly greased to glide smoothly in the tool tail and avoid shocks and vibrations which would harm the polishing. All the machinery is protected, during the polishing, by a tent made of a plastic transparent sheet.

2.3. SMOOTHING

During smoothing, one simply takes care to produce a finely and uniformly fine-ground surface. The brass concave smoothing tool works above the glass. Best results are obtained by employing garnets (W abrasives).

A permanent humidity must be maintained between the tool and the glass, by a permanent spray of fine water droplets; thus the abrasive forms a homogeneous paste (too liquid or too dry it could cause accidents).

The radius of curvature can be controlled by an interference gauge, grazing inci-dence during smoothing. It is better not to repeat it during polishing, and to take the optical power obtained during smoothing for the final one, as it is not advisable to attempt to reach a given value at the risk of destroying a surface state attained after a very long polishing time.

A method commonly used by opticians, by which the abrasive is crushed for a long time to produce a finer grain may often cause accidents. The same result is obtained without any risk by using an abrasive just finer in the series.

The tool has a diameter D, equal to the diameter of the lens, and moves $\frac{1}{3}D$ beyond its edge, on both sides (fig. 4). The total weight on the glass surface is of the order of 4 kg for $D = 200$ mm (about 13 g/cm^2).

Rounded bevels at 45° from the faces, ground with a fine-grain abrasive, must be provided to avoid the production of small glass chips. Both surfaces of the lens must be smooth before polishing begins. When turning the lens upside down to smooth and polish the second surface, the first, one is coated with black mat chemically neutral varnish. Then it is malleted with hot optical cement to a rigid aluminium support, 12 to 15 mm thick.

2.4. POLISHING

The polisher, 4 to 5 mm thick, is made of soft baked pitch, cast on an aluminium tool having about the same radius of curvature as the surface to be polished. The rotation speed is about 30 to 40 rpm for the glass; for the polisher, which is left free on the glass, the speed is a function of the amount by which it goes beyond the glass ($\frac{1}{3}D$ as for the smoothing) and of the frequency of the driving spindle (20 to 30 beats per minute). This spindle is loaded so that it has an average pressure of 8 g/cm^2, depending on the hardness of the pitch.

The best results in fine polishing are obtained by using as abrasive iron oxide Fe_2O_3 produced by calcination of iron oxalate. The polisher should not carry too much abrasive which otherwise would build up a crust with the resultant danger of producing very fine scratches (sleeks). Working with the polisher too wet also would be dangerous because of its non-uniform temperature which would cause it to fit improperly on the glass and thus to scratch.

The polishing time to obtain micro-ripples of the order of one angstrom is theoretically about 20 hours for a 200 mm diameter. In practice however, one can start examining the surface after about 15 hours of regular friction. As soon as the polisher slides on the glass leaving on it a slight film of water containing abrasive, thin enough to show interference colours changing rapidly by evaporation, the work should be stopped by lifting the nozzle of the spindle in order to have the polisher out of action suddenly. If this first surface looks satisfactory, the glass should be cooled, then detached from its holder by giving one or several blows on the latter with a hard wood or leather mallet.

By this time the polished surface should not be touched, but spray varnished and malleted on a concave holder having about the same radius of curvature. The surface which has been first smoothed is then polished, taking the same precautions.

The second knocking-off may be done as above described. Cleaning the glass is done by dissolving the residuals of cement and varnish, the solvent being changed until it comes out unspoilt. It is just a matter of patience.

2.5. POLISHING OF FUSED SILICA

Grinding is the same as for ordinary glass, but polishing is different. When Fe_2O_3 is used, very small pits are formed on the surface of the silica; they are wiped out during polishing, but new ones are formed at once (fig. 5a). Experience has shown that by

 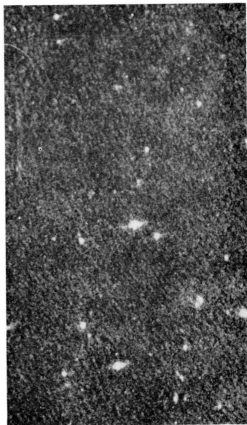

. 5a. Phase contrast pattern of a fused silica surface ished with Fe_2O_3 (depth of micro-ripples: about ˚).

Fig. 5b. Phase contrast pattern of a Calex glass surface, polished with Fe_2O_3 (bright points are due to dust on the surface).

replacing Fe_2O_3 by CeO_2, one gets a fused silica surface free of pits, with micro-ripples comparable to the residual obtained on ordinary glass (fig. 5b, *Calex glass*).

2.6. POLISHING OF FLINT GLASS

There is no special problem in grinding flint glass lenses, but polishing is more difficult. The pitch should be slightly softer, but again the best results are obtained with Fe_2O_3 as abrasive. The only point is to add some water containing 5 cm^3 of acetic acid per litre; thus the risks of oxidization, although greater than for borosilicate glass, remain small. Rotation and beat speeds should be reduced to two-thirds of the values for crown glass.

2.7. CLEANING A CORONAGRAPH OBJECTIVE

To restore a surface which has been scratched would mean a complete re-polishing. The method for cleaning hereafter tends to avoid such accidents. The objective must be handled only in its mounting which should be such that when laid flat, the objective has no contact with the table. The room must have been cleaned of dust with a wet sponge. The table is covered with a carefully degreased oilskin. Cotton-wool packets are selected as being free from any hard particles, by wiping on a clean soft glass surface (flint glass, for instance;) any packet scratching the glass is rejected. Those retained are kept in a clean glass container after ether drying to remove fat. On the other hand, a small quantity of iodine is added to 95 per cent alcohol (scarcely enough to give a light yellow colour) just before use. The surface is wiped with cotton-wool soaked with alcohol, then it is quickly dried. The operator must wear rubber gloves, to avoid greasing the pad. One starts describing circles, from the centre outwards to the edge; the stains, fat deposits, tracks left by insects, remains from drying of liquid drops, etc. are removed.

The cotton pad is changed after several runs from centre to edge; the surface becomes progressively cleaner and remains only slightly blurred by the iodine residual. The work must be resumed by a dry cotton pad previously wiped on a silicon paper as used for cleaning spectacles. Repeating the operation with several successive pads, but without using further silicone, one should get a clean surface. The last dust grains which adhere to it until it becomes electrically neutral can be removed by means of either a soft wooden rod recently knife sharpened, or an ebonite rod electrified by rubbing.

If the objective has been left exposed to dust (which is often abrasive) care must be taken, before wiping, to pour on each surface a solution of collodion in ether. After drying, all the dust grains are removed when the collodion film is pulled off. Then the cleaning is conducted as descibed above.

3. Variants of the coronagraph

Starting from the Lyot coronagraph, several more or less different devices have been used. The external disc coronagraph and the mirror coronagraph will be described in §§ 4 and 5, this one being restricted to some less distant variations.

3.1. ACHROMATIC CORONAGRAPH

Lyot restricted himself to a single lens objective, to avoid the light scattering by the cement. He had shown, however (LYOT et al [1948]), that Canada balsam, properly employed, could be used for a coronagraph objective. Since that time, cementing by polimerisable liquids has definitely solved this question. One could use, for instance, Stratyl 28 polyester resin, a transparent liquid; catalyser and accelerator are added at ambient temperature before use (BESSE and DEMARCQ [1956, 1957]). Bubbles can be avoided very easily, and, due to the low viscosity, the thickness of the resin film can be reduced to a few hundredths of a millimetre. The scattered light is negligible; we found no change after two years in an objective cemented by this method. No more light was scattered than during its first days.

The technique for polishing flint glass mentioned above is by no means final. Moreover, for the cemented surface, micro-ripples twelve times deeper may be acceptable, assuming the refractive index or the cement is midway between those of the glasses. However, the external surface will be subject, during use, to greater risks of scratching, because of the softness of the flint glass. Thus, it would be safer to build a *cemented triplet* by splitting the convergence of the crown glass between two lenses cemented on both sides of the flint glass. One more degree of freedom then becomes available in the computation of the objective (DEMARCQ et al. [1965]).

3.2. CORONAGRAPH WITHOUT A DISC

This system has been used at the Pulkovo Observatory, U.S.S.R. The primary image of the Sun is formed directly onto a roof-shaped spectrograph slit, the jaws of which reflect sideways the photospheric light. The open length of the slit is limited, of course, in order to admit the corona, not the photosphere. A field lens, following the slit, forms an image of the objective on to the spectrograph grating. As an objection to this mounting, attractively simple as it is, one should mention, that, if the slit is narrow, the image of the objective on the grating is widely spread by diffraction, in the direction normal to the slit, so that it becomes difficult to eliminate the light diffracted by the edge of the objective as in the original Lyot mounting.

3.3. MULTIPLE OCCULTATIONS

When the objective is a single lens, one can take advantage of its longitudinal chromatic aberration to separate two wavelengths which otherwise would fall in the same region of the focal plane of the grating spectrograph, in different orders. That is the case for the lines 3388 Å (Fe XIII) in the third order and 5303 Å (Fe XIV) in the second order. In the focal plane for the wavelength to be observed, the conventional occulting disc is surrounded by a plate in which a hole has been bored concentric with the disc, but slightly larger in diameter, thus leaving free a narrow circular zone. As the cross-section of the light beam carrying the undesired wavelength is not small (in this plane) most of it is stopped; the remaining light is stopped in its own focal plane by a metallic ring concentric with the axis, whereas this ring stops only a small fraction of the light in the wavelength to be observed (HUGON et al. [1963]).

3.4. TOOTHED OR SEMI-TRANSPARENT DISCS

It is of utmost importance to know at which altitude above the photosphere the corona is observed, because of the rapid decrease in its density as a function of this altitude. Now its measurement is made more difficult by the unavoidable excess of the diameter of the disc over the diameter of the solar image. This leads to the idea of hollowing out some cuts in the edge of the disc, then covered by neutral glass dense enough to let the Sun itself appear with about the same brightness as the corona. Four cuts, 90° apart from one another, are enough to localise the Sun for a photograph of the whole corona. For a reference to the solar limb on a spectrograph slit in any position angle, a pyrex disc (or even better, fused silica disc) must be used, its front surface being coated with a metallic layer of suitable density, so that the solar limb is seen through the disc all around the Sun.

3.5. CORONAGRAPH WITH EXTERNAL OCCULTATION

It has long been tried to observe the sky at small angles from the Sun, by simply casting a shadow of an opaque disc on to an objective. In such conditions, scattering property requirements are much less drastic. But, due to the angular diameter of the Sun itself, to have the objective inside the geometrical shadow of the disc, the inner corona has to be occulted too; the less distance the disc from the objective the larger the extent of the corona lost. Thus, the mounting will in any case by very long, and yet the lowest part of the corona, which is also the brightest, will not be observed.

For this reason, the mounting has been primarily used for studies on the law of decrease of the scattered light as a function of the angular distance from the Sun (NEWKIRK and EDDY [1956]). However, interest in it has been renewed by its possible use for small balloon, rocket or satellite-borne coronagraphs; indeed, because of the large angular extent of the occultation, the guiding problem is not so stringent. In any case, the light diffracted by the disc towards the axis of the instrument must be stopped either by a disc conjugate to the first one, or by other discs of suitable diameters conveniently located between the first one and the objective (NEWKIRK and BOHLIN [1965]; TONSEY [1965]).

3.6. MIRROR CORONAGRAPH

In view of observing the corona in the range 2000 to 3000 Å, BONNET and COURTÈS [1964] have built a rocket-borne coronagraph in which the objective is an aluminised mirror, in order to avoid chromatic aberrations. Not only, in this case, micro-ripples on the glass surface have to be reduced, but also the reflecting layer should not scatter light. The coating should be done in such conditions that no dust grain could leave a hole in the layer. This would unavoidably diffract light. Moreover, the mirror should be kept in vacuum until launching, to prevent oxidization of the coating; otherwise the dielectric aluminium film formed would attract dust.

References

ARNULF, A., 1927, Rev. Opt. **6**, 1.

BESSE, Y. and J. DEMARCQ, 1956, Rev. Opt. **35**, 21; 1957, Rev. Opt. **36**, 476.

BONNET, R. and G. COURTÈS, private communication.

FRANÇON, M., 1948, Rev. Opt. **27**, 595, 761.

HUGON, M., J. RÖSCH and M. TRELLIS, 1963, L'Observation depuis le sol de la couronne d'émission: la raie 3388Å, *in*: J. W. Evans, ed., The solar corona (Academic Press, New York) p. 215.

LYOT, B., 1939, Monthly Notices Roy. Astron. Soc. **99**, 580.

LYOT, B., 1946, Compt. Rend. **222**, 765.

LYOT, B. and M. FRANÇON, 1948, Rev. Opt. **27**, 398.

LYOT, B. and M. FRANÇON, 1950, Rev. Opt. **29**, 499.

LYOT, B., M. FRANÇON and M. CAGNET, 1948, Rev. Opt. **27**, 657.

NEWKIRK, Jr., G. and J. D. BOHLIN, 1965, Ann. Astrophys. **28**, 234.

NEWKIRK, Jr., G. and J. A. EDDY, 1956, J. Atmospheric Sic. **21**, 35.

TONSEY, R., 1965, Ann. Astrophys. **28**, 600.

ZERNIKE, F., 1942, Physica **9**, 686, 974.

CHAPTER 11

FIBER OPTICS

RENÉE DROUGARD AND ROBERT J. POTTER*

International Business Machines Corporation
Thomas J. Watson Research Center
Yorktown Heights, New York

*Present address: Xerox Corporation, Rochester, New York

CONTENTS

1. Introduction

An optical fiber is a very long thin solid glass rod with a length to diameter ratio which is usually greater than 1000. An individual fiber is not an image forming device. Light incident on one end of the fiber is simply transmitted by means of multiple total internal reflections. When individual fibers are held together to form a 'fiber bundle', an image can then be conducted from one end of the fiber bundle to the other. Each fiber is independent, and the image is reconstructed point by point, that is, fiber by fiber. Fiber bundles can be obtained in various forms: flexible, rigid, or in some special arrangement to form an image dissecting device.

Fiber optical components, actively introduced about fifteen years ago, have been developed to become practical for certain specialized optical systems. The optical fiber bundle can be designed to perform a variety of functions, including optical operations not usually available in most optical systems. In this chapter, we will attempt to outline the key features of fiber optics.

It is known (REVI [1957]) that in the first century B.C., the ancient Palestinians made glass portraits by drawing together various colored glass rods arranged to form a picture and then cutting them into sections, much as fused fiber bundles are made today. Fiber optical imaging devices were conceived in the 17th and 18th centuries and again in the late 1920's. With the recent work of VAN HEEL [1953], [1954], HOPKINS and KAPANY [1954] and O'BRIEN [1958], the interest in fiber optics has steadily increased, reaching its present status as an important component in several branches of optical and related technologies.

We will first review the important properties of single fibers and fiber bundles, and then describe some of the applications of fiber optics in modern technology. Finally, some properties of optical fibers with very small diameters will be described in terms of electromagnetic theory.

2. The geometrical optics of a single fiber

Transmission of light through a small diameter glass rod is really a 'waveguide' phenomenon. When the diameter of the fiber is substantially larger than the wavelength of light, it is adequate to view theoretical properties of the fiber in terms of rays and to use the methods of geometrical optics. Waveguide effects will be discussed in § 6.

A longitudinal cross section of a fiber is shown in fig. 1, where the fiber core has an index of refraction n and the material surrounding the fiber has an index of refraction n'. When $n > n'$, a ray of light entering the fiber from a medium of index of refraction n_0 is refracted into the core at an angle θ, and internally reflected at the boundary between the core and the surrounding medium of index n' if the angle of incidence ψ satisfies the condition $\sin \psi > n'/n$. A ray passing through the axis of the fiber, assumed here to be an ideal cylinder of circular cross section, will again be reflected at the angle ψ when it next hits the boundary. Consequently, *the angle that an arbitrary meridional ray makes with the axis is preserved*. The maximum

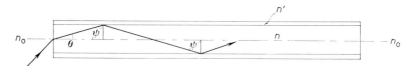

Fig. 1. Path of a meridional ray inside a fiber.

acceptance angle of the fiber θ_M, that is, the angle beyond which the ray will no longer be totally reflected at the wall, but rather will be transmitted through it, is given by eq. (1)

$$n \sin \theta_M = (n^2 - n'^2)^{\frac{1}{2}}. \tag{1}$$

The numerical aperture of the fiber (NA) has been defined (KAPANY [1958] and POTTER *et al.* [1963]) *as the quantity* $n \sin \theta_M$, by analogy with lens optics. An 'effective f/number' is also sometimes used to describe the light collecting capability of a fiber. The term must be used with discretion, however, since fibers have no focal length and the analogy to the f/number of a lens is not exact.

The numerical aperture of a lens is important because it determines the resolving power as well as the light collecting properties of the lens. In fiber optics, the numerical aperture is important primarily because it is a measure of the light collecting capability of the fiber. This is one of the properties of fiber optics which is exploited in many applications. Since the numerical aperture depends only upon the indices of refraction of two glasses, it is possible to make the numerical aperture approach, or, even exceed unity. Such efficient light collecting is not possible with most lens systems.

The fiber has in fact somewhat greater light collecting capability than is described by the numerical aperture because of the behavior of skew rays. This numerical aperture is actually an approximation (POTTER *et al.* [1963]), based on meridional rays only and is properly called a 'meridional numerical aperture'.

For an isolated fiber in air, n' is unity. An important technological advance in modern fiber optics was the introduction of *cladding*. The cladding is a very thin glass layer whose index of refraction is lower than that of the fiber core. It can be made to surround the fiber completely and thus provide 'optical insulation'. It is this technique that has allowed closely packed bundles of optical fibers to become commercially useful. The cladding also protects the fiber core from becoming scratched or dirty. A clad fiber often has a smaller meridional numerical aperture than one not clad, but it is now possible to find glass combinations such that $NA \approx 1.0$. The important technical advance making this possible was the development of satisfactory high index glasses.

A third glass may be used to surround the cladding. This coating is desirable in rigid fiber bundles to absorb those rays which are refracted out of one fiber and pass from fiber to fiber through the bundle. The desired characteristics of this glass, commonly called the extramural absorber (EMA), are low index of refraction and high absorption coefficient.

2.1. SKEW RAYS

In fiber optics as in lens optics, a skew ray is one which does not pass through the axis of the optical system. When a ray is incident on the fiber wall, the angle between it and the normal to the fiber wall at the point of reflection is still denoted ψ, as shown in fig. 2. The angle between the ray and the axis of the cylinder is θ; and γ

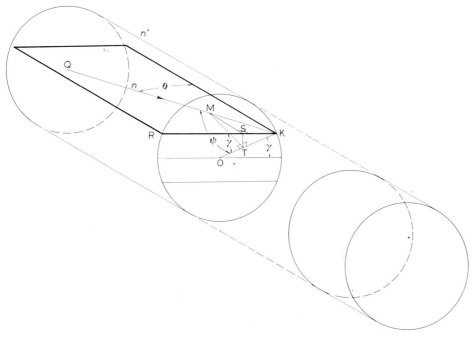

Fig. 2. Path of a skew ray.

is the angle between the projection of the ray on the circular cross section and the normal at the point of reflection. From the geometry defined by an arbitrary ray, QK, in fig. 2,

$$\frac{\cos \psi}{\sin \theta} = \frac{KT/KM}{KS/KM} = \frac{KT}{KS} = \cos \gamma; \tag{2}$$

and

$$\cos \psi = \sin \theta \cos \gamma. \tag{3}$$

Since the value of the angle ψ is preserved throughout the fiber by the law of reflection, eq. (3) is valid for any ray in any place in the cylindrical fiber. Moreover, γ has a constant value at each reflection. Consequently, *the angle that an arbitrary skew ray makes with the axis is preserved.* The important conclusion here is that a skew ray may make an angle θ with the axis of the fiber which exceeds the value of θ_M given by eq. (1). The condition $\sin \psi > n'/n$ must always be met. This implies

$$\sin \theta \cos \gamma \leq \sin \theta_M. \tag{4}$$

Therefore, for every value of $\theta > \theta_M$, γ must have a minimum value denoted $\gamma = \bar{\gamma}(\theta)$. Of course, for $\theta < \theta_M$, $0 < \gamma < \frac{1}{2}\pi$. It will be useful to define $\bar{\gamma}$ by

$$\cos \bar{\gamma} = \sin \theta_M / \sin \theta, \quad \text{with} \quad \theta > \theta_M. \tag{5}$$

When a single clad fiber is illuminated at all angles of incidence, but viewed at some particular exit angle corresponding to a value of θ smaller than θ_M, the light emerges from all parts of the fiber face (all values of γ are allowed). However, if the fiber is viewed at an angle corresponding to a value of θ larger than θ_M, rays (all of which are skew) are transmitted only for values of $\gamma > \bar{\gamma}$ and a 'black band' appears across the exit face of the fiber (POTTER [1961]). Only rays spiraling around the inside wall of the fiber can be transmitted without being refracted out of the fiber walls; consequently, the central band defined by $\gamma < \bar{\gamma}$ is dark.

Another restriction on the axial angle θ is determined by refraction at the entrance and exit faces. If we take the index of the entrance and exit media to be n_0, Snell's law determines an upper limit for θ, called θ_c, and given by

$$\sin \theta_c = n_0 / n. \tag{6}$$

Light that is incident on the face of a fiber at grazing incidence makes an angle θ_c with the axis after refraction into the fiber. There is a special application (REYNOLDS and CONDON [1957], REYNOLDS [1960]), of optical fibers in nuclear physics where the fibers are made of a luminescent material, excitable by high energy particles. In this case, light is created within the fiber (scintillation), then internally reflected at the walls of the fiber as the light progresses toward the exit face of the fiber, and some light is thus trapped within the fiber. The maximum angle for which a ray can be refracted out of the fiber in this case is also θ_c. Therefore, the limit θ_c applies to both scintillating and passive straight glass fibers and is defined exactly the same way in both cases.

2.2. TRANSMISSION OF LIGHT

Many of the applications of optical fiber bundles have been developed because the fiber bundle is usually capable of much greater light collecting and transmission than a corresponding lens system. The collection and transmission properties can be adequately described in terms of the geometrical optics of a single fiber.

Since the fiber can actually accept light incident at angles larger than θ_M, an effective numerical aperture (POTTER et al. [1963]) can be used in some cases. The details are beyond the scope of this chapter, except to point out that when we are to calculate all of the flux which a fiber is capable of collecting, we must include values of θ larger than θ_M in our calculations.

Given a certain numerical aperture, there are attenuation effects that depend on the fiber geometry, its material, and its imperfections. Since the light incident on the end of a fiber is in a medium whose index of refraction is different from that of the fiber core, the reflection losses at the ends of an individual fiber are accurately described in terms of Fresnel coefficients (see BORN and WOLF [1959] for the appropriate equations). There is another similar reflection loss as the light leaves the fiber at the exit face. Consequently, many practical optical fiber devices are immersed; that is, the source of light is made available in a medium whose index is very close to that of the fiber core. This minimizes the Fresnel reflection losses.

Additional factors which contribute to light losses in a fiber include imperfect reflections at the walls of the fiber, due either to irregularities or defects along the wall. Some light may be scattered from the expected geometrical path. One can characterize the phenomena by a reflection coefficient, α, which may be a function of the angle θ. Experimental results (POTTER [1961]) indicate that a value of α of 0.999 or greater can be achieved in commercial optical fibers. Losses due to surface phenomena (imperfect reflections) may be expected to be roughly proportional to α^{η}, where η is the number of reflections made by a given ray. Another major cause of light loss in an optical fiber is due to the bulk properties of the fiber materials. The absorption of light in the core is a function of wavelength and pathlength. One would expect the bulk losses for light at a given angle and a given wavelength in the fiber to be proportional to $\exp(-\beta P)$ where β is the absorption coefficient and P is the actual path length of the ray.

In practically every case of interest, individual optical fibers are cylinders; in the calculations to follow, we are assuming that the cross section is circular. The optical properties of fibers whose cross sections are polygonal or irregular, are observed to be very similar to the properties of circular fibers.

The whole entrance face of a fiber uniformly illuminated by a convergent cone of light may be considered as a source of luminance $L(\theta)$, emitting a flux in the fiber core. It can be shown that the total flux emerging from the exit face is given by (POTTER [1961])

$$
\begin{aligned}
F = 8\pi a^2 & \int_{\theta=0}^{\theta_M} \int_{\gamma=0}^{\frac{1}{2}\pi} L(\theta)t't''\alpha^{\eta}(\theta)e^{-\beta P} \cos^2 \gamma \sin \theta \, d\gamma \, d\theta \\
+ 8\pi a^2 & \int_{\theta=\theta_M}^{\theta_c} \int_{\gamma=\bar{\gamma}(\theta)}^{\frac{1}{2}\pi} L(\theta)t't''\alpha^{\eta}(\theta)e^{-\beta P} \cos^2 \gamma \sin \theta \, d\gamma \, d\theta.
\end{aligned}
\tag{7}
$$

a is the fiber radius; t' and t'' represent the Fresnel transmittance at the entrance and exit faces, resp. The angle θ_c is defined by eq. (6). Note that eq. (7) has two terms, the first of which is the total flux collected within the cone of half-angle θ_M. If we assume that the source of luminance $L(\theta)$ is Lambertian and that $t' = t'' = \gamma^{\eta} = e^{-\beta P} = 1$, this first term is proportional to $\sin^2 \theta_M$. The second term includes the contribution of only the skew rays for which $\theta > \theta_M$. The integration in eq. (7) has been performed for some cases and numerical results were given by KAPANY [1958] and POTTER et al. [1963] (see fig. 3). The case of a bright point on the entrance face (mentioned by KAPANY [1958]) and that of a parallel incident beam of light are interesting but, up to now, of no practical use; they will not be considered in this chapter.

By using an equation similar to eq. (7), but for meridional rays, it has been shown that the attenuation of light in a single fiber depends, to a first approximation,

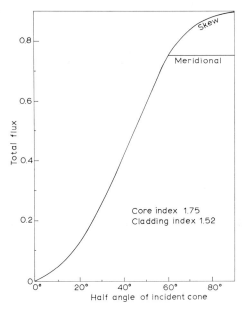

Fig. 3. The total flux (in arbitrary units) accepted and transmitted by a perfect circular fiber is shown as a function of the half angle of the incident cone of light.

on the length to diameter ratio if it is assumed that scattering at the core-cladding interface is the predominant attenuation factor. It is then possible to have the same relative attenuation in two fibers of very different dimensions, but with the same length to diameter ratio. When the diameter of the fiber becomes very small, i.e., several microns, this observation is no longer true because of irregular scattering and waveguide effects.

The spectral limitations of fiber bundles are due to absorption in the core glasses. There are no glasses presently available, useful as core materials, which have absorption coefficients low enough to be used with light of wavelengths below 0.30 μm or above 12 μm. In the visible spectrum, an attenuation of 50 % in two meters of fiber length is typical for a 25 μm diameter fiber at the present state of the technology.

At the short wavelength limit, low index crown core glasses are best, but since appropriate cladding glasses of lower index are not available, the numerical aperture and the transmission are reduced in the wavelength region below 4000 Å. For certain applications, isolated quartz fibers may be used for wavelengths below 0.3 μm.

For wavelengths longer than 2.5 μm, most common glasses attenuate light strongly and other fiber materials must be used. Several have been studied, but the combination generally used at present is an arsenic sulfide glass (As_2S_3) for the core (index 2.47) and a modified arsenic sulfide glass of lower index for the cladding*. The trans-

---

* *Note added in proof*: New oxide glasses (KAPANY and SIMMS [1965], notably germanate and lanthanate glasses are used for the spectral range of 0.4 to 5 μm and arsenic glasses for the range 1 to 12 μm.

mission, of course, still depends upon the length and diameter of the fibers. For fibers 50 μm in diameter, there is no perceptible transmission through lengths of 7 mm for wavelengths beyond 12 μm, or through lengths of 0.5 m for wavelengths beyond 6 μm. The water absorption band at about 7 μm limits many applications of these fibers in an open environment.

2.3. CONICAL FIBERS

There are some special cases where it is advantageous to use a tapered fiber bundle, offering a magnifying power different from unity. There is a significant equation giving the behavior of light in a perfect conical fiber:

$$d_S \sin \theta_S = d_L \sin \theta_L \tag{8}$$

where d is the diameter of the cross section of the fiber and θ is the axial angle. The subscript S refers to the small end and the subscript L refers to the large end.

The conical fiber changes the numerical aperture of the light beam. The angle of the rays with the axis decreases as the diameter increases. If one uses a fiber which has a varying diameter, it is the smallest diameter which determines the acceptance angle of the system.

A conical fiber does have one characteristic by which it differs from the cylindrical fiber: If the side of the fiber is illuminated, some rays are refracted into the fiber core, trapped, and transmitted in the fiber. This may be considered an advantage or disadvantage, depending upon the application.

3. Fiber bundles

One single fiber cannot transfer an image from one face to the other one because multiple reflections occurring inside one fiber tend to average out the illuminance on the entrance face. Fibers may be bound together, to form a fiber bundle capable of transferring an image, fiber by fiber, from the entrance face to the exit face. Any detail smaller than a fiber diameter cannot be transmitted, and the resolving power of the bundle is therefore limited by the diameter of the fibers. If the cladding is poor, the leakage of light between fibers blurs the image and causes a further loss of resolving power. *The only two conjugate surfaces are the two faces of the bundle.* Because the numerical aperture is usually high, the depth of focus is very small, and the object cannot be far removed from the entrance face without an appreciable blur of the image. Image formation and resolution properties of fiber bundles are discussed in § 4.

3.1. FABRICATION

Although there are several methods of manufacturing optical fibers, we shall mention only the most common one already described by KAPANY [1960].

3.1.1. *Single fibers*

A high refractive index glass rod is inserted into a tubing of lower index, and the assembly is drawn in a furnace, at the exit of which it is wound on a drum. It seems that better mechanical strength is obtained when the thermal expansion coefficient of the cladding is smaller than that of the core. The melting temperatures cannot of course be too different. The rod tube assembly may be further inserted in another tube of absorbing glass (extramural absorber) and the rod with two glass coatings is drawn as described above. Fibers may be drawn down to a diameter of a few microns with a cladding of the order of one micron.

3.1.2. *Fiber bundles*

When several fibers are fused together the major problem is that of alignment of the individual fibers (the arrangements of fibers at both ends must be identical in order to obtain an undistorted image). This alignment may be achieved by different processes which are often kept as trade secrets by manufacturers. One described by KAPANY [1958] involves the use of a rotating drum, with a very accurate lead mechanism to wind the fiber. After the required number of layers has been wound, the fibers are bound together, sawed at the desired length and cemented (usually with an epoxy resin) or fused together. The problem becomes difficult with fibers less than 25 μm in diameter which are hard to see and to handle. In that case, a number (a few hundred) of high index rods are inserted into lower index tubes and bundled together before the fusing and drawing operation. The resulting assembly is called a multifiber. When multifibers are joined together, the alignment presents a very difficult problem because of the smallness of the diameter of the individual fibers. Satisfactory solutions have however been worked out.

When fiber bundles are used not to transfer images but only to guide light, the alignment is, of course, unimportant.

3.2. SHAPES

The shape of the individual fibers in a fused bundle depends upon the relative viscosity of the core and cladding glasses (SIEGMUND [1963]) and upon the type of array. If the cladding glass is less viscous than the core glass, the fiber cores tend to keep their original shape, (generally circular) during the fusion while the cladding glass flows into all interstices. If the cladding glass is more viscous than the core glass the fibers tend to take a polygonal shape. A perfect packing of identical circular fibers before fusion results in a hexagonal close-packed structure of circles in the first case, and a hexagonal close-packed structure of hexagons in the second case (square arrays are also used). Rigid bundles are made of single fibers or multifibers by cementing or fusing them together along their whole length; flexible bundles are fused or cemented at the ends only. Fused rigid fiber bundles may be bent by heating to follow any prescribed path.

Fibers can also be deliberately misaligned in special bundles, and the two faces can be given completely different arrangements (see § 5).

In the great majority of cases, bundles are made of cylindrical fibers, but tapered fibers (or even fibers with more complicated shapes) have also been used.

3.3. DIMENSIONS

Bundles of aligned fibers may be very long (several meters) or very short (1 mm). With short bundles, cross sections up to 900 cm^2 have been achieved. With long flexible fiber bundles the area seldom exceeds 1 cm^2, but with rigid bundles about one meter long, areas up to 25 cm^2 have been obtained. If no alignment is necessary, the cross section and the length may be of course much greater.

3.4. TRANSMISSION PROPERTIES

There are several factors which govern the transmission of light by fiber bundles as well as by single fibers, such as: transmittance properties of the materials, quality of the reflecting interface, light leakage through the cladding, end losses, length and diameter of individual fibers. The numerical aperture which governs the light gathering capacity of a bundle is, theoretically, the numerical aperture of the single fiber components. However, the quality of the reflecting interface is slightly degraded when fibers are fused together, and the actual numerical aperture of the bundle may be appreciably smaller than that of the individual fibers. Rays which are not properly conducted by the fibers must be absorbed, or they will appear as stray light.

Another factor of attenuation which is characteristic of fiber bundles is the so-called 'packing fraction', i.e., the ratio of core area to the total area in a cross section. It is desirable, of course, that the thickness of the cladding be kept to a minimum, but this thickness cannot be less than one to two wavelengths because of the penetration of light into the second medium in the case of total reflection (the light may reach the next fiber and this leakage is often referred to as 'cross talk'). Hence, the packing fraction decreases with decreasing fiber diameter. The 'extramural absorber', which is a second thin coating of strongly absorbing glass, has little effect on 'cross talk' but it has the advantage of eliminating stray light due to the rays which are not totally reflected inside fibers; as it is very thin, it does not appreciably reduce the packing fraction which, for fibers of 3 to 5 μm, is no better than 0.6. This low value is due chiefly to the area occupied by the clear cladding (about 37 %), the extramural absorber occupying only 3 % of the total surface in a cross section.

Moreover it will be shown in § 6 of this chapter that the waveguide properties of fibers become more and more apparent when the diameter d decreases. In visible light, for $d \approx 3$ μm, patterns due to pure modes or to mixtures of modes may be visible on the exit face of some fibers.

These factors (added to the difficulties of fabrication when d becomes very small) explain why there is not much to gain by using bundles with fiber diameters of less than 3 μm. Thus for most applications and unless maximum resolution is needed, bundles of fibers with 10 μm diameter show a number of advantages: easier fabrication and alignment, a packing fraction about 0.7, reasonably good resolution and little or no waveguide effects.

4. Image formation. Resolution properties of fiber bundles

4.1. GENERAL REMARKS

Experimentally, it is found that in most cases, the illuminance on the exit face of an isolated fiber appears quite uniform, due to the many reflections occurring inside the fiber. As long as the light stays inside the properly clad fiber and the losses are negligible, the uniform illuminance over the exit face is the average of the illuminance on the entrance face. The image of an object appears as a juxtaposition of uniform circles (or polygons) of different or equal illuminances separated by the thin dark regions of the cladding which transmit no light (see figs. 4 and 5). Occasional dark spots correspond to broken fibers or defects in the bulk. A misalignment of fibers, especially at the junction of multifibers, gives the image a broken look. We shall assume that the fiber bundle is faultless and made of well clad circular fibers of the same diameter. If we suppose that an object is scanned by a single randomly moving rigid fiber of diameter d, *each fiber of the bundle may be then considered as a fixed position of the scanning fiber.* That is why some authors, like HOPKINS and KAPANY [1954] call a fiber bundle a 'static scanner'. This consideration enables us to determine the illuminance at any point on the exit face of the bundle. For this purpose, we shall,

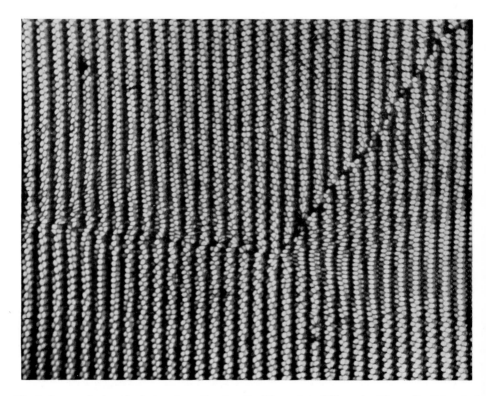

Fig. 4. Image of a bar chart given by a fiber bundle. Dimension of fibers $d \approx 10 \ \mu$m. Spatial period of the object $1/\nu \approx 3d$.

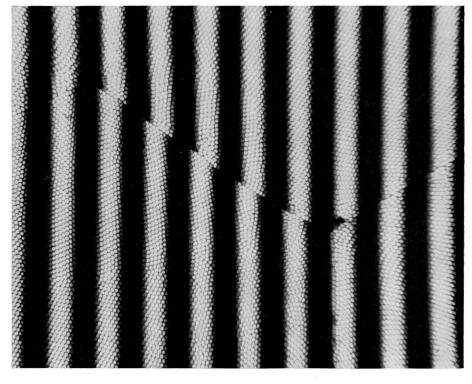

Fig. 5. Same as fig. 4. Spatial period $1/\nu \approx 10d$ or $12d$.

as DROUGARD [1964] did, study first the general problem of a scanning circular aperture of diameter d, and then see how it applies to the case of the fiber bundle.

4.2. PROBLEM OF THE SCANNING FIBER

Let us consider a fixed object, the illuminance of which, at a point (x, y) in its plane,
is represented by an integrable function $f(x, y)$. Let us suppose that this object is
scanned by one circular rigid fiber of diameter d moving in random directions, and
let (x', y') be the coordinates of the center of the exit face of the fiber, measured with
respect to axes parallel to the xy-axes of the object plane. The origin is such that
$x' = y' = 0$ when the center of the entrance face is at the origin of the xy-system.

The illuminance over the exit face of the fiber is equal to the average of the illuminance falling on the entrance face. Thus, the illuminance $f'(x', y')$ over the
exit face of the fiber, when its center is at the point (x', y'), is given by:

$$f'(x', y') = \frac{1}{\pi a^2} \int f(x, y)\,\mathrm{d}x\,\mathrm{d}y \qquad (9a)$$

in which the integration extends over the entrance face of the fiber and where a,
the radius of the fiber, is $\frac{1}{2}d$. Eq. (9a) may be usefully written:

$$f'(x', y') = \frac{1}{\pi a^2} \int_{-\infty}^{+\infty} f(x, y)e(x'-x, y'-y)\mathrm{d}x\mathrm{d}y, \tag{9b}$$

with $\begin{cases} e(x'-x, y'-y) = 1 & \text{for} \quad (x'-x)^2+(y'-y)^2 \leq a^2, \\ \qquad\qquad\qquad = 0 & \text{elsewhere.} \end{cases}$

The function $e(x', y')$ centered on (x, y) is equal to unity inside a circle of radius a and is zero outside. The function $f'(x', y')$ now appears in the form of a convolution of the function $f(x, y)$ representing the object, and the function $e(x', y')/\pi a^2$ centered on the point (x, y). Thus, if we define the function $f'(x', y')$ as the image of the object, given at every point (x', y') by the scanning fiber, eq. (9b) defines $e(x', y')/\pi a^2$ as the point-spread function of the scanning fiber. This implies that the system is linear, and 'spatially invariant'. This expression means that the point-spread function is the same at all points in the plane of the object. It should be emphasized that eq. (9b) does not imply anything about the actual image of one point; it defines mathematically a fictitious point-spread function for the fictitious 'image' $f'(x', y')$.

For this image defined by $f'(x', y')$ at any position (x', y') of the center of the scanning fiber, it is possible to speak of an optical transfer function $T(v)$, which is the Fourier transform of the function $e(x', y')/\pi a^2$

$$T(v) = \frac{2J_1(\pi vd)}{\pi vd} \tag{10}$$

in which J_1 is the Bessel function of the first kind of the first order, v is the spatial frequency, and d is the diameter of the fiber.

4.3. STATIONARY FIBER BUNDLE

In a stationary fiber bundle, the center (x', y') of the scanning fiber is allowed to occupy only discrete positions (x'_i, y'_i); and eqs. (9a) and (9b) are valid only at the centers of the N fixed fibers:

$$f'(x'_i, y'_i) = \frac{1}{\pi a^2} \int_{-\infty}^{+\infty} f(x, y)e(x'_i-x, y'_i-y)\mathrm{d}x\mathrm{d}y. \tag{11}$$

At any other point (x'', y'') on the exit face of one fiber, the illuminance $f''(x'', y'')$ is equal to the illuminance at the center of that fiber, and given by:

$$f''(x'', y'') = f'(x'_i, y'_i)e(x''-x'_i, y''-y'_i); \tag{12}$$

hence, if $f'(x', y'_i)$ is replaced by its expression in eq. (11)

$$f''(x'', y'') = \frac{1}{\pi a^2} \int_{-\infty}^{+\infty} \sum_{i=0}^{N} f(x, y)e(x'_i-x, y'_i-y)e(x''-x'_i, y''-y'_i)\mathrm{d}x\mathrm{d}y \tag{13}$$

in which, for any value of (x'', y''), there can be no more than one non-zero term in the summation, since only one fiber may cover any given point; eq. (13) can be written in the form of convolution $f(x, y)$ and a function:

$$E = \sum_{i=0}^{N} e(x_i' - x, \ y_i' - y) \ e(x'' - x_i', \ y'' - y_i'). \tag{14}$$

The function E thus defined can be called the point-spread function of the static fiber bundle, but it must be emphasized that E is not spatially invariant. It involves the coordinates of the centers of the fibers and shows discontinuities when (x, y) passes on the entrance face from one fiber to the next one. A point located between fibers yields no image. The Fourier analysis cannot be usefully applied to such a system. It does not enable us to describe the optical transfer properties of a fiber bundle by means of an optical transfer function *depending only on the spatial frequency v.*

In the general case, the optical transfer properties of the system are expected, *to vary not only with the spatial frequency, but also with the position of the fiber bundle.* It is, however, of much practical interest to know the limits between which it varies, whether its minimum value is acceptable and whether its variations are not too large. In the following we shall use an intuitive approach to analyze this problem.

A natural approach to the problem is to study the image formation of sine wave gratings of different spatial frequencies by the fiber bundle. We assume that the thickness of the cladding is negligible and that the circular fibers have a hexagonal close-packed structure (which is the most probable), and that one of the particular directions of that structure is vertical, as shown in fig. 6. The distance between two

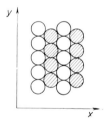

Fig. 6. Image of a sine wave grating given by a properly oriented fiber bundle. Spatial period $1/v = d\sqrt{3}$.

consecutive vertical rows is $\frac{1}{2}d\sqrt{3}$. If the grating object is also vertical, all the fibers of the same row show the same illuminance.

The illuminance of the object is represented by the function:

$$f(x, y) = A + B \cos 2\pi v x, \quad \text{contrast} \ \ C_0 = B/A, \quad |B| \leq A. \tag{15}$$

The illuminance $f'(x', y')$ over the exit face of one single scanning fiber, when its center is at the point (x', y') is represented by a sine wave of contrast $C_0 T(v)$, where $T(v)$ is the optical transfer function defined by eq. (10),

$$f'(x', y') = A + BT(v) \cos 2\pi v x'. \tag{16}$$

To the discrete positions (x_i', y_i') occupied in fact by the point (x', y'), correspond discrete points of the sine wave [eq. (16)] having abscissae distant by $\frac{1}{2}d\sqrt{3}$. The location of these points on the sine wave depends upon the relative position of the object and the fiber bundle. If two of the points occupy a maximum and the following minimum of the sine wave, i.e., when the middles of two vertical rows are on a maximum and a minimum of the object, then the contrast C_i, of the image is as good as possible, and equal to the contrast $C_0 T(v)$ given by one scanning fiber. If, from this position, the fiber bundle is horizontally translated by the quantity $\frac{1}{4}d\sqrt{3}$, two consecutive points become located symmetrically with respect to a maximum of the sine wave represented by eq. (16) and two others symmetrically with respect to the next minimum; the contrast C_i, of the image drops then to $C_0 T(v) \cos \frac{1}{2}\pi v d\sqrt{3}$.

These two cases are extreme. In the first one, all fibers covering a maximum or a minimum line of the object are centered on it; in the second one, all fibers covering a maximum or a minimum of the object have their centers as far as possible from it. It seems obvious that, when the fibers are oriented differently or not in order, those which cover a maximum or a minimum of the object are located not as well as in the first case, but not as badly as in the second one. All values of the optical transfer function, $T(v) = C_i/C_0$ are included between the two curves, J representing $T(v) = 2J_1(\pi v d)/\pi v d$ and C representing $T(v) \cos \frac{1}{2}\pi v d\sqrt{3}$, both shown on fig. 7. The

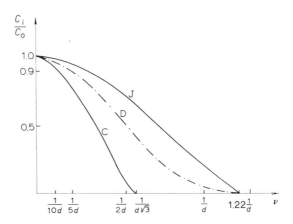

Fig. 7. Optical transfer C_i/C_0 vs spatial frequency v. For a static fiber bundle the values of C_i/C_0 are included between curve J representing $T(v) = [2J_1(\pi v d)]/\pi v d$ and curve C representing $T(v) \cos \frac{1}{2}\pi v d\sqrt{3}$. The dotted line represents $\tau(v) = [2J_1(\pi v d)]^2/(\pi v d)^2$, the optical transfer function for a randomly moving fiber bundle.

quantity $1/(d\sqrt{3})$ may be considered as the cut-off frequency. In that case, when the middle of one row of fibers is on a maximum and the middle of next row on a minimum, as shown on fig. 6, the contrast has the corresponding value of $T(v)$, i.e., 65%; if the fiber bundle is horizontally translated by $\frac{1}{4}d\sqrt{3}$, all rows show the same illuminance and the contrast is zero. In the limit of very small object frequencies, the dimension of fibers become negligible, there is practically a transmission point by point, the image is then as good as the object, and it is not surprising to see the two curves J and C tend to unity when v tends to zero.

From fig. 7, the optical transfer C_i/C_0 is larger than 90 % for $v < 1/8d$; a very good image can then be expected. For $v = 1/4d$, the image may still be considered as acceptable, but for $v > 1/4d$, drawbacks of the fiber bundle become very apparent, the difference between the two extreme values of C_i/C_0 increases rapidly with v: though the image might be recognizable, it cannot be expected to be good.

This is true as long as the fiber bundle may be considered as perfect, which is approximately the case inside one multifiber, as shown in figs. 4 and 5, but a misalignment of fibers at the junction of two multifibers spoils the image.

4.4. CASE OF THE RANDOMLY MOVING FIBER BUNDLE

It was shown by KAPANY et al. [1957] and KAPANY [1959a, b] that several advantages appear if the fiber bundle is moved randomly with respect to the object: the defects, broken fibers, and dislocations lose much of their importance, the fiber structure is blurred out, the orientation of the fiber bundle becomes irrelevant as well as the order or disorder of fibers. It seems that such a system should give a spatially invariant point-spread function. Every fiber is acting like the scanning fiber considered at the beginning of this section. The illuminance $f'(x', y')$ over its exit face, when its center is at the point (x', y'), is given by eq. (9a).

Let us suppose that a stationary photographic plate is located in the plane of the exit face and that the fiber moves in all directions. In each position, the fiber uniformly illuminates a circle on the plate. This illuminance varies with the position of the fiber and is simply $f'(x', y')$. At a fixed point of the plate, the illuminance in the image which is recorded will be the time integral of this varying illuminance from the moving fiber. When the center of the fiber is at (x', y'), the illuminance at the point (x'', y'') of the plate is $f'(x', y') e(x'' - x', y'' - y')$, then the level of illuminance is given by $f'(x', y')$ inside and is zero outside the fiber aperture, which is described here by the aperture function $e(x'', y'')$ centered on (x', y').

If now the fiber moves such that the point (x'', y'') on the plate is exposed to each point on the fiber exit face for the same length of time (as long as the plate may be considered as a linear system), the integrated illuminance will be given by:

$$f''(x'', y'') = \int f'(x', y') \, e(x'' - x', y'' - y') \, dx' \, dy'. \tag{17}$$

This condition is clearly satisfied for the case of uniform motion, and also for suitably random motion; eq. (17) then describes the image on the plate; $e(x'' - x', y'' - y')$ is again the function defined in eq. (9b).

If we compare the expressions for $f'(x', y')$ and $f''(x'', y'')$ given by eqs. (9b) and (17) the similarity, except for an irrelevant constant, is obvious. It shows that the entry face of the fiber is a scanning aperture, and that the exit face then acts as a 'writing aperture'. The system is composed of two parts, each having a normalized transfer function of the form of $T(v)$ given by eq. (10). For the whole system the optical transfer function is the product of the transfer functions of the two components:

$$\tau(v) = [T(v)]^2 = \left[\frac{2J_1(\pi vd)}{\pi vd} \right]^2 \tag{18}$$

which is represented by the dotted line D on fig. 7. This result is in agreement with the previsions of ROETLING and GANLEY [1962].

The point-spread function emerging from the analysis has circular symmetry, is the Fourier transform of $\tau(v)$, and is the autocorrelation function of a function which is constant inside a circle of diameter d and zero outside. Its shape is well-known.

The results obtained in the case of one randomly moving fiber obviously apply to the case of a whole fiber bundle of well coated fibers, merely by using the trivial result that the transform of the sum of partial functions is the sum of the partial transforms. Such a randomly moving fiber bundle is sometimes called a 'dynamic scanner'.

It is, of course, necessary that the total range of motion of the bundle be at least equal to two fiber diameters. Curve D (fig. 7) representing $\tau(v)$ is located between curves J and C, which is not surprising. It represents an average of the contrast transfer C_i/C_0 for all values given by all possible positions of the static fiber bundle. The gain in resolution is clearly evident in fig. 7. At the frequency $1/2d$, the static fiber bundle cannot give an acceptable image. The randomly moving fiber bundle gives a good image with a contrast transfer higher than 50 % and the cut-off frequency is about twice as high. This gain in resolution has been foreseen and shown experimentally by KAPANY et al. [1957] and KAPANY [1959a, b].

All the results of this analysis represent a good approximation when the fibers are polygonal, d being their average dimension. If the fiber structure is square-packed instead of hexagonal close-packed, curve C (fig. 7) drops a little faster, the cut-off frequency is then $1/2d$ instead of $1/(d\sqrt{3})$.

4.5. CONCLUSION

The point-spread function of a static fiber bundle is not spatially invariant and the system cannot therefore be strictly characterized by an optical transfer function. In the case of circular fibers of diameter d, the contrast of the image of an object varies with the position of the fiber bundle and lies between two extreme values which become closer together as the spatial frequency decreases (see fig. 7, curves J and C). A randomly vibrating fiber bundle is found to have a spatially invariant point-spread function and can therefore be characterized by an optical transfer function (see fig. 7, curve D). The latter has the advantage not only of giving a better resolution, but also of blurring out the fiber structure and the defects of the bundle.

5. Applications of fiber optics

There are many potential applications (KAPANY [1958, 1965] CAPELLARO [1963], KROLAK [1963], SIEGMUND [1963]) of fiber optics to various problems of image and light transfer. Some of them have been already put into practice, while others are still under development. These applications may be grouped roughly into two categories: light conduits, and image forming systems. In some of them, the fibers are bent. The propagation of light in bent glass rods has been studied by KAPANY [1958] for different radii of curvature. In most practical cases the radius of curvature is appreciably larger than the fiber diameter, and it is shown experimentally that when it is more than twenty times the fiber diameter, there is no appreciable change in numerical aperture, transmission properties and image quality.

5.1. LIGHT CONDUITS

These can be made of one single rod, or of a rigid or flexible bundle. The arrangement of fibers may be random, and such bundles scramble any input image; the exit faces may be used as screen illuminators or as ground glasses. They can have a great variety of shapes and sizes. Special illuminators can be made to concentrate light on an object. For example, the circular entrance face of a fiber bundle is placed at the image of a star; at the other end of the bundle the fibers are made to lie in a row covering the entrance slit of a stellar spectrograph, which then receives a much larger flux density than it would if the image were formed directly on it.

At this time, apparently, a very large market for fiber optics is in the data processing field to optically sense holes in punched cards*. The entrance face of an assembly of small flexible fiber bundles is illuminated by a small bright lamp. The exit faces of these bundles are located at each hole position in a row parallel to the smaller edge of a punched card. Facing each bundle is a clad glass rod followed by a lens and a phototransistor. The punched card moves parallel to its long dimension between the fiber bundles and the rods. Whenever a hole in the card allows light (with practically no heat) to pass from a fiber bundle to the rod facing it, the phototransistor passes a current large enough to drive a reed relay directly. In addition, another fiber bundle is used in the timing mechanism of the electronic system.

Such a system has several advantages over conventional electromechanical card verifiers and readers: The machine is quieter since fewer mechanical parts are required, it reads about four times faster, and less maintenance is necessary since the vibrations are reduced and the lamp is isolated from them.

Fiber bundles are also used (for proximity indication in document handling equipment, mark sensing, etc.) to collect the light reflected from documents.

Single flexible fibers are sometimes used as remote spot scanners: one end scans the object, while the other end is relayed to a photomultiplier.

5.2. IMAGE FORMING SYSTEMS

Fiber bundles used to transfer images must be made of well clad and carefully arranged fibers. The variety of shapes and sizes gives them several advantages over

---

* STAHL and POTTER [1966].

other optical systems. They can be long or short, have a large or small cross section, be flexible, rigid, bent, or tapered. They have other advantages, particularly the absence of aberrations and the large numerical aperture. We already know the disadvantages: defects due to broken fibers and to misalignment, the existence of only two possible conjugate planes, and a very short depth of focus. If the fibers are conical, the bundle can magnify or demagnify an image, but the magnifying and demagnifying power has a fixed value.

Such bundles are used as fiberscopes, faceplates for cathode ray tubes, field flatteners, and image dissectors. There are many other applications, but we shall consider only the most common ones.

5.2.1. *Fiberscopes*

These transfer images along rigid or flexible paths (SIEGMUND [1963]). The fibers or multifibers are generally not fused, but are cemented together. Rigid bundles, also called image conduits, are cheaper; they can be bent by heating to conform to any prescribed path, and the fibers are less breakable. But the advantage of flexibility is very important and fiber optics is probably best known for the flexible fiberscopes which are particularly useful for the inspection of hard-to-reach areas, for example, complex structures in aircraft, remote dials, level of liquids in tanks, etc. Another area of application is the endoscopic examination of internal portions of the body. A gastroscope made of fibers has a much better flexibility and gives a brighter image than the conventional periscopic systems.

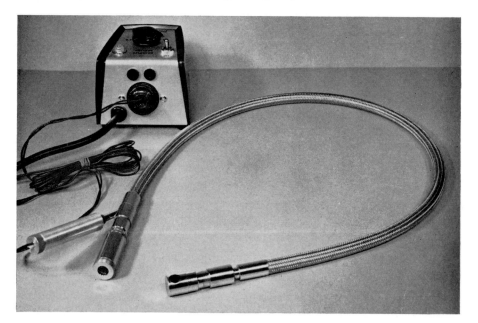

Fig. 8. Fiberscope. The box contains a variable transformer which supplies power to the lamp near the eyepiece. (Courtesy of American Optical Co.)

In a fiberscope (see fig. 8) an objective lens forms the image of an object on the entrance face of the fiber bundle, and the exit face is examined through an eyepiece or projected onto a photographic film. When the object cannot be illuminated directly, another flexible fiber bundle is used to carry light from a small lamp located near the eyepiece to the surface of the object, both fiber bundles being contained in a common flexible sheath.

Generally fiberscopes have diameters of approximately 10 to 25 mm and lengths up to 4 meters. Two of them can be used in series, but this causes additional losses in transmission and resolution.

Because of the gain in resolution and image quality due to a random movement of the fiber bundle, fiberscopes are available in which 'dynamic scanning' (cf. § 4.4) is used. The amplitude of scanning, which could be of a few fiber diameters for a faultless bundle must in fact be much larger because of the defects in real bundles.

5.2.2. *Field flatteners and electron tube faceplates*

Fiber bundles can be used to correct the field curvature of a lens system, thus allowing the lens designer to concentrate his efforts on achieving better correction of other aberrations. This problem of field flattening has been studied in some detail by KAPANY and HOPKINS [1957]. The entrance face of a fiber bundle is given the shape corresponding to the field curvature of the preceding lens, the exit face is planar and may be put in contact with a photographic film. If another lens follows, the exit face can be given the suitable curvature, so that the final image is planar.

Another application lies in the photography of the face plate of a cathode ray tube (see KAPANY and CAPELLARO [1961]). Every point of the phosphor emits light in all directions and only a small portion of this light can be collected by a lens which images the phosphor onto a photographic film. The face plate is made of a vacuum-tight fiber bundle, a few mm thick. The multifibers are always fused together, and any inclusion of gas is carefully avoided. The inside face, which can be planar or curved, carries the phosphor and the planar outside face is in contact with the photographic plate. Each fiber collects the light emitted in a cone angle close to 90° and transmits it with very few losses. The advantages are obvious: no halo, shorter exposure times and flattening of the field.

High index lead glasses are not satisfactory for the fabrication of fiber faceplates of television camera tubes or image intensifiers because lead poisons the photo-cathodes. This disadvantage is eliminated with the use of new lead-free glasses which can now be made with indices of refraction of about 1.80. As electron optical systems do not usually have spot sizes smaller than 20 μm (exceptionally 10 μm) there is no point in making the fibers smaller than 5 μm in diameter.

When an image is formed on the photocathode of an image tube with a fiber faceplate, as long as the object is of reasonable dimensions and not too far away, the best image-forming system is a fiber bundle. POTTER and HOPKINS [1960] have compared the efficiency of a fiber bundle to that of a specially designed lens system for unit magnification and a field of 12 cm, and they have shown that the fiber bundle gives an image luminance more than twice that obtained with the lens.

5.2.3. *Image dissectors*

Image dissectors sample an image into elements which can be arranged differently at the other end of the fibers. For example a straight line can be converted into a circular line and we shall show in the following how this conversion can be used to increase the resolution of a television transmission system. Square multifibers are bound together so that their entrance faces are arranged in a straight continuous line while exit faces lie on a circular ring, attached to the fiber faceplate of a television camera tube, and the camera spot scans this ring (if the individual fibers of the ring have dimensions around 10 μm, the spot always covers several of them). A lens images a portion of the scene onto the input end (straight line) of the fiber optics converter and the image is moved in a direction perpendicular to the straight line of fibers. Thus, since the camera tube is the limiting factor in resolving power, the circle-to-line converter increases the resolution of the system by a factor $\approx \pi$. Conversion is by no means limited to circle-to-line, and spiral-to-line converters have been also considered, as well as the breaking up of a straight line into several parallel segments.

Several applications of this device are given by KROLAK [1963]; one of the most useful is the transmission of images from planes and satellites.

5.3. OTHER APPLICATIONS

A new application of optical fibers results from the discovery of the glass laser by SNITZER [1961]. Using optical glasses doped with neodymium, Snitzer demonstrated laser action in fibers without end mirrors, thus making a high intensity flexible laser probe available. The technique appears to be appropriate for certain medical areas. KOESTER [1963] has studied the properties of a fiber laser as a light amplifier, also he has used a fiber laser as a switch in combination with two or more fiber lasers. Application of this switching action to very high speed optical logical circuits has also been suggested.

Instruments such as a hypodermic probe for microscopic inspection of living tissue *in vivo*, and a camera for examination of the interior water ways of a nuclear reactor have been described by CAPELLARO [1963]. An *in vivo* oxymeter with a flexible optical fiber probe for blood analysis in the circulatory system including the heart has been described by POLANYI and HEHIR [1962].

There is another possible application in coding and decoding systems: A flexible fiberscope in which the middle section is deliberately scrambled, is potted and sawed. Each half can code a picture, which the other half can decode.

Many other applications are suggested in fields as different as high speed recording, measurement of indices of liquids, control of high speed bacon slicing systems, etc.

6. Waveguide properties of fibers

Section 2 of this chapter has been mostly devoted to properties of fibers in the framework of geometrical optics and with the corresponding approximations. A fiber is in fact a dielectric waveguide in which both electric and magnetic fields $\mathcal{E} = \mathcal{E}_0 \exp(j\omega t)$ and $\mathcal{H} = \mathcal{H}_0 \exp(j\omega t)$ must satisfy the Maxwell equations and the boundary conditions. We shall see presently that these are satisfied for particular field distributions or 'modes'. This is also true of course for dielectric waveguides with metallic walls, the mode patterns of which are well known, but in this case, since all fields in a conductor are equal to zero, the boundary conditions are very simple. If the core is surrounded by a dielectric cladding of lower index, the fields in the cladding are generally not zero, and the boundary conditions are much more complicated. Up to now, in the field of optics, the problem has received little attention. However, at present, with the importance of lasers and with the development of fiber optics, the problem receives new interest and will be considered in this section. Since only a few experimental results are to be found in the literature, the present section will be mostly of a theoretical nature. The problem is to determine the components of the fields $\mathcal{E}$ and $\mathcal{H}$ at every point in the core and in the cladding. The results are summarized at the end of this section.

6.1. STATEMENT OF THE PROBLEM

For a wave propagating in a cylinder along the z-direction, the field amplitudes, at a point of cylindrical coordinates r, θ, z, may be written in the form:

$$\mathcal{E}_0(r, \theta, z) = [E_t(r, \theta) + uE_z(r, \theta)] \exp(-jhz),$$
$$\mathcal{H}_0(r, \theta, z) = [H_t(r, \theta) + uH_z(r, \theta)] \exp(-jhz),$$

(19)

where u is the unit vector along the z-axis, $E_t \exp(-jhz)$ and $H_t \exp(-jhz)$ are the transverse components of $\mathcal{E}_0$ and $\mathcal{H}_0$.

As a consequence of the Maxwell equations $\nabla \times \mathcal{H} = j\omega\mathcal{E}$ and $\nabla \times \mathcal{E} = -j\omega\mathcal{H}$, it may be shown (see, for example, TORALDO DI FRANCIA [1956]) that E_t and H_t may be written in terms of $\mathbf{grad}\, E_z$ and $\mathbf{grad}\, H_z$. They are given by

$$E_t = \frac{j}{\omega^2\mu\varepsilon - h^2} [+\omega\mu u \times \nabla H_z - h\nabla E_z],$$

(20)

$$H_t = \frac{j}{\omega^2\mu\varepsilon - h^2} [-\omega\varepsilon u \times \nabla E_z - h\nabla H_z],$$

where ε and μ are the dielectric constant and magnetic permeability of the medium which we will assume to be real (no absorption). *The problem is thus reduced to finding the functions E_z and H_z.* Further, since the z-components of $\mathcal{E}$ and $\mathcal{H}$ must satisfy the wave equation, E_z and H_z satisfy the Helmholtz equations (see TORALDO DI FRANCIA [1956]):

$$\nabla^2 E_z + (\omega^2 \mu \varepsilon - h^2) E_z = 0,$$
$$\nabla^2 H_z + (\omega^2 \mu \varepsilon - h^2) H_z = 0. \tag{21}$$

We shall in the remainder concentrate our attention on unattenuated waves, that is, we shall assume that h is real, so that $\omega^2 \mu \varepsilon - h^2 = \pm k^2$ is also real, positive or negative.

The solutions of eq. (21) are given by

$$\begin{cases} E_z \\ H_z \end{cases} \propto F_n(kr) \exp(jn\theta) \tag{22}$$

(SCHELKUNOFF [1943a]). As $\exp(jn\theta)$ must be the same for θ equal to multiples of 2π, n is an integer.

(1) If $\omega^2 \mu \varepsilon - h^2 = k^2$ ($k^2 > 0$), F_n may be any linear combination of Bessel functions of the first kind $J_n(kr)$, or of the second kind, $N_n(kr)$.

(2) If $\omega^2 \mu \varepsilon - h^2 = -k^2$, F_n may be any linear combination of modified Bessel functions of the first kind, $I_n(kr) = \exp(-\tfrac{1}{2}j\pi n)J_n(jkr)$ or of the second kind,

$$K_n(kr) = \tfrac{1}{2}j\pi \exp(\tfrac{1}{2}j\pi n) [J_n(jkr) + jN_n(jkr)].$$

K_n is also called a modified Hankel function of the first kind.

Of all these solutions of eq. (21), only a Bessel function of the first kind, J_n, which has a finite value for $r = 0$, is adequate to represent fields inside the core. Hence, if ε_i and μ_i are the dielectric constant and magnetic permeability of the core, we must have: $\omega^2 \mu_i \varepsilon_i - h^2 > 0$.

On the other hand, only a modified Bessel function of the second kind K_n, which decreases fast enough for large r to give a finite value to the energy, is adequate to represent fields in the cladding, which is assumed to be infinitely thick and characterized by the constants ε_e, μ_e. Hence we must have $\omega^2 \mu_e \varepsilon_e - h^2 < 0$. It appears that h^2 satisfies $\omega^2 \mu_e \varepsilon_e < h^2 < \omega^2 \mu_i \varepsilon_i$, which means that the phase velocity along the z-axis is included between the velocities of light in both media.

The expressions of E_{zi} and H_{zi} inside the core and of E_{ze} and H_{ze} outside the core can be written:

$$E_{zi} = A J_n(k_i r) \cos(n\theta + \phi_n),$$
$$H_{zi} = B J_n(k_i r) \cos(n\theta + \psi_n), \tag{23}$$

with

$$k_i^2 = \omega^2 \mu_i \varepsilon_i - h^2; \tag{24}$$

$$E_{ze} = C K_n(k_e r) \cos(n\theta + \phi_n),$$
$$H_{ze} = D K_n(k_e r) \cos(n\theta + \psi_n), \tag{25}$$

with

$$-k_e^2 = \omega^2 \mu_e \varepsilon_e - h^2. \tag{26}$$

To know the fields distributions, the quantities to be determined are k_i, k_e, A, B,

C, D, $\phi_n - \psi_n$ and h. In the case of a perfect metallic cladding both C and D must be zero.

All these formulae are general for fields satisfying eq. (19), and valid in any straight waveguide, regardless of the shape of the cross section. *In the following we shall now restrict ourselves to fibers with a circular cross section of radius a.* The unknown quantities will be determined by the boundary conditions. The tangential components of both electric and magnetic fields are continuous at the wall:

$$E_{zi} = E_{ze}, \qquad H_{zi} = H_{ze},$$
$$E_{\theta i} = E_{\theta e}, \qquad H_{\theta i} = H_{\theta e}. \tag{27}$$

These equations must be satisfied for $r = a$ and all values of θ. When these conditions are satisfied, the continuity of the normal components of the magnetic induction and the electric displacement can be shown to be automatically satisfied. Since the conditions concerning the z-components must be satisfied independently of θ, the factors including θ in eqs. (23), (25) are the same for E_{zi} and E_{ze} and similarly for H_{zi} and H_{ze}. Since ϕ_n or ψ_n may be chosen arbitrarily equal to $\frac{1}{2}\pi$, we see immediately that the condition $n = 0$ may result either in E_{zi} and $E_{ze} = 0$, or in $H_{zi} = H_{ze} = 0$. That is, transverse electric (TE) or transverse magnetic (TM) modes are possible in dielectric waveguides but only with circular symmetry (HONDROS and DEBYE [1910]). TEM-waves are not allowed in a dielectric waveguide. Note also that when n is different from zero, both the electric and magnetic fields have a z-component, giving so-called 'hybrid' modes.

The θ-components are obtained from eq. (20). For instance, inside the core:

$$E_{\theta i} = j \left[\frac{Anh}{k_i^2 r} J_n(k_i r) \sin (n\theta + \phi_n) + \frac{B\omega\mu_i}{k_i} J_n'(k_i r) \cos (n\theta + \psi_n) \right],$$
$$H_{\theta i} = j \left[-\frac{A\omega\varepsilon_i}{k_i} J_n(k_i r) \cos (n\theta + \phi_n) + \frac{Bnh}{k_i^2 r} J_n(k_i r) \sin (n\theta + \psi_n) \right]. \tag{28}$$

$E_{\theta e}$ and $H_{\theta e}$ are given by similar expressions with $J_n(k_i r)$ and $J_n'(k_i r)$ being replaced by $K_n(k_e r)$ and $K_n'(k_e r)$, k_i by k_e, and k_i^2 by $-k_e^2$, A and B by C and D.

If n is different from zero, the equalities (27) result in four equations which are linear and homogeneous with respect to the constants A, B, C, D (when $n = 0$ there are only two equations, and this case will be treated separately). The determinant Δ of their coefficients must be equal to zero. To make the expression of this condition more compact, we define X_n and Y_n by:

$$X_n(x) = \frac{K_n'(x)}{x K_n(x)}, \qquad Y_n(y) = \frac{J_n'(y)}{y J_n(y)}, \tag{29}$$

with $x = k_e a$ and $y = k_i a$, x and y are real and positive. Then the relation $\Delta = 0$ takes the form:

$$\frac{(\varepsilon_i Y_n + \varepsilon_e X_n)(\mu_i Y_n + \mu_e X_n)}{n^2 (\varepsilon_i \mu_i / y^2 + \varepsilon_e \mu_e / x^2)(1/x^2 + 1/y^2)} = -\frac{\sin (n\theta + \phi_n) \sin (n\theta + \psi_n)}{\cos (n\theta + \phi_n) \cos (n\theta + \psi_n)}. \tag{30}$$

The right-hand side of eq. (30) must, like the left-hand side, be independent of θ, which is realized only if $\psi_n - \phi_n = \pm\frac{1}{2}\pi$. If we now assume $\mu_i = \mu_e = \mu$ and $\varepsilon_e/\varepsilon_i = p$, $p < 1$, eq. (30) becomes (see SCHELKUNOFF [1943], ABELE [1948], SNITZER [1961a]):

$$(Y_n + pX_n)(Y_n + X_n) - n^2 \left(\frac{1}{y^2} + \frac{p}{x^2} \right)\left(\frac{1}{y^2} + \frac{1}{x^2} \right) = 0. \tag{31}$$

From eqs. (24), (26), x and y must also satisfy the condition:

$$x^2 + y^2 = a^2\omega^2\mu(\varepsilon_i - \varepsilon_e), \tag{32}$$

and the problem is thus compleetly solved by solving the system of eqs. (31), (32). The latter equation is that of a circle in the xy-plane and the solutions can be found as the intersections of this circle with the curve $x(y)$ obtained from eq. (31). This method was used by HONDROS and DEBYE [1910] in the particular case $n=0$. When x and y are known, the constants A, B, C, D are easily deduced from the boundary conditions and h is given by: $h^2 = \omega^2\mu\varepsilon_i - y^2/a^2$. All components of $\mathscr{E}$ and $\mathscr{H}$ are then completely determined.

6.2. DISCUSSION OF THE CHARACTERISTIC EQUATION

The characteristic equation (31) may be written, in the general case $n \neq 0$,

$$Y_n = -\tfrac{1}{2}(1+p)X_n \pm \left[\tfrac{1}{4}(1-p)^2 X_n^2 + n^2 \left(\frac{1}{y^2} + \frac{p}{x^2} \right)\left(\frac{1}{y^2} + \frac{1}{x^2} \right) \right]^{\frac{1}{2}}. \tag{33a}$$

If the two values of the right hand side corresponding to signs $+$ and $-$ are called f_+ and f_-, eq. (33a) becomes:

$$Y_n(y) = f_+(y, x) \quad \text{and} \quad Y_n(y) = f_-(y, x). \tag{33b}$$

There are thus two sets of solutions. We can obtain them as ABELE [1948] did by plotting on the same figure Y_n as a function of y, and f_+ and f_- as functions of y, x being considered as a parameter. The function $Y_n = J_n'(y)/yJ_n(y)$ becomes infinite for values of y which are roots of $J_n(y) = 0$ and are represented by $y_{n0} = 0$, y_{n1}, $y_{n2}, \ldots y_{nm} \ldots$. The function has an infinite number of branches (see fig. 9). All kinds of Bessel functions satisfy recurrence formulae *, from which Y_n may be written:

$$Y_n = \frac{n}{y^2} - \frac{J_{n+1}}{yJ_n} = \frac{J_{n-1}}{yJ_n} - \frac{n}{y^2}. \tag{34a}$$

For y included between 0 and the first root y_{n1} of $J_n(y) = 0$, J_{n+1}/yJ_n is certainly positive. Eq. (34a) shows therefore that the first branch of the curve Y_n is under the curve n/y^2 (see fig. 9).

---

* For more details on Bessel functions, see JAHNKE, EMDE and LÖSCH [1960]. The more useful properties are also given by SCHELKUNOFF [1943a] and SNITZER [1961a, appendix].

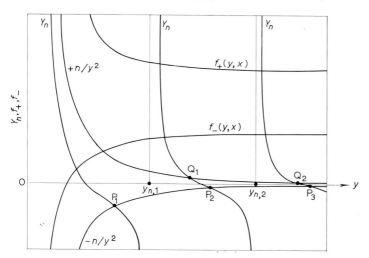

Fig. 9. Graphical solution of the characteristic equation (31) or (33a) from ABELE [1948] when $n>1$. $f_+(y,\,\infty)=+n/y^2$, $f_-(y,\,\infty)=-n/y^2$. The abscissae of Q_1, Q_2, ... Q_m are roots of $J_{n+1}(y)=0$. The abscissae of P_1, P_2, ... P_m are roots of $J_{n-1}(y)=0$. The asymptotes of the different branches of curve Y_n intersect the y-axis at points of abscissae $y_{n0}=C$, y_{n1}, y_{n2}, ... y_{nm}, roots of $J_n(y)=0$.

As the curve Y_n is composed of branches, for a given x and given n, we shall find two infinite sets of values of y which satisfy eq. (31). The corresponding modes are distinguished by the notation $\mathrm{EH}_{n,\,m}(Y_n=f_+)$ or $\mathrm{HE}_{n,\,m}(Y_n=f_-)$, where the integer m is different for the different branches of Y_n. This mode designation is the one suggested by SNITZER [1961a]. We now want to find out how the points of intersection of the curve Y_n with the curves f_+ and f_- vary when x varies from 0 to $+\infty$. For that purpose we need some knowledge about the behavior of the function X_n. From recurrence formulae $-X_n$ may be written

$$-X_n = \frac{n}{x^2} + \frac{K_{n-1}}{xK_n}.\tag{34b}$$

The function $-X_n$ is positive, monotonically decreasing when x varies from 0 to $+\infty$.

(a)   When $x\to+\infty$, $\dfrac{K_{n-1}}{K_n}\to 1$ and $-X_n\to 0,$ (35)

(b)   When $x\to 0$, $\dfrac{K_{n-1}}{xK_n}\to\dfrac{1}{2(n-1)}$ if $n>1,$ (36a)

$$\frac{K_0}{xK_1}\to\log(2/\gamma x)\quad\text{if}\quad n=1,\tag{36b}$$

where $\gamma=1.781$ is the Euler constant. Therefore when $x\to 0$, in any case $-X_n\to+\infty$.

Furthermore, it is possible to show that the derivatives with respect to x of f_+ and f_- are both negative for any value of y and for realistic values of p not close to zero. This means that, when x decreases from $+\infty$ to zero, both curves f_+ and f_- are going up continuously, and that x and y decrease together. Let us first concentrate on the set of solutions $Y_n = f_+$. When x becomes infinitely large, X_n approaches zero, and

$$f_+(y, \infty) \to n/y^2. \tag{37a}$$

From eqs. (34a), (37a) we see that the abscissae of $Q_1, Q_2, \ldots Q_m$, points of intersection of curves $Y_n(y)$ and $f_+(y, \infty)$, are roots of $J_{n+1}(y) = 0$ (denoted by $y_{n+1,1}$, $y_{n+1,2}, \ldots y_{n+1,m}$). We note (see fig. 9) that Q_1 is located on the second branch of Y_n. When x approaches zero, $-X_n$ becomes infinitely large positive, and f_+, which is the sum of two infinitely large positive quantities, approaches infinity regardless of the value of y. Thus, the curve f_+ goes continually up as x decreases from $+\infty$. The corresponding points of intersection of the curve f_+ with the curve Y_n go up the different branches of Y_n (the first branch excluded), starting from $Q_1, Q_2, \ldots Q_m$.

When $x \to 0$, their abscissae approach the roots of $J_n(y) = 0$ (the root zero being of course excluded). From these results, it is possible to draw roughly now, for the EH-modes, the curve $x(y)$ (see fig. 10).

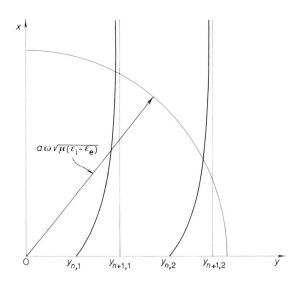

Fig. 10. EH$_{nm}$-modes for given values of n and of $p = \varepsilon_e/\varepsilon_1$. $y_{n+1,1}, y_{n+1,2}, \ldots y_{n+1,m}$ are roots of $J_{n+1}(y) = 0$. When $p = \varepsilon_e/\varepsilon_1$ varies, the curves vary slightly but the values of y for $x=0$ or $x \to \infty$ remain the same. The figure may also represent the TM$_{0m}$- or TE$_{0m}$-modes.

Turning now to the set of solutions $Y_n = f_-$, we see that for large x,

$$f_-(y, \infty) \to -n/y^2, \tag{37b}$$

and from eqs. (34a), (37b) the abscissae of the points $P_1, P_2, \ldots P_m$ of intersection of Y_n and $f_-(y, \infty)$ are seen to the be roots of $J_{n-1}(y) = 0$, which we denote

$y_{n-1,1}, y_{n-1,2}, \ldots y_{n-1,m}$. We note that point P_1 is located on the first branch of Y_n.

On the other hand, when x approaches zero, f_- is the difference between two infinitely large positive quantities, and to find its limit when $x\to0$ we replace in it X_n by an equivalent expression. From eqs. (36a) and (36b) the cases $n>1$ and $n=1$ are different.

If $n>1$, from eqs. (34b) and (36a) we have $-X_n\to n/x^2+1/2(n-1)$ when $x\to0$, which leads to

$$f_-(y, 0) = -\frac{n}{y^2} + \frac{p}{(n-1)(1+p)}. \tag{38}$$

This expression shows that, unlike curve f_+, curve f_- moves very little when x varies and remains close to curve $-n/y^2$. From eq. (34a) the equality $Y_n(y)=f_-(y, 0)$ leads to

$$\frac{J_{n-1}}{yJ_n} = \frac{p}{(n-1)(1+p)} = \frac{\varepsilon_e}{(n-1)(\varepsilon_i+\varepsilon_e)},$$

or, alternatively   (39)

$$\frac{yJ_{n-2}}{J_{n-1}} = -(n-1)\frac{\varepsilon_i-\varepsilon_e}{\varepsilon_e}.$$

We call $u_{n1}, u_{n2}, \ldots u_{nm}$ the values of y which satisfy eq. (39). The corresponding curves $x(y)$ are qualitatively drawn on fig. 11.

If $n=1$, from eqs. (34b), (36b), we have $-X_n\to1/x^2+\log(2/\gamma x)$ when $x\to0$, and $f_-(y, 0)$ is given by

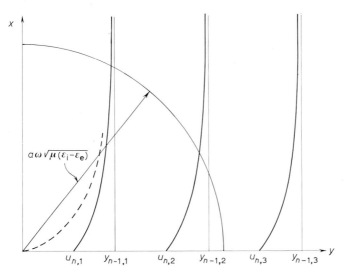

Fig. 11. HE$_{nm}$-modes for given values of n and of $p=\varepsilon_e/\varepsilon_i$, $y_{n-1,1}, y_{n-1,2}, \ldots y_{n-1,m}$ are roots of $J_{n-1}(y)=0$. When $n>1$, $u_{n1}, u_{n2}, \ldots u_{nm}$ are roots of eq. (39) and depend upon p. When $n=1$, $u_{11}=0$, $u_{12}, u_{13}, \ldots u_{1m}$ are roots of $J_1(y)=0$.

$$f_-(y, 0) = -\frac{1}{y^2} + \frac{p}{1+p} \log \frac{2}{\gamma x}.$$

This expression approaches infinity regardless of the value of y. Curve $f_-(y, x)$ then, as curve $f_+(y, x)$, goes continually up as x decreases from $+\infty$ to zero. Correspondingly its points of intersection with curve $Y_1(y)$ starting from $P_1, P_2, \ldots P_m$, go up the different branches of Y_1 (*including the first one*) and their abscissae tend for x infinitely large, to roots of $J_1(y)=0$, *including the root zero*. We call them $u_{11}=y_{10}=0$, $u_{12}=y_{11}=3.83$, $u_{13}=y_{12}=7.02$. The corresponding curves $x(y)$ are again qualitatively represented by fig. 11 with the notable difference that the first branch starts exactly at the origin (dotted line).

There remains to examine another special case, which has up to now been left aside, that is $n=0$. This case has been studied directly by HONDROS and DEBYE [1910]. They found that eq. (31) is replaced by

$$Y_n + pX_n = 0 \qquad \text{for the TM-modes,}$$
$$Y_n + X_n = 0 \qquad \text{for the TE-modes.}$$

These equations are in agreement with eq. (31) in which $n=0$. They showed that in both cases, for large x, y approaches one of the set of values $y_{11}, y_{12}, \ldots y_{1m}$, roots of $J_1(y)=0$. For small x, y approaches one of the set of values $y_{01}, y_{02}, \ldots y_{0m}$, roots of $J_0(y)=0$. The corresponding curves $x(y)$ may be quantitatively represented by those of fig. 10, the subscript n being replaced by zero.

At this point, we have completed our main task, which was to determine the important features of the function $x(y)$ defined in implicit form by eq. (31). As mentioned before, for any given value of ω the solution of the problem will be completed by taking the intersections of a circle centred on the origin and of radius $a\omega\mu^{\frac{1}{2}}(\varepsilon_i - \varepsilon_e)^{\frac{1}{2}}$ with the curves of fig. 10 (EH-modes) or fig. 11 (HE-modes); fig. 10 shows that the mode EH_{nm} exists only if the radius is larger than y_{nm}, i.e., if

$$\omega > \frac{y_{nm}}{a[\mu(\varepsilon_i - \varepsilon_e)]^{\frac{1}{2}}} \tag{40a}$$

and fig. 11 that the HE_{nm}-mode exists if

$$\omega > \frac{u_{nm}}{a[\mu(\varepsilon_i - \varepsilon_e)]^{\frac{1}{2}}}. \tag{40b}$$

For every mode, there is a cut-off frequency below which waves cannot be guided, with a remarkable exception corresponding to the fact that for $n=1$, the first branch of the curve on fig. 11 extends all the way to the origin. *The mode HE_{11} is very particular in that it has no cut-off frequency.*

The results displayed in figs. 10 and 11 for EH- and HE-modes at cut-off $(x=0)$ and far from cut-off $(x \to +\infty)$ are in full agreement with those given by SNITZER [1961a].

When ω increases from its cut-off value to $+\infty$ the radius of the circle on figs. 10, 11 increases, x varies from 0 to $+\infty$, y increases also, but for a given mode its range of variation is small. The fields inside the core are expressed in terms of y and their distribution varies only slightly from cut-off conditions ($x=0$) to conditions far from cut-off ($x \to +\infty$). The fields in the cladding on the other hand are expressed in terms of x. Their distribution varies then considerably. The function $K_n(k_e r) = K_n(xr/a)$, when r becomes very large, is equivalent to $(\exp k_e r)/(k_e r)^{\frac{1}{2}}$. When x is very large this function decreases very rapidly as r increases; the fields in the cladding extend to a very short distance beyond the radius a of the core. The energy is mostly confined to the core and strongly guided by it; h^2 is then equal to $\omega^2 \varepsilon_i \mu$, which means that the phase velocity is equal to light velocity in the core.

As x becomes smaller and smaller, $\exp(-k_e r)$ decreases more and more slowly for increasing r, the fields in the cladding extend to a larger and larger distance beyond the radius a of the core and the energy is only loosely guided by the core. In this case, h^2 approaches $\omega^2 \varepsilon_e \mu$, which means that the phase velocity approaches the velocity of light in the cladding.

It is interesting to note that eq. (40a) may be written in the form:

$$\lambda_c = \frac{2\pi a}{Y_{nm}} \left(\frac{\varepsilon_i - \varepsilon_e}{\varepsilon_0} \right)^{\frac{1}{2}},$$

where λ_c is the cut-off wavelength (in air) of the light entering the guide; $[(\varepsilon_i - \varepsilon_e)/\varepsilon_0]^{\frac{1}{2}}$ represents the 'numerical aperture' of the dielectric cylinder defined in eq. (1). If the numerical aperture is close to one, for low values of n and m, λ_c is of the order of $2a$, the diameter of the cross section. If the numerical aperture is 0.1, then λ_c is only $2a/10$.

6.3. FIELD DISTRIBUTIONS

We shall consider only the fields inside the core and give a simple example: the case of the TE_{02}-mode, in which, from eq. (23)

$$H_{zi} = BJ_0(k_i r) = BJ_0(yr/a), \qquad E_{zi} = 0.$$

The other components are deduced from eq. (20)

$$E_{\theta i} = \frac{jBa\omega\mu}{y} J_0'(yr/a), \qquad E_{ri} = 0$$

$$H_{ri} = \frac{-jBah}{y} J_0'(yr/a), \qquad H_{\theta i} = 0.$$

(a) Suppose first that ω is far above its cut-off value, then y is the second root of $J_1(y)=0$, i.e., $y_{12}=7.02$. $E_{\theta i}$ and H_{ri} are both plotted on fig. 12. They vary like $J_0'(yr/a)=J_1(yr/a)$ which is zero for $r=0$, for $yr/a=3.83$, and $yr/a=7.02$. H_z on the other hand is maximum or minimum when its derivative, i.e., when the transverse

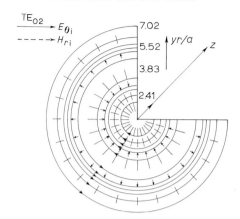

Fig. 12. Field plot in cross section of the core for the TE_{02}-mode far from cut-off. 2.41 and 5.52 are roots of $J_0(y) = 0$, 3.83 and 7.02 are roots of $J_1(y) = J_0'(y) = 0$.

components are zero. Along a radius H_z passes twice through zero with a change of sign for $yr/a = 2.41$ and for $yr/a = 5.52$. This mode is very similar to the TE_{02}-mode in a waveguide with metallic walls.

(b) When ω decreases and tends towards its cut-off value, the field distribution varies progressively and, at cut-off, y takes the value $y_{02} = 5.52$, the second root of $J_0(y) = 0$. There is a change of scale for yr/a so that now, on the wall, $yr/a = 5.52$ instead of 7.02. On the wall H_z is then zero but the transverse components are not.

To find the true field components, we must now multiply H_{zi}, $E_{\theta i}$, H_{zi} by the factor $\exp j(\omega t - hz)$. The distribution shown on fig. 12 is propagated along the z-axis with a phase velocity $v = \omega/h$.

In the general case, for $n \neq 0$, the field distribution shows no circular symmetry and becomes more and more complicated as n and m increase. For the HE_{11}-mode, the distribution is symmetrical with respect to a longitudinal plane passing through the z-axis, and its transverse electric field resembles that of a TM_{11}-mode inside a circular guide with metallic walls.*

The experiments performed by SNITZER and OSTERBERG [1961] and SNITZER [1961b] with visible light are in good agreement with the theory. We shall not attempt to describe the experiments here but shall only mention that, if the illumination on the entrance face of the fiber shows circular symmetry, the superposition of identical modes with different ϕ_n (see eqs. 23) gives on the exit face of the fiber a pattern which also shows circular symmetry. In the case of the mode HE_{11}, the illuminance decreases continuously from the center to the wall and for these conditions, the exit face of a single fiber of small diameter can be used as a nearly ideal point source (SNITZER [1961b]).

As the fiber diameter $2a$ increases, the radius of the circle on figs. 10, 11 and the number of possible modes increase also, and the superposition of many modes

* *Note added in proof:* Previous work has shown only those models which are capable of propagating, but SNYDER [1966] shows which modes are actually launched under a particular excitation.

generally gives a uniform illuminance on the exit face. It becomes difficult then, though not impossible, to excite single modes, that is why with visible light and fibers around 10 μm diameter the waveguide effects are generally not visible.

From a practical point of view a dielectric structure has limited applicability as a waveguide. A dielectric guide of finite length is susceptible to considerable radiation loss when it is mismatched at the input and output ends, when it is curved, or when conducting bodies are near it (see CHANDLER [1949]). Dielectric rods and tubes are used principally as radiators (KIELY [1953]).

In a fiber bundle, if a mode is excited in one single fiber, the energy may penetrate far enough in the cladding to reach another fiber core, The penetration increases when the frequency approaches cut-off but the same frequency may be far from cut-off for one mode and close to cut-off for another mode; different modes therefore behave differently and independently. There may be important coupling between the different fibers, the field distribution inside one fiber being affected by the field distribution in other fibers. This 'cross talk' has been studied in detail by SNITZER [1961b].

6.4. SUMMARY

The field distributions in the core and in the cladding have been determined, by assuming that the fields $\mathscr{E}$ and $\mathscr{H}$, (a) are propagated along the z-axis of a cylinder, (b) satisfy the Maxwell equations, (c) satisfy the boundary conditions.

(a) The fields $\mathscr{E}$ and $\mathscr{H}$ propagated along the z-axis may be written in the form:

$$\mathscr{E}(r, \theta, z) = E(r, \theta) \exp j(\omega t - hz),$$

$$\mathscr{H}(r, \theta, z) = H(r, \theta) \exp j(\omega t - hz).$$

(b) As a consequence of the Maxwell equations, the transverse components of E and H may be written in terms of the z-components E_z and H_z, as shown by eq. (20). The problem is thus reduced to finding E_z and H_z, which are given by:

$$E_{zi} = A\,J_n(yr/a)\cos n\theta \qquad E_{ze} = C\,K_n(xr/a)\cos n\theta$$
$$\text{and}$$
$$H_{zi} = B\,J_n(yr/a)\sin n\theta \qquad H_{ze} = D\,K_n(xr/a)\sin n\theta$$

in the core   in the cladding

A, B, C, D are constants, n is an integer. The quantities $\cos n\theta$ and $\sin n\theta$ may be interchanged. It appears immediately that if $n=0$, the field distribution shows circular symmetry and is either transverse electric (TE) or transverse magnetic (TM). In the general case $n \neq 0$, both E and H have a z-component and the corresponding modes are 'hybrid'. The quantities x and y are related by eq. (32) which is represented on figs. 10, 11 by a circle centered on O, with a radius proportional to the frequency $\omega/2\pi$.

(c) The boundary conditions result in eq. (31) which is another relation between x and y and gives two possible expressions for the function $x(y)$. Both of them depend upon the parameters n and $p = \varepsilon_e/\varepsilon_i$, the ratio of the dielectric constants of the cladding and the core. Both of them are represented on figs. 10, 11 and show an infinite number of branches designated as branches $1, 2, 3, \ldots, m \ldots$. For a given value of the frequency $\omega/2\pi$, the pairs of values of x and y are the coordinates of the points of intersection of the circle with the two curves $x(y)$. There are two sets of them, to which correspond two sets of modes, the EH_{nm}-modes (fig. 10) and the HE_{nm}-modes (fig. 11). The figures show clearly that a given mode, characterized by the subscripts n and m, exists only if the radius of the circle is larger than the value of y associated with $x=0$ for that mode. In other words, there is a cut-off frequency below which the mode cannot exist, as shown by eqs. (40a), (40b). For the HE_{11}-mode, the cut-off frequency is zero. When x and y are known, quantities proportional to the constants A, B, C, D are easily deduced from the boundary conditions and the propagation constant h is given by:

$$h^2 = \omega^2 \mu \varepsilon_i - y^2/a^2 = \omega^2 \mu \varepsilon_e + x^2/a^2.$$

All components of $\mathscr{E}$ and $\mathscr{H}$ are then determined. As an example, the fields have been plotted (see fig. 12) for the case $n=0$.

Acknowledgements

Mrs. E. J. Weichel–Moore has contributed a great deal to this work through her constructive review of this chapter. Also we wish to thank J. W. Hicks, W. P. Siegmund and E. Snitzer for their critical reading of the manuscript.

References

ABELE, M., 1948, Nuovo Cimento **5**, 274.

BORN, M. and E. WOLF, 1959, Principles of optics (Pergamon Press, London) pp. 39–40.

CAPELLARO, D. P., 1963, Optical systems using fiber optics, *in*: H. J. Merrill, ed., Light and heat sensing, 6th AGARD avionics panel meeting, Paris, 1962 (Pergamon Press, London, and MacMillan, New York) pp. 311–324.

CHANDLER, C. H., 1949, J. Appl. Phys. **20**, 1188.

DROUGARD, R., 1964, J. Opt. Soc. Am. **54**, 907

HOPKINS, H. H. and N. S. KAPANY, 1954, Nature **173**, 39.

HONDROS, D. and P. DEBEYE, 1910, Ann. Physik **32**, 465.

JAHNKE, E., F. EMDE and F. LÖSCH, 1960. Tables of higher functions, 6th ed. (McGraw-Hill, New York), and Teubner, Stuttgart) p. 131.

KAPANY, N. S., 1958, Appendix N, *in*: J. Strong, ed., Concepts of classical optics (Freeman, San Francisco) pp. 553–579.

KAPANY, N. S., 1959a, J. Opt. Soc. Am. **49**, 770.

KAPANY, N. S., 1959b, J. Opt. Soc. Am. **49**, 779.

KAPANY, N. S., 1960, Opt. Acta **7**, 210.

KAPANY, N. S., 1965, Japan J. Appl. Phys. **4**, Suppl. 1, pp. 312–322.

KAPANY, N. S. and J. CAPELLARO, 1961, J. Opt. Soc. Am. **51**, 23.

KAPANY, N. S., J. A. EYER and R. E. KLEIM, 1957, J. Opt. Soc. Am. **47**, 423.

KAPANY, N. S. and R. E. HOPKINS, 1957, J. Opt Soc. Am. **47**, 594.

KAPANY, N. S. and R. J. SIMMS, 1965, Infrared Phys. **5**, 69.

KIELY, D. G., 1953, Dielectric aerials (Methuen, London, and J. Wiley, New York).

KOESTER, C. J., 1963, Some properties of fiber optics and lasers, *in*: D. K. Pollack, C. J. Koester and J. T. Tippet, eds., Optical processing of information, Washington, 1962 (Spartan Books, Baltimore, and Cleaver-Hume Press, London) pp. 74–84.

KROLAK, L. J., 1963, Fiber optics in electro-optical devices, *in*: H. J. Merrill, ed., Light and heat sensing, 6th AGARD avionics panel meeting, Paris, 1962 (Pergamon Press, London, and MacMillan, New York) pp. 297–310.

O'BRIEN, B., 1958, U.S. Patent 2.825.260, issued 1958.

POLANYI, M. L. and R. M. HEHIR, 1962, Rev. Sci. Instr. **33**, 1050.

POTTER, R. J., 1961, J. Opt. Soc. Am. **51**, 1079.

POTTER, R. J., E. DONATH and R. TYNAN, 1963, J. Opt. Soc. Am. **53**, 256.

POTTER, R. J. and R. E. Hopkins, 1960, IRE Trans. Nucl. Sci. NS7, 150.

REVI, A. C., 1957, Glass Ind. **38**, 328.

REYNOLDS, G. T., 1960, IRE Trans. Nucl. Sci. NS7, 115.

REYNOLDS, G. T. and P. E. CONDON, 1957, Rev. Sci. Instr. **28**, 1098.

ROETLING, P. C. and W. P. GANLEY, 1962, J. Opt. Soc. Am. **52**, 99.

SCHELKUNOFF, S. A., 1943a, Electromagnetic waves (Van Nostrand, New York) ch. 3, pp. 44–51.

SCHELKUNOFF, S. A., 1943b, Electromagnetic waves (Van Nostrand, New York) ch. 10, pp. 425–428.

SIEGMUND, W. P., 1963, Fiber optics, *in*: H. J. Merrill, ed., Light and heat sensing, 6th AGARD avionics panel meeting, Paris, 1962 (Pergamon Press, London, and MacMillan, New York) pp. 265–296.

SNITZER, E., 1961a, J. Opt. Soc. Am. **51**, 491.

SNITZER, E., 1961b, Optical dielectric waveguides, *in*: J. R. Singer, ed., Advances in quantum electronics, 2nd Intern. Congr. Berkeley, 1961 (Columbia Univ. Press, New York) pp. 348–369.

SNITZER, E., 1964, Neodymium glass laser, *in*: P. Grivet and N. Boembergen, eds., Quantum electronics, Proc. 3rd Intern. Congr., Paris, 1963, vol. 2 (Dunond, Paris, and Columbia Univ. Press, New York) pp. 999–1019.

SNITZER, E. and H. Osterberg, 1961. J. Opt. Soc. Am. **51**, 499.

SNYDER, A. W., 1966, J. Opt. Soc. Am. **56**, 601.

STAHL, W. and R. J. POTTER, 1966, Appl. Opt. **5**, 1203.

TORALDO DI FRANCIA, G., 1956, Electromagnetic waves (Interscience, New York) pp. 258–259. Translated from Italian: Onde elettromagnetiche (1953, Nicola Zanichelli, Bologna).

VAN HEEL, A. C. S., 1953, Ingenieur **65**, 25.

VAN HEEL, A. C. S., 1954, Nature **173**, 39.

CHAPTER 12

A PRECISION INTERFEROMETER

WITH HIGH LIGHT-GATHERING POWER

A. MARÉCHAL, P. LOSTIS AND J. SIMON

Institut d'Optique de Paris

CONTENTS

1. Introduction

ZERNIKE [1950] has shown how, by replacing the two slits in Young's classical experiment by three slits, F_0, F_1, F_2 (fig. 1) one can obtain very great sensitivity for detecting slight changes in the central optical path (through F_0) relative to the mean of the lateral optical paths (through the slits F_1 and F_2). He demonstrated the possibility of detecting optical path changes of order $10^{-3}\lambda$ by visual observation. Unfortunately the original Zernike system has low luminosity or light-gathering power, because it is necessary to use a very narrow entrance slit. We shall show that this slit can be replaced by a suitably arranged periodic structure illuminated by an extended source without affecting the sensitivity of the system; thus the high sensitivity is retained but the luminosity is improved.

The apparatus is generally suitable for detecting slight changes in the central optical path with respect to the lateral paths. In particular, its geometry is well adapted for measuring the curvature of an optical surface (it is thus a three-beam spherometer), and for refractometry and thickness measurement of thin films. Examples of these applications will be given.

2. Zernike's experiment

In the very important experiment of Zernike the three slits F_0, F_1, F_2 are equidistant and have the same width; they are illuminated by coherent light from a plane wave originating at a single source S (fig. 1). In the plane of the image S' of the slit S

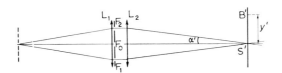

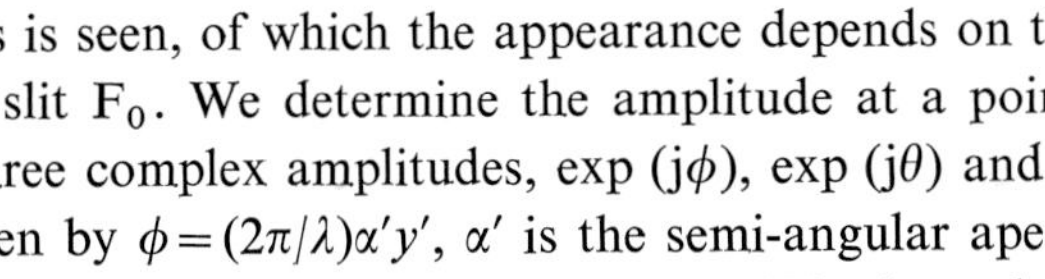

Fig. 1. Apparatus with a slit source.

a system of fringes is seen, of which the appearance depends on the phase change θ introduced at the slit F_0. We determine the amplitude at a point B' of the plane of S' by adding three complex amplitudes, exp ($j\phi$), exp ($j\theta$) and exp ($-j\phi$), where the phase ϕ is given by $\phi=(2\pi/\lambda)\alpha'y'$, α' is the semi-angular aperture of the pencil in image space and y' is the lateral displacement. We thus obtain

$$A(\phi) = \exp(j\phi)+\exp(-j\phi)+\exp(j\theta)$$
$$= 2\cos\phi+\cos\theta+j\sin\theta.$$

The intensity distribution in the plane of S' is given by

$$I(\phi)/I(0) = 1+4\cos^2\phi+4\cos\phi\cos\theta.$$

Fig. 2. shows this fringe distribution in three particular cases. Considering fig. 2c, if ε can be compensated by any means, as for example by a change of focus, we again

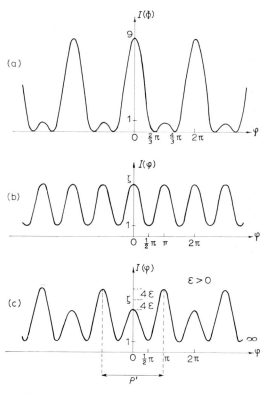

Fig. 2. Light distribution in the plane of S' due to phase change θ at the slit F_0;

(a) $\theta = 0$, $I(\phi) = (1 + 2 \cos \phi)^2$

(b) $\theta = \frac{1}{2}\pi$, $I(\phi) = 1 + 4 \cos^2 \phi$

(c) $\theta = \frac{1}{2}\pi + \varepsilon$ $(\varepsilon \ll \pi)$, $I(\phi) = 1 + 4 \cos^2 \phi - 4\varepsilon \cos \phi$

obtain fringes as in fig. 2b, where the maxima are equal; in this way ε can be measured. The assessment of equality of the maxima can be done visually with a precision of order 5 Å but the illumination is very low because the source must be a very narrow slit.

3. Use of an incoherently illuminated periodic object

In order to obtain more light but with similar precision we now replace the slit source S by a periodic object, such as a Foucault grating, illuminated incoherently. The aim is to superimpose the fringe systems formed by each of the slits in the Foucault grating. This will occur if the period p of the Foucault grating is such that its geometrical image has a period $p' = pg$ (where g is the geometrical magnification) exactly equal to the period of the fringes produced by a single element of the grating. In this way the incoherent images which are modulated with the same period are superimposed.

To determine the image of the grating formed by three slits (fig. 3) we use some general theorems on the formation of images in incoherent illumination derived from Fourier transform theory (MARÉCHAL and FRANÇON [1960]).

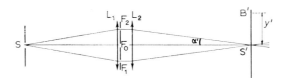

Fig. 3. Apparatus with a grating in the object plane.

It is known that, if $O(y)$, $D(y')$ and $I(y)$ are functions representing respectively the object, the image of a single point source and the image of the object under consideration, then I can be expressed as a convolution between O and D:

$$I = O \otimes D.$$

This can be very simply expressed by Fourier transform theory by the following equation, in which i, o and d are the transforms of I, O and D:

$$i = o \cdot d.$$

This implies that the instrument behaves as a filter of spatial frequencies and is characterized by the function d, which is known as the contrast transfer function. It can also be shown that d is the auto-correlation function of the complex amplitude distribution in the pupil when a point source is placed at the centre of the field. The final image is thus obtained as indicated in fig. 4, where at (a) is shown the 'spectrum' $o(\mu)$ of the object (a Foucault grating) as a function of the spatial frequency μ; fig. 4b shows the transfer function $d(\mu)$, which is equal to the auto-correlation function of the three-slit pupil, the amplitudes in the slits being respectively unity, $\exp(j\theta)$ and unity; fig. 4c shows the 'spectrum' of the image, which reduces substantially to the three frequencies $-1/p'$, 0, $1/p'$. Thus we have for the final image:

$$I(y') = I_0[1 + \tfrac{8}{3\pi} \cos \theta \cos (2\pi y'/p')].$$

Depending on the magnitude of the phase change θ introduced at the slit F_0 the following kinds of fringe system are obtained:

$\theta = 0$	$I(y') = I_0[1 + \tfrac{8}{3\pi} \cos (2\pi y'/p')]$	sinusoidal fringes,
$\theta = \tfrac{1}{2}\pi$	$I(y') = I_0$	no fringes,
$\theta = \tfrac{1}{2}\pi + \varepsilon$	$I(y') = I_0[1 - \tfrac{8}{3\pi} \cos (2\pi y'/p')]$	sinusoidal fringes with low modulation,
$\theta = \pi$	$I(y') = I_0[1 - \tfrac{8}{\pi} \cos (2\pi y'/p')]$	sinusoidal fringes like those for $\theta = 0$ except for a linear shift.

Among other ways, this phase change θ can be introduced by a change of focus from the true optical image (defined by equality of the two optical paths). If x is the longitudinal displacement from the focus, θ is given by

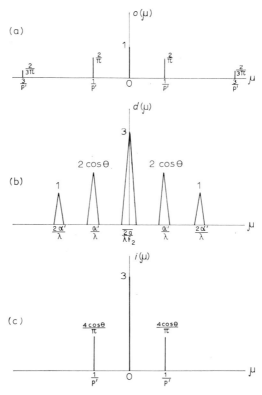

Fig. 4. (a) Fourier transform of the object grating, (b) transfer function of the three-slit pupil for phase change θ at the slit F_0, (c) Fourier transform of the image.

$$\theta = \pi\alpha'^2 x/\lambda.$$

The angle α' is generally small, so that the corresponding displacements are relatively large and easily measured accurately; thus very small phase changes can be precisely measured.

4. Effect of absorption in the specimen

We denote by A^2 the attenuation of the incident flux of reflection at or transmission by the specimen to be measured; let ϕ_1, ϕ_0 and ϕ_2 be the phases at the slits F_1, F_0 and F_2. We now give the normalized intensity distributions in the image, $I(y')/(I(0))$, for different positions of the specimen in relation to the three slits, taking account of the factor A. We omit details of the computation since the method is exactly as above.

(a) If the specimen is placed in front of the central slit:

$$\frac{I(y')}{I(0)} = 1 + \frac{4A}{\pi(2+A^2)}\left[\cos\left(\frac{2\pi y'}{p'} + \phi_0 - \phi_1\right) + \cos\left(\frac{2\pi y'}{p'} + \phi_2 - \phi_0\right)\right].$$

(b) If the specimen is placed in front of one of the outer slits, say F_2:

$$\frac{I(y')}{I(0)} = 1 + \frac{4A}{\pi(2+A^2)} \left[\cos\left(\frac{2\pi y'}{p'} + \phi_0 - \phi_1\right) + A\cos\left(\frac{2\pi y'}{p'} + \phi_2 - \phi_0\right) \right].$$

(c) If the specimen is placed in front of two adjacent slits, say F_0 and F_2:

$$\frac{I(y')}{I(0)} = 1 + \frac{4A}{\pi(1+2A^2)} \left[\cos\left(\frac{2\pi y'}{p'} + \phi_0 - \phi_1\right) + A\cos\left(\frac{2\pi y'}{p'} + \phi_2 - \phi_0\right) \right].$$

(d) If the specimen covers all three slits we obtain the result already stated, apart from the factor A^2:

$$\frac{I(y')}{A^2 I(0)} = 1 + \frac{4}{3\pi} \left[\cos\left(\frac{2\pi y'}{p'} = \phi_0 - \phi_1\right) + \cos\left(\frac{2\pi y'}{p'} + \phi_2 - \phi_0\right) \right].$$

In all these cases it is possible to compensate the phase change due to the specimen by a change of focus, as before; this produces a phase change $-\theta$ at the central slit F_0 and the original fringe system used as reference is regained. This changes ϕ_0 into $\phi_0 - \theta$ in the expressions above; we thus obtain the following equation relating θ to the phase change introduced by the specimen:

$$\theta = \phi_0' - \tfrac{1}{2}(\phi_1' + \phi_2'),$$

where ϕ_0, ϕ_1' and ϕ_2' are the phase changes produced at the three slits when the specimen is introduced. This is valid only if the reference condition used is either that of equal contrast of the two fringe systems or maximum or zero contrast.

Thus we conclude that the method is equally applicable whether the specimen produces attenuation by reflection or transmission and irrespective of the position of the specimen relative to the slits; however, the greatest precision is usually obtained when it is opposite the central slit.

5. The gain in luminosity of the light signal

We now consider the gain in luminosity of the three-slit system when the single object slit is replaced by a grating; we shall also consider the possibility of using a grating at the image plane. We take separately the two cases in which the light is received by the eye or by a physical detector.

For simplicity we suppose the slit source to be the same length (in the appropriate space) as the grating structure under consideration. Then the light distribution in the image of an infinitely narrow source formed by a three-slit pupil with slits of angular width $2h'$ is given by

$$\frac{I(\phi)}{I(0)} = \left(\frac{\sin\Delta\varphi}{\Delta\varphi}\right)^2 (1 + 4\cos^2\phi + 4\cos\phi\cos\theta)$$

with $\Delta\varphi = 2\pi h' y'/\lambda$ and $\phi = 2\pi\alpha' y'/\lambda$.

If the object grating consists of n_1 identical slits the gain g_1 over the original

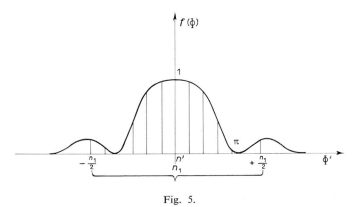

Fig. 5.

system is obviously equal to the sum of the vertical line elements in fig. 5. Thus

$$g_1 = \sum_{-\frac{1}{2}n_1}^{\frac{1}{2}n_1} \left(\frac{\sin \Delta\varphi_j}{\Delta\varphi_j}\right)^2 \quad \text{with} \quad \varphi_j = 2j\pi h' p'/\lambda$$

If the image of the grating is to be analyzed by a grating of n_2 lines with $n_2 < n_1$, the gain g_2 is given by $n_2 g_1$, so that

$$g_2 = n_2 \sum_{-\frac{1}{2}n_1}^{\frac{1}{2}n_1} \left(\frac{\sin \Delta\varphi_j}{\Delta\varphi_j}\right)^2.$$

Obviously, if the image grating is to be used away from the true focal plane a telecentric optical system must be used.

5.1. THE EYE AS DETECTOR

The use of the interferometer in incoherent light produces a gain in luminosity g_1: however, the following precautions must be taken to ensure the required precision; (a) the observing instrument must have a magnifaction sufficiently large to render negligible the effect of the power of accommodation of the eye;

(b) two gratings displaced in depth should be used (SIMON [1961]), forming a precise reference or match-point for focussing by the criterion of equality of contrast of the fringe systems covering the areas of the two gratings. The maximum sensitivity is obtained for a distance between the two gratings such that at the position of equal contrasts this contrast is just greater than the minimum perceptible; then a slight

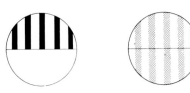

Fig. 6.

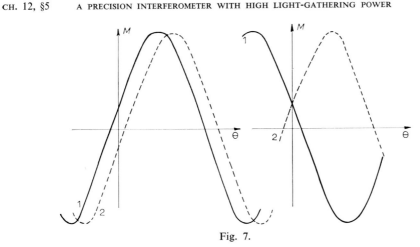

Fig. 7.

phase change caused by a change of focus will cause the fringes to vanish in one area and to increase in contrast in the other, as in fig. 6. There are two possible ways in which the required relative displacement of the gratings can be arranged, as shown in fig. 7.

5.2. USE OF A PHYSICAL DETECTOR

In this case, in order to analyze the image by means of either a slit (gain g_1) or a grating (gain g_2) it is necessary to be able to translate the image grating or slit relative to the detector. As in the case of the eye, it is desirable to use the criterion of equality of modulation. This can be done by presenting to the same detector sequentially in time the light signals 1 and 2 of fig. 7, each for accurately constant periods. The electrical signal produced by the detector will then be as in fig. 8. Such a signal is

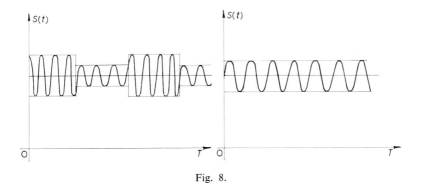

Fig. 8.

easily handled by a synchronous rectifier, which system also makes it conveniently possible to determine whether the true match position is in front of or behind the plane of focus.

6. The apparatus as constructed

We used two gratings M (fig. 9), each covering half the field and displaced longitudinally with respect to the focus f_1 of the objective O_1; this relative displacement is pre-set for optimum conditions as explained above. The two gratings can be il-

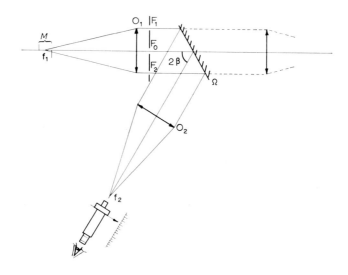

Fig. 9.

luminated incoherently in either white or monochromatic light. In the image space, near the focus f_2 of the objective O_2, the effects shown in fig. 7 can be observed by means of a microscope; the position of the microscope can be measured for each focal setting.

The phase change is determined in this way only *modulo* π; to eliminate this indeterminacy we use Young's two-slit method by masking the central slit and placing the sample in front of one of the outer slits; we then find the position of the achromatic fringe. In some cases it has been necessary to use other interference methods to determine the integral multiple of π in the phase change produced by the sample.

The relation between θ and x can be found by measuring the distance x_0 between two consecutive match-points.

From the distance x between the settings made before and after the introduction of the specimen we can obtain the following expression for the fractional part of the phase change:

$$\theta = x\pi/x_0 = \phi_0' - \tfrac{1}{2}(\phi_1' + \phi_2').$$

With the apparatus built at the Institut d'Optique (fig. 10) it is possible to measure path differences at varying angles of incidence in either reflection or transmission. The setting can be made to 0.01 mm, which corresponds to a precision of 3 Å.

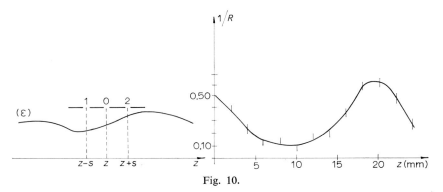

Fig. 10.

7. Some applications of the interferometer

The technique has been applied to the measurement of varying curvature of a substrate, the measurement of thickness of thin films and the measurement of refractive index differences in solids and liquids.

7.1. MEASUREMENT OF VARYING CURVATURE OF A SUBSTRATE

The measurement is carried out by placing the uncoated substrate in front of the three slits (fig. 11). We measure at each position of the substrate the difference between the phase at the central slit and the mean of the phases at the other slits, so for slowly varying ϕ the result is

$$\theta = \phi_0 - \tfrac{1}{2}(\phi_1 + \phi_2) = \phi(z) - \tfrac{1}{2}[\phi(z-s) + \phi(z+s)] \approx \tfrac{1}{2}s^2\phi''(z).$$

Thus we obtain directly the second derivative, i.e. the curvature. It can be seen that small rotations of the substrate do not affect the measurements. Fig. 12 shows the variation of curvature $1/R$, where R is in kilometres, of a silica plate as a function of the abscissa z.

7.2. MEASUREMENT OF THE PHASE CHANGE DUE TO A THIN FILM]

A thin film is characterized by its refractive index and its metrical thickness d. By means of the three-slit method we can measure the phase change relative to the substrate both in reflection and in transmission. For this purpose the film is deposited over only part of the substrate; thus we measure the relative phase change between film and substrate and then by covering the whole with an opaque metal film we can measure the metrical thickness of the film.

To eliminate the effect of irregularities of figure of the substrate we measure in the same regions of the substrate before and after deposition of the film. We measure the phase change due to the substrate first with the three slits opposite the full area and then with one or the other overlapping the edge. If θ is the phase change corresponding to the metrical thickness we have in this case $\theta = 2\pi d/\lambda$.

We have compared the results obtained by this method with those from other interference techniques. In table 1, we give some measurements made on films of thicknesses ranging through some hundreds of ångströms (Lostis [1964]).

TABLE 1

Three-slit method		Other methods	
$d(\text{Å})$	Δd	$d(\text{Å})$	Δd
236	±3	239	±7
707	±6	695	±9
873	±7	870	±7
1220	±12	1216	±10

7.3. MEASUREMENT OF DIFFERENCES IN REFRACTIVE INDEX

The three-slit method is also well suited for problems of refractometry of solids' liquids and gases. For example, it is possible to compare the refractive indices of two solid specimens, of a solid and a liquid, or other combinations.

For measurement of index differences in solids we obtained the results shown in table 2 for two sets of samples 2 mm thick in wavelength 5461 Å. Results from the Pulfrich method are given for comparison.

TABLE 2

	Pulfrich method		Three-slit method	
	$n'-n$	$\delta(n'-n)$	$n'-n$	$\delta(n'-n)$
First experiment	1×10^{-5}	$\pm 2 \times 10^{-5}$	1.1×10^{-5}	$\pm 10^{-6}$
Second experiment	7×10^{-5}	$\pm 2 \times 10^{-5}$	5.6×10^{-5}	$\pm 10^{-6}$

8. Conclusion

The interference method proposed enables high precision to be obtained in the measurement of phase changes; the samples can be slightly absorbing without loss of precision. The apparatus has high luminosity and the use of a physical detector in place of the eye gives additional advantages in the electrical processing of the signal.

References

Lostis, P., 1964, J. Phys. Radium **25**, 118.
Maréchal, A. et M. Françon, 1960, Diffraction, structure des images (Editions de la Revue d'Optique, Paris).
Simon, J., 1961, Rev. Opt. **40**, 213.
Zernike, F., 1950, J. Opt. Soc. Am. **40**, 326.

CHAPTER 13

ALIGNMENT

A. C. S. VAN HEEL†

(Technological University, Delft)

CONTENTS

1. Alignment and testing the flatness of large surfaces

Putting three or more points on a straight line is easily done by sighting: an illuminated hole is looked at through two other holes in series. Only when the three holes are on a straight line light is seen. It is inconvenient, that, before this state is reached, the observer is in the dark how to find the right position of the holes. Moreover, precision is not high, between 10 and 20 seconds of arc.

Therefore it is desirable to look out for other methods, presenting brighter patterns to the observer, and allowing determinations with better precision.

As telescopes have to be focussed for each distance, they are of no avail, when precision is aimed at. A lateral displacement of the eye piece of say 5 μm in a telescope of 30 cm length already gives rise to an error in the line of view mounting to 3 seconds of arc.

The parts of the observing telescopes need not be touched when a collimator is put into use. The combination of a collimator and a telescope is widely used for testing the straightness of the bed of lathes and the like. The collimator, resting on three feet of appropriate form on the surface to be tested, is placed in adjoining positions, thus covering the whole length step by step. For each position the measurement gives the mean slope.

The form of the bed is found by approximate integration, which can give rise to accumulation of errors. Deviations from straightness at intermediate points can furthermore easily stay undetected.

Ways of improving on these older procedures will be described below. Some of these, having been published elsewhere (VAN HEEL [1949, 1961, 1962], VAN HEEL and DE VEER [1962], DE VEER [1966]) will be treated only briefly.

2. Zone-plates

An adequate improvement on the sighting method is obtained by the use of zone-plates. The first 'point' of the three to be aligned is a small hole in a screen, illuminated by white or monochromatic light. The second point is the centre of a plate with a series of concentric alternately black and transparent rings, the zone-plate. The third point is a glass plate carrying an appropriate form of fiducial mark, e.g. two or more concentric circles.

The zone-plate produces a pattern of concentric circular rings. On account of diffraction the rings show more or less brilliant colours when white light is used. The black rings of the fiducial mark can be put concentrically with the rings of the pattern, and even with low magnifications (3 to 10 times) the precision is very high.

For differential measurements where only changes in the direction of alignment are of importance, the zone-plates may consist of plane-parallel glass plates with an aluminium coating in which the open zones are formed by scratching with a chisel on a lathe. For absolute alignments it seems better not to trust the parallelity and the homogeneity of a glass plate; it is preferable to form the zone-plate out of metallic rings held together by three or four spokes.

The thickness of the rings and the width of the open rings are not very important, provided the radii are not proportional to the square roots of the integers, as in that case there are foci, whose presence is undesirable; a smooth change of the pattern with the distance from the zone-plate is recommendable.

Observation of the pattern is preferably done by means of a lower power lens, a spectacle lens of say 8 dioptries being sufficient for most purposes. Its presence gives the additional advantage to screen off stray light by placing a stop in its back focus; see fig. 1, where the screen S with zone plate is imaged on the stop T. The aperture in T admits only light proceeding from the zone-plate. In this way it is possible to make observations in full daylight, even against a highly luminous background.

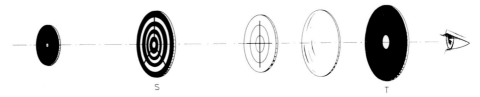

Fig. 1. Alignment with zone-plate.

The favourable spacing of the (equidistant) rings of the zone-plate depends on the distances a and b between the luminous hole and zone-plate and zone-plate and fiducial mark respectively. For a and b from 5 to 20 m a spacing of about 1 mm proves suitable. For smaller distances a proportionally smaller spacing is preferable. In order to give an impression of the precision that can be attained, we give an example in fig. 2. Here a and b were 2.46 and 1.60 m respectively, there were 16 equidistant

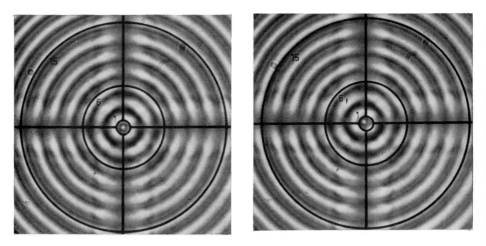

Fig. 2. Pattern produced by zone-plate; a) fiducial mark centred on pattern; b) not centred.

rings in the zone, the open rings had the same width as the black rings, the outer circle having a diameter of 23 mm. The black rings in the figure are produced by the fiducial mark. In fig. 2a the setting is practically perfect, in fig. 2b it is defective by 0.25 mm. This error corresponds to an error of 0.6 seconds of arc in the straightness of the three 'points' as defined above.

Under favourable circumstances a precision of 0.2 seconds of arc can be attained without too much trouble.

The diameter of the aperture which materializes the first 'point' needs some consideration. For patterns with good contrast it is necessary that the light incident on the zone-plate be coherent. With a diameter p of the zone-plate the diameter q of the aperture must for that reason not be greater than $a\lambda/2p$, where λ is the wave length of the light. Putting $\lambda = 0.56 \times 10^{-3}$ mm, we have $q = 0.28 \times 10^{-3} a/p$, all lengths expressed in mm. When $a = 10$ m and $p = 1$ cm, the upper limit of q is 0.28 mm; a larger aperture would impair contrast in the pattern, though observations can be made with q twice as large.

Precision is obtained with these simple means, because the eye is able to set the mark symmetrical to the pattern. It is well known this can be done with a very high precision.

For further details the reader is referred to DE HAAS [1953] where also the still simpler procedure with a *double slit* instead of the zone-plate is described. The diffraction lines are too far apart to practise the setting on symmetry. The setting is done on a colour transition in the pattern, giving the same precision.

By using two sets of double slits, perpendicular to one another, alignment in two dimensions can be achieved. Examples are given in VAN HEEL [1949] and DE HAAS [1953].

It is worth noting that with a set-up with zone-plate or double slit *no* extrapolation is made. Taking for instance the case that the second 'point' (the zone-plate) is to be put on a line with the first and third point, a vibration of 0.1 mm of the zone-plate gives an uncertainty in the alignment of only 2 seconds of arc, when $a = b = 10$ m. With the increase of the values of a and b, the *influence of vibration* is proportionally lowered.

A good example of the use of zone-plates is the transposition of the north-south line from the ground level to a level 500 m lower in a mining shaft (MOONEN [1955]). In the schematic drawing of fig. 3 the orientation of the line a is known. At A and B two illuminated holes admit light to the zone-plate at Z, somewhere at half the depth of the shaft. At the lower level a fiducial mark at C and another at D are put on the lines AZ and BZ respectively. The line b is parallel to a. The observations by Moonen performed with this method gave a precision for the orientation of 0.5 to 1 minute of arc, the depths varying from 150 to 500 m and with shaft diameters of 5 m. The ventilation gale was blowing during the observation, securing a good mixture of the air.

A more recent use of the method was the alignment of a section of 700 m for the ship's towing slope near Nivelles, south of Brussels. The distances in this case were so large that a helium-neon gas-laser was used as a light source. In this way the precision of below 0.5 second of arc could be reached. For the necessary correction of the deviations of the light path from straightness, deviations produced by the variation of temperature and barometric pressure, observations of temperature and pressure were made along the light path. The corrections then were readily found.

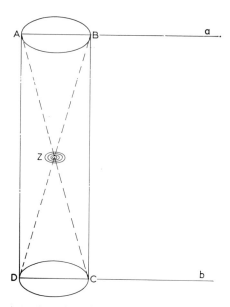

Fig. 3. Transferring orientation of line a at ground level to b in mining shaft.

In these applications and the like an important advantage is to be mentioned: even when alignment is not attained, the observer sees a part of the ring pattern and he is easily able to change the position of the third 'point' or to order by signals to adjust either the first or the second 'point'. This proved especially useful in noisy and untidy surroundings, like in a ship's hull under construction, in which the bearings of the main shaft have to be aligned.

The testing of an experimental runway at Schiphol Airport (Amsterdam) during burdening with a running motor lorry up to 100 tons, was done by means of build-in light sources, zone-plates and film camera's, each giving every half second a picture of the pattern, together with the fiducial mark (LIEM [1960]).

Evaluation of the nine film strips for the nine lines of observation showed that precision was between 0.1 and 0.2 seconds of arc, enabling the observers to calculate (in combination with observations with stress gauges) the influence of different underlayers.

Still another application is the placing of the many axes of machinery, like machines for the fabrication of paper and of asphalt-paper. These axes, lying in different levels, must be put in parallel positions. In some cases with 30 to 60 axes, placing was done in 4 to 6 nights. A long 'light line', produced by a zone-plate, was bent over 90° at the appropriate places by means of pentagon prisms.

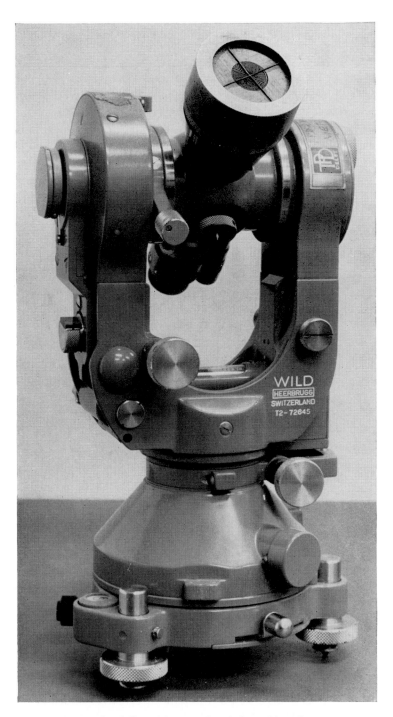

Fig. 4. Theodolite with zone-plate before object-glass.

3. Theodolite with zone-plate

The zone-plate can be used with advantage in conjunction with a theodolite for geodetic measurements. In the first place it is possible to point with utmost precision at points lying at different distances *without* touching the telescope, provided the points consist of illuminated small holes. By pushing the eyepieces well within the focus, all images will be unsharp. With a zone-plate mounted before the object-glass (fig. 4) all these blurred patches are adorned with coloured rings at which the fiducial mark can be adjusted in a most satisfactory manner.

Even for geodetic measurements of the highest order, where the objects are all at great distances, the zone-plate provides a useful means to attain the highest precision (REITZ [1963]). Moreover, in a hazy atmosphere the coloured pattern gives a better contrast to the grey background without zone-plate.

4. Axicon

Diffraction and the interference of diffracted light have thus proved to be helpful in alignment problems. Another way of making use of this help is described by Mc-LEOD [1954]. A well made conical surface on a glass plate, of which the other side is either flat or spherical, also gives rise to interference patterns that can be used for alignment; see fig. 5. The centres of the circular symmetrical patterns lie on the alignment line. The precision with which the centres can be set is very high and the

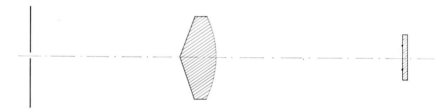

Fig. 5. Axicon.

brightness of the images is better than with zone-plates. It must be noted, however that the precision with which the optical piece, the *axicon*, is manufactured, determines the straightness of this line. Any small deviation, for instance, of the centre of curvature of the spherical surface from the axis of the conical surface impairs the trueness of this line.

5. Use of aberration

Satisfactory though it is that one of the bogeys of optical precision measurements, *diffraction*, is converted from enemy to ally, it appears that another bugbear, *aberration*, can also be put to our cart. In the methods described here the idea of no-extrapolation is dropped. The gain in brightness of the images and the possibility to test not only lines but also flat surfaces seems to justify their study.

Let us start with a wave front with axial symmetry, having no convergence or divergence on the axis, but curved by spherical aberration (fig. 6). With a point P on the axis as centre we imagine a sphere A, touching the wave front W along a circle QR. A number of similar spheres B, C, . . . is indicated, whose radii are smaller by amounts $\frac{1}{2}\lambda, \frac{2}{2}\lambda, \frac{3}{2}\lambda, \ldots$. In this way the circle through P is surrounded by zones having some similarity to Fresnel's zones. In practical cases the wave front can be represented by a surface of revolution whose meridian curve is of pure fourth degree. It can easily be shown that the wave front lies on one side of the sphere, as in fig. 6.

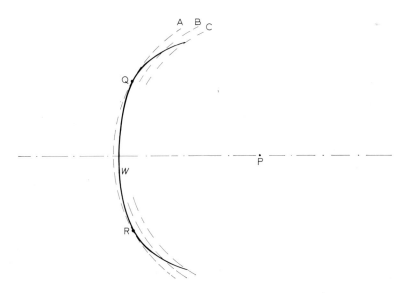

Fig. 6. Wave front W with axial symmetry and with spherical aberration of first order only. Sphere A around P touches W along a circle QR.

The stronger the aberration, the narrower the zones are. For a given point P the effect is, as if the light reaches P within a narrow ring and will give rise to the circular diffraction patterns of the type as already mentioned by Lord RAYLEIGH [1888]. For a small amount of aberration the zones are broad, which favours brightness. With growing distance of P the brightness decreases with distance, as the area of the effective zone is a constant and illumination at P is inversily proportional to the square of the distance.

When the wave front is somewhat divergent on the axis, the form of the wave front becomes like that of fig. 7, when the aberration is undercorrected. Even when P is not far away, the zone has an appreciable diameter QR. Larger diameters like Q'R' correspond to smaller distances of P'. The region of the wave front around the axis gives stray light at the axial points. This impairs contrast of the pattern and can be intercepted by a circular screen whose centre lies on the axis.

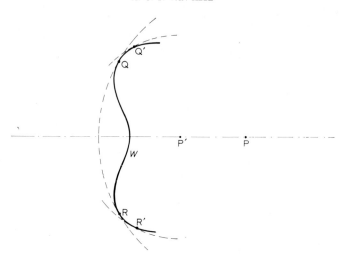

Fig. 7. Diverging wave front W with axial symmetry and again with spherical aberration of first order only. Sphere around P touches W along circle QR, sphere around P' touches W along circle Q'R'.

6. Sphere with cap

Without too much trouble a *glass sphere* can be made by the optical shop within so small a deviation from its true form that it can be considered as perfect. This is especially the case as the exact size does not play a part in the alignment experiments.

Spheres of optical glass of utmost homogeneity proved very useful. When a very small hole is placed in such a position that the sphere forms an image of it at a great distance, the emergent wave front has the form of fig. 6; when it is placed somewhat nearer to the sphere the form of fig. 7 is produced. It appears that for our purpose only the first aberration term need to be taken into account.

Stability of the set-up is best secured if the screen with aperture is attached to the sphere. Therefore the shape of fig. 8 is better; the sphere *with cap*. The cap is of the

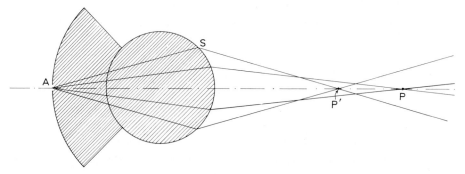

Fig. 8. Sphere with cap.

same glass. Its thickness is such that a small hole A in the aluminium coating, when illuminated by a light source, gives rise to an emergent wave front like that of fig. 6

(hole at paraxial front focus of the diopter S), or, better still, like that of fig. 7 (hole somewhat nearer to S). Cap and sphere are cemented together. The outer surface of the cap need not be a perfect sphere.

The small hole must have a diameter of a few microns for spheres with a diameter from say 1.5 to 5 cm. It can be realized by evaporating aluminium on the cap in a vacuum, after a thin thread of a few microns thickness and drawn from an appropriate plastic glue is laid on the surface. After removal of the thread a second thread is put on the surface square to the position of the first. The slit left open after the first coating is now reduced to a square window of the required dimensions.

It is astonishing how the light transmitted through such a small hole from a 35 watt car lamp, put at some distance before it, is sufficient to produce circular patterns of satisfactory brightness at distances up to 40 m or more. The straight line connecting the centres of these patterns can be regarded as a straight 'light line'.

It can be proved that with homogeneity of the glass to within 1 or 2 units of the sixth decimal place of the refractive index and with sphericity of the refracting surface

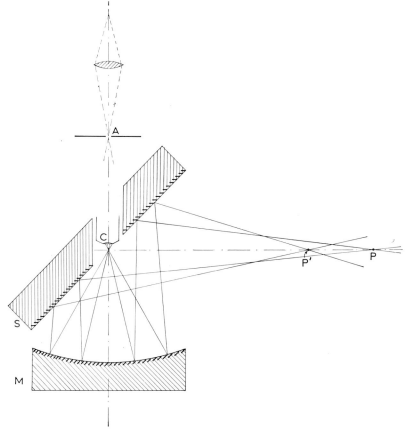

Fig. 9. Producing a straight line PP' (viz. connecting the centres of the circular diffraction patterns around points like P and P') by making use of a concave spherical mirror M and a flat mirror S.

to within $\frac{1}{4}\lambda$ wave length, deviations from the straightness are not more than 0.2 seconds of arc.

In order to obviate the necessity to procure very homogeneous glass a concave spherical mirror can be substituted for the sphere. This must be combined with a perfect flat mirror in order to prevent the presence of supports in the reflected light.

In fig. 9 a greatly diminished image of an illuminated aperture A is formed by a tiny sphere C. This image can be considered as a point source and is a little within the focal distance of the concave mirror M.

The reflected wave fronts have the form of fig. 7. With exception of the central part they are reflected by the plane mirror S in the direction PP'. The line PP' in this case is the "light line". The reader is referred to VAN HEEL [1961] for further details, where also an independent test of the straightness of the "light line" is described. It must be admitted that for technical applications this set-up is rather clumsy.

In the case of the concave mirror the colours in the circular pattern are white in the centre and a colour scale, more or less like Newton's colour scale, for the first few rings. It is perhaps astonishing, that for the sphere with cap it is allowed to use white light. It must be remembered, however, that for smaller wave lengths the refractive index increases, and the zone, of which the wave normal reaches the same point P, has a smaller diameter d (and smaller spherical aberration). If these diameters were directly proportional to the wave length, the patterns would consist of white and black rings, for the diameter of a given ring in the pattern is proportional to $1/d$ and to λ. In reality the rings are coloured, but well observable.

7. Testing of flatness

The traditional way of testing the flatness of a surface is to make use of an axis of very good quality. There are theodolites on the market of which the vertical axes can be trusted to be true within 0.5 seconds of arc, provided the instrument is carefully handled. Let us assume a horizontal surface is to be tested. A theodolite is placed in the neighbourhood of the surface. In some cases it may even be placed within the boundary of the surface. One of the axes is to be placed vertically, the other axis is clamped. The telescope then can be turned around the vertical axis and pointed to the several points to be tested. These can be realized by cross wires, each placed at the same height above the surface, or at least at a height that must be known for each of the cross wires.

When their distance from the theodolite is not the same for all of them, the telescope must be focussed for each of them and this impairs seriously the precision, as has been mentioned in the introduction of this chapter.

To obviate the necessity of focussing, the points can be realized by small circular holes, each transmitting light from a small lamp. The object glass of the telescope is provided with a zone-plate and the telescope is sensible defocussed by pushing the eye piece inward. By each point a diffraction pattern is produced, consisting of coloured concentric rings.

Passing from one to another point the telescope need not, and indeed must not, be touched. In this way full advantage is taken of the high quality of the axis.

In another way a good axis can be employed to 'produce' a flat optical surface. We take as an example a vertical surface to be tested. A hollow axis of good quality is mounted in a horizontal position and provided with an illuminated hole at one end and a lens at the other end. The lens mounting carries a zone-plate and pentagonal prism. By turning this equipment around the optical axis of the lens the 'light line' emerging from the prism describes a plane vertical surface (see fig. 10). The hole must be placed on the optical axis and the deviation of the pentagonal-prism must be 90°. A similar contrivance has been used to test the vertical end faces of the concrete caissons of the traffic tunnel under construction near Amsterdam.

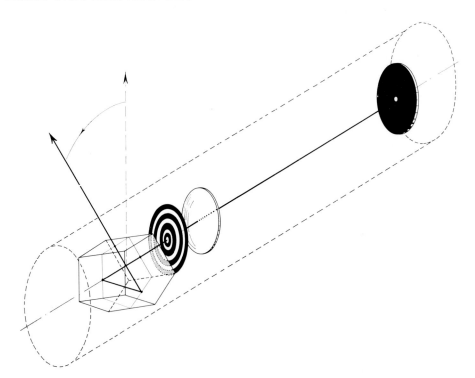

Fig. 10. Testing a flat surface by means of collimator, zone-plate and pentagonal prism.

Of the many other optical devices to form an optical plane surface, we will mention two more, referring the reader to chapter 7, where also the use of the rainbow is described (see also below under the head of unconventional methods).

8. Unconventional methods

Making two holes in the coating of the cap, two 'light lines' can be produced, which intersect in the centre of the sphere. These straight lines define a plane surface and one might try to use them to test the deviations of a surface from flatness. This might be done by interconnecting the points of each of the lines, but the auxiliary apparatus for such a procedure is not easy to handle and it is therefore advisable to look out for a more practicable method to test the flatness of surfaces.

One might think of a narrow slit instead of a hole on the outer surface of the cap. The diffraction would then become a band with coloured fringes, parallel to the slit.

When the centre of the sphere lies in the flat containing the slit, this set up would produce a flat surface, defined by the central fringe of the pattern. Now, it is impossible to make a slit of a few microns width on the cap, which should be lying in a flat surface to within a few tenths of a micron, while moreover the centre of the sphere should be a point of this flat.

This indeed is the tolerance for spheres of 2 to 5 cm diameter in order to be sure that the surface produced by the patterns is flat to within a few tenths of a second of arc.

A solution that was just feasible, consisting of a half sphere cemented on a half cylinder of the same glass, on the outer aluminized surface of which a fine scratch was made on a lathe of the best quality, is described in VAN HEEL [1962]. The range of distances is from say 2 m to 40 m or more. The angle of the light surface, having its top in the centre of the sphere, is about 90°. The flatness of the optical plane surface, created in this way, is about 0.4 seconds of arc.

A much easier way to realize this flatness, though the angle is appreciably smaller (25°), is as follows (fig. 11). A piece of optical glass of selected homogeneity is formed

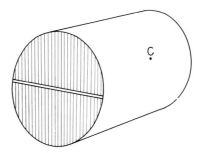

Fig. 11. Optical dome to produce a sector of a flat optical surface.

into a cylinder of which one end surface is fairly flat, and the other is spherical to a high degree of precision. The radius of the sphere can be chosen between 1 and 2 cm. The flat end surface is aluminized and a scratch is made on it. The scratch should have a width of about 2 μm and it should be as straight as possible. The scratch can also be made on an aluminized plane-parallel glassplate, which is cemented to the flat surface of the cylinder, the aluminized surfaces next to that surface.

Once this optical piece having been made, it is ready for use, not only to produce an optical flat surface, but also for alignment purposes. Let us see, how such an 'optical dome', as we might call it, functions.

The light passing through the slit at point A, and its immediate neighbourhood, gives rise to a diffraction pattern consisting of parallel bands with brilliant hues, of which fig. 12 gives an inadequate impression due to the lack of colour. The pattern

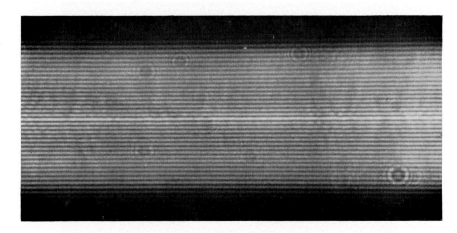

Fig. 12. Pattern produced by optical dome.

is much brighter than the circular patterns described in section 6, as the adjacent parts of the slit are sufficiently coherent to increase the amplitude. The central fringes of the diffraction patterns all lie in one plane. In this way, the optical dome can be considered to produce an optical plane.

If the slit had a circular form with the centre C of the spherical surface as its centre, each part of the slit should give the same pattern. In reality the outer parts of the slit are further away from C. It is therefore fit to make the length of the cylinder between the top of the spherical surface and the flat surface somewhat smaller than the front local length of the spherical surface. The wave fronts, originating from the central parts of the slit, have a form, corresponding to fig. 7. Towards the outer parts the form approaches to that of fig. 6.

Seeing from any point P of the optical plane to the spherical surface, one observes the bright zone, which is responsible for the production of the diffraction pattern around P (see fig. 13).

Parts of the slit that lie too far from the centre, cannot illuminate the complete luminous circle. Thus the useful length of the slit is limited. Only an angle of about 25° (fig. 14) can be covered. This is a disadvantage, for, in order to cover a square with sides p, the optical dome has to put at a distance of at least $2.25p$, the distance between the dome and farthest point being $3.3p$. With a half sphere, combined with a half cylinder, as mentioned earlier in this section, an angle of 90° is covered. The necessary distance is $0.5p$ and the distance to the farthest point is $1.1a$. As the position of pointing is proportional to the distance, the optical dome is clearly at a disadvantage compared to half sphere plus half cylinder. It is, however, much easier to make.

Precision proved to be a few tenths of a second of arc, that is 0.0015 mm at 1 m distance, 0.015 mm at 10 m distance.

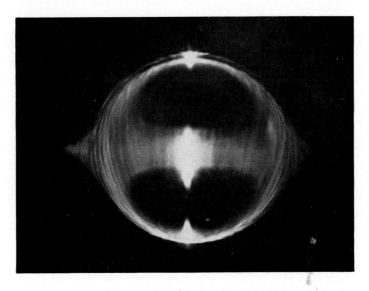

Fig. 13. Luminous zone of optical dome, produced by spherical aberration and responsible for the linear diffraction pattern of fig. 12.

The addition of two transverse scratches to the main straight scratch, makes it possible to use the instrument for alignment uses, with the advantage, that the pattern is easy to find on account of its brightness. It should be mentioned again, that the apparatus works by extrapolation.

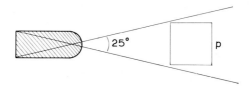

Fig. 14. Sector covered by optical dome.

After much experimenting to assure the straightness of the narrow slit, we found that this practical problem can be solved in a simple way. Instead of a scratch one can make use of the edge of a roof prism of the type used in many military instruments. The flat surface of the optical dome is polished and left blank. Quite near to it the edge is mounted (see fig. 15a). As it is the intersection of two optically flat surfaces, its straightness is guaranteed to within a few tenths of a micron. It is perhaps surprising that the width of the edge is so small, indeed between one and two microns; this is just the width wanted for our purpose. Surprising, because the roof prisms are made by (a very skilled) hand. In the reverse position (fig. 15b) this contrivance can be used in the same way.

In the above some examples have been given of the use of comparatively simple

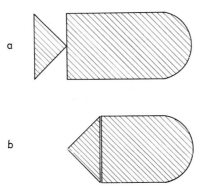

Fig. 15. Optical dome with edge of roof prism acting as slit.

optical methods to obtain a good precision with alignments and the like. Application of fundamental principles can often make superfluous the use of complicated apparatus.

References

DE HAAS, E., 1953, J. Arctic Inst. North America **6**, 260.

DE VEER, J. D., 1966, Some optical devices for testing alignment and flatness, to be published.

LIEM, S. H., 1960, A new application of the alignment method of van Heel (Laboratorium voor Grondmechanica, Delft) 22 pp. (in Dutch, short English summary).

McLEOD, J. H., 1954, J. Opt. Soc. Am. **44**, 592.

MOONEN, J. G. D., 1955, Z. Deut. Markscheider-Ver. **62**, 1.

RAYLEIGH, Lord, 1888, Wave theory of light. Scientific Papers, III (1902) p. 88.

REITZ, O. G., 1963, Height measurement by triangulation. Federal Dept. of Trigon. and Topogr. Surveys, Salisbury, Tech. Paper no. 1.

VAN HEEL, A. C. S., 1949, Appl. Sci. Res. **B1**, 306.

VAN HEEL, A. C. S., 1961, Modern alignment devices, *in*: E. Wolf, ed., Progress in optics, I (North-Holland Publ. Co., Amsterdam) p. 289.

VAN HEEL, A. C. S., 1962, Trans. Soc. Instr. Technol. (London) **14**, 270.

VAN HEEL, A. C. S. and J. D. DE VEER, 1962, Testing the straightness and the flatness of surfaces, *in*: Proc. Conf. Opt. Instr., 1961 (Chapman and Hall, London) p. 383.

CHAPTER 14

LASERS

H. G. FREIE AND A. L. SCHAWLOW

Department of Physics, Stanford University

CONTENTS

1. Introduction

Optical masers are quite commonplace today, although their development lies totally within the last few years. Excited atoms have long been used in light sources as diverse as flames, gas discharges and fluorescent lamps. However, it is only recently that we have learned how to make them emit in synchronism to produce coherent light. Townes (GORDON et al. [1954]) and independently BASOV and PROKHOROV [1954] realized that excited atoms placed in a suitable resonator could be stimulated to emit coherently. A maser oscillator was first operated in the microwave region (GORDON et al. [1954]) by using an ammonia beam which was electrically deflected so that only excited molecules entered a resonator cavity. A more widely applicable method of providing excited atoms is the three-level pumping scheme proposed by BLOEM-BERGEN [1956] and by BASOV and PROKHOROV [1955]. This method was first realized, also in the centimeter wave region, by Scovil et al. [1957] who used a microwave oscillator tube to provide the pumping energy.

However, it follows from the principles of the maser that the excitation energy need not be coherent. Thus, SCHAWLOW and TOWNES [1958] showed that conventional light sources could provide sufficient pumping power for maser operation in the optical region. They also showed that a simple resonator structure with two small parallel end mirrors could select a few of the enormous number of modes in a volume of centimeter dimensions.

In 1960 optical maser action was attained in several very different systems. First MAIMAN [1960] obtained strong pulses of visible stimulated emission with pink ruby pumped by a xenon flash lamp. The predicted optical maser properties (SCHAWLOW and TOWNES [1958], SCHAWLOW [1960]) of producing highly monochromatic directional and coherent beams of light were verified by R. J. COLLINS et al. [1960]. JAVAN et al. [1961] obtained continuous coherent radiation in the near infrared from a gas discharge optical maser.

Since that time a large number of new active materials, new methods of excitation and of construction have greatly extended the wavelength range in which these phenomena have been observed. Here we will be concerned with masers which operate in the near infrared, visible or ultraviolet regions, with describing the development of their properties and applications, and with discussing their future prospects and the ways in which these can be realized.

2. Fundamental principles

The principles of operation of optical masers have been described extensively in other places (SCHAWLOW and TOWNES [1958], LENGYEL [1962], TROUP [1963], YARIV and GORDON [1963], SCHAWLOW [1963], HEAVENS [1964], and BIRNBAUM [1964]) but they will be summarized here.

Any maser, as the name implies, makes use of microwave amplification by stimulated emission of radiation. This amplification is a true negative absorption. Thus, a wave passing through the amplifying medium grows in amplitude without changing its frequency, its phase or the shape of its wavefront. Like absorption, stimulated emission occurs when the frequency of the incoming wave is equal to the energy difference between two energy levels of the medium divided by Planck's constant, h, that is, if the emitting or absorbing transition takes place between an upper energy level E_2 and a lower energy level E_1; the frequency v of maximum amplification or attenuation is given by $E_2 - E_1 = hv$. The absolute amount of amplification or attenuation depends on the number of atoms in the two levels, commonly called the population. If these numbers are equal, there is neither gain nor loss of intensity. If more atoms are in the lower state, absorption dominates; if more atoms are in the upper state, there is amplification. The condition for absorption is the usual one in nature, as the population density of an energy level E at absolute temperature T in systems which are in thermodynamic equilibrium is proportional to the Boltzmann factor $\exp(-E/kT)$. Thus, the lower state will normally have a larger population than the upper state. It is quite possible to prepare a system with most of its atoms in the upper state, but such a system is not stable and, if left alone, will eventually return to equilibrium either by spontaneous emission or by non-radiative processes.

The most straightforward way to put atoms in the upper state E_2 from the lower state E_1, is to excite them with electromagnetic radiation of just the frequency $v_{12} = (E_2 - E_1)/h$. However, it is impossible to do this continuously, for when an atom is brought into the upper state the same radiation stimulates it to emit and return to the lower state, with the same probability as for absorption. The end result of vigorous excitation of this kind is at most an equalization of populations in the levels E_1 and E_2.

However, if there are three levels available, it is possible to produce a surplus of atoms in an upper state in two ways, illustrated in fig. 1a and b. As at optical frequencies the energy levels are thousands of reciprocal centimeters apart and at $273°K$ the factor kT is equivalent to 200cm^{-1}, it may be assumed that only the lowest level (ground state) is initially populated. When intense light of frequency $v_{13} = (E_3 - E_1)/h$ is applied atoms are excited to level E_3 and stimulated emission at frequency $v_{23} = (E_3 - E_2)/h$ can occur, as there were no atoms in level E_2 initially, as assumed. This

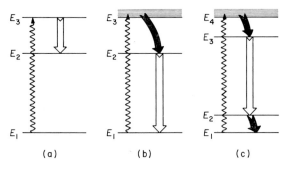

Fig. 1. Three-level and four-level pumping scheme for masers.

process, however, starts the absorption from E_2 to E_3 and so amplification by stimulated emission at frequency ν_{23} can only continue if atoms are sufficiently rapidly removed from level E_2. The three-level scheme of fig. 1a will show stimulated emission only if the rate of relaxation from E_2 to E_1 is faster than the rate from E_3 to E_2, when both radiative and non-radiative processes are included.

The three-level scheme of fig. 1b on the other hand can be used when atoms, pumped by the light to level E_3, relax rapidly to level E_2 and accumulate there, e.g. because the transition $E_2 - E_1$ is forbidden by some selection rule, that is, has a very low probability. In this case the process of pumping atoms from E_1 to E_3, followed by relaxation to E_2 can be continued till more than half of the atoms have accumulated in the last level, after which amplification by stimulated emission can occur at frequency $\nu_{12} = (E_2 - E_1)/h$.

The first scheme has the advantage that a population inversion is more easily established between E_3 and E_2 than between E_2 and E_1, as E_2 is initially empty and E_1 full. However, the second scheme has the advantage that the conflicting requirements of a broad absorption band and a narrow emission line are not combined in one energy level; thus, E_3 may be a broad band that can effectively absorb a wide range of pumping light while E_2 may remain sharp for strong stimulated emission.

Some advantages of both schemes may be obtained by using four levels as depicted in fig. 1c. Here E_4 may be a broad band while E_3 and E_2 may be sharp levels; E_2 is normally empty and might be kept that way by rapid relaxation to the ground-state level E_1.

Once a population inversion has been established in a suitable material a wave of the right frequency passing through it will be amplified. However, to make an oscillator which continually generates coherent light it is necessary to feed back some of the output so that the system provides its own input. Moreover, as with an electrical oscillator, this feedback loop can be used to narrow the output frequency width.

Rectangular resonator boxes of convenient size, say a few centimeters, can support many millions of different optical modes, even within the small frequency range of the active medium. If many modes are equally likely to build up, the ensuing oscillation might jump rapidly from one mode to another or the energy might be drained in several oscillating modes at the same time. The simplest way to make a resonator

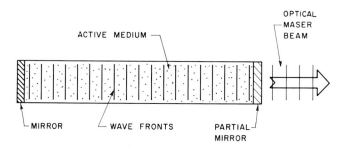

Fig. 2. Optical maser arrangement with two plane parallel mirrors.

which has practical dimensions and which strongly favors one (spatial) mode is shown in fig. 2. A long narrow column of active medium is terminated by two small flat mirrors perpendicular to the longitudinal axis of the medium. This allows only the axial modes to build up, as any light wave which starts at an angle with the optic axis of the system will leave it after a small number of reflections. Moreover, this scheme also has the advantage of leaving the sides open to admit pumping radiation.

A sustained oscillation will only take place if the amplification in the medium exceeds the loss at the reflections. This threshold condition will be further examined in § 4. Even for waves traveling along the optic axis more than one mode of oscillation is possible, the resonator condition being that the wave, when it retraces its own path through the medium, should have the same phase at the same point, or

$$\lambda = 2d/n \tag{1}$$

where λ is the wavelength, d is the spacing between the mirrors and n is any integer. These axial modes are regularly spaced on a frequency axis; the number of modes that participate in stimulated emission is, however, limited by the narrow amplifying band of the active medium. For a typical optical maser this is shown in fig. 3. By adjusting the rate of excitation it is usually possible to confine the oscillation to a few modes with frequencies closest to the center of the band, while at higher pumping rates several axial modes might oscillate simultaneously.

From these considerations follow the remarkable properties of the light beam

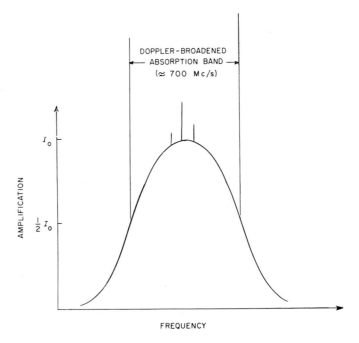

Fig. 3. Gain profile of the spectral line and sharpened axial mode resonances exhibited by a typical optical maser.

which emerges through one of the end mirrors (which should be only partially reflecting). It is *highly directional*, as only the light that has been reflected in the axial mode has interacted long enough with the active medium to obtain a large intensity; ideally its beamwidth is λ/a radians where a is the diameter of the active column. The light is *powerful*, as the atoms are stimulated to emit at a higher rate than they would have done spontaneously. It is *monochromatic* as the stimulated emission is a resonance process and takes place most strongly at the center of the range of amplification. Finally, since many atoms are forced to contribute in the proper phase to the emerging beam, it has a *high degree of spatial coherence*, i.e., in the plane mirror geometry described above the phase in one point of the plane perpendicular to the optic axis is related to that of all other points in the same plane.

3. Amplification of radiation

When an atomic system is in its lowest energy state, E_1, it is said to be in its ground state. By absorption of an energy quantum of frequency v it may change to a higher energy level E_2 such that

$$E_2 - E_1 = hv \tag{2}$$

where h is Planck's constant. The rate with which this occurs is the Einstein coefficient for absorption B_{12} and thus the probability that such an event will take place during one unit of time is then

$$p_{12} = I_v B_{12} \tag{3}$$

where I_v is the intensity of the radiation of frequency v defined by (2). Now, with the system in state E_2 the electromagnetic radiation field of the same frequency may stimulate the system to fall back to the ground state again, with a probability defined by the Einstein coefficient of stimulated emission B_{21}. However, this is not the only way in which the atomic system can return to the ground state: it can also give up radiation spontaneously. Thus, the total probability that an atomic system will go from the higher level E_2 to the lower level E_1 during one unit of time is

$$p_{21} = B_{21} I_v + A_{21} \tag{4}$$

where A_{21} is called the Einstein coefficient of spontaneous emission. The relations between these coefficients were first deduced by EINSTEIN [1917] by considering the thermodynamic equilibrium between the radiation and the atoms. They can be formulated as

$$g_1 B_{12} = g_2 B_{21} \tag{5}$$

$$A_{21} = 8\pi h v^3 n^3 B_{21}/c^3 \tag{6}$$

where g_1 and g_2 are the multiplicities of the levels E_1 and E_2, n is the index of refraction of the medium and c the velocity of light *in vacuo*. FÜCHTBAUER [1920], LADENBURG [1921], and later MILNE [1924] extended this theory to the relation between the absorption coefficient k and the Einstein coefficient of spontaneous emission, showing that

$$\int k_\nu d\nu = \frac{\nu_0^2 n^2 g_2}{8\pi c^2 g_1} N_1 A_{21} \left(1 - \frac{g_1 N_2}{g_2 N_1}\right) \tag{7}$$

where N_1 and N_2 are the number of atoms per cubic centimeter in energy state E_1 and E_2 respectively and ν_0 is the frequency of the center of the absorption line. This equation can also be written as

$$\int k_\nu d\nu = N_1 \kappa \left(1 - \frac{g_1 N_2}{g_2 N_1}\right) \tag{8}$$

defining κ. Normally, in the optical wave length region where $E_2 - E_1 = h\nu \gg kT$, where the ratio of atoms in the excited state to those in the ground state, N_2/N_1, is extremely small, this formula may be replaced by $\int k_\nu d\nu = \kappa N$, where N is the total number of active atoms per cubic centimeter. Written thus, this formula states that the integral of the absorption coefficient over the total width of the absorption line is proportional to the number of atoms per cubic centimeter available.

However, in some special cases, as in electrically excited gases, the ratio N_2/N_1 is not negligible. Following the Maxwell–Boltzmann distribution law we get for thermodynamic equilibrium

$$N_2/N_1 \leqq g_2/g_1 \tag{9}$$

where the equality is valid for the case $T \to \infty$. However, this inequality can be reversed; the system will be then in a definite nonequilibrium situation, and insertion in (8) will give a negative value for the integral of the absorption coefficient. The light wave of frequency ν_{12} traveling through such a system will grow in intensity following

$$I = I_0 \exp[\alpha x] \tag{10}$$

where x is the distance through the medium. This is exactly the usual absorption formula with α replacing $-k_\nu$. The necessary condition for this amplification is a system having a population inversion between two energy levels. This now can be done in various ways which will be considered in § 7.

Eq. (6) shows that the rate of spontaneous emission is proportional to the rate of stimulated emission by a factor which contains ν^3. Everything else being equal this means that the shorter the wavelength the more difficult it becomes to keep such a system even for a short time in such a nonequilibrium state: stimulated emission of, say, X-rays, will be very difficult to achieve as the energy necessary to put the system in a state of inverted population would break down most materials. On the other hand the spontaneous emission at microwave frequencies is lower than the thermal noise, hence these systems have to be cooled to take full advantage of their signal-to-noise characteristics. The optical frequencies take up a midposition between these two extremes: the preponderance of optical masers in the near infrared range is due both to this above mentioned A/B ratio and to the availability of intense excitation sources in the frequency range just above, i.e., in the visible region.

4. Threshold conditions

If the amplification by stimulated emission in the active medium exceeds the losses, a steady oscillation will build up, limited in amplitude by the available number of excited atoms.

Consider a resonator with plane parallel mirrors, as illustrated in fig. 2, with length L and with an amplification coefficient α, then, according to (10), the intensity will increase during one round trip through the medium by $I = I_0 \exp[2L\alpha]$. Neglecting all losses except the reflectivities r_1 and r_2 of the end mirrors, the intensity has decreased to $I = I_0 r_1 r_2$. So, after passing the same point in the same direction, the intensity of the beam has changed by the factor $r_1 r_2 \exp[2L\alpha]$. Disregarding spontaneous radiation but for the inception of oscillation, the necessary condition for oscillation can be stated as

$$\alpha_{\text{thr}} = -(\ln r_1 r_2)/2L. \qquad (11)$$

This is the threshold condition. We can also derive this condition in a slightly different way by looking at the energy balance, where the energy radiated out of the resonator cavity must be equal to or smaller than the energy supplied by induced emission, or

$$P_1 \leqq P_2 \qquad (12)$$

in order to have sustained oscillation. The energy going out is

$$P_1 = -\left(\frac{dI}{dt}\right)_1 \approx \frac{I(1 - r_1 r_2)c}{Ln} \qquad (13)$$

where n is the refractive index of the active medium. This can be written $I = I_0 \exp[t/T]$ with $T = Ln/c(1 - r_1 r_2)$ from which we can deduce in a conventional way a quality factor

$$Q \stackrel{\text{ref}}{=} 2\pi\nu T_1 = \frac{2\pi\nu Ln}{c(1 - r_1 r_2)}.$$

In the same way we can deduce quality factors for the other causes of energy loss, as diffraction loss, loss by scattering on inhomogeneities in mirrors and medium, and loss due to mirror imperfections. All these quality factors we can lump together into a single quality factor representing total loss $Q_1 = 2\pi\nu T_1 = 2\pi\nu[\sum T^{-1}]^{-1}$ giving

$$I = I_0 \, \Pi \, \exp[t/T] = I_0 \exp[t/T_1] \qquad (14)$$

for the total decrease in intensity. The increase in intensity due to induced emission on the other hand is

$$P_2 = \left(\frac{dI}{dt}\right)_2 = h\nu(N_2 - N_1 g_2/g_1)\frac{c}{n}W_i(\nu) \qquad (15)$$

where $W_i(v)$ is the total transition rate.

To derive this formula we have to reconsider some simplifications made before. This is obvious in the case of the bandwidth, which is extremely small, so that the radiation density $\varrho(v)$ cannot be taken constant over the frequency range where amplification is possible. Also the lineshape will have to be taken into account by introducing the normalized curve for absorption or emission intensity versus frequency, $g(v)$. Thus, $g(v)dv$ is the probability that a given transition will result in absorption or emission of one photon of frequency between v and $v+dv$.

For a curve with Gaussian lineshape, with full width at half maximum Δv and mean frequency v_0 the peak value of the lineshape curve is

$$g_G(v_0) = 2(\pi \ln 2)^{+\frac{1}{2}}/\pi \Delta v. \tag{16}$$

For a curve with a Lorentzian lineshape, however, the peak value is

$$g_L(v_0) = 2/\pi \Delta v. \tag{17}$$

Taking this into account (see e.g., YARIV and GORDON [1963]) the balance between decrease and increase of intensity reduces to:

$$N_2 - N_1 g_2/g_1 \gtrsim \frac{8\pi v^2 n^3}{T_1 A_{12} c^3 g(v_0)}. \tag{18}$$

The left-hand side of (18) is called the population inversion density. If the equal sign applies in (18) we have the threshold population inversion density which can be evaluated by calculating the right-hand side, while replacing $g(v_0)$ by either (16) or (17) depending on whether the transition has a Gaussian or a Lorentzian lineshape.

Another way of calculating threshold conditions is based on calculation of the population changes of the different levels of the system. These rate equations (see e.g., MAIMAN [1961]) can be very helpful in calculating the threshold power. However, all transition probabilities involved have to be known. As soon as the number of levels taking part in the process increases it is difficult to predict which transition will show stimulated emission. A good example is given by the helium–neon system (energy level scheme shown in fig. 8) where as yet only 13 of the 30 allowed transitions between 2s and 2p states have been shown to give maser action.

5. Linewidths of maser output

We will briefly return to the question of output linewidth. As has been shown in the very first papers on the possibility of stimulated emission (GORDON et al. [1955], SCHAWLOW and TOWNES [1958]), the linewidth of the maser beam is smaller than both the linewidth of the atomic transition and that of the resonator. If the active medium is a gas with a very narrow emission line, the transition linewidth is almost entirely due to Doppler broadening caused by thermal agitation. In a gas of molecular weight M at absolute temperature T the Doppler width of a line of frequency v is $\Delta_{vD} = 7.16 \times 10^{-7}(T/M)^{\frac{1}{2}}$. For the neon line of wavelength 1.153 μm (wavenumber

$8670\,\mathrm{cm}^{-1}$) this is $710\,\mathrm{Mc/s}$. This corresponds to a fractional linewidth $\Delta v_D/v$ of 2.72×10^{-6} or a quality factor for the medium, Q_{med}, of 3.6×10^5. The linewidth of the cavity is approximatively given by $\Delta v_{\mathrm{cav}} \approx c(1-r)/L$, which, for a typical gaseous optical maser with mirror separation $L=1\,\mathrm{m}$ and reflectivity $r=0.98$, gives $6\,\mathrm{Mc/s}$. The linewidth of the resulting induced emission is given by the formula

$$\delta v \approx (2\pi h v/P)(\Delta v_{\mathrm{cav}})^2 \tag{19}$$

where δv is the frequency range in which the energy is chiefly radiated and P is the power output. Both theoretically and experimentally the minimum power that must be supplied in order to sustain oscillation is found to be around 10^{-3} watts, so that for pumping power about twice the threshold value and Δv_{cav} equal to $6\,\mathrm{Mc/s}$, follows $\delta v \approx 6\,\mathrm{c/s}$, which is indeed very monochromatic. The different linewidths outlined above are illustrated in fig. 4. To resolve linewidths of this order, standard optical

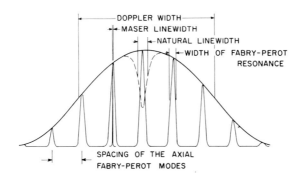

Fig. 4. Linewidth factors in an optical maser. (After HERRIOTT [1962].)

instruments like spectrometers cannot be used without considerable difficulty, but a multiplier phototube which is exposed to two modes of slightly different frequency will record the frequency difference (beat frequency), as was shown by JAVAN et al. [1961] and HERRIOTT [1962]. High stability is a requirement for these experiments, especially in as far as mirror separation is concerned. Every change in the distance between the mirrors due to vibration or thermal fluctuation will result in a linear shift of the center of resonator modes and of a nonlinear shift of the frequencies of the operating modes. These nonlinearities can be compensated and the resulting beat frequency is very stable. JAVAN et al. [1962] found a short-term stability of $2\,\mathrm{c/s}$ over a period of several seconds. At an operating frequency of $260\,\mathrm{Tc/s}$ ($1.153\,\mu\mathrm{m}$ wavelength) this indicates a fractional linewidth of around 5×10^{-15}. The frequency drift observed by mixing the output of two independent optical masers can be held as low as $30\,\mathrm{c/s}$ per second, representing a stability of 10^{-12}, as was shown by JASEJA et al. [1963]. This implies that the resonator length changes by no more than $0.001\,\text{Å}$ per second.

These results show that a gaseous optical maser can be useful as a secondary standard of wavelength; its reproducibility, however, is still not as good as the short-term stability. It has been found possible to reset a helium–neon optical maser to the center of the atomic line with an accuracy of 10^{-9} or nearly 4×10^{-3} times the linewidth of the Doppler-broadened transition (JASEJA et al. [1963]).

6. Resonator systems

Although two parallel mirrors in the classic arrangement of Fabry and Perot have long been used as an interferometer filter, the use of mirrors in laser resonators differs in several important ways. The structure is different, for the laser mirrors almost always have diameters small in comparison with their separation. Thus while edge effects and diffraction losses can usually be neglected for the interferometer, they play an important part in the mode-selective resonator.

Instead of plane waves traveling through the resonator, in a self-oscillating system one must consider the normal modes of oscillation. However, unlike modes of the closed boxes used for a microwave resonator, all modes of the open optical resonator are more or less lossy even when the mirrors are perfect. Thus, edge diffraction plays a role in determining both the frequency and field distribution of the normal modes, and also inevitably introduces losses.

From a microwave point of view, we could approach the optical resonator by considering first a rectangular box of centimeter dimensions with reflecting walls. In any narrow frequency band in the optical region, such a box would have very many resonant modes. These modes could be identified by their values of k_x, k_y and k_z, the propagation vectors parallel to the three edges of the box. Those modes for which k_x and k_y are small would have field configurations and losses relatively insensitive to the x- and y-dimensions of the resonator. Thus, these modes might be little affected by removing the side walls entirely. It is, therefore, reasonable to expect that the lowest-loss modes of the open resonator would be something like the corresponding modes of the rectangular box (SCHAWLOW [1961], WAGNER and BIRNBAUM [1961]).

An exact electromagnetic-field calculation for the open resonator is extremely difficult. However, since all dimensions are typically many times larger than a wavelength of the radiation, we can ignore waves with longitudinal components and use a scalar or 'optical' approximation. The problem then is reduced to finding field distributions on one end mirror which are reproduced after passage one or more times through the system.

FOX and LI [1961] calculated the field distributions, resonant frequencies and losses for the lowest modes of a plane-parallel resonator. As might be expected, the lowest mode has an electric-field distribution on the end mirror which falls smoothly from center to edges without any nodes. The diffraction loss of this mode is actually less than that of a uniform field distribution across the aperture – in this respect a laser operating in the lowest-loss mode is self-apodizing.

Still lower diffraction losses can be obtained by using confocal spherical mirrors in an arrangement resembling the CONNES [1958] interferometer. This system can be solved exactly in the scalar approximation (BOYD and GORDON [1961]). Their analysis confirms the low losses of low order modes; this structure is thus very suitable for use with gas discharges which give only small amplification factors. However, higher order modes, of both even and odd symmetry relative to the resonator axis, were also observed (KOGELNIK and RIGROD [1962]). Moreover, a wide range of mirror spacings and radii of curvature can be used (BOYD and KOGELNIK [1962]). A two-dimensional diagram can be constructed showing the regions of high and low losses, illustrated in fig. 5. Coordinates are $d/r_1 - 1$ and $d/r_2 - 1$, where r_1 and r_2 are the radii of curvature of the mirrors and d is their spacing. The solid hyperbola represents the concentric systems, while the dotted hyperbola represents the confocal systems. The intersection of the lower left to upper right diagonal with these hyperbolae gives the points A, plane parallel mirrors, and B, two concentric mirrors of equal curvature. The origin gives the third singular point C, corresponding to two mirrors of equal curvature placed confocally. It follows from this diagram that this last case is rather sensitive to changes in curvature or spacing. The boundaries between these high and low loss

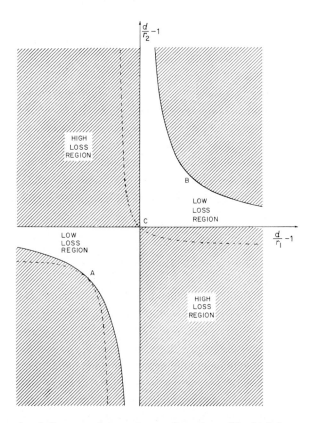

Fig. 5. Two-dimensional diagram of resonator configurations. The high loss regions are shown shaded. The solid hyperbolic curves represent the concentric systems, the dotted curves represent the confocal systems. Point A corresponds to the plane parallel mirrors, point B to concentric mirrors of equal radii of curvature and point C to the symmetrical confocal configuration. (After BOYD and KOGELNIK [1962].)

regions are sharp for large Fresnel numbers only, as shown by Fox and Li [1963]. One of the most useful of these nonconfocal systems is the hemispherical in which one mirror is plane and is placed at the center of curvature of the other.

Besides these approaches from the microwave field some from geometrical and physical optics should be mentioned. TORALDO DI FRANCIA [1963] showed that a very large family of optical systems can be treated as variations of an ideal resonator so that their resonant modes may quickly be found.

Alternatively the radiation through an aperture can be described by a set of plane waves whose amplitudes are the Fourier transforms of the amplitude distribution over the aperture. This method was followed by e.g. KOTIK and NEWSTEIN [1961] and by CULSHAW [1962]. In an iterative procedure a self-reproducing distribution of phase and relative amplitude over the apertures may be found. This feature of self-reproducing is the proper characteristic for a resonant mode. Most methods involve integral equations, but the resonant frequencies for all systems having two planes of symmetry perpendicular to the optic axis can be found without solving these equations. An analysis of the field conditions inside a large number of resonator configurations especially ring resonators, is given by S. A. COLLINS [1964]. Other configurations featuring lenses or refracting surfaces on the active medium were proposed but have disadvantages due to increased geometric aberrations. To reduce the number of axial modes without introducing other deleterious effects, RONCHI et al. [1964] have proposed end mirrors with periodic reflectance, say in the form of diffraction gratings.

Another arrangement for suppressing some of the axial modes, which was suggested by KLEINMAN and KISLIUK [1962], made use of a second resonator with a different mirror spacing that should be tuned so as to suppress most axial modes of the first resonator. This can either be done with an air-spaced Fabry–Perot type interferometer (KOGELNIK and PATEL [1962]) or with a simple plane-parallel plate (MANGER and ROTHE [1963]).

Some mirror arrangements give quite high losses. In particular, if one of the mirrors of the plane-parallel arrangement is even slightly convex toward the other, the diffraction losses increase considerably. However, it is not always advisable to seek the lowest diffraction losses. Indeed, for good mode selection, the *difference* in diffraction losses between two modes must be appreciable in comparison with the difference in other losses. In a carefully constructed gas laser, these other losses can be negligible, and if the gain is small, a low loss mirror arrangement is desirable. In solid state lasers, on the other hand, the laser material usually is far from ideally homogeneous, but large amplifications are obtainable to compensate for this. Thus, for solid lasers, plane mirrors are most commonly used. Even a system deliberately given high diffraction losses by making one mirror convex toward the other has been proposed (MOLLENAUER et al. [1963]), and found to give improved mode selection for ruby (SIEGMAN [1964]).

All of these devices give a standing wave pattern inside the resonator. One can obtain traveling wave maser action in a ring resonator (ROSENTHAL [1962], MACEK and DAVIS [1963]), in which waves can circulate continuously in the same direction.

Traveling wave 'whispering gallery' modes also exist in a spherical resonator (GARRETT *et al.* [1961]). However, in both of these cases there is degeneracy between modes circulating in clockwise and counterclockwise directions, and these degenerate modes can combine to produce an alternate stationary mode. One of the traveling wave modes in a ring resonator can be suppressed by inserting an optical isolator. Laser action is then obtained with a purely circulating mode having no nodes or loops (TANG *et al.* [1963a]). A special kind of circulatory laser is the twisted-mode structure in which the wave traverses a rod medium, but with different polarizations for the two directions of travel (EVTUHOV and SIEGMAN [1965]).

Many laser materials, such as ruby at room temperature, have a homogeneously broadened emission line. One would expect that once the threshold is achieved for laser action in one most favored mode, rapid stimulated emission would prevent further increase in the excited state population. Thus, other modes would never reach the threshold of oscillation. However, ruby lasers often oscillate simultaneously in several modes. This arises because any one mode can only draw on those excited atoms which lie close to its loops and not near nodes. Unless spatial energy transfer is fast, the excited atoms at nodes remain available for oscillation in another resonant mode. On the other hand, traveling-wave circulatory lasers have no nodes, and so they are more likely to oscillate in a single mode. A frequency-stabilized, single-mode optical maser is very valuable for many applications, e.g. for modulation. One way to achieve this is by choosing the mirror spacing so small that only one axial mode falls within the Doppler-broadened linewidth, and then stabilizing the frequency by keeping the gain constant. Feedback can be achieved by mounting one of the resonator mirrors on a piezoelectric crystal (WHITE *et al.* [1964]). Other multi-mode stabilizing techniques have been realized, e.g., by HARGROVE *et al.* [1964] and by FOSTER *et al.* [1965] based on interlocking different axial modes. This method can be used to control an optical maser in such a way that its spectral output resembles a central frequency oscillator with frequency-modulated sidebands, as shown by HARRIS and TARG [1965]. By demodulating this light at the proper frequency and phase, MASSEY *et al.* [1965] showed that the resulting output consisted then of one single stabilized mode.

One other phenomenon which is influenced by the spatial nonuniformity of field in standing wave lasers, is the 'spiking' or relaxation oscillation (R. J. COLLINS and NELSON [1961]). Almost all solid state lasers produce pulses of radiation, typically of about one microsecond duration separated by a few microseconds. Indeed, such relaxation oscillations can be inferred from the rate equations. As the population of excited atoms is initially built up by pumping, a threshold is reached for laser oscillation. Oscillation begins and it starts to deplete the excited state population, slowly at first and then more rapidly. Meanwhile, the excited state population continues to increase until the rate of stimulated emission overtakes and exceeds the rate at which atoms are supplied. The population then decreases toward the threshold value, but when threshold population inversion is reached there are still many photons in the resonator, and they continue stimulating emission. Thus, the excited state population continues to decrease, and oscillation stops with a population consideraby below the threshold value. Then, if pumping has continued, the excited state population builds up again and the process repeats.

While the rate equations are nonlinear, they have been extensively investigated (STATZ and DEMARS [1960], DUNSMUIR [1961], BURCH [1962], KOROBKIN and USPENSKII [1963]). It is found that they predict regularly spaced spikes of oscillation, which damp out to give continuous oscillation. This is indeed observed in some materials, such as $CaF_2:U^{3+}$ (SOROKIN and STEVENSON [1961]). For ruby, however, spiking is usually irregular and does not disappear even in continuous operation. TANG et al. [1963b] have shown that the prolonged spiking in ruby is associated with the mode competition arising from the spatially nonuniform energy density.

A number of methods for regulating the onset of stimulated emission has been proposed. Mostly these are used to enhance the output of one single pulse in that the population inversion is built up to as high a value as possible before stimulated emission is allowed to take place. The 'giant pulse' method of Hellwarth (MCCLUNG and HELLWARTH [1962]) uses a Kerr-cell shutter between the mirrors. This system lowers the reflectivity of one end mirror for the plane of polarization which the ruby amplifies and thus increases the threshold. The Kerr-cell shutter can be switched off in an extremely short time, typically 20 ns therewith lowering the threshold and giving the stimulated emission a chance to start. This technique is also called 'Q-spoiling'.

Mechanical shutters are mostly too slow for producing one single giant pulse, but rotating sectors, mirrors and prisms have been used successfully for periodically changing the reflection coefficient of an end mirror and for thus modulating the output of the optical maser. The same effect was achieved by DEMARIA and GAGOSZ [1962] by setting up a standing wave pattern of ultrasonic waves in a suitable cell between the mirrors. This pattern acts as a diffraction grating that appears and disappears at twice the frequency of the ultrasonic waves. Finally, a whole series of dyes will serve the same purpose either by absorbing the first amount of monochromatic radiation and subsequently undergoing phase change and clearing the path for stimulated emission, or by showing a nonlinear effect in getting more transparent at stronger electromagnetic fields (see e.g., MASTERS and MURRAY [1965]).

7. Active materials and methods of excitation

7.1. SOLID MATERIALS

Most interest has been centered around chromium and rare earth ions in different host lattices. Chromium in aluminum oxide is commonly called ruby. The theoretical aspects of this material have been thoroughly studied by SUGANO and TANABE [1958] and the energy level scheme is shown in fig. 6. The first maser action was reported in this material by MAIMAN [1960] on a transition from one of the ^2E levels to the $^4A_2$ ground state called the R_1 line, situated at 6943Å. Further research has shown that the R_2 line at 6929Å can show stimulated emission also (MCCLUNG

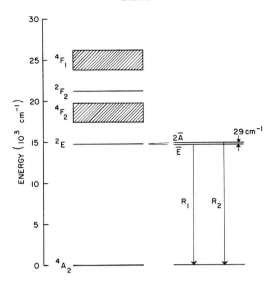

Fig. 6. Energy level diagram of ruby. The left side shows the blue ($^4F_1$) and green ($^4F_2$) pumping bands, the right side shows the splitting of the ^2E and $^4A_2$ levels due to the crystalline field.

et al. [1962]) and that the same is the case even for the N_1 and N_2 lines at 7040Å and 7009Å respectively (SCHAWLOW [1960], WIEDER and SARLES [1961], SCHAWLOW and DEVLIN [1961]). The most common method of excitation of solids is still pumping with visible light because in this region of the electromagnetic spectrum both the sources and the energy levels of the materials have been studied extensively beforehand. This method has been applied to stimulate emission in a large number of other materials including crystals, glasses, plastics, organic liquids, two gases and one semiconductor material. The usual arrangement is to bring the light in perpendicular to the optic axis of the resonator, using different lamp and mirror geometries like elliptical cylinder, sphere or even simple close coupling of the lamp and laser rod inside a reflecting housing. Notwithstanding the fact that ruby was the first material to show stimulated emission, it requires much higher threshold pumping energy than most other common solid maser materials, e.g., neodymium-doped glasses. This is due to the fact that ruby operates on the three-level principle (see fig. 1b) or nearly so. Here the ground state, which is normally full, has to be at least half emptied to bring about an inversion in the population, and this leads to a high threshold. However, once threshold has been attained, a small fractional increase in pumping power can produce a large laser output power.

Much effort has been bestowed on devices to lower the power requirements for the pumping light. We might mention the arrangement of NELSON and BOYLE [1962], that resulted in continuous maser action at 77°K, the cladding arrangement of DEVLIN *et al.* [1962], that resulted in halving the threshold power, and finally the continuous operation at room temperature achieved by EVTUHOV and NEELAND [1965].

In contrast to this, many of the rare earth (4f transition) ions have energy levels suitable for the four-level scheme of fig. 1c and hence show very low threshold values. Moreover, they possess very sharp levels due to the effective shielding from the crystal field provided by the two 5s and six 5p electrons. A good example is trivalent neodymium, extensively studied by usual spectroscopic methods by CARLSON and DIEKE [1961] and CARLSON [1960]. It might be said that stimulated emission at around 1.06 μm due to Nd^{3+} has been observed in almost every conceivable host material, with threshold ranging from 88 to 1 joule. Nd^{3+} has also shown stimulated emission at room temperature and $CaWO_4:Nd^{3+}$ was the first solid material used in a continuous optical maser (JOHNSON *et al.* [1962]). The transition involved here is $^4F_{\frac{3}{2}}-^4I_{\frac{11}{2}}$, as shown in fig. 7. The absorption of pumping radiation takes place in all

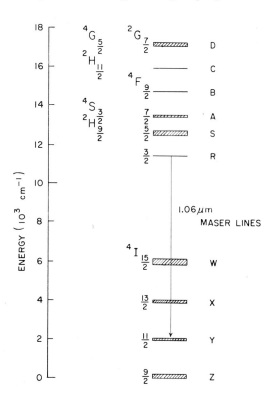

Fig. 7. Energy level diagram of Nd^{3+}.

bands in the visible region and is quite efficiently transferred via the crystal lattice down to the last ^4F level, which then acts as a springboard for all transitions to the ^4I group. The lowest level in this group is the ground state and thus normally filled, but the next highest level, situated at around $2000 \, cm^{-1}$, will be empty up to room temperature and thus sustain maser action.

Good reviews of solid materials that have shown optical maser action are presented by JOHNSON [1963] and NASSAU [1965].

7.2. LIQUID AND PLASTIC HOST MATERIALS

A definite periodicity in the surroundings, as in the crystalline state, tends to keep
the linewidths in the active medium narrow, which gives also a lower threshold,
as is well illustrated by the behavior of neodymium in crystals as compared to glasses.
Most crystals have problems however relating to imperfections, polish and orientation of the crystal axes. The availability of pure, single crystals with the desired quality
(strainfree, not hygroscopic, small coefficient of expansion) is mainly limited by
manufacturing techniques. Most liquids and plastics do not have these problems while
still retaining the advantage of high concentration of active ions. Promising host
materials are the chelates in solvents, as reported by LEMPICKI and SAMELSON [1963]
and SAMELSON et al. [1964] or in plastic, as reported by WOLFF and PRESSLEY [1963],
both containing Eu^{3+} as active material. These chelate molecules have a double
function: they provide the active ions with a shield against random effects, such as
collisions in the liquid and strains in the plastic, so that the linewidths are not unduly
broadened, and they provide the strong absorption bands for the pump energy,
which is then transferred to the trivalent europium ion. A review of the chelate maser
materials is given by NUGENT et al. [1964].

7.3. GASEOUS SYSTEMS

Electric discharges in low pressure gaseous media can create large numbers of fast
electrons, which can in colliding with gas atoms excite these to high levels (JAVAN
[1959]). It is possible to distinguish several mechanisms to obtain a population inversion between two specific states: in the first place, electron collisions are more effective
in exciting to some particular levels than to others; in the second place, even if all
states are populated at equal rates, some will empty faster than others, either by
radiation or by collision. The main advantage of these types of excitations is their high
ratio of excited to ground-state atoms, while the density of atoms is quite low compared
to that in solid state devices. The first gas-discharge optical maser, realized by JAVAN
et al. [1961], used a mixture of helium and neon and was the first optical maser to
work continuously. The energy level diagram for helium and neon is shown in fig. 8.
The 2^3S and 2^1S states of helium are metastable and thus have a long lifetime. Energy
transfer from these states to the energetically near 2s and 3s neon levels by collision
is thus very probable. As moreover the 2p levels tend to depopulate very rapidly, the
2s–2p and 3s–2p transitions are very suitable for optical maser action, which they
have shown in respectively the infrared (1.06 μm) and red (6328Å) spectral regions.
A description, complete with drawings, is given by HERRIOTT [1962] for the first
working model with internal plane parallel mirrors, and by RIGROD et al. [1962]
for the now common type with external spherical mirrors and a discharge tube with
flat windows set at Brewster's angle to minimize reflection losses for one polarization
plane. In some mixtures of a rare gas, like neon, with a molecular gas, such as oxygen,
the discharge can bring about a dissociation of the molecule into two atoms in particular
excited states. This leads to many far-infrared maser wavelengths, as e.g., in carbon-

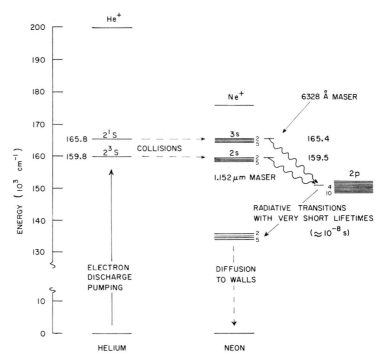

Fig. 8. Energy level diagram for helium and neon.

dioxide as reported by PATEL *et al.* [1964a], in water vapor (CROCKER *et al.* [1964] and WITTEMAN and BLEEKRODE [1964]) or in cyanides (GEBBIE *et al.* [1964]). Finally, the excited states of ionized atoms have yielded many new wavelengths in which stimulated emission was reported. The disadvantage of having first to spend ionization energy is largely offset by the large amplification factors achieved. Also the lower level empties rapidly by radiation, so that power output can be high. Good examples here are the many transitions found in four noble gases by FAUST *et al.* [1964], in xenon by BRIDGES [1963], in neon up to $133\,\mu$m by PATEL *et al.* [1964b] and those in iodine down to 5407Å as reported by FOWLES and JENSEN [1964]. These gas discharge masers fall at the present time within a frequency range from $337\,\mu$m to 2358Å. Most transitions in the noble gases are summarized by BENNETT [1962], while useful tabulations of transitions in all types of materials can be found in BIRNBAUM [1964].

7.4. SEMICONDUCTORS

Coherent light can also be generated in semiconductors. Some advantages are a very direct excitation process by means of a direct current flowing through the junction, a high efficiency (up to 50%) and a simple modulation technique by just superimposing an alternating current up to 10Gc/s on the pumping current. Fig. 9 shows the energy level scheme of a p–i–n semiconductor diode. As is well known a p-type semiconductor material has a small percentage of impurity atoms called acceptors,

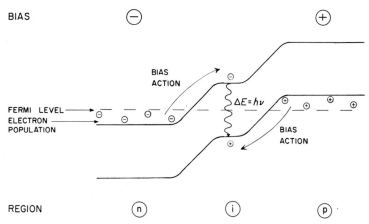

Fig. 9. Level scheme for a p–i–n semiconductor.

as a result of which an excess of holes is created in the valence band. In a n-type material, which contains donors, an excess of electrons is found; the boundary (or junction) region is essentially a recombination space with high conductivity for both kinds of charge carriers. The recombination process is responsible for the emission of light of certain wavelengths and, as is the case with other types of masers, a suitable population inversion has first to be created to counteract the competing recombina-

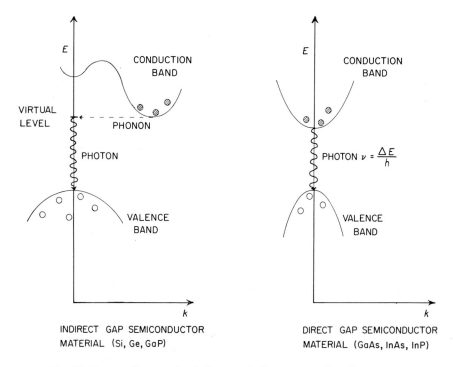

Fig. 10. Energy diagrams for indirect and direct gap semiconductors.

tion mechanisms, e.g., spontaneous emission, phonon emission of the same energy, light and phonon emission via impurity levels in the forbidden band and Auger, i.e., selfexcitation, effects. The transition which has the smallest time constant will be dominating, so the radiative transitions have to have high probabilities. The distinction between two types of semiconductors, those with direct and those with indirect gap, is usually made: the former have electrons in the conduction band and holes in the valence band showing a similar distribution in momentum space, which the latter have not (fig. 10). Most ordinary junction diodes used in electronic equipment are made of indirect gap semiconductor materials e.g., silicon, germanium, and consequently the electrons, in jumping from the higher energy conduction band into the lower energy valence band need not only to give off their excess energy in the form of photons, but also its excess momentum in the form of phonons. Usually recombination then takes place near an impurity atom which provides the necessary coupling to the crystal lattice. The above considerations show that for light emission the favorable material is the direct gap material. Thus, maser action has been described in indium antimonide, indium arsenide, gallium arsenide and in intermediate mixed compounds, in silicon carbide, indium phosphide, lead selenide and lead telluride and finally in $GaAs_xP_{1-x}$ up to $x=0.6$ where GaP is an 'indirect gap' material. Recently, some advances have been made in pumping semiconductor materials with electron beams of discrete velocities, as reported by HURWITZ and KEYES [1963] and BENOIT and DEBEVER [1964]. This technique will be valuable for pumping unusual semiconductor materials in which p–n junctions are difficult to produce.

8. Modulation and generation of second harmonics

Whenever the dielectric tensor of a medium, and consequently its optical properties, are influenced by an electric field one speaks of an electro-optic effect. Linear electro-optic effects can only exist in crystals without a center of inversion, i.e., in the same crystal classes that permit piezoelectric effects (FRANKEN et al. [1961]). In modulating light at high frequencies this linear (Pockels) effect is much more efficient than the quadratic (Kerr) effect, as a result of the absence of a direct current component and of high dielectric loss. Single crystals of ammonium dihydrogen phosphate (ADP) and potassium dihydrogen phosphate (KDP) as first proposed by KAMINOW [1961] have received most attention. These crystals are already optically anisotropic in zero field so they can be used only with the light propagating along the optic axis, which in turn constitutes an alignment problem. It is advantageous to use, if possible, cubic crystals without inversion center as e.g., zincblende, CuCl, hexamethylenetetramine, which show both optic isotropy at zero field and a linear electro-optic effect.

For modulation purposes a division can be made between internal modulating techniques, which are limited by the bandwidth of the active device, and external modulation, which takes place in the frequency range between two successive axial modes. Internal modulation (see e.g., KAMINOW [1965]) is chiefly limited by the quality of the resonator and, according to the peculiar characteristics of the light source,

can only be in the order of 10 Mc/s, while external modulation, which is dependent on the spacing of the resonator mirrors only, can achieve a much larger bandwidth. If only one optical mode is present there is in principle no limit to the external modulation bandwidth.

Demodulation can be performed in a photodiode or photomultiplier. The first device is limited in frequency response by the transit time of the photon-excited carriers (BERNARD [1963]). McMURTRY and SIEGMAN [1963] were able to detect beats between axial modes of a ruby optical maser, spaced at 600 Mc/s, in a traveling-wave phototube. Both semiconductor and photoelectric detectors have been made to work at microwave frequencies.

Conversion of FM to AM by means of a Lyot filter was demonstrated by HARRIS [1963] and thus FM demodulation can also be achieved.

The effect of the internal electromagnetic field generated in a dielectric by incident radiation is to create a polarization P, which is a function of the electric field E. Extremely strong fields, where P can then no longer be taken proportional to E alone but to a sum of terms containing E, E^2 and higher orders, give rise to nonlinear effects as generation of second and higher order harmonics. This was demonstrated by FRANKEN et al. [1961] and reviewed by KLEINMAN [1962], FRANKEN and WARD [1963], BLOEMBERGEN [1963], and BLOEMBERGEN [1965]. Both crystals without inversion center, where even-order harmonic generation is permitted and crystals with inversion center are discussed. A simple system which consists of a plane boundary between two media does not have a center of inversion and thus can give rise to nonlinear effects, which were discussed in detail by BLOEMBERGEN and PERSHAN [1962]. The efficiencies reported for pulsed harmonic generation have been generally quite high, up to 20 percent, because of the large electric fields produced by optical masers.

Finally, the optical maser can be used advantageously as an intense and monochromatic light source in observing both the Raman and the Brillouin scattering. These phenomena are due to creation of phonons, of the acoustical branch in the latter case and of the optical branch in the former, resulting in a frequency shift of the scattered lightwaves. The coherent generation of Raman-scattered light in organic liquids, where the higher level is populated by means of an optical maser and the lower level is situated at E_{vibr} above the ground state, has been demonstrated by ECKHARDT et al. [1962]. For a comprehensive survey, see BLOEMBERGEN [1965].

9. Applications

The optical maser has tremendous advantages as a light source due to its narrow spectral linewidth (temporal coherence, monochromaticity). This, of course, makes it ideally suited as a source for spectroscopy. As a spectroscopic tool it has already given renewed impetus to spectroscopic research and new transitions in stimulated emission have been found by FAUST et al. (1964) which were never seen before.

For interferometric purposes stability and reproducibility should be added; then the optical maser will have also the desired properties of a tertiary, secondary and may be even primary standard of frequency or time. These characteristics are necessary for experiments testing effects of relativity theory, as already performed by JASEJA et al. [1964].

Monochromatic light is used in all aspects of metrology such as measuring alignments, velocities or distances. Short distances can be measured by straight interferometric methods and long distances by using either pulsed beams and measuring the time elapsed between sending and receiving or microwave-modulated beams and measuring the phase difference between outgoing and returning beams, i.e. interferometry on the microwave level. This last method is also applicable to velocity measurements as is the Doppler shift technique. The Doppler effect gives, for instance, a 3 kc/s beat note with an object speed of 1 mm/sec.

Thus, monochromaticity lies chiefly at the basis of most of the following uses: experiments on Thompson scattering, scattering of light by light, and testing of diffraction gratings, in particular on Rowland ghosts. Very small changes in absorption or refractive index can be detected over a small frequency range in using the steep shoulder of the maser gain versus frequency curve as shown by HERZIGER et al. [1964]. In this group belong also the measurements of refraction, absorption and scattering of the transmitting medium as used in schlieren technique, plasma probing, Rayleigh scattering and atmospheric turbulence measurements. Spectral broadening of Rayleigh-scattered light has been observed by CUMMINS et al. [1964], using heterodyne detection. This has also been applied on electrons moving in a plasma; here the Doppler broadening of the scattered light was used to calculate the electron temperature, which can be extended even to nonequilibrium situations, as shown by SCHWARZ [1963]. The use of the radiation field of the optical maser for accelerating electrons has been proposed by SHIMODA [1962].

The small beamwidth (spatial coherence, directionality) of the optical maser is important in another series of experiments, in particular for ophthalmological applications and long distance communications. In this last field the small relative bandwidth and the directionality of the single-mode continuous gas optical maser are very promising for information transmission, especially for space applications. For earthbound connections this last advantage turns into a disadvantage, however, as the uncertainty of pointing due to atmospheric turbulence ('seeing') is far greater than the divergence of the beam. The same difficulties are encountered when trying to ascertain the position of an object, where directionality implies object selectivity.

Sometimes the applications require additional power as e.g., in stimulated Brillouin scattering and consequent production of coherent phonon beams and in industrial applications as welding, cutting and refractory melting. It has been often demonstrated that it is possible to drill very fine holes of say $40 \mu m$ diameter in a variety of hard materials like diamonds, razor blades and behind-the-iron-curtain rulers, but the very low efficiency of high-power experiments will delay large-scale industrial use. By using a Q-spoiling device ELLIS and FOURNEY [1963] forced a ruby maser to emit strong, regular pulses of light at frequencies up to $5 \times 10^{-5} s^{-1}$, which allowed them to apply this as a light source in high-speed photography. This technique will undoubt-

edly be pursued to still higher frequencies as exemplified by the research of HARGROVE et al. [1964] who succeeded in producing trains of very short light pulses at frequencies of $10^8 s^{-1}$.

The most interesting high power density applications, however, are in pumping single and multiple photon and phonon processes, i.e. for parametric amplifiers, Raman oscillators and the nonlinear effects encountered in practically all materials at these power levels. Due to these effects, for instance, the spot size of a focussed, high-intensity light beam is limited (aside from diffraction effects) and will rather be spread along the optic axis into a focal line, as shown by CHIAO et al. [1964].

Construction of high-power optical masers leads to physically bigger units, i.e. to longer ruby rods, which in turn relaxes the reflectivity requirements. Totally uncoated ruby rods of 10cm length will emit stimulated emission on the strength of the reflection coefficient at normal incidence alone, which is 8 % in this case. As the total power available for stimulated emission is independent of the number of modes that take part in the oscillation process, mode restriction should lead to higher power output in the remaining mode(s), unless scattering prevents this.

Two important characteristics of the maser might be mentioned here: firstly, it is the most powerful infrared source known: to compare the infrared maser with traditional infrared sources as incandescent lamps these last ones would have to be blackbody radiators at temperatures of 10^{10} °K; secondly, the maser is not a Lambertian source (see e.g., BORN and WOLF [1964]) and thus the field at the focus can be much higher than that at the source.

Finally, for some successful applications a wider frequency range would be preferred also. Examples are infrared spectroscopy, communications and photochemistry, where the optical maser will be able to influence chemical reactions specifically in time, space and kind, i.e. certain molecular vibrations might be strongly excited by an infrared maser spectral line while others are left unaffected.

All three types of masers can be tuned to a small degree by changes in temperature or by applying electric or magnetic fields; this means conversely that frequency stability requires temperature stability. By varying the stochiometric composition of the semiconductor diodes from $GaAs_{0.6}P_{0.4}$ through GaAs, InAs to InSb, they can be almost continuously tuned to emit luminescence in the range from around 0.6 to 5.2 μm. Semiconductor materials have been grown whose injection luminescence band (i.e. spontaneous emission band) or whose stimulated emission in the visible region matched the pumping bands of the infrared maser material, thus creating a very efficient pumping source (OCHS and PANKOVE [1964], PHELAN and REDIKER [1965]). This characteristic, added to the small physical size, high efficiency and excellent modulability of the semiconductor optical maser, makes it advantageous as an emitter, detector and amplifier in the field of communications. Due to its high signal-to-noise ratio it also can be used as an electro-optical logic component, minimizing inductance and capacitance problems.

The most active research in the optical maser field is mainly directed toward the higher power applications and the search to extend the frequency range from the present limit of 337 μm into the millimeter range.

References

BASOV, N. G. and A. M. PROKHOROV, 1954, Zh. Eksperim. i Teor. Fiz. **27**, 431.

BASOV, N. G. and A. M. PROKHOROV, 1955, Zh. Eksperim. i Teor. Fiz. **28**, 249; Soviet Phys.-JETP **1**, 184.

BENNETT, W. R., 1962, Applied Optics, Supplement on Optical masers, p. 24.

BENOIT À LA GUILLAUME, C. and J.-M. DEBEVER, 1964, Compt. Rend. **259**, 2200.

BERNARD, M., 1963, Appl. Phys. Letters **2**, 9.

BIRNBAUM, G., 1964, Optical masers, Advan. Electron. Electron Phys., Suppl. 2 (Academic Press, New York).

BLOEMBERGEN, N., 1956, Phys. Rev. **104**, 324.

BLOEMBERGEN, N., 1963, Proc. IEEE **51**, 124.

BLOEMBERGEN, N., 1965, Non-linear optics (Benjamin, New York).

BLOEMBERGEN, N. and P. S. PERHAN, 1962, Phys. Rev. **128**, 606

BORN, M. and E. WOLF, 1964, Principles of optics, 2nd ed. (Pergamon Press, London) p. 188.

BOYD, G. D. and J. P. GORDON, 1961, Bell System Tech. J. **40**, 489.

BOYD, G. D. and H. KOGELNIK, 1962, Bell System Tech. J. **41**, 1347.

BRIDGES, W. B., 1963, Appl. Phys. Letters **3**, 45.

BURCH, J. M., 1962, in: K. J. HABELL, ed., Proc. Conf. Opt. Instr. Tech., London, 1961 (Chapman and Hall, London) p. 463.

CARLSON, E. H., 1960, Thesis, John Hopkins Univ., Spectrosc. Rept. 16.

CARLSSON, E. H. and G. H. DIEKE, 1961, J. Chem. Phys. **34**, 1602.

CHIAO, R. Y., E. GARMIRE and C. H. TOWNES, 1964, Phys. Rev. Letters **13**, 479.

COLLINS, R. J. and D. F. NELSON, 1961, J. Opt. Soc. Am. **51**, 473.

COLLINS, R. J., D. F. NELSON, A. L. SCHAWLOW, W. BOND, C. G. B. GARRETT and W. KAISER, 1960, Phys. Rev. Letters **5**, 303.

COLLINS, S. A., 1964, Appl. Opt. **3**, 1263.

CONNES, P., 1958, J. Phys. Radium **13**, 262.

CROCKER, A., H. A. GEBBIE, M. F. KIMMITT and L. E. S. MATHIAS, 1964, Nature **201**, 250.

CULSHAW, W., 1962, IRE trans. Microwave Theory Tech. MTT10, 331.

CUMMINS, H. Z., N. KNABLE and Y. YEH, 1964, Phys. Rev. Letters **12**, 150.

DEMARIA, A. J. and R. GAGOSZ, 1962, Proc. IRE **50**, 1522.

DEVLIN, G. E., J. MCKENNA, A. D. MAY and A. L. SCHAWLOW, 1962, Appl. Opt. **1**, 11.

DUNSMUIR, R., 1961, J. Electron. Control **10**, 453.

ECKHARDT, G., R. W. HELLWARTH, F. J. MCCLUNG, S. E. SCHWARZ, D. WEINER and E. J. WOODBURY, 1962, Phys. Rev. Letters **9**, 455.

EINSTEIN, A., 1917, Physik. Z. **18**, 121.

ELLIS, A. T. and M. E. FOURNEY, 1963, Proc. IEEE **51**, 942.

EVTUHOV, V. and J. K. NEELAND, 1965, Appl. Phys. Letters **6**, 75.

EVTUHOV, V. and A. E. SIEGMAN, 1965, Appl. Opt. **4**, 142.

FAUST, W. L., R. A. MCFARLANE, C. K. N. PATEL and C. G. B. GARRETT, 1964, Phys. Rev. **133**, A1476

FOSTER, L. C., M. D. EWY and C. B. CRUMBLY, 1965, Appl. Phys. Letters **6**, 6.

FOWLES, G. R. and R. C. JENSEN, 1964, Appl. Opt. **3**, 1191.

FOX, A. G. and T. LI, 1961, Bell System Tech. J. **40**, 453.

FOX, A. G. and T. LI, 1963, Proc. IEEE **51**, 80.

FRANKEN, P. A., A. E. HILL, C. W. PETERS and G. WEINREICH, 1961, Phys. Rev. Letters **7**, 118

FRANKEN, P. A. and J. F. WARD, 1963, Rev. Mod. Phys. **35**, 23.

FÜCHTBAUER, C., 1920, Physik. Z. **21**, 322.

GARRETT, C. G. B., W. KAISER and W. L. BOND, 1961, Phys. Rev. **124**, 1807.

GEBBIE, H. A., N. W. B. STONE and F. D. FINDLAY, 1964, Nature **202**, 685.

GORDON, J. P., H. J. ZEIGER and C. H. TOWNES, 1954, Phys. Rev. **95**, 282.

GORDON, J. P., H. J. ZEIGER and C. H. TOWNES, 1955, Phys. Rev. **99**, 1264.

HARGROVE, L. E., R. L. FORK and M. A. POLLACK, 1964, Appl. Phys. Letters **5**, 4.

HARRIS, S. E., 1963, Appl. Phys. Letters **2**, 47.

HARRIS, S. E. and R. TARG, 1964, Appl. Phys. Letters **5**, 202.

HEAVENS, O. S., 1964, Optical masers (Methuen, London, and Wiley, New York).

HELLWARTH, R. W., 1961, *in*: J. R. Singer, ed., Advances in quantum electronics (Columbia Univ. Press, New York) p. 334.

HERRIOTT, D. R., 1962, J. Opt. Soc. Am. **52**, 31.

HERZIGER, G., H. LINDNER and H. WEBER, 1964, Z. Angew. Physik **17**, 67.

HURWITZ, C. E. and R. J. KEYES, 1964, Appl. Phys. Letters **5**, 139.

JASEJA, T. S., A. JAVAN, J. MURRAY and C. H. TOWNES, 1964, Phys. Rev. **133**, A1221.

JASEJA, T. S., A. JAVAN and C. H. TOWNES, 1963, Phys. Rev. Letters **10**, 165.

JAVAN, A., 1959, Phys. Rev. Letters **3**, 87.

JAVAN, A., E. A. BALLIK and W. L. BOND, 1962, J. Opt. Soc. Am. **52**, 96.

JAVAN, A., W. R. BENNETT and D. R. HERRIOTT, 1961, Phys. Rev. Letters **6**, 106.

JOHNSON, L. F., 1963, J. Appl. Phys. **34**, 897.

JOHNSON, L. F., G. D. BOYD, K. NASSAU and R. R. SODEN, 1962, Phys. Rev. **126**, 1406.

KAMINOW, I. P., 1961, Phys. Rev. Letters **6**, 528.

KAMINOW, I. P., 1965, Appl. Opt. **4**, 123.

KLEINMAN, D. A., 1962, Phys. Rev. **128**, 1761.

KLEINMAN, D. A. and P. P. KISLIUK, 1962, Bell System Tech. J. **41**, 453.

KOGELNIK, H. and C. K. N. PATEL, 1962, Proc. IRE **50**, 2365.

KOGELNIK, H. and W. RIGROD, 1962, Proc. IRE **50**, 220.

KOROBKIN, V. V. and A. V. USPENSKII, 1963, Zh. Eksperim. i Teor. Fiz. **45**, 1003; 1964, Soviet Phys.-JETP **18**, 693.

KOTIK, J. and M. C. NEWSTEIN, 1961, J. Appl. Phys. **32**, 178.

LADENBURG, R., 1921, Z. Physik **4**, 451.

LEMPICKI, A. and H. SAMELSON, 1963, Phys. Letters **4**, 133.

LENGYEL, B. A., 1962, Lasers (Wiley, New York).

MACEK, W. M. and D. T. M. DAVIS, 1963, Appl. Phys. Letters **2**, 67.

MAIMAN, T. H., 1960, Nature **187**, 493.

MAIMAN, T. H., 1961, Phys. Rev. **123**, 1145.

MANGER, H. and H. ROTHE, 1963, Phys. Letters **7**, 330.

MASSEY, G. A., M. K. OHSMAN and R. TARG, 1965, Appl. Phys. Letters **6**, 10.

MASTERS, J. I. and E. M. E. MURRAY, 1965, Proc. IEEE **53**, 76.

McCLUNG, F. J. and R. W. HELLWARTH, 1962, J. Appl. Phys. **33**, 828.

McCLUNG, F. J., S. E. SCHWARZ and F. J. MEYERS, 1962, J. Appl. Phys. **33**, 3139.

McMURTRY, B. J. and A. E. SIEGMAN, 1962, Appl. Opt. **1**, 51.

MILNE, E. A., 1924, Monthly Notices Roy. Astron. Soc. **85**, 117.

MOLLENAUER, L. F., G. F. IMBUSCH, H. W. MOOS, A. L. SCHAWLOW and A. D. MAY, 1963, Proc. Symp. Optical masers, Brooklyn Polytechnic Inst. (Polytechnic Press, Brooklyn) p. 51.

NASSAU, K., 1965, Mater. Res. Std. **5**, 3.

NELSON, D. F. and W. S. BOYLE, 1962, Appl. Opt. **1**, 181.

NUGENT, L. J., M. L. BHAUMIK, S. GEORGE and S. M. LEE, 1964, J. Chem. Phys. **41**, 1305.

OCHS, S. A. and J. J. PANKOVE, 1964, Proc. IEEE **52**, 713.

PATEL, C. K. N., W. L. FAUST and R. A. McFARLANE, 1964a, Bull. Am. Phys. Soc. **9**, 500.

PATEL, C. K. N., W. L. FAUST, R. A. McFARLANE and C. B. G. GARRETT, 1964b, Proc. IEEE **52**, 713.

PHELAN, R. J. and R. H. REDIKER, 1965, Appl. Phys. Letters **6**, 70.

RIGROD, W. W., H. KOGELNIK, D. BRANGACCIO and D. R. HERRIOTT, 1962, J. Appl. Phys. **33**, 743.

RONCHI, L., A. M. SCHEGGI and G. TORALDO DI FRANCIA, 1964, Alta Frequenza **33**, 114, 526.

ROSENTHAL, A. H., 1962, J. Opt. Soc. Am. **52**, 1143.

RÖSS, D., 1963, Proc. IEEE **51**, 468.

SAMELSON, H., A. LEMPICKI, C. BRECHER and V. BROPHY, 1964, Appl. Phys. Letters **5**, 173.

SCHAWLOW, A. L., 1960, *in*: C. H. Townes, ed., Quantum electronics (Columbia Univ. Press, New York) p. 553.

SCHAWLOW, A. L., 1961, Solid State J. **2**, 3.

SCHAWLOW, A. L., 1963, Contemp. Phys. **5**, 81.

SCHAWLOW, A. L. and G. E. DEVLIN, 1961, Phys. Rev. Letters **6**, 96.

SCHAWLOW, A. L.,and C. H. TOWNES, 1958, Phys. Rev. **112**, 1940.

SCHWARZ, S. E., 1963, Proc. IEEE **51**, 1362.

SCOVIL, H. E. D., G. FEHER and H. SEIDEL, 1957, Phys. Rev. **105**, 762.

SHIMODA, K., 1962, Appl. Opt. **1**, 33.

SIEGMAN, A. E., 1964, Bull. Am. Phys. Soc. **9**, 729; 1965, Proc. IEEE **53**, 277.

SOROKIN, P. P. and M. J. STEVENSON, 1961, Phys. Rev. Letters **5**, 557.

STATZ, H. and G. DEMARS, 1960, *in*: C. H. Townes, ed., Quantum electronics (Columbia Univ. Press, New York) p. 530.

SUGANO, S. and Y. TANABE, 1958, J. Phys. Soc. Japan **13**, 880.

TANG, C. L., H. STATZ and G. DEMARS, 1963a, Appl. Phys. Letters **2**, 222.

TANG, C. L., H. STATZ and G. DEMARS, 1963b, J. Appl. Phys. **34**, 2289.

TORALDO DI FRANCIA, G., 1963, Proc. Symp. Opt. masers, Brooklyn Polytechnic Inst. (Polytechnic Press, Brooklyn) p. 157.

TROUP, G. J., 1963, Masers and Lasers, 2nd. ed. (Wiley, New York).

WAGNER, W. G. and G. BIRNBAUM, 1961, J. Appl. Phys. **32**, 1185.

WHITE, A. D., E. I. GORDON and E. F. LABUDA, 1964, Appl. Phys. Letters **5**, 97.

WIEDER, I. and L. R. SARLES, 1961, Phys. Rev. Letters **6**, 95.

WITTEMAN, W. J. and R. BLEEKRODE, 1964, Phys. Letters **13**, 126.

WOLFF, N. E. and R. J. PRESSLEY, 1963, Appl. Phys. Letters **2**, 152.

YARIV, A. and J. P. GORDON, 1963, Proc. IEEE **51**, 4.

CHAPTER 15

OPTICAL GLASS

H. MEYER

Laboratoire Sovirel, Le Vesinet (S.- & -O.), France

CONTENTS

1. Introduction

From other chapters in this book it is possible to gauge the progress made in optics in recent years in such fields as instrument design and computing methods. This is paralleled by progress in the optical glass industry; the extent of these developments cannot be explained in terms only of the present situation, it is necessary to recall the historical beginnings of the current many-sided developments.

2. Historical

We shall not recapitulate the story of the great pioneers, Guinand, who invented optical glass as such, Abbe and Schott, the originators of the modern techniques, and others. Through the work of all these the optical glass industry developed over a period of about 100 years to the fairly stable situation which prevailed before the 1939–1945 world war. At this period all glass factories used the classical process in which the glass was melted in fireclay pots; this process required skilled operatives and gave a low yield of good glass but it satisfied the requirements of the users. That is, the glass had refractive index homogeneity of 1 in 10^5 or occasionally 1 in 10^6, apart from certain almost unavoidable defects; the latter quality was suitable for astronomical applications, the former for ordinary optical purposes.

The main drawbacks were the high price of the glass, due to the low yield, the large number and size of the residual bubbles in the glass, due to inadequate 're-fining', defects of homogeneity and finally the residual colour from chemical attack on the pots.

Further developments to minimize these defects began in the period 1935–1940, the most notable of these being the new rare-earth glasses (see the Kodak publications from 1935 onwards). These glasses could only be melted in platinum pots because they attacked the usual refractory materials violently. The chief stimulus for the latest developments was the enormous demand created by the 1939–1945 war; the final result was a revolution in production techniques.

3. Recent developments

3.1. DEVELOPMENTS IN THE U.S.A.

In the U.S.A. the problems of mass production stimulated research; the ordinary sources of supply were abruptly cut off at a time when the demand due to the war was enormous. The most striking result was the development of the continuous melting process by Corning Glass Works. This solution to the problem of mass-production of optical glass involves a reversal of what had been regarded until then as firmly established principles; it had been assumed that only the discontinuous or batch process could produce glass of sufficient homogeneity. In the Corning process the continuous furnace is divided in three sections corresponding to the three principal operations in glass melting, namely (1) melting the raw material, (2) refining, (3) homogenization. Very good results were obtained by lining appropriate parts of the furnace. The homogenization section, which is the last part of the process, produces glass of suitable viscosity for drawing into bars of accurate section; by means well understood in other branches of the glass industry it is also possible to obtain 'gobs' of glass of accurate weight and even finished mouldings, using a completely automatic system. This solution of the problem of manufacturing optical glass is typical of American industry. It marks a turning point in optical glass manufacture and it will certainly be the method best suited to mass production.

However, it must be remembered that the continuous process is a compromise; it is impossible to obtain homogeneity to one part in 10^5 from one lot to the next in a furnace in which the raw materials are introduced at one end, but by careful construction and operation it is possible to ensure that the index variation through a complete operation is within the production tolerance for the glass type, namely $\pm 100 \times 10^5$ to $\pm 50 \times 10^5$. The variation is slow enough to permit useful sized pieces to be obtained, but of course the weight and therefore the maximum dimension of such a piece depends on the quality required. Much experience with such furnaces has now been obtained, the amplitude of the refractive index oscillations is known, and it is possible to calculate in advance the characteristics of a furnace to satisfy certain tolerances.

3.2. DEVELOPMENTS IN EUROPE

European studies during and after the last war led in quite a different direction. Traditionally the European optical glass industry has sought to produce top quality glass with a great variety of different properties, supplying an industry mainly manufacturing high-performance products rather than mass production. Thus the emphasis has been on the discontinuous process, which can produce extremely homogeneous glass; new crucible materials, in particular platinum, have been developed.

The technology has developed in different ways, partly owing to the non-reactivity of the crucible walls and partly by the use of new heating methods (radiant heating by electricity and high-frequency induction heating) and improved regulation and control methods; the most important result was that the batch process has developed into a semi-continuous process. A tapping outlet is fitted to the platinum crucible, so that one has at the same time the advantages of a flexible batch system giving very homogeneous glass and those of a continuous system, at least those which concern the possibility of manufacturing bars, gobs and mouldings.

4. Possible future developments

The two processes, American and European, are seen on comparison to be complementary to each other rather than in competition; together they can satisfy practically all requirements for optical glass, and the manufacturers who wish to offer a really complete catalogue of optical glasses must use both processes. A detailed comparison of their respective domains of applicability may be made as follows:

1) In the continuous process the production units are capable of making about 1 ton of glass per day, or sometimes even more. Thus this technique is only worthwhile where the same type of glass is to be made for several days on end, so as to make negligible the loss of time in cleaning the furnace and starting up production again on a new type.

2) The batch and semi-continuous processes can produce glass melts from tens to hundreds of kilograms in weight. The time spent in changing from one type to another is zero or negligible, so that there is no need to carry on making several similar melts consecutively. Thus the process is particularly useful for small quantities, and also when some of the raw materials are very expensive; this is the case in glasses containing certain rare-earth oxides, as tantalum oxide or niobium oxide. Moreover, this process is appropriate for the production of extremely homogeneous glass, since there is no slow variation of the refractive index during pouring; this is inevitable in the continuous process, so that, although extremely homogeneous glass is generally wanted only in small quantities the semi-continuous process has an important sphere of use.

5. The choice of optical glasses

The above brief description of the two processes and comparison of their respective domains of use is intended to show the designer the present range of manufacturing possibilities and to enable him to make informed choice. Of course, changes may come in the next few years by way of a different emphasis in manufacturing; for example, an improvement in the continuous process may come about in which smaller units are available, thus producing a gain in flexibility. Thus the designer who is working in a new field should always consult the glass manufacturer; in this way he will be kept informed of the present catalogue position and of planned changes. The manufacturer needs to strike a balance between ordinary and special glass making and such joint consultation is of advantage to both, since the designer must choose his glasses with due regard to the possibility of making them as well as for their optical properties and the number to be sold.

On the one hand, if mass-production instruments are to be made, such as binoculars of ordinary characteristics, it is desirable to choose continuous melted glass supplied in automatic mouldings, since such glass will probably remain standard for several years.

On the other hand, for specialized, non-standard, or advanced optical systems, non-standard optical glasses may be needed; here one must know exactly what is possible, both in respect of optical properties and of quantities and sizes. For example it is known that high-index glasses can be particularly useful for some design problems: the curvature of a lens of given power decreases as its refractive index increases and this decrease of curvature results in a corresponding decrease of aberrations. Thus the aberration correction of lenses may be improved through the use of higher index glasses, the aperture may be increased, or the number of components may be decreased.

The development of the high index glasses is important for another reason; it is known that the dense barium crowns are chemically not very stable and this situation is aggravated with the higher densities, in spite of efforts for improvement. However, as the index is increased by the addition of rare-earth oxides the reverse phenomenon occurs and greatly improved chemical stability is found. Thus it is found that the lanthanum and tantalum crowns, of which the refractive indices lie between 1.8 and 1.9, are much better from this point of view than the classical crowns with indices between 1.6 and 1.7.

The most impressive techniques have evolved for the glasses of highest index, since the densest crowns are the most difficult to manufacture and they also give rise to certain polishing problems, necessitating the adaptation of polishing methods; however, once finished they are chemically more stable and they have exceptionally valuable optical properties.

6. Classification of glasses; chemical composition

The relative merits of the classical and special glasses can be seen by referring to the wellknown diagram of refractive index plotted against reciprocal dispersion. Most catalogues give this diagram with linear coordinates, but in fact what interests the designer in studying a set of glasses is not only the absolute values of the refractive index and reciprocal dispersion but also the ratio between the dispersions (i.e. not their difference). It is therefore sensible to plot the diagram with a logarithmic abscissa scale, as in fig. 1. It can then be seen that the region covered by high-index glasses, at the top of the graph, is as great as that of the lower-index glasses. For example, for index 1.62 there

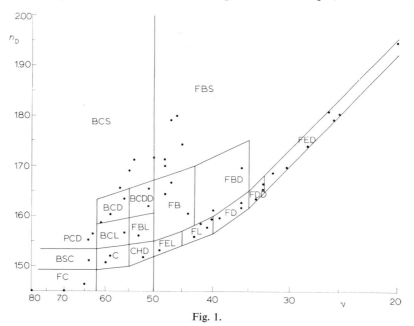

Fig. 1.

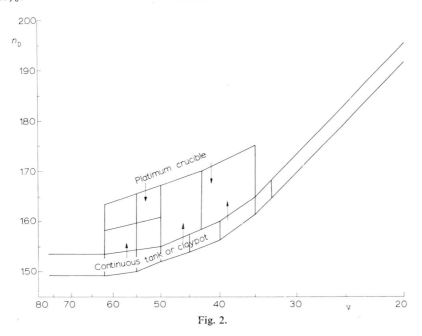

Fig. 2.

are two extreme glasses, both classical, with $v = 60$ and 35, of which the ratio is about 2; for index 1.8 we find the extreme values $v = 47$ and 25, a similar ratio, so that no sacrifice has been made to gain the advantage of the higher index. Fig. 2 shows approximately which glasses are made by which of the two manufacturing

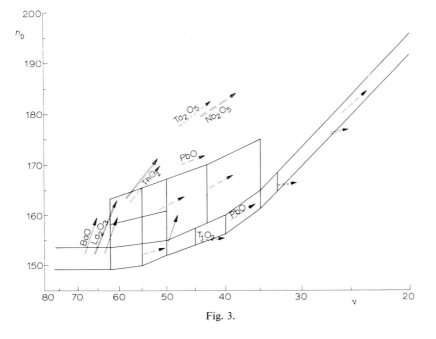

Fig. 3.

processes mentioned above. The lower group is clearly that of the older glasses and also of the mass-production glasses; the upper group contains the new glasses mostly and it is the group with the greater production flexibility. We stress that there is no exact line of dermarkation between the groups; the limit varies from one manufacturer to another, also it changes with time, tending generally to move upwards so as bring the high index glasses more into the large production range. The glasses in the graph have an enormous range of compositions; by contrast almost all industrial glasses, e.g. mirror glass, window glasses, glass fibres, bottles etc., have compositions like the crown and borosilicate crown glasses; only the group of so-called crystal

TABLE 1

	SiO_2	B_2O_3	Al_2O_3	Na_2O	K_2O	CaO	MgO	PbO	BaO	Remarks
Mass-production glasses										
Window glass	70.5	–	1.9	12.8	0.1	12.9	1.8	–	–	
Plate glass	72.9	–	1.3	13.9	–	8.5	3.4	–	–	
Bottle glass	73.3	–	1.9	14.1	0.5	6.4	3.8	–	–	
"Pyrex"	80.2	12.3	2.6	4.5	0.3	0.1	–	–	–	Low expansion 32 ⟩
Crystal	67.2	–	–	–	7.1	0.9	9.3	5.5	–	
Optical glasses										
801–51	68.4	19.0	3.2	0.3	9.1	0.8	–	–	–	Low expansion 51 ⟩
801–01 (BCS B 1664)	68.3	12.0	–	10.0	9.0	–	–	–	0.7	Index 1.516
800–03 (CB 2359)	67.4	8.0	–	7.4	9.6	0.8	–	6.8	–	Index 1.523
FD C 2036	45.7	–	0.4	2.1	6.1	–	–	45.8	–	Index 1.620
FeD C 8132	37.8	–	0.2	2.4	3.7	2.0	–	53.9	–	Index 1.681
FeD F 4820 (6.2)	16.6	–	1.5	–	0.3	–	–	81.6	–	Index 1.948
BCD C 2060	29.8	17.5	2.4	–	–	–	–	–	50.3	Index 1.620, low dispersion

	SiO_2	B_2O_3	Al_2O_3	La_2O_3	Ta_2O_5	ThO_2	WO_3		BaO	
Special optical glasses (*rare earth types*)										
BCS C 9154	14.0	17.1	1.3	10.4	–	9.0	–	–	4.82	Index 1.691, low dispersion
FBS E 0046	3.0	22.4	0.3	27.1	14.3	26.8	1.1	–	5	Index 1.800, low dispersion

glasses are like the light flints. The great range of optical glass compositions implied by fig. 3 is indicated also in table 1.

The first part of table 1 gives the compositions of the commonest industrial glasses; the actual values are usually within 2 to 3 % of those shown. The next section lists certain technical glasses with compositions markedly different from the mass-production glasses. Finally the compositions of some optical glasses are given; although the list is far from exhaustive it can be seen that the proportions of the constituents vary over large ranges. This wide range of variation creates, understandably, special manufacturing problems.

It should be noted here that the usual n_D–v diagram is insufficient to specify all relevant optical properties of glasses; a designer concerned with either microscope objectives or very large optics inevitably meets the problem of secondary spectrum. In order to be able to eliminate secondary spectrum completely it is necessary that the partial dispersions of all the glasses to be used should be linearly related through the spectrum, i.e., the relative partial dispersions should be independent of the reciprocal dispersions and the refractive indices. If we plot for example $(n_Q–n_F)/$ $(n_F–n_C)$ against the reciprocal dispersion $(n_D–1)/(n_F–n_C)$, using a logarithmic abscissa scale for the latter (fig. 4), we see that the points for almost all glasses lie on a straight line, which is *not* parallel to the abscissa axis. It is rather surprising that the representative points of the glasses depend only on the reciprocal dispersion, not on the refrac-

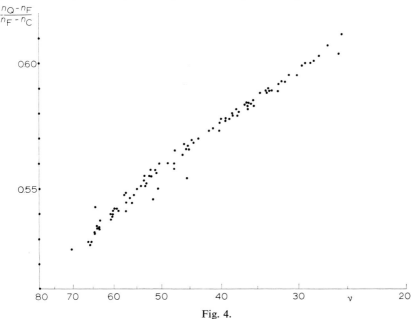

Fig. 4.

tive index. There are a few exceptions: the points for glasses with a boric oxide base lie somewhat below the line and those containing phosphorus lie slightly above it, particularly those containing also fluorine, but these are slight differences. At present the secondary spectrum problem cannot be solved perfectly, since this would require two glasses with their representative points at the same level but a considerable distance apart in the horizontal direction. This is not at the moment possible with commercial glasses but several glass firms are studying the problem.

7. The transmission of optical glass

To conclude this chapter we must stress the importance of good light transmission; this matter needs proportionally more attention with increase of complexity and size of optical systems. Progress is steady in this field, particularly with the high index glasses, these being the most sensitive to traces of colouring impurities. Some effort is being devoted to regions beyond the visible spectrum, as is indicated by the examples of figs. 5 and 6.

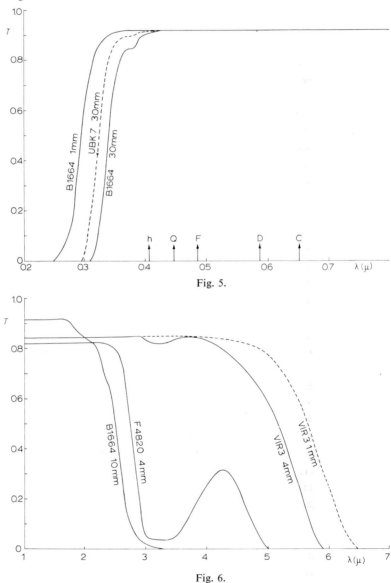

Fig. 5.

Fig. 6.

We do not wish here to expand beyond the part of this book devoted to classical optics, but it must be said in conclusion that, as the field of optics grows towards other branches of physics, particularly electronics, the glass manufacturers will meet new stimuli, and the resulting activity will undoubtedly react favourably on the domain of classical optics.

CHAPTER 16

GEOMETRICAL OPTICS

W. BROUWER AND A. WALTHER

Diffraction Limited, Inc.
Bedford, Mass.

CONTENTS

Contents continued overleaf

Contents, continued

1. Foundations of geometrical optics

1.1. INTRODUCTION

Geometrical optics describes the propagation of light in terms of rays. It is the oldest theory of light; in a rudimentary form it dates back to ancient Greece.

The speed of light depends on the medium it traverses, and may depend on the direction in which it travels. A medium in which the speed of light is direction dependent is called anisotropic. In this chapter we assume isotropic media: the speed of light is the same in all directions.

The speed of light may or may not vary within a medium. In the former case we call the medium inhomogeneous, in the latter case homogeneous.

In this chapter we shall, except in a very few instances, restrict ourselves to systems consisting of a number of homogeneous media separated by smooth surfaces.

The speed of light in vacuo is about 300000 km/s, independent of the color of the light. In material media the speed of light depends on the color. Not too close to absorption bands the speed of light decreases with the wavelength.

In geometrical optics a medium is described by its refractive index n: the ratio of the speed of light in vacuo (c) and the speed of light in the medium (v),

$$n = c/v. \tag{1}$$

Except for a few cases of X-ray propagation n is always greater than unity.

1.2. FERMAT'S PRINCIPLE

The entire edifice of geometrical optics can be built on one theorem: Fermat's principle. This principle states: The path chosen by the light in traveling from one

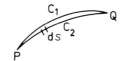

Fig. 1. Variation of a ray.

point to another is always such that the time required is stationary with respect to small variations in the path connecting the two points. Referring to fig. 1, the time it takes the light to travel along the actual path C_1 from P to Q is given by

$$\int_{P(C_1)}^{Q} \frac{ds}{v} = \frac{1}{c} \int_{P(C_1)}^{Q} n \, ds.$$

The value of this integral is stationary when we make small variations in the path, i.e. go from the path C_1 to some neighbouring curve C_2. The speed of light in vacuo is an absolute constant; consequently the factor $1/c$ is inconsequential. The integral

$$\int_{P}^{Q} n \, ds$$

taken along the actual path is called the optical pathlength between P and Q.

An immediate consequence of Fermat's principle is that in homogeneous media light travels along straight lines.

1.3. THE SINGLE THIN LENS

As a first application of Fermat's principle we consider the case of a single thin lens, as it is sketched in fig. 2.

We consider a plano convex lens with refractive index n, radius r and thickness t. The lens is located in vacuo, or in air, which has a refractive index quite close to

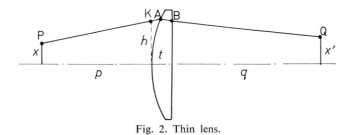

Fig. 2. Thin lens.

unity. Two points P and Q are given by their distances to the axis, x and x', and their distances to the lens measured along the axis, p and q. We wish to find the lightray that connects P with Q. This problem reduces to finding the intersection points A and B with the lens, because we know that both in the air and in the glass the lightrays are straight lines.

We further reduce the problem to bare essentials by assuming that p, q and r are large with respect to x and x' and the heights of incidence on the lens, which in turn are large with respect to the lens thickness.

On PA we introduce the auxiliary point K, perpendicularly above the vertex of the surface. Our assumptions with respect to the order of magnitude of the quantities involved allow us to neglect the differences in height of K, A and B. We denote this unknown height by h. We now have, to a sufficient approximation

$$
\begin{aligned}
PK &= p+(h-x)^2/2p, \\
KA &= h^2/2r, \\
AB &= t-h^2/2r, \\
BQ &= q+(h-x')^2/2q.
\end{aligned}
$$

The optical pathlength PKABQ, as a function of h, will be denoted by $S(h)$. We find this function by a simple addition, in which we take into account that AB is situated in glass:

$$
S(h) = p+\frac{(h-x)^2}{2p} + \frac{h^2}{2r} + n\left(t-\frac{h^2}{2r}\right) +q+ \frac{(h-x')^2}{2q},
$$

or

$$S(h) = (p+q+nt) + \tfrac{1}{2}\left(\frac{x^2}{p} + \frac{x'^2}{q}\right) - h\left(\frac{x}{p} + \frac{x'}{q}\right) + \tfrac{1}{2}h^2\left(\frac{1}{p} + \frac{1}{q} - \frac{n-1}{r}\right). \tag{2}$$

We find an equation for the value of h that makes $S(h)$ stationary by equating to zero the derivative of $S(h)$ with respect to h:

$$-\left(\frac{x}{p} + \frac{x'}{q}\right) + h\left(\frac{1}{p} + \frac{1}{q} - \frac{n-1}{r}\right) = 0. \tag{3}$$

The value of h that satifies this equation specifies the height of incidence of the actual lightray from P through the lens to Q. In solving it we must distinguish between three cases:

1. When the coefficient of h is not zero there is one and only one solution for h: the points P and Q together define one unique ray.

2. The coefficient of h is zero, but the constant is not zero. In that case there is no ray connecting P with Q.

3. Both the coefficient of h and the constant are zero:

$$\frac{1}{p} + \frac{1}{q} = \frac{n-1}{r}, \tag{4}$$

$$\frac{x'}{x} = -\frac{q}{p}. \tag{5}$$

In this case $S(h)$ does not depend on h at all, and consequently every ray departing from P arrives in Q. This, first of all, explains case 2: when all rays from P arrive in Q they cannot pass through another point of the plane through Q. P is in this case imaged in Q, and eq. (5) is the well known "lens formula". The object and image height are proportional; the magnification is given by the equally well-known formula (5).

We have to make one reservation as far as cases 1 and 3 are concerned: h may not come out larger than the semi-diameter of the lens. This seemingly trivial remark is of great practical importance and will be treated further in the section on pupils.

The stationary value of $S(h)$ is a minimum or a maximum, depending on the sign of the coefficient of h^2 in eq. (2). The minimum is a true minimum; the maximum is, however, not a true maximum when we allow a *general* variation according to Fermat's principle, i.e. when we vary not only h, but also vary the paths connecting P with A, A with B, and B with Q. We remind the reader that Fermat's principle only requires stationarity. The stationary value need not be a true maximum or minimum.

1.4. SNELL'S LAW

The technique used in the previous section to discuss the basic properties of a thin lens can be extended to systems containing more than two surfaces. Also the paraxial approximation can be overcome; this requires however an iteration method to obtain numerical results. An interesting ray tracing scheme based on this idea is given by SMITH [1945]. For many lens problems this approach is rather artificial, and it is more expedient to follow a ray step by step. Given a ray entering the lens, one first determines, from simple geometry, its point of intersection with the first surface. At the first surface the direction of the ray changes, and when the new direction is established one can determine its intersection point with the second surface, etc. The change in direction upon refraction by a surface is given by Snell's laws, which read as follows:

(1) The incident ray, the refracted ray and the normal to the surface in the point of incidence lie in one flat plane, called the plane of incidence.

(2) Let φ be the angle between the incident ray and the normal, and φ' the angle between the refracted ray and the normal.

Then

$$n \sin \varphi = n' \sin \varphi', \tag{6}$$

in which n and n' are the refractive indices before and after the surface. The angle φ is called the angle of incidence; φ' is called the angle of refraction.

This theorem is an immediate consequence of Fermat's principle. To prove it we choose two points P and Q on the incident and refracted ray, at a finite distance from the point of incidence A (fig. 3). Due to the symmetry about the plane of

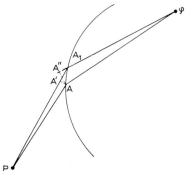

Fig. 3. Derivation of Snell's law.

incidence the optical path $\overline{\text{PAQ}}$ is stationary with respect to small movements of the point A perpendicular to the plane of incidence. When A is moved to A_1 the distance PA is augmented by $A'A_1$, and the distance AQ is reduced by $A''A_1$, A' and A'' being the projections of A on PA_1 and A_1Q respectively. These two variations in length cancel in the optical path calculation when

$$n \cdot A'A_1 = n' \cdot A''A_1.$$

But $A'A_1 = AA_1 \sin \varphi$, and $A''A_1 = AA_1 \sin \varphi'$, which leads directly to eq. (6).

Snell's law implies the case of reflection of a ray by a reflecting surface, provided that the refractive index after reflection is taken to be the negative of the index before reflection. The incident ray and the reflected ray lie on opposite sides of the normal and include equal angles with it.

1.5. APPLICATIONS OF FERMAT'S PRINCIPLE

We noted already that the straightforward application of Fermat's principle, as shown in the previous sections, becomes cumbersome in more complicated (i.e. more realistic) situations. In the section to follow we shall derive from Fermat's theorem a number of general results which shall prove to be indispensible in the further development of geometrical optics. The approach we shall take dates back to Hamilton. As stated before, we shall consider only isotropic media.

We consider a general optical system, consisting of inhomogeneous media separated by a finite number of surfaces where the index jumps discontinuously. In between these refracting surfaces the refractive index $n(x, y, z)$ is differentiable with respect to the space coordinates x, y, z. Fig. 4 exemplifies this situation; the line $P_0 P_1 \ldots P_n P_{n+1}$ represents a lightray connecting P_0 with P_{n+1}. Around this actual ray we consider a collection of other lines, in general *not* satisfying Fermat's principle. We label these

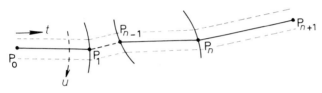

Fig. 4. General ray variation in piecewise continuous media.

lines with a parameter u (fig. 4). The points on each individual line are scanned by a parameter t. So the entire assembly of lines, running more or less from P_0 to P'_n is given by three functions of two parameters: $x(t, u)$, $y(t, u)$ and $z(t, u)$. Differentiation with respect to t shall be denoted by a prime.

The integral we must discuss is:

$$W(u) = \int_{P_0}^{P_{n+1}} n(x, y, z)\,ds = \sum_{0}^{n} \int_{P_i}^{P_{i+1}} \mathscr{L}(x, y, z, x', y', z')\,dt,$$

in which we have written

$$\mathscr{L}(x, y, z, x', y', z') = n(x, y, z)\,\sqrt{(x'^2 + y'^2 + z'^2)},$$

a quantity which will be recognized as the Lagrangian by students of analytical mechanics.

The variation of $W(u)$ with respect to u is described by

$$\frac{\partial W}{\partial u} = \sum_{0}^{n} \frac{\partial}{\partial u} \int_{P_i}^{P_{i+1}} \mathscr{L}\,dt. \tag{7}$$

We would like to interchange the differentiation and the integration. This is allowed, provided that we take care in the t calibration along the lines: each refractive surface must be a plane of constant t, and likewise the surface elements containing the starting point and the end point must be planes of constant t. We then have, for one term in the sum (7)

$$\frac{\partial}{\partial u}\int_{P_i}^{P_{i+1}} \mathscr{L}\,dt = \int_{P_i}^{P_{i+1}} \left(\frac{\partial\mathscr{L}}{\partial x}\frac{\partial x}{\partial u} + \frac{\partial\mathscr{L}}{\partial x'}\frac{\partial x'}{\partial u}\right)dt + (y, z)$$

$$= \int_{P_i}^{P_{i+1}} \frac{\partial\mathscr{L}}{\partial x}\frac{\partial x}{\partial u}\,dt + \int_{P_i}^{P_{i+1}} \frac{\partial\mathscr{L}}{\partial x'}\frac{d}{dt}\left(\frac{\partial x}{\partial u}\right)dt + (y, z)$$

$$= \frac{\partial\mathscr{L}}{\partial x'}\frac{\partial x}{\partial u}\bigg/\begin{array}{c}P_{i+n}\\P_i\end{array} + \int_{P_i}^{P_{i+1}}\left[\frac{\partial\mathscr{L}}{\partial x} - \frac{d}{dt}\left(\frac{\partial\mathscr{L}}{\partial x'}\right)\right]\frac{\partial x}{\partial u}\,dt + (y, z). \qquad (8)$$

The formulas are only written out for the x-terms; they must be completed by similar terms in y and z as indicated. Fermat's principle states that the actual light-ray is distinguished by $\partial W/\partial u$ being zero for any and all arbitrary collections of lines that we choose around the actual ray.

As a first application of this principle we choose our varied lines such that they coincide with the ray, except in between two points of refraction P_i and P_{i+1}.

Eq. (8) shows that in this case we must have

$$\frac{\partial\mathscr{L}}{\partial x} - \frac{d}{dt}\left(\frac{\partial\mathscr{L}}{\partial x'}\right) = 0,$$

and similar equations in y and z, for the actual ray in the inhomogeneous medium. We have here three differential equations, Euler's equations, that determine the path of a ray in an inhomogeneous medium. They express, implicitly, the curvature and the "twist" of the ray in every point, as a function of its direction and the properties of the medium.

We next assume that, at least between the refracting surfaces, all lines in the collection of lines chosen satisfy these equations. Eq. (7) then reduces to

$$\frac{\partial W}{\partial u} = \sum_1^n \frac{\partial\mathscr{L}}{\partial x}\frac{\partial x}{\partial u}\bigg/\begin{array}{c}P_{i+1}\\P_i\end{array} + (y, z). \qquad (9)$$

We now find the behavior of the actual ray at the refracting surfaces by requiring that, when P_0 and P_{n+1} are fixed, W shall be independent of small variations in the location of $P_1 \ldots P_n$ on the refracting surfaces.

When we use indices B and A to denote before and after refraction, we can write for eq. (9)

$$\frac{\partial W}{\partial u} = \left[\frac{\partial\mathscr{L}}{\partial x'}\frac{\partial x}{\partial u} + (y, z)\right]_{n+1} - \left[\frac{\partial\mathscr{L}}{\partial x'}\frac{\partial x}{\partial u} + (y, z)\right]_0$$

$$+ \sum_1^n \left\{\left[\frac{\partial\mathscr{L}}{\partial x'}\frac{\partial x}{\partial u} + (y, z)\right]_A - \left[\frac{\partial\mathscr{L}}{\partial x'}\frac{\partial x}{\partial u} + (y, z)\right]_B\right\}.$$

Keeping P_0 and P_{n+1} fixed, and requiring that $\partial W/\partial u$ shall be zero, we see that at each refraction the quantity

$$\frac{\partial\mathscr{L}}{\partial x'}\frac{\partial x}{\partial u} + \frac{\partial\mathscr{L}}{\partial y'}\frac{\partial y}{\partial u} + \frac{\partial\mathscr{L}}{\partial z'}\frac{\partial z}{\partial u}$$

must be the same before and after refraction. This is a disguised form of Snell's law, as we shall now demonstrate. We have:

$$\frac{\partial \mathcal{L}}{\partial x'} = n(x, y, z) \frac{x'}{\sqrt{(x'^2 + y'^2 + z'^2)}}$$

and similar equations in y and z. The expressions $x'(x'^2 + y'^2 + z'^2)^{-\frac{1}{2}}$ etc. are simply the direction cosines L, M and N of the ray direction with respect to the coordinate frame. The vector $\partial x/\partial u$, $\partial y/\partial u$, $\partial z/\partial u$ is tangential to the refracting surface, so we may conclude that the projection onto the tangential plane in the point of incidence of a vector along the direction of the ray, with a length equal to the local refractive index, is the same before and after refraction. This, however, comprises both parts of Snell's law.

A third result of fundamental importance may be derived from eq. (7). Let us assume that all lines chosen satisfy Euler's equations in between the refracting surfaces, and Snell's law at the refracting surfaces. Then all lines are legitimate lightrays and eq. (8) reduces to:

$$\frac{\partial W}{\partial u} = \frac{\partial \mathcal{L}}{\partial x'} \frac{\partial x}{\partial u} \Big/ \frac{P_{n+1}}{P_0} + (y, z).$$

We derived the meaning of $\partial \mathcal{L}/\partial x'$ etc. in the previous paragraph: they represent direction cosines multiplied with the appropriate refractive index. So we can write

$$dW = n(L\,dx + M\,dy + N\,dz) \Big/ \frac{P_{n+1}}{P_0}.$$

This equation specifies the variation of the optical path between two points when the points are moved over a small distance. Its geometrical interpretation is shown in fig. 5. Let $P_0 P_{n+1}$ be the original ray and $Q_0 Q_{n+1}$ the displaced ray. We project

Fig. 5. Geometrical interpretation of the nodal derivation of the characteristic function.

the displacements $P_0 Q_0$ and $P_{n+1} Q_{n+1}$ onto the original ray, finding points R_0 and R_{n+1}. Then we have

$$[Q_0 Q_{n+1}] - [P_0 P_{n+1}] = [P_{n+1} R_{n+1}] - [P_0 R_0],$$

the square brackets denoting optical path length. In our further discussions we shall assume that the space before the first refracting surface, called the object space, and the space beyond the last refracting surface, called the image space, are homogeneous, with refractive indices n and n' respectively. We shall use separate coordinate systems for these spaces: (x, y, z) and (x'_1, y'_1, z'_1) respectively. In general a prime shall indicate that a quantity belongs to the image space; so we shall write (L, M, N) and (L', M', N') for the direction cosines in the object and the image space.

The optical pathlength W measured along the ray connecting an arbitrary point in the object space with an arbitrary point of the image space is a function of the six variables (x, y, z) and (x'_1, y'_1, z'_1). This function is often called Hamilton's characteristic function.

According to the previous work, we have

$$dW = n'(L'dx'_1 + M'dy'_1 + N'dz'_1) - n(Ldx + Mdy + Ndz), \tag{10}$$

or

$$\frac{\partial W}{\partial x} = -nL, \qquad \frac{\partial W}{\partial x'_1} = n'L',$$

$$\frac{\partial W}{\partial y} = -nM, \qquad \frac{\partial W}{\partial y'_1} = n'M', \tag{11}$$

$$\frac{\partial W}{\partial z} = -nN, \qquad \frac{\partial W}{\partial z'_1} = n'N'.$$

So the direction of a ray in the object and image space can be found simply by differentiating the characteristic function with respect to the coordinates of the end points of the ray.

1.6. PERFECT SYSTEMS

The bulk of this chapter on geometrical optics shall be concerned with lenses, and in particular the image forming properties of lenses. But before we start a discussion of the properties of specific lens systems, it seems appropriate to first prove a theorem that severely restricts the possibility of perfect image formation: if a system forms a perfect image of a point and its immediate three-dimensional vicinity, the magnification for this image formation must be unity.

The point P in the object space (fig. 6) is imaged perfectly into the point P' of the image space when all rays emerging from P pass through the point P' after they have

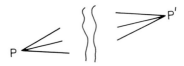

Fig. 6. Perfect system.

traversed the optical system. In order to satisfy Fermat's principle, the optical path length from P to P' must be the same along all rays connecting P and P'.

Let us introduce two cartesian coordinate systems (x, y, z) and (x', y', z') with their origins in P and P' respectively. We now require that not only P is imaged perfectly into P', but also that the immediate vicinity of P is imaged perfectly into the immediate vicinity of P'. For the coordinates of a point close to P we may write: (dx, dy, dz). This point shall be imaged into the point $Q'(dx', dy', dz')$, and we shall have relations of the type:

$$\begin{pmatrix} dx' \\ dy' \\ dz' \end{pmatrix} = \begin{pmatrix} \alpha_{11} & \alpha_{12} & \alpha_{13} \\ \alpha_{21} & \alpha_{22} & \alpha_{23} \\ \alpha_{31} & \alpha_{32} & \alpha_{33} \end{pmatrix} \begin{pmatrix} dx \\ dy \\ dz \end{pmatrix}, \tag{12}$$

where the α_{ij} are the derivatives of the image point coordinates with respect to the object point coordinates. Now let (L, M, N) and $(L'M'N')$ be the direction cosines of an arbitrary ray connecting P with P'. Then we have for the points Q and Q', according to the previous section

$$dW = n'(L'dx' + M'dy' + N'dz') - n(Ldx + Mdy + Ndz). \tag{13}$$

Given the image formation, the optical pathlength QQ' is fully determined by the coordinates of Q alone and is obviously independent of which ray from P to P' we choose.

So

$$dW = dF(x, y, z), \tag{14}$$

independent of the direction cosines. We can now rewrite (12), (13), and (14) in the form

$$[n'(\alpha_{11}L' + \alpha_{21}M' + \alpha_{31}N') - nL]dx +$$
$$+ [n'(\alpha_{12}L' + \alpha_{22}M' + \alpha_{32}N') - nM]dy +$$
$$+ [n'(\alpha_{13}L' + \alpha_{23}M' + \alpha_{33}N') - nN]dz =$$
$$= \frac{\partial F}{\partial x}dx + \frac{\partial F}{\partial y}dy + \frac{\partial F}{\partial z}dz.$$

The derivatives in the right-hand side of this equation are constants when the ray direction varies, hence the expressions between square brackets in the left-hand side must be constants. This shows that the relations connecting (L, M, N) with (L', M', N') are linear transformations. This linear transformation preserves length, because all direction cosines represent unit vectors. Consequently the matrix

$$\frac{n'}{n}\begin{pmatrix} \alpha_{11} & \alpha_{21} & \alpha_{31} \\ \alpha_{12} & \alpha_{22} & \alpha_{32} \\ \alpha_{13} & \alpha_{23} & \alpha_{33} \end{pmatrix}$$

constitutes a unitary transformation, and the derivatives of F are zero. From this it follows, first of all, that the angle between two rays upon departure from P is equal to the angle between these rays upon their arrival in P'. Secondly, observing that the transpose of a unitary matrix is its inverse, we see by observing eq. (12) that the ratio of the length of the line elements (dx', dy', dz') and (dx, dy, dz) is equal to n/n'. Consequently the perfect image formation for an element of space is only possible when the magnification of lengths is equal to the ratio of the refractive indices in the object and image space. We have proved at the same time that this circumstance obtains around one perfectly imaged point when the "angular magnification", i.e. the ratio of the angle between two rays in the image and object space, is unity.

Few systems are known that do satisfy this severe requirement on the image formation: the only example of practical importance is the plane mirror. We wish to emphasize, however, that the above proof is, in a sense, only of academic value: it does not indicate how closely perfect image formation can be approximated in practical cases.

1.7. ABBE AND HERSCHEL'S LAWS

The result of the previous section indicates that we have to settle for less than perfect image formation of a three-dimensional region. In this section we shall consider two more restricted cases: the perfect image formation of a line element perpendicular to the axis of a lens, and the perfect image formation of a line element along the axis of a lens.

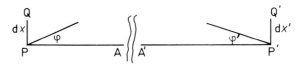

Fig. 7. Abbe's sine rule.

Let, in fig. 7, P and Q be imaged perfectly in P' and Q' respectively. We shall have

$$[QQ'] - [PP'] = n'L' \, dx' - nL \, dx,$$

and this expression must be independent of L and L'. It must in fact be zero, because along the axis (PAA'P') we have $L = L' = 0$. We can write $L = \sin \varphi$ and $L' = \sin \varphi'$; so it follows that

$$\frac{dx'}{dx} = \frac{n \sin \varphi}{n' \sin \varphi'}. \tag{15}$$

This formula is the condition under which a line element perpendicular to the axis is imaged perfectly, given that the point on axis is imaged without aberrations. It is known as Abbe's sine rule. For axially symmetric systems the condition applies to a surface element perpendicular to the axis. For an object at infinity, Abbe's sine rule must be slightly modified. A limiting procedure shows that for an incident

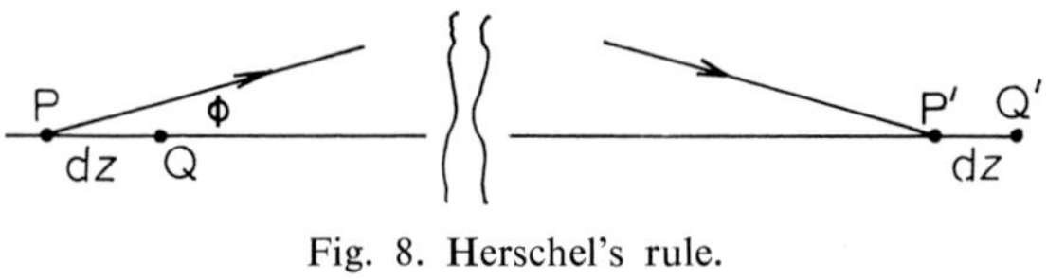

Fig. 8. Herschel's rule.

ray parallel to the axis the ratio of the height before the lens and the sine of the angle with the axis after the lens must be constant, the ratio being the focal length of the lens. This shows that a lens corrected for an object point at infinity, and its immediate vicinity, cannot have an F number (ratio of focal length and diameter of the incident pencil) smaller than 0.5.

We now consider a different problem. Let, in fig. 8, the points P and Q, both on the axis of the instrument, be imaged perfectly into P' and Q'. Then

$$[QQ'] - [PP'] = n'N' \, dz' - nN \, dz.$$

This expression must again be independent of the direction cosines. Along the axis both direction cosines are unity, hence

$$n'N' \, dz' - nN \, dz = n' \, dz' - n \, dz.$$

We now substitute $N = \cos \varphi$, and $N' = \cos \varphi'$, and arrive at

$$\frac{dz'}{dz} = \frac{n \sin^2 \frac{1}{2}\varphi}{n' \sin^2 \frac{1}{2}\varphi'}. \tag{16}$$

This formula is the condition under which a line element along the axis of an instrument is imaged perfectly, given that one of its points is imaged perfectly. It is known as Herschel's rule.

We see that Herschel's rule and Abbe's sine rule are only compatible when $\varphi = \pm \varphi'$. It then follows that

$$\left| \frac{dx'}{dx} \right| = \left| \frac{dz'}{dz} \right| = \frac{n}{n'},$$

which confirms the general result of the previous section.

1.8. EIKONAL FUNCTIONS

In section 1.5 we defined Hamilton's characteristic function $W(x, y, z, x'_1, y'_1, z'_1)$ as the optical pathlength from the point (x, y, z) in the object space to the point (x'_1, y'_1, z'_1) in the image space *.

We proved that the direction cosines in the object and image space are given by

$$-nL = \frac{\partial W}{\partial x}, \qquad n'L' = \frac{\partial W}{\partial x'_1},$$

$$-nM = \frac{\partial W}{\partial y}, \qquad n'M' = \frac{\partial W}{\partial y'_1},$$

$$-nN = \frac{\partial W}{\partial z}, \qquad n'N' = \frac{\partial W}{\partial z'_1}.$$

These six equations are not independent, as the sum of the squares for each set of

---

* The index 1 attached to the image space coordinates signifies that (x'_1, y'_1, z'_1) is not meant to be the image of (x, y, z).

direction cosines is one. In some cases this dependency is rather awkward in the applications *. For this reason the z and z'_1 coordinates are often taken for granted, and W is considered as a function of the four variables x, y, x'_1, and y'_1 only, signifying the optical pathlength from a point (x, y) in the plane $z=0$ to a point (x'_1, y'_1) in the plane $z'_1 = 0$. The coordinate axes are then usually chosen such that the ray traveling along the z-axis is transformed by the instrument into a ray along the z'_1 axis. The optical path function $W(x, y, 0, x'_1, y'_1, 0)$ is called the "point eikonal" $S(x, y, x'_1, y'_1)$ in this case, and we have

$$\frac{\partial S}{\partial x} = -nL, \qquad \frac{\partial S}{\partial x'_1} = n'L',$$

$$\frac{\partial S}{\partial y} = -nM, \qquad \frac{\partial S}{\partial y'_1} = n'M'. \tag{17}$$

We can also write

$$\mathrm{d}S = n'(L'\,\mathrm{d}x' + M'\,\mathrm{d}y') - n(L\,\mathrm{d}x + M\,\mathrm{d}y), \tag{18}$$

in which the variations in the endpoints of the ray are now required to take place in the planes $z=0$ and $z'=0$.

A wealth of important theorems can be derived from the mere fact that the right-hand side of eq. (18) is a total differential; lack of space impels us, however, to refer the reader to the literature, in particular HERZBERGER's [1931] classic treatise "Strahlen Optik". As an example we mention that by virture of the relation

$$\frac{\partial^2 S}{\partial x\, \partial x'_1} = \frac{\partial^2 S}{\partial x'_1\, \partial x},$$

we have

$$n'\left(\frac{\partial L'}{\partial x}\right)_{x'_1} = n\left(\frac{\partial L}{\partial x'_1}\right)_x.$$

Assuming that the differentiations take place around the origins, the physical interpretation of this formula leads to the following theorem, due to Christiaan Huygens: the angular size under which an eye sees an object through an optical system remains the same when object and eye reverse places.

Note that in this example there cannot be an object–image relation between the origins in the object and the image space. The entire argument would break down, because our basic assumption is that the four coordinates (x, y, x'_1, y'_1) determine one and only one ray. If this is not the case one can hardly expect that eq. (17) still yields ray directions. To overcome this difficulty we introduce three new functions, closely related to the point eikonal. The first of these functions is the *point angle eikonal* V, defined by

---

* In inhomogeneous media these relations are very useful: they lead to partial differential equations of the Hamilton–Jacobi type for the wavefront.

$$V(x, y, L', M') = S(x, y, x'_1, y'_1) - n'(L'x'_1 + M'y'_1).$$

Note that we do not only add terms to the point eikonal, we also choose a new set of variables. Differentiation of V yields

$$dV = -n'(x'_1 dL' + y'_1 dM') - n(L dx + M dy),$$

or

$$\frac{\partial V}{\partial L'} = -n'x'_1, \qquad \frac{\partial V}{\partial x} = -nL,$$

$$\frac{\partial V}{\partial M'} = -n'y'_1, \qquad \frac{\partial V}{\partial y} = -nM. \qquad (19)$$

We see that differentiation with respect to the direction cosines in the image space yields the coordinates of the point of intersection of the ray with the reference plane $z'_1 = 0$. The function V can be used whenever a ray is uniquely determined by its point of intersection with the object side reference plane $(z = 0)$ and its direction in the image space.

The physical meaning of the additional terms is easily found (see fig. 9) by observing that $(L'x'_1 + M'y'_1)$ is the length of the projection onto the ray of the vector

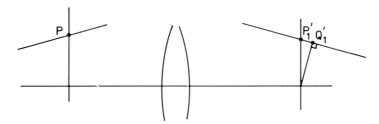

Fig. 9. Point angle eikonal.

drawn from the origin $(0, 0)$ to the point (x'_1, y'_1). So V is the optical pathlength from the point (x, y) in the reference plane at the object side to the projection of the coordinate origin in the image space onto the ray in the image space.

Two more eikonals are commonly used. Their definition goes along the same lines as the definition of V:

Angle point eikonal

$$V'(L, M, x'_1, y'_1) = S(x, y, x'_1, y'_1) + n(Lx + My),$$
$$dV' = n'(L' dx'_1 + M' dy'_1) + n(x dL + y dM).$$

Angle cikonal

$$E(L, L', M, M') = S(x, y, x'_1, y'_1) + n(xL + yM) - n'(x'_1 L' + y'_1 M'),$$
$$dE = -n'(x'_1 dL' + y'_1 dM') + n(x dL + y dM).$$

The geometrical meaning of the four eikonals is summarized in fig. 10.

Fig. 10. Eikonal functions: PP_1' point eikonal; PQ_1' point angle eikonal; QP_1' angle point eikonal; QQ_1' angle eikonal.

1.9. WAVEFRONTS

Let us consider all rays emanating from a point in the object space. Each of these rays passes through the optical system, and gives rise to a ray in the image space. On each of these rays in the image space we choose a point that has a predetermined optical distance to the object point. The locus of these points forms a surface, which is called a wavefront for reasons that are set forth in the theory of diffraction. A wavefront is perpendicular to all its rays, for in going in the wavefront from one point to another one we have

$$n'(L'\,dx' + M'\,dy' + N'\,dz') = 0.$$

Perfect image formation requires that the wavefronts in the image space be spheres. If the image formation suffers from aberrations, the wavefronts may be very complicated surfaces, especially when they are studied in a region where an image is approximately formed. Far away from such regions the wavefronts become more manageable surfaces, with a shape closely related to the point angle eikonal, as we shall show now.

If, on each ray in the image space, we move backwards from the point x_1', y_1' over a distance S (the point eikonal function) and from there move backwards further over a fixed distance p, then the points obtained in this way constitute a wavefront. The coordinates of the points so obtained are

$$x_1' - (S+p)L',$$
$$y_1' - (S+p)M',$$
$$- (S+p)N'.$$

We assume that p is large, and we now determine the distance from each point of this wavefront to a fixed point $x_0' y_0' z_0'$ which might be the point in which we would like to see the image formed. This distance is

$$\{[x_1' - x_0' - (S+p)L']^2 + [y_1' - y_0' - (S+p)M']^2 + [-z_0' - (S+p)N']^2\}^{\frac{1}{2}}.$$

If a perfect image were formed, this quantity would be constant and if the image were formed close to the plane $z_1' = 0$ its value would be about p.

So it is appropriate to subtract p from the expression given above; the result will be the deviation between the actual wavefront and a sphere centered around the point where we would like to see the image formed.

We now evaluate this difference Δ when p is very large. By using the theorem that in the limit when p goes to infinity $(p^2 + Ap + B)^{\frac{1}{2}} - p$ equals $\frac{1}{2}A$, we arrive at

$$\Delta = (S - n'L'x_1' - n'M'y_1') + n'(L'x_0' + M'y_0' + N'z_0'),$$

or

$$\Delta(L', M') = V(x, y, L', M') + n'(L'x_0' + M'y_0' + N'z_0'). \tag{20}$$

This formula clearly shows the close relation between the point angle eikonal and the wavefront deviation from a sphere centered around the point (x_0', y_0', z_0'), the deviation being evaluated at infinity.

This result is of prime importance in the development of the diffraction theory of aberrations.

We can use eq. (20) to derive the form that the point angle eikonal must have in order that each point of the (x, y) plane in the object space is imaged into a point x', y' of the (x_1', y_1') plane. The requirement is that Δ is independent of L' and M', so

$$V(x, y, L', M') = -n'x'L' - n'y'M' + f(x, y),$$

in which x' and y' are functions of x and y by virtue of the object image relation, and $f(x, y)$ is an arbitrary function of x and y.

The correctness of this expression can be seen immediately upon differentiation with respect to L' and M':

$$n'x_1' = -\frac{\partial V}{\partial L'} = n'x',$$

$$n'y_1' = -\frac{\partial V}{\partial M'} = n'y',$$

which shows that the point of incidence of a ray with the (x_1', y_1') plane is determined by x and y only; it is independent of L' and M'. In this case the direction of a ray in the object space is given by

$$nL = -\frac{\partial V}{\partial x} = n'L'\frac{\partial x'}{\partial x} - \frac{\partial}{\partial x}f(x, y),$$

$$nM = -\frac{\partial V}{\partial y} = n'M'\frac{\partial y'}{\partial y} - \frac{\partial}{\partial y}f(x, y).$$

When we apply these equations in the immediate vicinity around the origins, the ray $L = M = 0$ in the object space corresponds to the ray $L' = M' = 0$ in the image space. So the derivatives of $f(x, y)$ must be zero. This then verifies Abbe's sine rule.

1.10. MATRIX NOTATION

Most of the optical systems that shall be treated in this chapter will have axial symmetry. We shall always assume that the z- and z_1'-axes coincide with this axis of symmetry. The eikonal functions are restricted by the requirement of axial symmetry: they can only depend on combinations of their four variables that are rotationally invariant.

For the point angle eikonal this leads to the form

$$V(x, y, L', M') = V(u_1, u_2, u_3),$$

with

$$u_1 = \tfrac{1}{2}(x^2 + y^2),$$
$$u_2 = xL' + yM', \tag{21}$$
$$u_3 = \tfrac{1}{2}(L'^2 + M'^2),$$

in which the factors of $\tfrac{1}{2}$ are only introduced for convenience. Differentiation now leads to

$$-n'x_1' = \frac{\partial V}{\partial u_2}x + \frac{\partial V}{\partial u_3}L' \qquad -nL = \frac{\partial V}{\partial u_1}x + \frac{\partial V}{\partial u_2}L',$$

$$-n'y_1' = \frac{\partial V}{\partial u_2}y + \frac{\partial V}{\partial u_3}M' \qquad -nM = \frac{\partial V}{\partial u_1}y + \frac{\partial V}{\partial u_2}M'.$$

We can solve these equations for x', L', y' and M'; this leads to

$$\begin{pmatrix} n'L' \\ x' \end{pmatrix} = \begin{pmatrix} B & -A \\ -D & C \end{pmatrix}\begin{pmatrix} nL \\ x \end{pmatrix}, \qquad \begin{pmatrix} n'M' \\ y' \end{pmatrix} = \begin{pmatrix} B & -A \\ -D & C \end{pmatrix}\begin{pmatrix} nM \\ y \end{pmatrix},$$

in which

$$B = -n'\left(\frac{\partial V}{\partial u_2}\right)^{-1},$$

$$A = -B\left(\frac{\partial V}{\partial u_1}\right),$$

$$D = \frac{B}{n'^2}\left(\frac{\partial V}{\partial u_3}\right), \tag{22}$$

$$BC - AD = 1.$$

These formulas are the basic relations required in the description of image formation. They will be derived from the parameters specifying an optical system in the sections to follow, and will there be discussed at length.

2. Matrix description of optical instruments

2.1. COMPUTATION OF THE MATRIX ELEMENTS

In section 1.10 it is shown that the quantities A, B, C and D are sufficient to describe a lens system. We will derive the formulae to compute these quantities in terms of the parameters describing the optical system. We will only consider optical systems with an axis of symmetry.

We can describe a ray in such an optical system by four coordinates. Here we will again use the direction cosines L and M, and the intersection point (x, y) of the ray with a surface perpendicular to the z-axis which is the axis of symmetry. Basically then the problem consists of two transformations: 1) the transformation of these four coordinates at a refracting surface, 2) the transformation of these coordinates from one refracting surface to the next.

Before we consider these transformations we will establish a sign convention.

1. Unless otherwise stated, the light is always coming from the left.
2. A distance is positive if measured from left to right.
3. A distance is always measured from a refracting surface.
4. The vertex of a refracting surface is its intersection point with the axis of symmetry of the system.
5. A radius of curvature is positive if the direction from the vertex to the center of curvature is from left to right.
6. A ray coordinate before and after refraction will be denoted with the same letter; the one after the refraction will have a prime.
7. Subscripts will be used to indicate at what surface the refraction is taking place. The numbering of the surfaces will be in the order in which the light is passing through them.

We will first consider the refraction at a surface. This is completely described by Snell's law.

In fig. 11 an incident ray AP is refracted at point P into ray PB. Our coordinate system is chosen such that P is in the (x, y) plane and the z-axis coincides with the

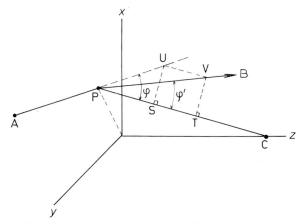

Fig. 11. Refraction by a surface with axial symmetry.

axis of symmetry. The refractive index to the left of the refracting surface is n_i; to the right of the surface it is n_i'. The ray AP is given by its direction cosines L_i and M_i and the coordinates x_i, y_i of point P. We want to find the coordinates L_i' and M_i' and x_i', y_i' of the refracted ray PB. Using the same coordinate system it is obvious that the point P belongs to both rays and therefore

$$x'_i = x_i,$$
$$y'_i = y_i.$$

(23)

Since the z-axis is an axis of symmetry, the normal to the refracting surface will intersect the z-axis in a point C.

We now have for the direction cosines of the normal PC

$$\cos \alpha = - \frac{x_i}{PC},$$

$$\cos \beta = - \frac{y_i}{PC}.$$

(24)

We now extend the ray AP with a distance PU such that

$$PU = n_i$$

and on the ray PB we take a distance PV so that

$$PV = n'_i.$$

Designating the angle UPC by φ_i and the angle BPC by φ'_i we have

$$US = n_i \sin \varphi_i,$$
$$VT = n'_i \sin \varphi'_i.$$

According to Snell's law PU, PV and PC are coplanar and

$$US = VT.$$

We now project the triangle PUV onto the x-axis and find

$$n'_i L'_i - UV \cos \alpha - n_i L_i = 0.$$

Similarly, projecting this triangle onto the y-axis we find

$$n'_i M'_i - UV \cos \beta - n_i M_i = 0.$$

Using the expressions (24) for $\cos \alpha$ and $\cos \beta$ we have

$$n'_i L'_i = n_i L_i - \frac{UV}{PC} x_i,$$

$$n'_i M'_i = n_i M_i - \frac{UV}{PC} y_i.$$

(25)

Again from geometry

$$UV = ST = n'_i \cos \varphi'_i - n_i \cos \varphi_i.$$

We will now introduce the quantity

$$\frac{UV}{PC} = \frac{n'_i \cos \varphi'_i - n_i \cos \varphi_i}{PC} = A_i.$$

(26)

Combining eqs. (23), (25) and (26) and writing the results in matrix form we find:

$$\begin{pmatrix} n_i'L_i' \\ x_i' \end{pmatrix} = \begin{pmatrix} 1 & -A_i \\ 0 & 1 \end{pmatrix} \begin{pmatrix} n_iL_i \\ x_i \end{pmatrix} = R_i \begin{pmatrix} n_iL_i \\ x_i \end{pmatrix}, \tag{27}$$

$$\begin{pmatrix} n_i'M_i' \\ y_i' \end{pmatrix} = \begin{pmatrix} 1 & -A_i \\ 0 & 1 \end{pmatrix} \begin{pmatrix} n_iM_i \\ y_i \end{pmatrix} = R_i \begin{pmatrix} n_iM_i \\ y_i \end{pmatrix}. \tag{28}$$

We notice that the transformation R_i is the same for the two sets of coordinates (n_iL_i, x_i) and (n_iM_i, y_i), and furthermore that the determinant of the matrix R_i equals $+1$. This transformation is valid for all surfaces with an axis of symmetry, including aspherics. For spherical surfaces the length PC equals the radius of curvature r of the surface. Introducing the quantity R, called the curvature of the surface, by

$$R_i = 1/r_i,$$

we can write eq. (26) for spherical surfaces in the form

$$A_i = (n_i' \cos \varphi_i' - n \cos \varphi_i)R_i. \tag{29}$$

For a computation scheme to determine the A_i for a ray we refer the reader to ch. 17, section 3.6.

We now have to consider the transformation of the ray coordinates between the surfaces i and $i+1$. We will choose the coordinate axis for surface $i+1$ such that its z-axis coincides with the z-axis of the previous surface.

The (x, y) plane for surface $i+1$ is again chosen such that the point of incidence of the ray with this surface is in this coordinate plane. The distance between the points of refraction at the surfaces i and $i+1$ measured along the ray is T'. We will label the coordinates at surface $i+1$ by L_{i+1}, M_{i+1} and x_{i+1}, y_{i+1}. From simple geometry we find

$$L_{i+1} = L_i', \qquad M_{i+1} = M_i',$$

or, since $n_{i+1}=n_i'$,

$$n_{i+1}L_{i+1} = n_i'L_i', \qquad n_{i+1}M_{i+1} = n_i'M_i'.$$

For the height we have

$$x_{i+1} = x_i' + T_i'L_i' = x_i' + \frac{T_i'}{n_i'} n_i'L_i',$$

$$y_{i+1} = y_i' + T_i'M_i' = y_i' + \frac{T_i'}{n_i'} n_i'M_i'.$$

Again writing eqs. (15) and (16) in matrix form we find

$$\begin{pmatrix} n_{i+1}L_{i+1} \\ x_{i+1} \end{pmatrix} = \begin{pmatrix} 1 & 0 \\ \dfrac{T_i'}{n_i'} & 1 \end{pmatrix} \begin{pmatrix} n_i'L_i' \\ x_i' \end{pmatrix} = T_i \begin{pmatrix} n_i'L_i' \\ x_i' \end{pmatrix}, \tag{30}$$

$$\begin{pmatrix} n_{i+1} M_{i+1} \\ \\ y_{i+1} \end{pmatrix} = \begin{pmatrix} 1 & 0 \\ \dfrac{T_i'}{n_i'} & 1 \end{pmatrix} \begin{pmatrix} n_i' M_i' \\ \\ y_i' \end{pmatrix} = T_i \begin{pmatrix} n_i' M_i' \\ \\ y_i' \end{pmatrix}. \tag{31}$$

We again notice that the transformation is the same for the sets of coordinates $n_i' L_i'$, x_i' and $n_i' M_i'$, y_i' and that the determinant of the matrix T_i equals unity.

Any ray passing through an optical system can now be described by the product of the appropriate R and T matrices for each surface. In general we thus find that a ray with coordinates L_1, M_1 and x_1, y_1 entering a system of e refracting surfaces, emerges with coordinates L_e', M_e' and x_e', y_e' given by

$$\begin{pmatrix} n_e' L_e' \\ x_e' \end{pmatrix} = R_e T_{e-1} \cdots R_2 T_1 R_1 \begin{pmatrix} n_1 L_1 \\ x_1 \end{pmatrix} = M_{1,e} \begin{pmatrix} n_1 L_1 \\ x_1 \end{pmatrix},$$

$$\begin{pmatrix} n_e' M_e' \\ y_e' \end{pmatrix} = R_e T_{e-1} \cdots R_2 T_1 R_1 \begin{pmatrix} n_1 M_1 \\ y_1 \end{pmatrix} = M_{1,e} \begin{pmatrix} n_1 M_1 \\ y_1 \end{pmatrix}.$$

The matrix $M_{1,e}$ is again a 2×2 matrix with a determinant $+1$. We shall write

$$M_{1,e} = \begin{pmatrix} B & -A \\ -D & C \end{pmatrix}$$

where

$$BC - AD = 1,$$

so that

$$\begin{pmatrix} n' L' \\ x' \end{pmatrix} = \begin{pmatrix} B & -A \\ -D & C \end{pmatrix} \begin{pmatrix} nL \\ x \end{pmatrix} \tag{32}$$

and

$$\begin{pmatrix} n' M' \\ y' \end{pmatrix} = \begin{pmatrix} B & -A \\ -D & C \end{pmatrix} \begin{pmatrix} nM \\ y \end{pmatrix}. \tag{33}$$

In these last formulas we have dropped the subscripts; the prime indicating the image space coordinates and no prime indicating the object space. This simplification in the notation will not lead to ambiguities when we only deal with the properties of the entire system.

We are usually not interested in studying rays between the first and last surface of an optical system, but in the quality of the images formed by these rays. It is easy to extend the matrix to include the object and the image plane. The distance between the object plane and the first surface, measured along a ray, we will call τ; and the distance to the image plane from the point of the intersection of the ray with the last surface, again measured along the ray, is τ'. It is easily seen that we then have the relation

$$\begin{pmatrix} n'L' \\ x' \end{pmatrix}_{im} = \begin{pmatrix} 1 & 0 \\ \dfrac{\tau'}{n'} & 1 \end{pmatrix} \begin{pmatrix} B & -A \\ -D & C \end{pmatrix} \begin{pmatrix} 1 & 0 \\ -\dfrac{\tau}{n} & 1 \end{pmatrix} \begin{pmatrix} nL \\ x \end{pmatrix}_{obj}$$

$$= \begin{pmatrix} B + \dfrac{\tau}{n} A & -A \\ \dfrac{\tau\tau'}{nn'} A + \dfrac{\tau'}{n'} B - \dfrac{\tau}{n} C - D & C - A \dfrac{\tau'}{n'} \end{pmatrix} \begin{pmatrix} nL \\ x \end{pmatrix}_{obj}$$

One of the requirements for perfect imagery is that

$$x'_{im} = \beta' x_{obj}$$

for all rays between object and image plane, where β' is the lateral magnification. Therefore we must require that

$$\frac{\tau\tau'}{nn'} A + \frac{\tau'}{n'} B - \frac{\tau}{n} C - D = 0$$

and

$$C - \frac{\tau'}{n'} A = \beta' = \text{constant}.$$

Any deviation of the values given by (25) and (26) leads to aberrations in the image formation. In order to come to some general conclusions about optical systems we will proceed to develop the quantities A, B, C and D into power series in the rotational invariants (see section 1.10). The first term in each of these series developments will be a constant. The approximation consisting only of this constant for each of the four matrix elements is called the paraxial approximation, because it can only be expected to give satisfying results for rays staying close to the axis.

2.2. PARAXIAL OPTICS

A first approximation to the refracting matrices can be found by considering that if φ_i and φ'_i are small we can write

$$\cos \varphi_i \sim 1 \quad \text{and} \quad \cos \varphi'_i \sim 1,$$

and therefore

$$A_i \sim (n'_i - n_i) R_i.$$

We shall denote this paraxial approximation to A_i by a_i. When φ_i and φ'_i are small all x_i and y_i will be small and all rays will travel close to the axis of symmetry. Therefore, the first term in the power series for T_i will equal the distance measured along the axis of the system between surface i and surface $i+1$. We will call this distance t_i; therefore

$$T'_i \sim t'_i \quad \text{and} \quad \frac{T'_i}{n'_i} \sim \frac{t'_i}{n'_i}.$$

The quantities x_i and y_i in this approximation will be measured in a plane tangent to the spherical refracting surface at the intersection point with the axis (called the vertex of the refracting surface). To distinguish in the equations between this approximation and the real values we introduce the paraxial notation

$$x_i \to h_i.$$

It can be easily seen that in this approximation L and M can be replaced by the angles α and β between the ray and the axis of symmetry:

$$L \sim \alpha \quad \text{and} \quad M \sim \beta.$$

Substituting these approximations in the fundamental relations (27), (28), (30) and (31) we have

$$\begin{pmatrix} n_i' \alpha_i' \\ h_i' \end{pmatrix} = \begin{pmatrix} 1 & -a_i \\ 0 & 1 \end{pmatrix} \begin{pmatrix} n_i \alpha_i \\ h_i \end{pmatrix}, \tag{34}$$

and similarly in the (M, y) plane. Also:

$$\begin{pmatrix} n_{i+1} \alpha_{i+1} \\ h_{i+1} \end{pmatrix} = \begin{pmatrix} 1 & 0 \\ \dfrac{t_i'}{n_i'} & 1 \end{pmatrix} \begin{pmatrix} n_i' \alpha_i' \\ h_i' \end{pmatrix}, \tag{35}$$

and the matrix for the system becomes

$$\begin{pmatrix} b & -a \\ -d & c \end{pmatrix},$$

where the lower case characters indicate the paraxial approximation. We now see that the quantities a, b, c and d in this approximation are functions of the system parameters n, R and t'; the dependence on the ray coordinates has been eliminated. The constants a, b, c and d are called the Gaussian constants of the system. The relation $bc - ad = +1$ still holds.

Again, if we introduce an object and image plane a distance respectively l and l' away from the first and last surface of the lens system we find

$$\begin{pmatrix} n' \alpha' \\ h' \end{pmatrix} = \begin{pmatrix} b + \dfrac{l}{n} a & -a \\ \dfrac{ll'}{nn'} a + \dfrac{l'}{n'} b - \dfrac{l}{n} c - d & c - \dfrac{l'}{n'} a \end{pmatrix} \begin{pmatrix} n\alpha \\ h \end{pmatrix}. \tag{36}$$

Image formation requires once more

$$\frac{ll'}{nn'} + \frac{l'}{n'} b - \frac{l}{n} c - d = 0, \tag{37}$$

$$c - \frac{l'}{n'} a = \beta' = \left(b + \frac{l}{n} a \right)^{-1}. \tag{38}$$

The last equality is due to the determinant of the matrix being $+1$.

We can easily see that for each object distance l we can find an image distance l'. (We presume both positive and negative values are possible.) Furthermore, we can find a location for an object and image plane for any required linear magnification. Using eqs. (37) and (38) we can write for (36)

$$\begin{pmatrix} n'\alpha' \\ h' \end{pmatrix}_{\text{im}} = \begin{pmatrix} 1/\beta' & -a \\ 0 & \beta' \end{pmatrix} \begin{pmatrix} n\alpha \\ h \end{pmatrix}_{\text{obj}}. \tag{39}$$

2.3. CARDINAL POINTS

In many problems in paraxial optics we really do not care or know what the configuration of the optical system is. It is, therefore, often advantageous to describe the image formation with slightly different variables. In order to arrive at this description we first find the location of the object and image plane with a magnification $+1$. These planes are called the "unit planes". We will denote the object and image distance of these planes by l_H and l'_H. From (38) we find

$$\frac{l'_H}{n'} = \frac{c-1}{a}, \qquad \frac{l_H}{n} = \frac{1-b}{a}. \tag{40}$$

We can now measure our object and image distances from the respective unit planes

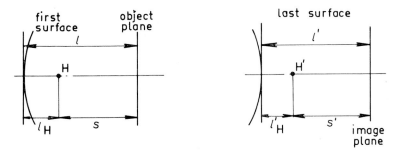

Fig. 12. Paraxial parameters.

instead of from the first and last vertex of the system (fig. 12). Calling these distances s and s' we have

$$\frac{l}{n} = \frac{s}{n} + \frac{l_H}{n}, \qquad \frac{l'}{n'} = \frac{s'}{n'} + \frac{l'_H}{n'},$$

or with eq. (40)

$$\frac{s}{n} = \frac{l}{n} - \frac{c-1}{a}, \qquad \frac{s'}{n'} = \frac{l'}{n'} - \frac{1-b}{a}.$$

Introducing this into eq. (36) we find (remembering that the matrix describes an object to image plane transformation)

$$
\begin{pmatrix} n'\alpha' \\ \\ h' \end{pmatrix}_{im} = \begin{pmatrix} 1 + \dfrac{s}{n}\,a & -a \\ \\ 0 & 1 - \dfrac{s'}{n'}\,a \end{pmatrix} \begin{pmatrix} n\alpha \\ \\ h \end{pmatrix}_{obj}
$$

and from eq. (38)

$$
\beta' = 1 - \frac{s'}{n'}\,a = \left(1 + \frac{s}{n}\,a\right)^{-1}. \tag{41}
$$

Rewriting this equation we find

$$
\frac{n'}{s'} = \frac{n}{s} + a. \tag{42}
$$

It further follows from eq. (41) that

$$
\frac{s'/n'}{s/n} = \beta'. \tag{43}
$$

The meaning of the quantity a is easily seen from eq. (42). Moving the object plane to infinity the image is a distance f' away from the image unit point. This distance is called the focal distance. We find for f' by letting s go to infinity in eq. (42)

$$
n'/f' = a. \tag{44}
$$

Similarly by demanding that the image be formed at infinity we find for the object distance

$$
n/f = -a, \tag{45}
$$

and therefore

$$
f'/n' = -f/n.
$$

We can now also deduce the meaning of the constants b and c. When we place the object at infinity the value of s is f' and therefore from eq. (41) we find $\beta' = 0$. We then find for the distance between the last surface of the lens system and the image plane, called the focal plane (the axial point of this plane is called the focal point) from eq. (38)

$$
\frac{l'_F}{n'} = \frac{c}{a} = c\frac{f'}{n'}. \tag{46}
$$

The quantity c, therefore, determines the portion of the focal distance which is located outside the optical system. Similarly, by moving the image to infinity we find for the distance between the first surface of the optical system and the object plane

$$
\frac{l_F}{n} = \frac{-b}{a} = b\frac{f}{n}, \tag{47}
$$

and b therefore determines the portion of the object focal length laying outside the optical system.

We can also investigate the relation between the angles a ray makes in object and image plane. If we restrict this investigation to rays leaving the axial point of the object, in other words $h = 0$ we find

$$n'\alpha' = \frac{1}{\beta'} \, n\alpha.$$

We can now try to find a pair of object and image planes such that $\alpha' = \alpha$; these object and image planes are called the nodal planes and the axial points of these planes the nodal points. A straightforward calculation shows that

$$-f = \text{FH} = \text{N}'\text{F}' = \frac{n}{a}, \qquad f' = \text{FK} = \text{H}'\text{F}' = \frac{n'}{A}.$$

We see that when object and image space are in air with refractive indices $+1$, the nodal and unit planes coincide.

2.4. TELESCOPIC SYSTEMS

The focal points, unit points and nodal points of a system are known collectively as the system's cardinal points. The calculation of their location always involves a division by the power a of the system. If this power is zero, the arguments of the previous section break down.

If a is zero we have, between the first vertex and the last vertex of the lens,

$$\begin{pmatrix} n'\alpha' \\ h' \end{pmatrix} = \begin{pmatrix} 1/c & 0 \\ -d & c \end{pmatrix} \begin{pmatrix} n\alpha \\ h \end{pmatrix}.$$

Hence:

$$\alpha' = \frac{n}{n'} \frac{1}{c} \alpha,$$

which means that a parallel pencil of rays entering the system emerges from the system as a parallel pencil of rays. A system with this property is called afocal (because it has no focal points) or telescopic (because telescopes are the best known instruments with zero power). Let us derive the object image relations for an afocal system. Eqs. (37) and (38) now read:

$$\frac{l'}{n'} \frac{1}{c} - \frac{l}{n} c - d = 0,$$

and

$$c = \beta',$$

or

$$l' = \beta'n'd + \frac{n'}{n} \beta'^2 l. \tag{49}$$

So the magnification of a telescopic system is independent of the object and image distance, and there is a simple linear relation between the object and image distance. For a system with a constant magnification the cardinal points obviously do not exist.

If the combination of two optical systems I and II is telescopic, the back focal point of system I must coincide with the front focal point of lens II, for lens I will focus a parallel pencil in its back focal plane. But the light must emerge as a parallel pencil from lens II, which requires that (for lens II) the light originates in a point of its front focal plane.

2.5. INVARIANTS

Let a system be specified by matrix (a, b, c, d) between any two reference planes in the object and the image space. We now consider two paraxial rays passing through the system, specified by (α_1, h_1) and (α_2, h_2).

The fundamental matrix relations yield

$$n'\alpha_i' = bn\alpha_i - ah_i, \qquad i = 1, 2.$$
$$h_i' = -dn\alpha_i + ch_i,$$

Some straightforward algebra yields

$$n(\alpha_1 h_2 - \alpha_2 h_1) = n'(\alpha_1' h_2' - \alpha_2' h_1'), \tag{50}$$

which shows that this crosswise combination of the paraxial ray coordinates of two rays is invariant upon passing through an optical instrument.

Let us assume $h_1 = h_2$. Then, if the two reference planes are imaged onto each other, we shall also have $h_1' = h_2'$. Hence

$$n(\alpha_1 - \alpha_2)h = n'(\alpha_1' - \alpha_2')h',$$

or, if we write $\alpha_1 - \alpha_2 = \eta$ and $\alpha_1' - \alpha_2' = \eta'$ (fig. 13)

$$n\eta h = n'\eta'h'. \tag{51}$$

This relation is attributed to various authors: Huygens, R. Smith, Lagrange and

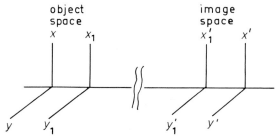

Fig. 13. Alternative ray coordinates.

Helmholtz. It is of particular importance in the design of periscopes, because it shows a direct relation between the width of a pencil and its angular spread at various points in the instrument.

2.6. ALTERNATIVE RAY COORDINATES

Up to this point we have used the coordinates α and h to describe a ray. It is some-times advantageous to use another set of coordinates. Let us consider for the moment again real nonparaxial rays. We select two sets of conjugated planes (fig. 13). A ray in the object space can now be described by giving its coordinates in the two choosen planes x, y and x_1, y_1. After passing through the system the ray can be described in the image space by its intersection points with the image planes of the two planes chosen in the object space: x', y' and x'_1, y'_1.

In any given optical system with power $a \neq 0$ the positions of these planes are completely given by their magnifications. We will call these magnifications β' and β'_1.

The advantages of this coordinate system will become clear in the description of pupils and the aberrations of an optical system.

The distance δ along the axis between the planes x and x_1 in the object space is given by

$$\frac{\delta}{n} = \frac{\beta' - \beta'_1}{\beta' \beta'_1 a},\tag{52}$$

which is easily derived from eq. (41).

In the image space the distance between the two planes is given by

$$\frac{\delta'}{n'} = \frac{\beta' - \beta'_1}{a}.\tag{53}$$

2.7. THIN LENSES

For initial computations it is often assumed that the thickness of a lens component equals zero since the formulas simplify a great amount. For a single "thin" lens we find

$$\begin{pmatrix} 1 & -a_2 \\ 0 & 1 \end{pmatrix}\begin{pmatrix} 1 & 0 \\ 0 & 1 \end{pmatrix}\begin{pmatrix} 1 & -a_1 \\ 0 & 1 \end{pmatrix} = \begin{pmatrix} 1 & -(a_1+a_2) \\ 0 & 1 \end{pmatrix}.$$

We can call $a_1 + a_2$ the power of the thin lens. It is therefore possible to compute only with matrices containing the powers of the thin components and the distances between these thin components.

2.8. PARAXIAL CALCULATIONS

The paraxial matrices of single surfaces and thin lenses contain many one's and zero's. For strictly numerical work this is rather awkward. We therefore present in this section a tabular calculation scheme which is rather more concise.

Upon refraction by a single surface or a thin lens the height of incidence of a ray remains the same, but its direction changes according to

$$n'_i \alpha'_i = n_i \alpha_i - a_i h_i.$$

A translation to the next surface leaves the direction of the ray unchanged, but the height changes according to

$$h_{i+1} = h'_i + \frac{t'_i}{n'_i}(n'_i\alpha'_i).$$

A ray can be followed through the system by alternate application of these two formulas.

As an example we consider a system with the following data (table 1).

TABLE 1

Surface	R	n'	t'	a	t/n
1	+1.000	1.500	0.150	0.500	0.100
2	−1.000	1.800	0.360	−0.300	0.200
3	−0.750	1		+0.600	

The surface powers and their reduced spacings are entered into table 2.

TABLE 2

		$n_1\alpha_1$	0.2000	0	1
$-a_1$	−0.500	h_1	−0.1000	1	0
t'_1/n'_1	0.100	$n_2\alpha_2$	0.2500	−0.5000	1
$-a_2$	+0.300	h_2	−0.0750	0.9500	0.1000
t'_2/n'_2	0.200	$n_3\alpha_3$	0.2275	−0.2150	1.0300
$-a_3$	−0.600	h_3	−0.0295	0.9070	0.3060
		$n'_3\alpha'_3$	0.2452	−0.7592	0.8464

Let an incident ray be given by its direction before, and its height at the first surface. In the first column of table 2 we took $n_1\alpha_1 = 0.2$, and $h_1 = -0.1$. Using first the refraction formula, we see that $n_2\alpha_2$ is found by adding $(-a_1)$ times h_1 to $n_1\alpha_1$:

$$n_2\alpha_2 = 0.2 + (-0.1)(-0.5) = 0.25.$$

The translation formula now gives:

$$h_2 = h_1 + (n_2\alpha_2)(t'_1/n'_1) = -0.1 + (0.25)(0.1) = -0.075.$$

From a computation point of view these two operations are identical: multiply the last entry with the system parameter on the same line, and add the previous entry. This routine is very convenient when a desk calculator is available.

This routine is in particular useful to find the Gaussian constants of the system. If we enter the system with the ray $n_1\alpha_1 = 0$; $h_1 = 1$, the emerging height is c, and the emerging direction is $-a$:

$$\begin{pmatrix} b & -a \\ -d & c \end{pmatrix}\begin{pmatrix} 0 \\ 1 \end{pmatrix} = \begin{pmatrix} -a \\ c \end{pmatrix}.$$

Similarly the ray with $n_1\alpha_1 = 1$ and $h_1 = 0$ yields $-d$ and b. This technique is demonstrated in columns two and three, the result being:

$$\begin{pmatrix} 0.8464 & -0.7592 \\ 0.3060 & 0.9070 \end{pmatrix}.$$

3. Pupils of optical systems

3.1. ENTRANCE AND EXIT PUPILS

It is clear that not all rays leaving an object point are refracted by the lens systems forming an image of this point. In this section we will describe how one determines which rays actually pass through the system.

The cones of light rays are restricted by the edges of the components of the lens system and sometimes by an aperture called the diaphragm, specifically built in to limit the rays.

Let us first consider a cone of light rays, leaving the point on the axis of the object plane. This cone will in the first instance be limited by the edge of the first component of the system. The rays passed by this component are, however, not by necessity all passed by the second component. The rays passed by the second component could again be restricted by some following component or diaphragm of the lens system. We would like to be able to tell which rays in the object space will be passed by *every* component of the system. There is a simple way to find the restricting edge or aperture that limits the cone the most. All rays inside this cone are passed through the system and contribute to the image formation.

Let us first consider the edge of the second component. We can image this edge backward through the first component into the object space. If we assume for the moment that the diameter of the first component is large enough to pass all the rays that will be passed by the second component, we know from the laws of image-formation that all rays going through the image of the edge of the second component in the object space will go, after passing through the first component, through the actual edge of the second component. All rays inside the cone defined by the image of the edge of the second component will now be passed by the first and second component.

We can now image the edge of the third component backward through the second and the first component into the object space. In general we can image the edge of the nth component backward into the object space through a system containing the first $n-1$ components. We do this for all edges and diaphragms in the system. In the object space we have now the images of all edges and diaphragms. We can now determine which image is smallest as seen from our axial object point. This image is called the entrance pupil. Since the entrance pupil limits the bundle most, all rays passing the entrance pupil are passed by the system and contribute to the image formation.

We can now image the entrance pupil through the whole system into the image space. This image is called the exit pupil. All rays passing through the edge of the entrance pupil will go through the edge of the exit pupil and all rays inside the edge of the entrance pupil will be inside the edge of the exit pupil.

In this way we have found an easy way to establish which rays leaving the axial point of the object will contribute to the image formation. For a point off-axis some of the other edges of components may again interfere with the passage of light. To illustrate this we refer to fig. 14. Here we show the object space of a lens system with the images of the edges of the lenses and diaphragms.

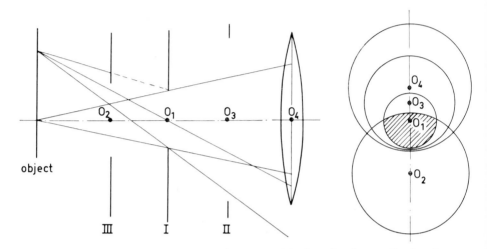

Fig. 14. (a) Obstructing edges in the object space. (b) Vignetting for an off-axis point.

It is clear that the image labeled I is the entrance pupil. When we take an off-axis object-point, the ray coming from this point and going through the center of the entrance pupil is called the principal ray for this object point. However, in considering the meridional rays above the principal ray we see that the edge forming the image labeled III is preventing rays from passing through the system. On the lower side of the bundle, in the given configuration, the edge of the first lens is the limiting factor. This effect is called vignetting, which is illustrated in fig. 14b. The entrance pupil is drawn, and also the projections of all the other edge images onto the plane of the entrance pupil, using the off-axis object point as the center of projection. The shaded area shows the area of the bundle which passes through the system. We should notice that in reality these circles are ellipses. This effect may become pronounced and should be taken into consideration. In extreme cases (wide angle lenses) the edge aberrations must also be taken into account. When rays are traced in an electronic computer, one can determine at each surface if it passes through the given diameters of the component. A ray going outside the given diameters is rejected by the computer.

It now becomes clear that in describing the rays it is easier to use the coordinate system consisting of two sets of conjugate planes. For the first set we use the object and image plane; for the second set we use the entrance and exit pupil planes. If the radius of the entrance pupil is ρ all axial rays for which $x_1^2+y_1^2 \leq \rho^2$ will pass through the system. Vignetting can be determined by testing in the computer at each surface if $x_i^2+y_i^2 \leq \rho_i^2$, where ρ_i is the radius of the clear aperture at each surface.

Vignetting is often used by optical designers to eliminate highly aberrated rays, coming from the edge of the field of view.

3.2. EXAMPLE OF A PUPIL DETERMINATION

Let us consider the following optical system (table 3) (we assume thin elements to make the computations simpler).

TABLE 3

Surface #	Radius	Thickness	Refractive index
1	+0.460 707	0	1.62
2	−0.460 707	0.111 461	1
3	−0.260 400	0	1.62
4	+0.260 400	0.144 899	1
5	+0.598 920	0	1.62
6	−0.598 920	−	1

From this we can compute the following quantities (table 4).

TABLE 4

Surface #	R	a	t/n
1	+2.170 573	+1.345 755	0
2	−2.170 573	+1.345 755	0.111 461
3	−3.840 245	−2.380 952	0
4	+3.840 245	−2.380 952	0.144 899
5	+1.669 671	+1.035 196	0
6	−1.669 671	+1.035 196	−

We can now write down the matrices for the system and make the necessary matrix multiplications (it is clear that all thickness matrices for lens thicknesses 0 reduce to the unit matrix and are therefore omitted):

$$\begin{pmatrix} 1 & -1.035\,196 \\ 0 & 1 \end{pmatrix}\begin{pmatrix} 1 & -1.035\,196 \\ 0 & 1 \end{pmatrix}\begin{pmatrix} 1 & 0 \\ 0.144\,899 & 1 \end{pmatrix}\begin{pmatrix} 1 & 2.380\,952 \\ 0 & 1 \end{pmatrix} \times$$

$$\times \begin{pmatrix} 1 & 2.380\,952 \\ 0 & 1 \end{pmatrix}\begin{pmatrix} 1 & 0 \\ 0.111\,461 & 1 \end{pmatrix}\begin{pmatrix} 1 & -1.345\,755 \\ 0 & 1 \end{pmatrix}\begin{pmatrix} 1 & -1.345\,755 \\ 0 & 1 \end{pmatrix}.$$

Since we will only investigate the edges of lenses we can first multiply the thin lens matrices. We then have:

$$\begin{pmatrix} 1 & -2.070392 \\ 0 & 1 \end{pmatrix} \begin{pmatrix} 1 & 0 \\ 0.144899 & 1 \end{pmatrix} \begin{pmatrix} 1 & 4.761904 \\ 0 & 1 \end{pmatrix} \times$$

$$\times \begin{pmatrix} 1 & 0 \\ 0.111461 & 1 \end{pmatrix} \begin{pmatrix} 1 & -2.691510 \\ 0 & 1 \end{pmatrix},$$

which gives

$$\begin{pmatrix} 1 & -2.070392 \\ 0 & 1 \end{pmatrix} \begin{pmatrix} 1 & 0 \\ 0.144899 & 1 \end{pmatrix} \begin{pmatrix} 1 & 4.761909 \\ 0 & 1 \end{pmatrix} \begin{pmatrix} 1 & -2.691510 \\ 0.111461 & 0.700002 \end{pmatrix} =$$

$$= \begin{pmatrix} 1 & -2.070392 \\ 0 & 1 \end{pmatrix} \begin{pmatrix} 1 & 0 \\ 0.144899 & 1 \end{pmatrix} \begin{pmatrix} 1.530767 & +0.641829 \\ 0.111461 & 0.700002 \end{pmatrix} =$$

$$= \begin{pmatrix} 1 & -2.070392 \\ 0 & 1 \end{pmatrix} \begin{pmatrix} 1.530767 & +0.641829 \\ 0.333268 & 0.793002 \end{pmatrix} =$$

$$= \begin{pmatrix} 0.840772 & -0.999995 \\ 0.333268 & 0.793002 \end{pmatrix}.$$

We have now all necessary paraxial values to image any edge or diaphragm back into the image space.

In order to avoid confusion we will in these computations consider the images in the object space as the objects, since then all our normal sign considerations hold. We ask therefore what object plane in the object space will be imaged in the second element by element one. We know that the second element is a distance 0.111461 behind the first lens with a power 2.691510. Therefore

$$\frac{1}{s} = \frac{1}{0.111461} - 2.691510 = +6.280237,$$

or

$$s = +0.159229.$$

The magnification of these two conjugated planes is

$$0.111461/0.159229 = 0.700002.$$

We then have to see which plane in the object space is imaged by the first two components in the plane of the third lens. For the system consisting of the first two elements we have found the following paraxial constants

$$a_{12} = -0.641829, \qquad b_{12} = 1.530767, \qquad c_{12} = 0.700002.$$

In this case it is easier to first compute the magnification with the help of eq. (38). We find

$$\beta' = 0.700002 - 0.144899(-0.641829) = +0.793002$$

and from this

$$l = \left(\frac{1}{0.793\,002} - 1.530\,767 \right) \Big/ -0.641\,829 = +0.420\,263.$$

When we assume the diameter of the first lens to be 0.25, the diameter of the second lens 0.14 and the diameter of the third lens 0.20, we find for the size of the image of lens 2 in the object space 0.2, and for the image of the element 3 we find 0.252 206.

For an object plane at infinity we find thus that the entrance pupil is formed by the image of the second element (fig. 15a). However, for an object placed in contact with the first element we find that the image of the third element is the entrance pupil (fig. 15b).

For a simpler computation scheme to compute the location of the entrance pupil see chapter 17, section 2–3.

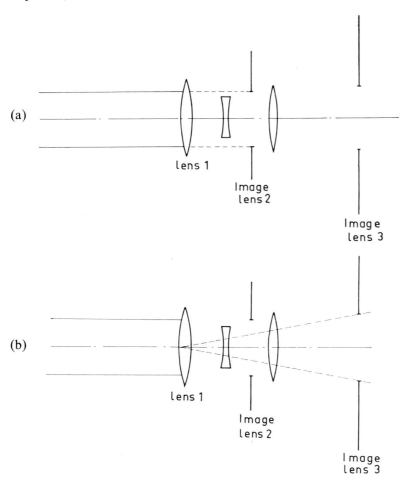

Fig. 15. (a) Object side obstructing edges for a Cooke triplet; object at infinity; lens 2 limits the axial pencil. (b) The same lens system, but the object coinciding with the first lens element; lens 3 limits the axial pencil.

In the design of optical instruments the study of the pupils is of eminent importance for three reasons:

(1) The pupils determine the amount of light that can be passed through the system.

(2) The pupils determine which rays pass through the system and so have a profound influence on the aberrations.

(3) In combining optical systems the relative location of the pupils of the first and second system determines which rays will pass through both systems.

This last item is especially of great concern in the design of instruments for visual use, e.g., a microscope or telescope. The exit pupil of these systems is the key hole we have to look through to see the object. If the eye is not put right in the exit pupil only a part of the object will be observed, as shown in fig. 16.

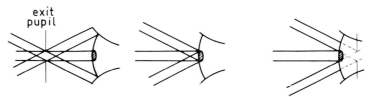

Fig. 16. The eye in relation to the exit pupil.

A convenient distance between the last lens surface and the eye is 15 mm. This must be taken into account in the design of eye pieces.

3.3. PHOTOMETRY OF OPTICAL INSTRUMENTS

In fig. 17 we have sketched two small apertures with area dA and dA', separated by a distance r. The first aperture is illuminated by a light source L that is large enough

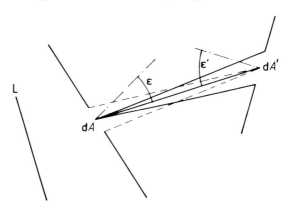

Fig. 17. Basic photometric relations.

to "fill" both apertures: there is a light ray going from each and every point of dA to each and every point of dA'.

The basic experimental fact of photometry is that the amount of energy ϕ passing through both the first and the second aperture per unit of time is proportional to the projected area of dA onto a plane perpendicular to the line connecting the two apertures, and proportional to the solid angle subtended by dA' as seen from dA. We have

$$\phi = B \cdot dA \cos \varepsilon \frac{dA' \cos \varepsilon'}{r^2}, \tag{54}$$

in which B is a constant of proportionality as related to dA. We can also say that ϕ is proportional to the projected area of dA', and to the solid angle subtended by dA as seen from dA'. We then have

$$\phi = B' \cdot dA' \cos \varepsilon' \frac{dA \cos \varepsilon}{r^2}, \tag{55}$$

in which B' is a constant of proportionality as related to dA'. Comparison of eqs. (54) and (55) shows that $B = B'$. B must be expressed in units of ϕ per unit of area and per unit of solid angle. It is called the luminance (brightness), and we see that it is invariant along the tube of rays connecting the two apertures.

When the tube of light rays is refracted or reflected by an optical instrument, some light will be lost due to absorption and reflection losses. Apart from this, it can be proved that the brightness, after division by the square of the refractive index, is invariant when the tube passes through an optical instrument. So the brightness is really a property of the light source only. For a further discussion of this matter we refer the reader to section 2.5 on condensing systems.

The general proof of the brightness invariance depends on the eikonal methods described in section 1.8. In the object and image space of an optical system we introduce two coordinate systems (x, y, z) and (x', y', z') such that the ray along the z-axis emerges along the z'-axis. We assume that the (x', y') plane is not the image of (x, y) plane. If it is, an intermediate plane must be introduced and the proof can be given in two steps. Direction cosines are denoted as usual by (L, M, N) and (L', M', N').

We consider two rectangular surface elements (dx, dy) and (dx', dy') around the points P and P′ in the two reference planes, and we shall calculate the light flux passing through both surface elements.

Looking from P, the two end points of the line element dx' are seen in the directions (L, M, N) and $L+d_1 L, M+d_1 M, N+d_1 N)$ respectively. Similarly the line element dy' subtends a variation in the direction of observation of $(d_2 L, d_2 M, d_2 N)$. So, looking from P, the surface element (dx', dy') is seen under a solid angle given by

$$d\Omega = \frac{1}{N} (d_1 L d_2 M - d_2 L d_1 M)$$

$$= \frac{1}{N} \left(\frac{\partial L}{\partial x'} \frac{\partial M}{\partial y'} - \frac{\partial L}{\partial y'} \frac{\partial M}{\partial x'} \right) dx' dy'.$$

The projected area of (dx, dy) is $N dx dy$. Hence the light flux through (dx, dy) and (dx', dy') follows from

$$d\phi = B \cdot N \, dx \, dy \cdot \frac{1}{N} \left(\frac{\partial L}{\partial x'} \frac{\partial M}{\partial y'} - \frac{\partial L}{\partial y'} \frac{\partial M}{\partial x'} \right) dx' dy'$$

$$= \frac{B}{n^2} \left(\frac{\partial nL}{\partial x'} \frac{\partial nM}{\partial y'} - \frac{\partial nL}{\partial y'} \frac{\partial nM}{\partial x'} \right) dx \, dy \, dx' dy', \tag{56}$$

in which B is the brightness at P.

Reversing the argument we can also write

$$d\phi' = \frac{B'}{n'^2} \left(\frac{\partial n'L'}{\partial x} \frac{\partial n'M'}{\partial y} - \frac{\partial n'L'}{\partial y} \frac{\partial n'M'}{\partial x} \right) dx' dy' \, dx \, dy, \tag{57}$$

in which B' is the brightness at P'. Barring transmission losses $d\phi$ and $d\phi'$ are equal.

We now consider the total differential of the point eikonal function between (x, y) and (x', y')

$$dS = n'L' dx' + n'M' dy' - nL \, dx - nM \, dy.$$

It follows from the properties of total differentials that the partial derivatives in (56) and (57) are pair wise equal, hence, with $d\phi = d\phi'$ we have

$$B/n^2 = B'/n'^2,$$

which completes the proof.

We shall apply the brightness invariance theorem to calculate the image intensity in two special cases: a wide-aperture image forming lens used on axis, and a wide angle lens, with a moderate aperture, used off axis.

1) *High aperture lens on axis*

In fig. 18 we show an axially symmetric lens forming an image S' of the light source S. We assume that the light source has an axially symmetric radiation pattern $B(\varphi)$.

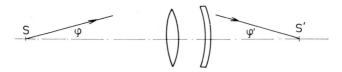

Fig. 18. Image plane illumination on axis.

(Note that we only proved the invariance of the brightness along a tube of light rays, it will in general vary from one tube to the next.)

An annular solid angle of light rays

$$2\pi \sin \varphi' d\varphi'$$

in the image space produces a light flux

$$d\phi = B(\varphi) \cdot dA' \cos \varphi' \cdot 2\pi \sin \varphi' d\varphi' \tag{58}$$

through the surface element dA in the image plane. The angles φ and φ' are functionally related in a manner depending on the lens aberrations.

The "illumination" E in the image plane is defined as the flux per unit area. From eq. (58) we have

$$dE = 2\pi B(\varphi) \sin \varphi' \cos \varphi' \, d\varphi',$$

and

$$E = 2\pi \int_0^{\varphi'_{max}} B(\varphi) \sin \varphi' \cos \varphi' \, d\varphi'.$$

In the special case that the brightness of the source does not depend on φ (a Lambertian radiator) we have

$$E = 2\pi B \int_0^{\varphi_{max}} \sin \varphi' \cos \varphi' \, d\varphi'$$

$$= \pi \frac{B}{n'^2} (n' \sin \varphi'_{max})^2.$$

The quantity $n' \sin \varphi'_{max}$ is called the (image side) numerical aperture, and plays an important role in the diffraction theory of optical instruments. We see that, for a Lambertian object, the illumination in the image is proportional to the square of the numerical aperture.

For photographic objectives the object may usually be considered to be at infinity (fig. 19). In this case $B(\varphi)$ is obviously constant because φ is zero throughout.

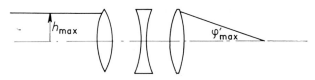

Fig. 19. Image illumination for an extended object at infinity.

If the lens is properly corrected for coma we have

$$h_{max} = f' \sin \varphi_{max}$$

according to Abbe's sine rule. Hence

$$E = \pi B(h_{max}/f')^2 = \tfrac{1}{4}\pi B/F^2,$$

in which the F number of the lens is defined as the ratio of the focal length to the diameter of the *entrance* pupil. One would indeed expect that the amount of light gathered is proportional to the area of the entrance pupil.

It is important to keep in mind that the entire discussion has been based on extended incoherent objects. In the image formation of point sources the argument breaks down because the distribution of the light in the image plane may not be considered uniform any more. A perfect lens will image a star as an airy disc, and the concept of "illumination" as flux per unit area loses its significance. The size of the detector now plays an important role and we must distinguish between two cases.

a) The detector is much larger than the Airy disc. Then the detector catches all the light entering the lens and the flux measured in the image plane is proportional to the square of the diameter of the entrance pupil.

b) The detector is much smaller than the Airy disc, and is placed in the center of the Airy disc. Then, first of all, a good deal of light is lost because it never hits the detector. But the amount of light reaching the detector is now proportional to the fourth power of the diameter of the entrance pupil. Apart from the increase in the total amount of light collected, proportional to h_{max}^2, the linear size of the Airy disc is, according to diffraction theory, inversely proportional to h_{max}, so that the percentage of the light in the Airy disc picked up by the detector is proportional to h_{max}^2.

2) *Wide angle lens off axis*

We shall now consider the light transmitting properties of a wide angle lens. We assume that an actual diaphragm in the center of the lens limits the rays; vignetting will not be taken into account. The optical system is sketched in fig. 20, which also specifies the notations used.

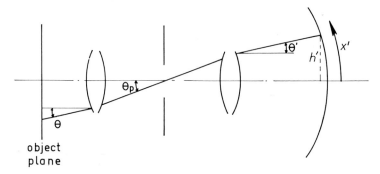

Fig. 20. Photometry of a wide angle lens.

The angles θ, θ_p and θ' are the angles between a principal ray and the axis in the object space, diaphragm space and image space respectively. We assume a curved image plane; x' is the image height measured along the curved image plane, and h' is the image height measured perpendicular to the axis.

We create a small rectangular element of surface area by (1) varying θ by an amount $d\theta$ and (2) rotating the figure around the axis over an angle $d\alpha$.

The flux through this area $h' dx' d\alpha$ can be calculated in the diaphragm space. If ρ is the semi-diameter of the diaphragm we have

$$d\phi = B\pi\rho^2 \cos \theta_p \cdot d\theta_p \sin \theta_p \, d\alpha,$$

provided that the diaphragm aperture is reasonably small so that an integration over its area is not called for. B is the brightness in the object element corresponding to the image element considered.

The illumination of the image element follows from

$$E = \frac{d\phi}{h'\,dx'\,d\alpha}$$

$$= B\pi\rho^2 \cos\theta_p \, \frac{\sin\theta_p}{h'} \frac{d\theta_p}{dx'} . \tag{59}$$

This formula tells us how the illumination in the image plane drops off when we move from the axis outwards. This "natural vignetting" must not be confused with the vignetting described in section 3.1.

We shall consider a number of special cases.

1) The diaphragm is in the image plane; the image is flat. Then

$$\theta_p = \theta'$$

and

$$x' = h' = t' \tan\theta',$$

t' being the distance from the diaphragm to the image. Substitution in (59) yields

$$E = B\pi \left(\frac{\rho}{t'}\right)^2 \cos^4\theta'.$$

So in this case the illumination in the image plane drops off with the fourth power of the cosine of the field angle in the image plane.

2) A concentric system with the diaphragm in its center. We have

$$\theta = \theta_p = \theta',$$
$$x' = t'\theta,$$
$$h' = t' \sin\theta.$$

Substitution yields

$$E = B\pi \left(\frac{\rho}{t'}\right)^2 \cos\theta.$$

So in this case the light drop off goes with the first power of $\cos\theta$.

3) If we only know that there is no field curvature we have

$$x' = h'.$$

Eq. (59) can now be rewritten in the form

$$E = B\pi\rho^2 \cos\theta_p \, \frac{\sin\theta_p \, d\theta_p}{x'\,dx'}$$

$$= B\pi\rho^2 \cos^4\theta_p \, \frac{d(\tan^2\theta_p)}{dx'^2} . \tag{60}$$

So if x' is proportional to $\tan\theta_p$ a $\cos^4$ law holds. In wide angle lenses the rear part of the lens must be so designed that the last factor partially compensates for the $\cos^4$ factor.

4. Color aberrations

4.1. OPTICAL PROPERTIES OF GLASS

In all our computations about lenses we assumed that the refractive index of glass is a constant. For real optical glass this is not the case for several reasons.

Due to improper mixing during fabrication and the fact that glass is a super-cooled liquid going through at least one phase change during the cooling process, there are usually slight local variations in refractive index in any piece of glass. The amount of variation that can be tolerated should be specified when a piece of optical glass is ordered. The best optical quality will have changes of refractive index not exceeding a few units in the 6th decimal place over distances of several inches.

The above mentioned phase changes can also lead to birefrigence in the glass. In good optical quality glass this can be smaller than 10 nm/cm. In large lens systems great care should be taken in the mounting of the elements, since any strain in the glass will again introduce birefringence. Any large optical system should therefore be checked for strain after mounting the elements. The above mentioned defects in glasses can all be eliminated by proper care during the manufacturing of the glass and of the elements. Glass also has the property of having different refractive indices for light of different wavelengths, the so-called dispersion. Since all properties of lenses, including the paraxial, are functions of the refractive index of the material used, each lens will form different images for different wavelengths, giving rise to the color aberrations.

Many attempts have been made to describe the change of refractive index with wavelength mathematically, from theoretical as well as empirical considerations. The most useful description for the optical designer is given by HERZBERGER [1959]. We will give here a description of his results.

The refractive index $n(\lambda)$ is given in general by:

$$n(\lambda) = n^{**}a_1(\lambda) + n_F a_2(\lambda) + n_C a_3(\lambda) + n^* a_4(\lambda), \qquad (61)$$

where

n^{**} is the refractive index for the wavelength 0.3650 μm,
n_F is the refractive index for the wavelength of the F-line of hydrogen (0.4861 μm),
n_C is the refractive index for the wavelength of the C-line of hydrogen (0.6563 μm),
n^* is the refractive index for the wavelength 1.014 μm

and

$$a_1(\lambda) = +0.66147196 - 0.40352796\lambda^2 - \frac{0.28046790}{\lambda^2 - \lambda_0^2} + \frac{0.03385979}{(\lambda^2 - \lambda_0^2)^2},$$

$$a_2(\lambda) = -4.20146383 + 2.73508956\lambda^2 + \frac{1.50543784}{\lambda^2 - \lambda_0^2} + \frac{0.11593235}{(\lambda^2 - \lambda_0^2)^2},$$

$$a_3(\lambda) = +6.29834237 - 4.69409935\lambda^2 - \frac{1.57508650}{\lambda^2 - \lambda_0^2} + \frac{0.10293038}{(\lambda^2 - \lambda_0^2)^2},$$

$$a_4(\lambda) = -1.758\,350\,59 + 2.362\,537\,94\lambda^2 + \frac{0.350\,116\,57}{\lambda^2 - \lambda_0^2} - \frac{0.020\,857\,82}{(\lambda^2 - \lambda_0^2)^2},$$

in which $\lambda_0 = 0.28\ \mu$m.

A tabulation of the values of $a_1(\lambda), \ldots, a_4(\lambda)$ for various wavelengths is given in table 5.

Many glasses can be described by only two constants. It is therefore useful to rewrite the above formula in the form

$$n(\lambda) = A(\lambda)n_C + B(\lambda)n_F + r(\lambda) \tag{62}$$

where $r(\lambda)$ is the deviation of the actual refractive index from the one predicted by the constants $A(\lambda)$, $B(\lambda)$ and n_F, n_C.

$$A(\lambda) = +1.998\,835\,50 - 0.087\,342\,07\lambda^2 - \frac{0.360\,264\,51}{\lambda^2 - \lambda_0^2} - \frac{0.010\,800\,30}{(\lambda^2 - \lambda_0^2)^2}$$

$$B(\lambda) = -0.997\,572\,65 + 0.080\,341\,76\lambda^2 + \frac{0.361\,638\,96}{\lambda^2 - \lambda_0^2} + \frac{0.010\,530\,95}{(\lambda^2 - \lambda_0^2)^2}.$$

For so called "normal" glasses $r(\lambda)$ can be neglected. The values for $A(\lambda)$ and $B(\lambda)$ are also tabulated in table 5.

In all glass catalogues glasses are classified by the value of the refractive index for the wavelength of the d-line of helium (0.5876 μm) and the Abbe number.

For the so called "normal" glasses we can rewrite Herzberger's formula in the form

$$\frac{n_\lambda - n_F}{n_F - n_C} = C_1(\lambda)v_d + C_2(\lambda), \tag{62A}$$

where

$$C_1(\lambda) = 0.001\,262\,21 - 0.006\,996\,79\lambda^2 + \frac{0.001\,373\,75}{\lambda^2 - \lambda_0^2} - \frac{0.000\,269\,25}{(\lambda^2 - \lambda_0^2)^2}$$

$$C_2(\lambda) = -1.997\,919\,48 + 0.082\,264\,49\lambda^2 \frac{0.361\,261\,44}{\lambda^2 - \lambda_0^2} + \frac{0.010\,604\,93}{(\lambda^2 - \lambda_0^2)^2}.$$

The values for $C_1(\lambda)$ and $C_2(\lambda)$ are also to be found in table 5.

4.2. SINGLE THIN LENS

We will now see what effect these changes in refractive index have on the image forming properties of lenses. To gain some insight in the problem we will first investigate a single thin lens. We find for the change in paraxial constants with wavelength

$$\Delta a = R\,\Delta n = a\,\frac{\Delta n}{n-1}, \tag{63}$$

$$\Delta b = \Delta c = \Delta d = 0.$$

TABLE 5

λ (μm)		$a_1(\lambda)$	$a_2(\lambda)$	$a_3(\lambda)$	$a_4(\lambda)$	$A(\lambda)$	$B(\lambda)$	$C_1(\lambda)$	$C_2(\lambda)$
3500		1.435709	−0.9178388	0.5817688	−0.0996392	−3.033593	4.018381	−0.0152037	3.022559
3600		1.128837	−0.2606635	0.1585677	−0.0267418	−2.604675	3.592466	−0.0122032	2.595819
3650	**	1.000000	0	0	0	−2.411430	3.400500	−0.0109248	2.403502
3700		0.8859134	0.2212860	−0.1285218	0.0213224	−2.232045	3.222259	−0.0097814	2.224947
3800		0.6927538	0.5702481	−0.3142354	0.0512335	−1.905964	2.898144	−0.0078156	1.900291
3900		0.5386521	0.8177094	−0.4242657	0.0679043	−1.618748	2.612532	−0.0062125	1.614239
4000		0.4154352	0.9873813	−0.4777961	0.0749796	−1.364267	2.359364	−0.0049006	1.360711
4047	h	0.3667395	1.045108	−0.4876394	0.0755916	−1.255436	2.251061	−0.0043725	1.252262
4100		0.3168017	1.097281	−0.4892674	0.0751838	−1.137577	2.133751	−0.0038241	1.134801
4200		0.2378489	1.161211	−0.4696264	0.0705657	−0.9346499	1.931709	−0.0029392	0.9325167
4300		0.1747309	1.189815	−0.4272202	0.0626735	−0.7521775	1.749964	−0.0222116	0.7505724
4341		0.1529573	1.193300	−0.4050817	0.0588238	−0.6834544	1.681498	−0.0019551	0.6820354
4358	g	0.1440049	1.193553	−0.3945990	0.0570406	−0.6541263	1.652276	−0.0018487	0.6527846
4400		0.1244083	1.191354	−0.3684439	0.0526814	−0.5874200	1.585805	−0.0016136	0.5862489
4500		0.0844625	1.172271	−0.2982161	0.0414818	−0.4380911	1.436967	−0.0011231	0.4372759
4800		0.0093269	1.036653	−0.0526307	0.0066506	−0.0648932	1.064759	−0.0001341	0.0647958

5876	d	−0.0254918	0.3363380	0.7354800	−0.0463262	0.7256999	0.2748024	0.0005020	−0.7253356
5893	D	−0.0249535	0.3263014	0.7445719	−0.0459198	0.7341189	0.2663755	0.0004942	−0.7337603
6000		−0.0213902	0.2658311	0.7980592	−0.0425002	0.7842733	0.2161657	0.0004388	−0.7839549
6328		−0.0090712	0.1001054	0.9315709	−0.0226052	0.9186776	0.0815306	0.0002082	−0.9185266
6438	C'	−0.0047923	0.0512767	0.9663730	−0.0128574	0.9581539	0.0419605	0.0001144	−0.9580710
6500		−0.0023982	0.0252553	0.9838484	−0.0067055	0.9793183	0.0207403	0.0000585	−0.9792758
6563	C	0	0	1.000000	0	1.000000	0	0	−1.000000
7000		0.0153054	−0.1458975	1.071191	0.0594007	1.125644	−0.1260986	−0.0004540	−1.125973
7065	b	0.0173054	−0.1632996	1.075910	0.0700835	1.141971	−0.1424989	−0.0005274	−1.142354
7500		0.0282773	−0.2522385	1.071357	0.1526041	1.237879	−0.2389259	−0.0010456	−1.238638
7682	A'	0.0315549	−0.2761967	1.051954	0.1926871	1.272222	−0.2734983	−0.0012749	−1.273148
8000		0.0353359	−0.3006700	0.9952632	0.2700710	1.325433	−0.3271238	−0.0016898	−1.326659
8500		0.0362820	−0.2980634	0.8523147	0.4094667	1.394599	−0.3969738	−0.0023731	−1.396321
9000		0.0313292	−0.2505083	0.6502625	0.5689166	1.449730	−0.4528211	−0.0030887	−1.451972
9500		0.0208456	−0.1631564	0.3953830	0.7499279	1.493920	−0.4977558	−0.0038335	−1.496702
10000		0.0052354	−0.0402777	0.0927296	0.9423128	1.529419	−0.5340279	−0.0046062	−1.532762
10140	*	0	0	0	1.000000	1.538040	−0.5428706	−0.0048275	−1.541544
10500		−0.0151121	0.1146179	−0.2536288	1.154123	1.557900	−0.5633097	−0.0054064	−1.561824
11000		−0.0398440	0.2986513	−0.6404053	1.381598	1.580629	−0.5868664	−0.0062344	−1.585153
11500		−0.0686490	0.5094582	−1.064932	1.624123	1.498576	−0.6056705	−0.0070905	−1.603722

We see that for a single thin lens only the power is affected by the properties of the glass. Often the quantity $\Delta n/(n-1)$ is called $1/v$. In that case Δn is taken as $n_F - n_C$. The quantity v is called the Abbe number of the glass. With the Abbe number we can write

$$\Delta a/a = 1/v.$$

From the relation between a and f' we find

$$\Delta a/a = -\Delta f'/f' = 1/v. \tag{64}$$

For different wavelengths therefore the focal length changes, but if the lens is thin, the position of the unit points is unaffected.

4.3. THIN SYSTEMS

For a thin system consisting of e lenses without airgaps in between, we find

$$\Delta a = \sum_{i=1}^{e} \frac{a_i}{v_i}$$

$$\Delta b = \Delta c = \Delta d = 0.$$

For a thin system it is advantageous to introduce the equivalent dispersion v, defined by:

$$\Delta a = \sum_{i=1}^{e} \frac{a_i}{v_i} = \frac{a}{v}. \tag{65}$$

By a proper choice of the powers a_i and the dispersion v_i, Δa can always be made zero for one pair of wavelengths. This will be discussed later in this section.

4.4. TWO THIN LENSES SEPARATED BY A DISTANCE

Before giving a general description of the calculation of color aberrations for any system we will discuss the system consisting of two thin lenses, separated by a distance t. From its paraxial constants it is easily seen that

$$\Delta a = \frac{a_1}{v_1} + \frac{a_2}{v_2} - t a_1 a_2 \left(\frac{1}{v_1} + \frac{1}{v_2} \right),$$

$$\Delta b = -t \frac{a_2}{v_2},$$

$$\Delta c = -t \frac{a_1}{v_1},$$

$$\Delta d = 0.$$

In order to achromatize b and c we have to achromatize each individual element and therefore we have to make each one at least a thin doublet. We notice that if

$\Delta b = \Delta c = 0$, we also have $\Delta a = 0$. A system of two separated single lenses is often used however as an eyepiece, without achromatizing b and c. If one only achromatizes the power one may use the same glass for each element. Taking $v_1 = v_2$ we have, if we require Δa to be zero:

$$t = \frac{1}{2}\left(\frac{1}{a_1} + \frac{1}{a_2}\right) = \tfrac{1}{2}(f_1' + f_2').\tag{66}$$

In this case $\Delta a = 0$ for all wavelengths. When we take f_1' a few times larger than f_2' we have a so called Huygens eyepiece. When we take f_1' approximately equal to f_2', we have a Ramsden eyepiece. In this case we usually deviate slightly from the above condition for t in order to bring the object plane slightly outside the first lens, so that we can insert cross hairs and we do not focus on the small scratches and dust that might collect on the first surface.

We notice, however, that in the above solutions we have only achromatized the power and the images presented to the eye do suffer from the chromatic errors. To minimize these effects one makes the lenses from a glass type with a v value as large as possible.

4.5. GENERAL DESCRIPTION OF COLOR ABERRATIONS

In order to describe the color aberrations of any system in a general way, we use the following set of equations

$$n'(x_\lambda' - x_{\lambda_0}') = n'\Delta x' = c_1(\lambda)\xi_1 + c_2(\lambda)\xi,\tag{67A}$$

$$n'(x_{1\lambda}' - x_{1\lambda_0}') = n'\Delta x_1' = c_3(\lambda)\xi_1 + c_4(\lambda)\xi.\tag{67B}$$

The x and x_1 coordinates used here are the heights of intersection with the two reference planes introduced in section 2.6. The ξ and ξ_1 variables are reduced coordinates in the object and the pupil, as further explained in section 5.4.

We can show that the coefficients c_i can be computed from

$$c_1 = -\sum_{i=1}^{e} h_i d_i P_i \left(\frac{\Delta n_i'}{n_i'} - \frac{\Delta n_i}{n_i}\right),\tag{68A}$$

$$c_2 = \sum_{i=1}^{e} h_i d_i' P_i \left(\frac{\Delta n_i'}{n_i'} - \frac{\Delta n_i}{n_i}\right),\tag{68B}$$

$$c_3 = -\sum_{i=1}^{e} h_i' d_i P_i \left(\frac{\Delta n_i'}{n_i'} - \frac{\Delta n_i}{n_i}\right),\tag{68C}$$

$$c_4 = \sum_{i=1}^{e} h_i' d_i' P_i' \left(\frac{\Delta n_i'}{n_i'} - \frac{\Delta n_i}{n_i}\right),\tag{68D}$$

where:

$$\Delta n_i = n_{i\lambda} - n_{i\lambda_0}$$
$$\Delta n_i' = n_{i\lambda}' - n_{i\lambda_0}'.$$

For the notation employed here we must refer the reader to ch. 17, section 3.1 on the calculation of third order aberrations.

Examination of eq. (67A) shows that the coefficient c_1 represents a shift of the image plane with wavelength, while the coefficient c_2 represents a change in size of the image with wavelength. With these equations the color aberrations of any optical system can be computed.

We will now investigate the properties of systems due to special configurations of the elements and the influence of the glass properties.

In the first place we notice that there is a simple relationship between c_2 and c_3. When n_1 is the refractive index of the object space and n_e' the refractive index of the image space, we can easily derive:

$$c_2 + c_3 = \frac{n_e'(\beta' - \beta_1')}{a}\left(\frac{\Delta n_e'}{n_e'} - \frac{\Delta n_1}{n_1}\right),$$

which reduces for a system in air to:

$$c_2 + c_3 = 0.$$

In general, one tries to design optical systems such that c_1 and c_2 are zero for one specific pair of wavelengths. In that case, the system has the same image position and magnification for the standard wavelength and the selected second wavelength. For visual instruments, the selected wavelengths are usually the F- and C-line. However, the above formula holds for the entire optical spectrum by selecting the proper two wavelengths for which to correct the system.

For a system consisting only of thin elements in air, we find (the subscripts refer to the elements and not to surfaces):

$$c_1 = -\sum_{i=1}^{e} h_i^2 \frac{a_i}{v_i}, \tag{69A}$$

$$c_2 = +\sum_{i=1}^{e} h_i h_i' \frac{a_i}{v_i} = -c_3, \tag{69B, C}$$

$$c_4 = +\sum_{i=1}^{n} h_i'^2 \frac{a_i}{v_i}, \tag{69D}$$

in which the h_i and h_i' are the heights of intersection of the object ray and the pupil ray, as explained in chapter 17, section 3.1.

When a system contains only "normal" glasses, we can use eq. (62A) to describe the glasses and we find:

$$c_1(\lambda) = -C_2(\lambda)\sum_{i=1}^{e} h_i d_i P_i \left[\frac{\Delta n_i'}{n_i'} - \frac{\Delta n_i}{n_i}\right] - C_1(\lambda)\sum_{i=1}^{e} h_i d_i, \tag{70A}$$

$$c_2(\lambda) = C_2(\lambda) \sum_{i=1}^{e} h_i d_i' P_i \left[\frac{\Delta n_i'}{n_i'} - \frac{\Delta n_i}{n_i} \right] + C_1(\lambda) \sum_{i=1}^{e} h_i d_i', \tag{70B}$$

where:

$c_1(\lambda)$ is the c_1 coefficient for wavelength λ,

$c_2(\lambda)$ is the c_2 coefficient for wavelength λ,

$C_1(\lambda)$ and $C_2(\lambda)$ are the coefficients in Herzberger's dispersion formula, and

$$\Delta n' = n_F' - n_C',$$

$$\Delta n = n_F - n_C.$$

The first terms in these formula's represent the normal F–C correction, the second terms the "secondary" spectrum, the amount by which the image position and the magnification change with the color after the "primary correction" has been effected.

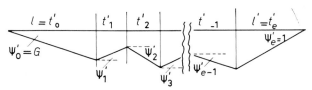

Fig. 21. Secondary spectrum calculation for "normal" glasses.

These last terms can be evaluated in a rather interesting manner. We trace a paraxial ray through the system from the axial point of the object plane to the axial point of the image plane, such that its direction in the image space is unity. Then, using the notation specified in fig. 21, we have:

$$\sum_{i=1}^{e} h_i d_i = \sum_{i=0}^{e} t_i' \psi_i'^2. \tag{70C}$$

Tracing a similar ray through the center of the entrance and exit pupil, and indicating its parameter with an index P, we also have:

$$\sum_{i=1}^{e} h_i d_i' = \sum_{i=0}^{e} t_i' \psi_i' \psi_{iP}'. \tag{70D}$$

These equations show that the secondary spectrum for a lens system composed of "normal" glasses is fully determined by the geometry of the rays, and is independent of which "normal" glasses are used. Eq. (70C) also shows that for lenses that form a real image of a real object, the secondary spectrum cannot be corrected with "normal" glasses, and that complicated lenses will tend to have a large secondary spectrum. (Wide angle lenses are notorious in this respect.)

4.6. COLOR CORRECTION FOR A THIN SYSTEM

For a system of thin lenses in contact, we may write (the subscripts refer, in this case, to elements and not to surfaces):

$$c_1 = -h^2 \sum_{i=1}^{e} \frac{a_i}{v_i},$$

$$c_2 = hh' \sum_{i=1}^{e} \frac{a_i}{v_i} = -c_3,$$

$$c_4 = h'^2 \sum_{i=1}^{e} \frac{a_i}{v_i}.$$

The quantities h and h' are all the same for each element and depend only on the position of the object and the entrance pupil. The system is, therefore, fully corrected by making the quantity $\sum_{i=1}^{e} a_i/v_i$ equal to zero.

In eq. (65) we already introduced the concept of equivalent dispersion for a thin system. For a doublet of unit power, we have:

$$a_1 + a_2 = 1, \qquad \frac{a_1}{v_1} + \frac{a_2}{v_2} = \frac{1}{v}.$$

Solving these equations for a_1 and a_2 we find:

$$a_1 = \frac{v_1}{v_1 - v_2}\left(1 - \frac{v_2}{v}\right), \qquad a_2 = -\frac{v_2}{v_1 - v_2}\left(1 - \frac{v_1}{v}\right). \qquad (71)$$

By taking $v = \infty$ we find the powers required for normal color correction. The reason for leaving the quantity v in these equations is that it is possible to get v values which are not available with a single glass and are helpfull in correcting more com-

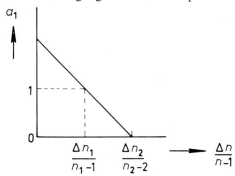

Fig. 22. Equivalent dispersion.

plicated systems. By replacing single elements by such doublets, the freedom of the designer is greatly enlarged (ch. 17, section 3.7).

When we return to the notation with Δn we can rewrite eq. (71) in the form:

$$a_1\left(\frac{\Delta n_1}{n_1 - 1} - \frac{\Delta n_2}{n_2 - 1}\right) = \frac{\Delta n}{n - 1} - \frac{\Delta n_2}{n_2 - 1}, \qquad (72A)$$

$$a_2\left(\frac{\Delta n_1}{n_1 - 1} - \frac{\Delta n_2}{n_2 - 1}\right) = -\left(\frac{\Delta n}{n - 1} - \frac{\Delta n_1}{n_1 - 1}\right). \qquad (72B)$$

These linear relations are summarized in fig. 22.

It is often desirable to correct for two wavelengths. This leads to the conditions:

$$c_{1_{\lambda 1}} = -h^2 \sum_{i=1}^{e} a_i \frac{\Delta n_{i\lambda 1}}{n_i - 1} = 0,$$

$$c_{1_{\lambda 2}} = -h^2 \sum_{i=1}^{e} a_i \frac{\Delta n_{i\lambda 2}}{n_i - 1} = 0.$$

For a thin doublet, c_2 is automatically zero for both wavelengths.

We have already shown that we cannot fulfill these conditions with "normal" glasses. Some of the glasses, however, deviate enough from "normal" so as to make it possible to fulfill these conditions. From eq. (62A) for the "normal" glasses for two wavelength's λ_1 and λ_2 we find:

$$\frac{n_{\lambda 1} - n_F}{n_d - 1} = \frac{\Delta n_{\lambda 1}}{n - 1} = C_1(\lambda_1) + C_2(\lambda_1) \frac{n_F - n_C}{n_d - 1},$$

$$\frac{n_{\lambda 2} - n_F}{n_d - 1} = \frac{\Delta n_{\lambda 2}}{n - 1} = C_1(\lambda_2) + C_2(\lambda_2) \frac{n_F - n_C}{n_d - 1},$$

or

$$\frac{\Delta n_{\lambda 2}}{n - 1} = \frac{C_2(\lambda_2)}{C_2(\lambda_1)} \frac{\Delta n_{\lambda 1}}{n - 1} + \left\{ C_1(\lambda_2) - \frac{C_2(\lambda_2)}{C_2(\lambda_1)} C_1(\lambda_1) \right\}. \tag{73}$$

Here $\Delta n = n_\lambda - n_F$, however, it is easily shown that in general with $\Delta n = n_\lambda - n_{\lambda_0}$ we have for "normal" glasses a relationship of the same form:

$$\frac{\Delta n_{\lambda 2}}{n - 1} = \alpha \frac{\Delta n_{\lambda 1}}{n - 1} + \beta. \tag{73A}$$

For glasses that deviate from this dispersion formula, we will then find that $\Delta n_{\lambda 2}/(n-1)$ is different from the value computed by the above equation. We can now define:

$$\frac{\Delta n_{\lambda 2}}{n - 1} - \left(\frac{\Delta n_{\lambda 2}}{n - 1} \right)_{\text{computed}}.$$

As an example we give the following glasses from the Schott catalogue in table 6.

TABLE 6

Type	$n_{A'}$	n_d	n_F	n_g
PSKS5	1.613 30	1.619 62	1.626 41	1.631 71
K6	1.497 34	1.502 76	1.508 53	1.513 03
BaF8	1.615 41	1.623 74	1.633 06	1.640 55
LaSF5	1.867 22	1.880 69	1.895 76	1.907 90
LaF7	1.736 27	1.749 50	1.764 61	1.777 05
F16	1.582 61	1.592 70	1.604 45	1.614 31
SFS1	1.892 70	1.917 61	1.948 37	1.975 27

We can now compute the values of $(n_g - n_F)/(n_d - 1)$ and $(n_{A'} - n_F)/(n_d - 1)$ for these glasses and also the value of $(n_{A'} - n_F)/(n_d - 1)$ according to eq. (73) with the proper values for the constants C_1 and C_2 for the above wavelengths (table 7).

TABLE 7

Type	$(n_g - n_F)/(n_d - 1)$	$(n_{A'} - n_F)/(n_d - 1)$	Computed	C_1	C_2
PSKS5	0.008 553	−0.021 158	−0.021 562	+0.004 04	−2.473 751
K6	0.008 950	−0.022 257	−0.022 336	+0.000 079	−2.486 815
BaF8	0.012 008	−0.028 297	−0.028 300	+0·000 003	−2.356 512
LaSF5	0.013 784	−0.032 406	−0.031 764	−0.000 732	−2.350 986
LaF7	0.016 597	−0.037 811	−0.037 250	−0.000 561	−2.278 182
F16	0.016 635	−0.036 848	−0.037 325	+0.000 477	−2.215 088
SFS1	0.029 315	−0.060 668	−0.062 055	+0.001 387	−2.069 520

We can now make a plot $(n_g - n_F)/(n_d - 1)$ versus $(n_{A'} - n_F)/(n_d - 1) - [(n_{A'} - n_F)/(n_d - 1)_{computed}]$ as shown in fig. 23. In this plot we can again represent all possible values of $\Delta n/(n-1)$, which one can make with a doublet by drawing a line through the two points representing the two glasses used. We also find $\Delta n_{\lambda_2}/(n-1) - \Delta n_{\lambda_2}/(n-1)_{computed}$ for each doublet in this diagram.

In general we cannot make an apochromatic doublet, even with glasses that are not "normal". This is easily seen by the fact that we have to fulfill three conditions (the equation for the power of the doublet and two conditions for $C_1(\lambda)$). It is advantageous to introduce the quantity

$$\frac{\Delta n_{\lambda_1}}{\Delta n_{\lambda_1}} = \phi = \frac{\Delta n_{\lambda_1}/(n-1)}{\Delta n_{\lambda_2}/(n-1)}. \tag{74}$$

We see that only for glasses with the same value for ϕ we can make an apochromatic doublet, since in this case the two color conditions reduce to one condition. In fig. 23 we can draw lines for which ϕ is constant. These will be straight lines since:

$$\frac{\Delta n_{\lambda_2}}{n-1} - \left(\frac{\Delta n_{\lambda_2}}{n-1}\right)_{computed} = (\phi - \alpha)\frac{\Delta n_{\lambda_1}}{n-1} - \beta, \tag{75}$$

where α and β are the constants given in eq. (73A). In general, we need three elements to fulfill the three conditions and in our diagram we can draw a line through two glasses representing all possible doublets with these glasses. Where this line intersects the line of constant ϕ going through our third glass is the proper combination for our doublet to be combined with our third glass to form an apochromatic triplet.

Taking the glasses K6, LaSF5 and F16 to make an apochromatic triplet we have to solve the three following equations:

$$a_1 + a_2 + a_3 = 1,$$
$$0.008\,950\,a_1 + 0.013\,784\,a_2 + 0.016\,635\,a_3 = 0,$$
$$0.022\,257\,a_1 + 0.032\,406\,a_2 + 0.036\,848\,a_3 = 0.$$

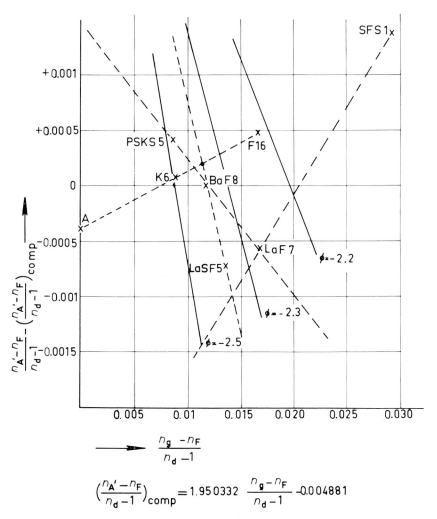

Fig. 23. Glass chart for use in the design of apochromatic system.

We find:

$$a_1 = +4.175\,946, \qquad a_2 = -5.421\,655, \qquad a_3 = +2.245\,709.$$

We could also have proceeded by noticing in our diagram that we could combine the glasses K6 and F16 into a doublet with a ϕ value equal to the glass LaSF5 by giving the first component a power $+0.650\,291$ and the second a power $+0.349\,709$. The doublet power would be $+1$ while $\Delta n_{\lambda_1}/(n-1)$ equals $0.011\,638$; $\Delta n_{\lambda_2}/(n-1)$ equals $-0.027\,360$ and, therefore, $\Delta n_{\lambda_2}/(n-1) - (\Delta n_{\lambda_2})/(n-1)_{\text{computed}}$ equals $+0.000\,219$ and $\phi = 2.350\,985$. We can now combine this doublet as a unit with the glass LaSF5 to correct for only one wavelength and find that the LaSF5 component needed a power $-5.421\,655$ and the doublet a power $+6.421\,655$ to correct the color. This way of computing has many advantages, since we can easily see in our glass diagram what powers to expect in the components. On the line connecting K6 and F16 we can see that we have to combine two positive powers, roughly in the ratio 2 : 1, to achieve a doublet with the same ϕ value as LaSF 5. All possible combinations of this doublet with LaSF5 are now represented by the constant ϕ line through this glass while the power ratio of the components is given by the distances between the doublet-glass-point (point B in fig. 23) and the point $\Delta n_{\lambda_1}/(n-1)=0$.

We notice also that by starting with the glasses LaSF5 and BaF8, which are approximately on the same ϕ line, we would have approximately apochromatic color correction with a doublet by correcting only for the g-line. By using eqs. (71) we find:

$$a_1 = -6.761\,203, \qquad a_2 = +7.761\,203.$$

The coefficient c_1 for the A'-line for this doublet is $-0.000\,515$. It was also clear from the glass diagram that we would have to use larger component powers to accomplish color correction as compared to our example of the triplet. It is interesting to compare this result with a simple doublet, color corrected for one color (the g-line) made with the glasses K6 and F16. We compute $a_1 = +2.164\,608$. For the A'-line the color coefficient of this doublet is $c_1 = -0.005\,264$ or approximately $10\times$ larger than in our previous example. (The value of C_1 for the A'-line of any combination can be directly read in our diagram. All constant p-lines go through one point B on the $(n_{A'}-n_F)/(n_d-1)-(n_{A'}-n_F)/(n_d-1)_{\text{computed}}$-axis, coordinate $+0.004\,881$. Any color corrected doublet is given by the intersection point of the line through these two glasses with this coordinate axis, in our last example given by point A, coordinate $-0.000\,383$. The value of c_1 is then represented in the length AB. For doublets of "normal" glasses c_1 has, therefore, a constant value $-0.004\,881$ for this combination of wavelengths.)

To show how great the difference in secondary spectrum can be, we will give two more examples of possible doublets which the glasses shown. First, the combination LaF7 with SFS1; we need powers $a_1 = +2.305\,000$ and $a_2 = -1.305\,000$ and for the A'-line we have $c_1 = -0.007\,983$.

Second, the combination PSKS5 with 4aF7, which gives $a_1 = 2.063\,276$ and $a_2 = -1.063\,276$ and $c_1 = -0.003\,451$. We see that in this case, the color correction is more than twice as good as in the first combination.

4.7. LIMITS FOR THE COEFFICIENTS c_1 AND c_2

From the definition of c_1 one can easily compute how large c_1 can be before we have wavefront aberrations larger than 1λ. This leads to the relation $c_1 < 8\lambda F^2/f'$, where c_1 is computed for a focal length $+1$ and F is the F number of the system. For a doublet with a focal length of 10 cm we can use the first combination with $c_1 = -0.007\,983$ to an F number of 11, while the other with $c_1 = -0.003\,451$ can be used diffraction limited to F number 7.5.

For c_2 we find along the same lines the relation $c_2 < \lambda/d\theta_{max}$, where d is the diameter of the system and θ_{max} the half field angle over which the lens is used.

For many applications these limits are much to severe and the allowable values have to be determined from the quality of the desired image.

4.8. SYSTEMS CONSISTING OF THIN COMPONENTS

In general, we have to solve the equations for c_1 and c_2 and find a glass and power distribution for which these coefficients are zero. When a better color-correction is needed, we can see that each thin element can be replaced by a thin system. This way our freedom in glass constants is enormously enlarged. Furthermore, we can then design each thin group such that all groups have the same ϕ value. Correcting then, for the whole system c_1 and c_2 for wavelength λ_1, the system will automatically be corrected for λ_2.

5. Aberrations

5.1. INTRODUCTION

In section 1 we have proved the theorem that a finite volume of space can only be imaged perfectly if the angular magnification is unity throughout. Fortunately there are two reasons why this theorem is not of great practical importance. First of all, a system that forms a perfectly stigmatic image of a point source, according to geometrical optics, does in practice not behave in this way: due to the diffraction of the light the "point image" will have a certain finite size. Reversing this argument we see that we need not require an entirely perfect geometrical point image. Secondly, the detector observing the image always has a finite resolution, again indicating that perfection in the geometrical image formation need not be essential to an adequate performance of the optical instrument.

Furthermore, there is usually no requirement that a finite volume of space is imaged to a certain degree of faithfulness: in the majority of practical cases one is only interested in imaging a single plane, with a specified magnification β'. In the context of geometrical optics this can always be done by using an optical system with a point angle eikonal from object to image plane given by:

$$V = -n'\beta'(xL'+yM')+f(x^2+y^2), \tag{76}$$

in which we have assumed that the system has axial symmetry. Eq. (76) yields the required image formation, for

$$x' = -\frac{\partial V}{\partial(n'L')} = \beta'x, \qquad y' = -\frac{\partial V}{\partial(n'M')} = \beta'y. \tag{77}$$

The arbitrary function $f(x^2+y^2)$ can be used to satisfy some condition extraneous to the imaging requirement for the planes, e.g. the perfect image formation for one additional isolated point on axis (SMITH [1921–22]).

Eq. (76) provides us with an eikonal that will image to perfection one plane with a specific magnification. Constructing this eikonal is of course only the first step in constructing the instrument realizing this eikonal. In most of the literature it is silently assumed that any eikonal function can be realized by an instrument, at least in principle. No theorem to this effect has ever been proved, however, and the problem of the realizability of eikonal functions remains an open question (see CARATHEODORY [1937]). In this chapter we shall not delve into questions of this type; our main concern will be with the various possibilities of deviation from the perfect image formation. We shall see that the forms these aberrations can take are restricted both by the assumed axial symmetry of the instrument and by the fact that the instrument must possess an eikonal function.

5.2. SERIES DEVELOPMENT

The point angle eikonal from the object plane to the image plane of a system with axial symmetry depends on only three vairables (see section 1.10):

$$\begin{aligned}
u_1 &= \tfrac{1}{2}(x^2+y^2), \\
u_2 &= n'(xL'+yM'), \\
u_3 &= \tfrac{1}{2}n'^2(L'^2+M'^2).
\end{aligned} \tag{78}$$

For a perfect system we have

$$V = -\beta'u_2+f(u_1), \tag{79}$$

and the paraxial form is

$$V = -\beta'u_2-a\beta'u_1 \tag{80}$$

in which a is the paraxial power of the system.

We shall now consider an optical instrument that is not perfect. We shall develop its point angle eikonal in powers of u_1, u_2 and u_3, and interpret the physical meaning of the various terms. The linear terms must correspond to the paraxial approximation; so we shall have

$$\begin{aligned}
V = {}&-a\beta'u_1-\beta'u_2+ \\
&-\tfrac{1}{2}[\bar{K}_{11}u_1^2+2\bar{K}_{12}u_1u_2+\bar{K}_{22}u_2^2+2\bar{K}_{13}u_1u_3+2\bar{K}_{23}u_2u_3+\bar{K}_{33}u_3^2]+ \\
&+[\dots].
\end{aligned} \tag{81}$$

In this section we shall be primarily concerned with the third order aberrations. These aberrations are the image errors due to the terms of V quadratic in the u_i. Differentiation of eq. (81) with respect to L' and M' yields

$$\begin{pmatrix} x' \\ y' \end{pmatrix} = \beta'\begin{pmatrix} x \\ y \end{pmatrix} +(\bar{K}_{12}u_1+\bar{K}_{22}u_2+\bar{K}_{23}u_3)\begin{pmatrix} x \\ y \end{pmatrix}$$

$$+(\bar{K}_{13}u_1+\bar{K}_{23}u_2+\bar{K}_{33}u_3)\begin{pmatrix} n'L' \\ n'M' \end{pmatrix}. \tag{82}$$

Due to the axial symmetry of the system we do not impair the generality of the discussion by choosing the object point on the x-axis. Substituting $y=0$ in the equations defining u_1 and u_2 we have

$$u_1 = \tfrac{1}{2}x^2,$$
$$u_2 = n'xL', \tag{83}$$
$$u_3 = \tfrac{1}{2}n'^2(L'^2+M'^2).$$

We substitute this in eq. (82) and find

$$x' = \beta'x+\tfrac{1}{2}K_{12}x^3+\tfrac{1}{2}(K_{13}+2K_{22})x^2L'+\tfrac{1}{2}K_{23}(3L'^2+M'^2)x+\tfrac{1}{2}K_{33}(L'^2+M'^2)L',$$
$$y' = \tfrac{1}{2}K_{13}x^2M'+K_{23}L'M'x+\tfrac{1}{2}K_{33}(L'^2+M'^2)M'. \tag{84}$$

Here we have absorbed the factors n' into the K coefficients, which is indicated by omitting the bar over the coefficients. Eqs. (84) must be understood as follows. An object point is located on the x-axis at a height x measured from the axis. Rays emerge from the object point; each individual ray can be identified by its direction in the image space, L' and M'. Ideally all these rays would intersect the image plane in the point $x'=\beta'x$, $y'=0$. But in reality the various rays intersect the image plane in slightly different points. For each ray this point of intersection is given by eq. (84).

If we consider the entire ensemble of rays emerging from the object point and arriving at the image plane, then the ensemble of intersection points gives a picture of the blur pattern representing the "image" of the object point. We must, however, caution the reader against thoughtless application of these "spot diagrams". Only if the wavefront aberration (i.e. the non-linear part of the point angle eikonal) is large with respect to the wavelength of the light employed, the spot diagrams give a fairly realistic picture of what will be observed in practice.

The connection of the K_{ij} with the wavefront aberrations is of great practical importance. In section 1.9 we have derived that the wavefront deviation for an object point (x, y), evaluated with respect to the image point (x'_0, y'_0, z'_0), is given by

$$\Delta(L', M') = V(x, y, L', M')+n'(L'x'_0+M'y'_0+N'z'_0). \tag{85}$$

Upon substitution of the series development for V we arrive at

$$\Delta(L', M') = -a\beta'u_1-\tfrac{1}{2}\sum_{ij}\bar{K}_{ij}u_iu_j+n'N'z'_0+(x'_0-\beta'x)n'L'+(y'_0-\beta'y)n'M'. \tag{86}$$

This expression enters into the diffraction integral as follows

$$\text{Ampl}\,(x'_0, y'_0) = \exp\,(-ika\beta'u_1)\int\!\!\int\text{Ampl}\,(L', M')\exp ik[-\tfrac{1}{2}\sum_{ij}\bar{K}_{ij}u_iu_j+n'N'z'_0]\times$$
$$\times\exp ikn'[(x'_0-\beta'x)L'+(y'_0-\beta'y)M']\,\mathrm{d}L'\,\mathrm{d}M'. \tag{87}$$

This shows that the amplitude distribution in the receiving plane is the Fourier transform of

$$\text{Ampl}\,(L', M')\exp ik[-\tfrac{1}{2}\sum_{ij}\bar{K}_{ij}u_iu_j+n'N'z'_0], \tag{88}$$

except for a phase term only depending on x and y.

This is not the place to discuss the amplitude distribution Ampl (L', M') over the wavefront. It is often assumed to be uniform. The last expression shows that the aberration terms added to the perfect point angle eikonal enter into the diffraction integral in a very direct manner. The term containing N' represents a defocussing. In the third order approximation it may for small z_0 be replaced by $-\frac{1}{2}n'z_0'(L'^2 + M'^2)$, the constant being irrelevant.

5.3. INTERPRETATION

We shall now discuss the geometrical significance of the K coefficients one by one. In this work we shall wish to single out rays with a specific direction in the image space. This can be accomplished (albeit only geometrically) by assuming that the entrance pupil is located in the front focal plane. A point (x_1, y_1) in the front focal plane corresponds to a direction

$$L' = -x_1/f', \qquad M' = -y_1/f'. \tag{89}$$

in the image space. One may consider this point as a pinhole in the front focal plane. This is even feasible experimentally provided that the pinhole is made large enough to obviate diffraction effects and small enough to single out essentially one direction. The eqs. (89) themselves are of course only a paraxial approximation. This approximation is, however, good enough for use in eqs. (84), for the use of correction terms in eqs. (89) leads to terms in eq. (84) of a degree higher than 3 in x, L' and M'. These terms we have however left out of consideration for the time being. We shall now discuss the coefficients in eqs. (84) one at a time.

A. *Distortion*

We first consider the case in which all K_{ij} coefficients are zero except K_{12}. In that case we have

$$x' = \beta'x + \tfrac{1}{2}K_{12}x^3, \qquad y' = 0. \tag{90}$$

For a given object point the height of intersection of the rays in the image plane is independent of L' and M'. Hence a sharp image is formed. The location of this image is, however, in error by an amount that is proportional to the third power of the distance from the object point to the axis. As a result a straight line is imaged as a curved line, as indicated in fig. 24a.

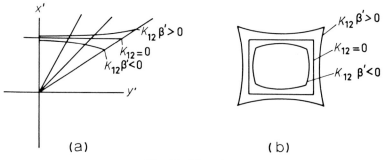

Fig. 24. Distortion.

The effect of this aberration on the image of a rectangle is shown in fig. 24b, which explains the expressions pin-cushion distortion and barrel distortion for the cases $\beta' K_{12} > 0$ and $\beta' K_{12} < 0$ respectively.

B. *Spherical aberration*

If K_{33} is the only coefficient differing from zero, we have

$$
\begin{aligned}
x' &= \beta'x + \tfrac{1}{2}K_{33}(L'^2 + M'^2)L', \\
y' &= \phantom{\beta'x + {}} \tfrac{1}{2}K_{33}(L'^2 + M'^2)M'.
\end{aligned}
\tag{91}
$$

Let ψ be the angle between a ray in the image space and the z-axis, and θ an azimuth angle. Then

$$
L' = \sin\psi\cos\theta
$$

and

$$
M' = \sin\psi\sin\theta.
\tag{92}
$$

Substitution in eqs. (91) yields

$$
\begin{aligned}
x' &= \beta'x + \tfrac{1}{2}K_{33}\sin^3\psi\cos\theta, \\
y' &= \phantom{\beta'x + {}} \tfrac{1}{2}K_{33}\sin^3\psi\sin\theta.
\end{aligned}
\tag{93}
$$

A narrow annulus in the front focal plane selects a fixed value for ψ, and allows all values of θ from 0 to 2π. If we eliminate θ from eq. (93) we arrive at

$$
\sqrt{\{(x' - \beta'x)^2 + y'^2\}} = \tfrac{1}{2}K_{33}\sin^3\psi.
$$

Hence all rays passing through this annulus intersect the image plane in a small circle, concentric with the ideal image point. The radius of this circle grows with the third power of $\sin\psi$ (fig. 25).

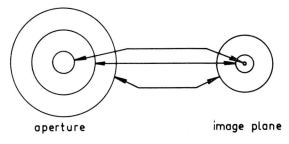

aperture image plane

Fig. 25. Spherical aberration.

Next considering the entire aperture, it follows that all rays passing through a circular aperture in the front focal plane will intersect the image plane in a blur circle concentric with the ideal image point, and with a radius given by $\tfrac{1}{2}K_{33}\sin^3\psi$.

Eqs. (91) are independent of x, hence this aberration does not vary over the field. It is the only third order aberration that can occur on axis.

In fig. 26 we have sketched the ray pattern in the image space when this aberration is present. This figure indicates that a smaller blur circle is obtained if we move the receiving plane from the paraxial image plane to the plane denoted by S. This can

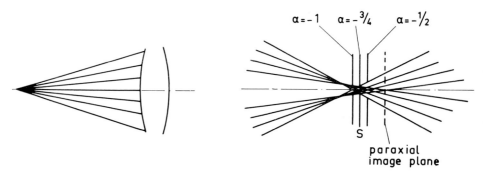

Fig. 26. Spherical aberration ray pattern.

be found algebraically as follows: if the receiving plane is moved over a distance $\Delta z'$ to the right, the heights of intersection $\bar{x}'$ and $\bar{y}'$ with this new plane follow from

$$\bar{x}' = x' + \frac{L'}{N'} \Delta z', \qquad \bar{y}' = y' + \frac{M'}{N'} \Delta z'. \tag{94}$$

As long as $\Delta z'$ is small, N' may be approximated by unity. We then have, substituting eqs. (93) for x' and y'

$$\bar{x}' = \beta' x + (\tfrac{1}{2} K_{33} \sin^2 \psi + \Delta z') \sin \psi \cos \theta,$$
$$\bar{y}' = \qquad (\tfrac{1}{2} K_{33} \sin^2 \psi + \Delta z') \sin \psi \sin \theta. \tag{95}$$

It follows that the ray intercepts with the receiving plane still cover a circle concentric with the ideal image point. The radius of this circle is now equal to the maximum absolute value of the function $\tfrac{1}{2} K_{33} \sin^3 \psi + \Delta z' \sin \psi$ over the range of ψ values allowed by the size of the aperture in the front focal plane. We can bring this function in the standard form

$$\tfrac{1}{2} K_{33} \sin^3 \psi_{\max} (u^3 + \alpha u), \qquad -1 \leqq u \leqq 1,$$

by writing

$$\sin \psi / \sin \psi_{\max} = u \tag{96}$$

and

$$2 \Delta z' / K_{33} \sin^2 \psi_{\max} = \alpha. \tag{97}$$

The function $(u^3 + \alpha u)$ is plotted in fig. 27 for various values of u.

An algebraic calculation shows that $\alpha = -\tfrac{3}{4}$ is the optimum curve. A refocussing, corresponding to this α value, reduces the size of the blur circle by a factor of 4 compared to the blur circle in the paraxial image plane. It is important to note that the value $\alpha = -\tfrac{3}{4}$ minimizes the size of the *geometrical* blur circle. If the aberrations are

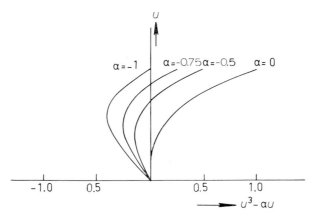

Fig. 27. Refocussing to improve 3rd order spherical aberration.

small it is rather more important to minimize the mean square wavefront aberration. Working our way backwards from eq. (95) to the point angle eikonal, we find for the wavefront aberration:

$$\Delta(L', M') = \tfrac{1}{2}n'K_{33} \sin^4 \psi_{\max}[\tfrac{1}{4}u^4 + \tfrac{1}{2}\alpha u^2 + \varepsilon], \tag{98}$$

in which ε is a constant that determines the choice of the reference sphere. It can be proved that the mean square value of Δ is minimal for $\alpha = -\tfrac{1}{2}$ and $\varepsilon = \tfrac{1}{24}$. So the optimum amount of defocussing is determined by different criteria depending on the amount of aberration present. A further discussion of these matters would lead us beyond the realm of geometrical optics; we refer to O'NEILL [1963]. In fig. 26 the results of this section are shown pictorially. The paraxial image plane corresponds to $\alpha = 0$. The plane $\alpha = -\tfrac{1}{2}$ is the optimum refocussing plane for small aberrations, the plane $\alpha = -\tfrac{3}{4}$ for large aberrations. The plane $\alpha = -1$ is distinguished by the fact that the edge rays pass through the center of the blur circle.

C. *Coma*

We next assume that only K_{23} differs from zero. Then

$$x' = \beta'x + \tfrac{1}{2}K_{23}(3L'^2 + M'^2)x,$$
$$y' = \qquad K_{23}L'M'x. \tag{99}$$

Again introducing the angles ψ and θ we have

$$x' = \beta'x + \tfrac{1}{2}K_{23} \sin^2 \psi \cdot x \cdot (2 + \cos 2\theta),$$
$$y' = \qquad \tfrac{1}{2}K_{23} \sin^2 \psi \cdot x \cdot \sin 2\theta. \tag{100}$$

So the rays passing through an annulus in the front focal plane once more intersect the image plane in a circle instead of in one point. The size of this circle is proportional to the object height, and proportional to the square of the aperture. This circle of ray intercepts is *not* concentric with the ideal image point; it is displaced over a distance equal to the diameter of the circle. Moreover, we observe that if the intersection point of a ray with the front focal plane travels around the annulus once, its point of intersection with the image plane travels twice around the circle of ray intercepts (fig. 28). Drawing the circles of ray intercepts for the various sizes of

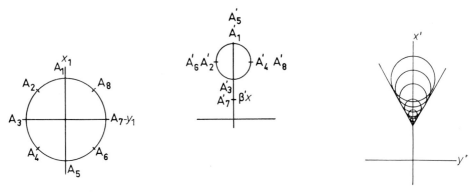

Fig. 28. Coma.   Fig. 29. Coma.

annuli in the entrance pupil, we arrive at a peculiar aberration pattern shown in fig. 29. The size of this pattern grows linearly with the distance from the object point to the axis, and is proportional to the aperture sin ψ squared. The center of gravity of the aberration pattern does not coincide with the ideal image point, which is detrimental in astronomic direction determinations.

D. Astigmatism and field curvature

The two remaining coefficients, K_{13} and K_{22}, we shall consider jointly. If the three other coefficients are zero and we introduce a defocussing $\Delta z'$, we have

$$x' = \beta'x + [\tfrac{1}{2}(K_{13}+2K_{22})x^2 + \Delta z']L',$$
$$y' = \qquad [\tfrac{1}{2}K_{13}x^2 + \Delta z']M'. \tag{101}$$

Again introducing the angles ψ and θ we have

$$x' = \beta'x + [\tfrac{1}{2}(K_{13}+2K_{22})x^2 + \Delta z']\sin\psi\cos\theta,$$
$$y' = \qquad [\tfrac{1}{2}K_{13}x^2 + \Delta z']\sin\psi\sin\theta. \tag{102}$$

Hence an annulus in the front focal plane specified by the angle ψ leads to an ellipse of ray intercepts with the image plane:

$$\frac{(x'-\beta'x)^2}{a^2} + \frac{y'^2}{b^2} = 1,$$

with

$$a = [\tfrac{1}{2}(K_{13}+2K_{22})x^2 + \Delta z']\sin\psi,$$
$$b = [\tfrac{1}{2}K_{13}x^2 + \Delta z']\sin\psi.$$

This ellipse is centered around the paraxial image point. In the paraxial image plane ($\Delta z' = 0$) its size is proportional to the square of the object height x. It grows linearly with the aperture $\sin \psi$.

A special case is obtained when $K_{22} = 0$. Then a stigmatic image can be obtained by curving the image such that $\Delta z'$ has the proper value for each x:

$$\Delta z' = -\frac{K_{13}}{2\beta'^2}(\beta'x)^2.$$

So the image plane must be curved to a radius of $-\beta'^2/K_{13}$. This case is known as pure field curvature.

In general K_{22} will not be zero. There are then three special cases to be considered: $a=0$, $a=-b$ and $b=0$. These cases obtain when the image plane is curved according to

$$\Delta z' = -\frac{K_{13}+2K_{22}}{2\beta'^2}(\beta'x)^2, \tag{103A}$$

$$\Delta z' = -\frac{K_{13}+K_{22}}{2\beta'^2}(\beta'x)^2, \tag{103B}$$

and

$$\Delta z' = -\frac{K_{13}}{2\beta'^2}(\beta'x)^2 \tag{103C}$$

respectively.

In the first case we have

$$x' = \beta'x,$$
$$y' = -K_{22}x^2M'.$$

The ellipse is degenerated into a line segment perpendicular to the meridional (x, z) plane. All rays intersecting the entrance pupil in a line parallel to the x-axis (i.e. M' is constant, L' is variable) intersect the image plane in one point of this line segment. By varying M' the entire line segment is created. The length of the line segment is proportional to the square of the object height x, and grows linearly with the aperture M' (see fig. 30).

In the last case we have

$$x' = \beta'x + K_{22}x^2L',$$
$$y' = 0.$$

This situation is similar to the previous one, except that x and y are reversed. The line segment now lies in the (x, z) plane. All rays intersecting the entrance pupil in a line perpendicular to the (x, z) plane (i.e. L' constant, M' variable) converge to one point of the line segment, and by varying L' the entire line segment is created. The length of the line segment is the same as in the previous case.

In the first case all rays traveling in the meridional plane ($M'=0$) converge to one point on the image line. This line segment is therefore called the meridional image, formed in the meridional image plane give by eq. (103A). In the opposite case rays traveling in a plane perpendicular to the meridional plane ($L'=0$, M' variable) converge to one point. This second image line is therefore called the sagittal image line, formed in the sagittal image plane given by eq. (103C).

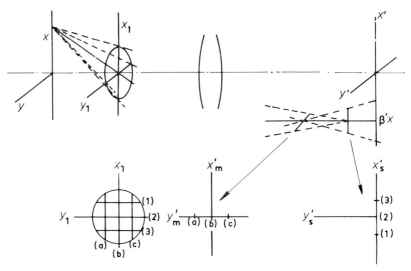

Fig. 30. Astigmatism.

The plane specified by eq. (103B) is midway between the meridional and the sagittal image plane. In this plane we have

$$x' = \beta'x + \tfrac{1}{2}K_{22}x^2 \sin \psi \cos \theta,$$
$$y' = \tfrac{1}{2}K_{22}x^2 \sin \psi \sin \theta.$$

So in this plane a blur circle will be observed with a diameter equal to one-half of the length of each of the astigmatic lines. In fig. 31 we have sketched an object, a wheel with spokes, and its image in the three image planes considered.

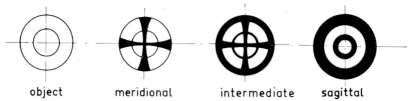

object   meridional   intermediate   sagittal

Fig. 31. Astigmatism: image of a wheel with spokes.

Summary

Spherical aberration – gives a blur circle centered around the ideal image point. The size of the blur circle is the same everywhere in the field, but grows with the third power of the aperture sin ψ.

Coma – causes an asymmetric aberration pattern with a size proportional to the distance from the object point to the axis, and the square of the aperture.

Astigmatism and field curvature – cause aberration patterns that are elliptical and centered around the ideal image point. By curving the image plane the ellipse can be made to degenerate in a meridional or sagittal image line, or a circle. In any case, the size of the aberration pattern is proportional to the square of the object height, and the first power of the aperture.

Distortion – produces stigmatic images in which the location of the image points is in error proportional to the third power of the object height.

5.4. INFLUENCE OF THE PUPIL POSITION

In the previous work we have assumed that the image forming rays were limited by a round stop in the front focal plane of the lens. This was done to bring out the close relationship between the point angle eikonal, the wavefront aberrations and the geometrical aberration patterns. But in most lenses the pupil is not located in the front focal plane. This makes it necessary to remove this restriction.

Let the actual pupil magnification be β'_1, and let the coordinates in the entrance pupil plane be x_1 and y_1. Then we have, paraxially

$$n'L' = \frac{a}{\beta'_1 - \beta'} (\beta' x - \beta'_1 x_1),$$

$$n'M' = \frac{a}{\beta'_1 - \beta'} (\beta' y - \beta'_1 y_1).$$

To simplify the formulas we introduce the reduced variables

$$\xi = \frac{a\beta'}{n'(\beta'_1 - \beta')} x, \qquad \xi_1 = \frac{a\beta'_1}{n'(\beta'_1 - \beta')} x_1,$$

$$\eta = \frac{a\beta'}{n'(\beta'_1 - \beta')} y, \qquad \eta_1 = \frac{a\beta'_1}{n'(\beta'_1 - \beta')} y_1.$$

The variables ξ and η are the paraxial direction cosines of the line connecting the

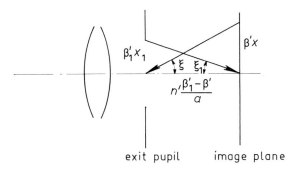

Fig. 32. Reduced ray parameters.

paraxial image point with the center of the exit pupil, and ξ_1 and η_1 are minus the paraxial direction cosines of the line connecting a point in the exit pupil with the center of the image plane (fig. 32). We have

$$L' = \xi - \xi_1, \qquad M' = \eta - \eta_1.$$

These expressions must now be substituted in eq. (82).

We have, writing q for the distance between the exit pupil and the image plane devided by the object magnification β',

$$x = q\xi, \qquad L' = \xi - \xi_1,$$
$$y = q\eta, \qquad M' = \eta - \eta_1,$$

and, if we write

$$\tfrac{1}{2}(\xi^2 + \eta^2) = w_1,$$
$$\xi\xi_1 + \eta\eta_1 = w_2,$$
$$\tfrac{1}{2}(\xi_1^2 + \eta_1^2) = w_3,$$

we also have

$$u_1 = q^2 w_1,$$
$$u_2 = n'q(2w_1 - w_2),$$
$$u_3 = n'^2(w_1 - w_2 + w_3).$$

We shall forego the details of the algebraic work. The result of the substitution is

$$\begin{pmatrix} n'x' \\ n'y' \end{pmatrix} = \frac{n'}{n}\beta'\begin{pmatrix} nx \\ ny \end{pmatrix} + (C_{12}w_1 + C_{22}w_2 + C_{23}w_3)\begin{pmatrix} \xi \\ \eta \end{pmatrix} +$$
$$+ (C_{13}w_1 + C_{23}w_2 + C_{33}w_3)\begin{pmatrix} \xi_1 \\ \eta_1 \end{pmatrix}, \quad (104)$$

in which

$$\begin{pmatrix} C_{12} \\ C_{22} \\ C_{23} \\ C_{13} \\ C_{33} \end{pmatrix} = \begin{pmatrix} q^3 & 2n'q^2 & 3n'^2 q & q^2 n' & n'^3 \\ 0 & -n'q^2 & -2n'^2 q & 0 & -n'^3 \\ 0 & 0 & n'^2 q & 0 & n'^3 \\ 0 & 0 & -2n'^2 q & -q^2 n' & -n'^3 \\ 0 & 0 & 0 & 0 & n'^3 \end{pmatrix} \begin{pmatrix} n'\overline{K}_{12} \\ n'\overline{K}_{22} \\ n'\overline{K}_{23} \\ n'\overline{K}_{13} \\ n'\overline{K}_{33} \end{pmatrix}. \quad (105)$$

The interpretation of this result is exactly the same as the interpretation of the original formula (84):

C_{12}:   distortion
C_{22} and C_{13}:   astigmatism and field curvature
C_{23}:   coma
C_{33}:   spherical aberration.

We invite the reader to verify that the relation between the old and the new coefficients is dimensionally correct; the new C coefficients all have the dimension of a length.

It further follows that upon a shift of the pupil the coefficients are subject to a linear homogeneous transformation among each other. It is well to keep in mind, however, that the path of a ray is independent of the location of the pupil. The place and size of the pupil only determines *which* rays contribute to the image formation. So, for instance, if the pupil is shifted and its size is adjusted such that the maximum value of ξ_1 (i.e. $\sin \psi$) does not change, one would expect the spherical aberration to be unchanged. This is in fact the case, as follows from the above relations. The above relations also show that $C_{22} - C_{13}$ only changes by a proportionality factor. The reason for this simple behavior of $C_{22} - C_{13}$ will become clear later.

Aberrations can actually sometimes be annulled by a proper choice of the pupil location. We have for instance

$$C_{23} = n'^3 q \overline{K}_{23} + n'^4 \overline{K}_{33},$$

so C_{23} can be made zero by an appropriate choice of q, provided that the spherical aberration is not zero. Conversely, one can obtain the effect of a mixture of coma and spherical aberration for a point on axis by using a pupil not centered with respect to the axis.

A further development of the theory would require a study of the variation in the C coefficients when the object magnification is changed. This would lead us too far afield however; SMITH [1921–22] and BROUWER [1964] may be referred to for further details on this subject. The applicable formulae will be stated later.

5.5. THE ADDITION OF THIRD ORDER ABERRATIONS

When two lens systems in series are used to form an image of an object, the third order aberrations of the combination can be expressed in the third order aberrations of the two partial systems. Let all quantities relating to the first system be marked by an index A, for the second system we use an index B. No special index indicates that a quantity is related to the system as a whole. In particular we have

$$\beta'_A \beta'_B = \beta', \qquad \beta'_{1A} \beta'_{1B} = \beta'_1.$$

Denoting the aberrations by a Δ symbol, and singling out the x-variables (the y-variables behave exactly the same) we can write

$$x'_B = \beta'_B x_B + \Delta x'_B, \qquad x'_A = \beta'_A x_A + \Delta x'_A.$$

x'_B equals x', the height in the final image plane, and x'_A equals x_B. Also x_A equals x, the height in the object plane. So

$$\begin{aligned} x' &= \beta'_B(\beta'_A x_A + \Delta x'_A) + \Delta x'_B \\ &= \beta' x + \beta'_B \Delta x'_A + \Delta x'_B. \end{aligned} \tag{106}$$

In the calculation of the third order aberrations it is sufficient to use the variables

ξ, η, ξ_1 and η_1 in the paraxial approximation. We have

$$\xi = \xi_B = \left(\frac{n_B}{n'_B \beta'_B}\right) \xi_A, \tag{107A}$$

$$\xi_1 = \xi_{1B} = \left(\frac{n_B}{n'_B \beta'_{1B}}\right) \xi_{1A}. \tag{107B}$$

We can now write down eq. (104) once for the combined system, and once for each of the partial systems. Eq. (106) then yields, after application of eq. (107):

$$C_{12} = C_{12A} G_B S_B^3 + C_{12B}, \tag{108A}$$

$$C_{22} = C_{22A} G_B^2 S_B^2 + C_{22B}, \tag{108B}$$

$$C_{23} = C_{23A} G_B^3 S_B + C_{23B}, \tag{108C}$$

$$C_{13} = C_{13A} G_B^2 S_B^2 + C_{13B}, \tag{108D}$$

$$C_{33} = C_{33A} G_B^4 + C_{33B}, \tag{108E}$$

in which

$$G = \frac{n'}{n} \beta' \quad \text{and} \quad S = \frac{n'}{n} \beta'_1, \tag{109}$$

i.e. the reciprocals of the angular object and pupil magnification.

5.6. FURTHER DEVELOPMENTS

The next step in developing the theory of third order aberrations is to find the aberration coefficients for a given optical system as a function of its construction parameters. The derivation of these formulae is very lengthy and devoid of any interest. We refer the reader to ch. 17, section 3.1 for further information on this subject.

References

BROUWER, W., 1964, Matrix methods in optical instrument design (W. A. Benjamin, Inc., New York).
CARATHEODORY, C., 1937, Geometrische Optik (Springer-Verlag, Berlin).
HERZBERGER, M., 1931, Strahlen Optik (Springer-Verlag, Berlin).
HERZBERGER, M., 1959, Opt. Acta 6, 197.
O'NEILL, E. L., 1963, Introduction to statistical optics (Addison-Wesley, Reading, Massachusetts).
SMITH, T., 1921–22, Trans. Opt. Soc. 23, 311.
SMITH, T., 1945, Proc. Phil. Soc. 57, 286.

CHAPTER 17

DESIGN OF OPTICAL INSTRUMENTS

W. BROUWER AND A. WALTHER

Diffraction Limited, Inc.
Bedford, Mass.

CONTENTS

1. Plane mirror systems

1.1. MATRIX FORMULATION

The reflection of a light ray by a mirror surface is governed by Snell's laws when we put $n' = -n$. We then arrive at:

(1) The angle of reflection equals the angle of incidence;

(2) The reflected ray lies in the plane defined by the incident ray and the normal to the mirror in the point of incidence.

For one plane mirror this leads to a simple law of image formation, which reads:

A plane mirror forms a perfect image of every object point. The line segment connecting an image point with its object point is perpendicular to the mirror and is divided by the mirror into two segments of equal length.

For a proof of this theorem we refer to any elementary textbook on optics.

The need for an advanced mathematical description of this simple image formation arises when light has to pass through a sequence of plane mirrors arbitrarily oriented in space. Unless one chooses a convenient mathematical scheme, the description of the successive reflections tends to get rather involved.

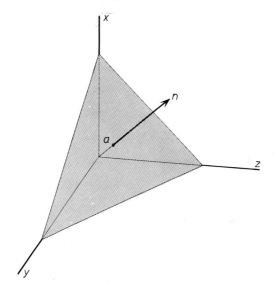

Fig. 1.

In this section we shall develop a simple matrix model for a sequence of flat mirrors. We shall use vectors in a fixed Cartesian coordinate system to describe the parameters occurring in the problem. Quantities before a reflection will be unprimed; after reflection they will be primed. All vectors are column vectors, so transposed vectors (v^{T}, etc.) are row vectors.

We shall first consider the case of one mirror (fig. 1). The normal to the mirror is defined by the unit vector n, and the distance from the origin of the Cartesian coordinate system to the plane of the mirror be a. Then the equation satisfied by all points $\bar{r}$ in the plane of the mirror is

$$\bar{r} \cdot n = a. \tag{1}$$

Here we use the dot notation for the scalar product. Let r be an object point and r' its image point. When 2λ is the distance between the object and the image point, we have

$$r' = r - 2\lambda n. \tag{2}$$

According to the law of image formation stated above the point

$$r - \lambda n$$

lies in the plane of the mirror. Substituting this in eq. (1) yields

$$(r - \lambda n) \cdot n = a,$$

or

$$\lambda = -a + n \cdot r.$$

Substitution of this value for λ in eq. (2) yields:

$$r' = r - 2n(n \cdot r) + 2an. \tag{3}$$

We now switch to the matrix notation, in which a scalar product is represented by the matrix product of a transposed vector with an untransposed vector. Rewriting eq. (3) in this fashion yields:

$$r' = r - 2nn^{\mathrm{T}}r + 2an,$$

or

$$r' = (E - 2nn^{\mathrm{T}})r + 2an,$$

in which E stands for the unit matrix.

When we write (L, M, N) for the components of the unit column vector n and (x, y, z) for the coordinates in space we can write for this relation:

$$\begin{pmatrix} x' \\ y' \\ z' \end{pmatrix} = \begin{pmatrix} 1-2L^2 & -2LM & -2LN \\ -2LM & 1-2M^2 & -2MN \\ -2LN & -2MN & 1-2N^2 \end{pmatrix} \begin{pmatrix} x \\ y \\ z \end{pmatrix} + \begin{pmatrix} 2aL \\ 2aM \\ 2aN \end{pmatrix}. \tag{4}$$

It is often convenient to cast this equation in a 4×4 matrix form:

$$\begin{pmatrix} x' \\ y' \\ z' \\ 1 \end{pmatrix} = \begin{pmatrix} 1-2L^2 & -2LM & -2LN & 2aL \\ -2LM & 1-2M^2 & -2MN & 2aM \\ -2LN & -2MN & 1-2N^2 & 2aN \\ 0 & 0 & 0 & 1 \end{pmatrix} \begin{pmatrix} x \\ y \\ z \\ 1 \end{pmatrix}. \tag{5}$$

We shall write A_i for the 3×3 matrix in eq. (4) and B_i for the 4×4 matrix in eq. (5). The index i is used to indicate that we refer to a single reflection only; the index shall be used later to indicate which reflection is referred to when a more complicated system is considered.

The determinant of both A_i and B_i is -1. This can be verified by noting that the determinants are independent of a rotation of the coordinate axes, and then taking a special case for n.

We also note that A_i represents an orthogonal transformation, which implies that the inverse of A_i is equal to A_i transposed. But A_i is symmetric, which makes it its own inverse. This was to be expected: the mirror image of a mirror image is the original image.

1.2. COMPOUND SYSTEMS OF PLANE MIRRORS

The image formed of an object by a sequence of plane mirrors can now be obtained by a successive application of eq. (5)

$$\begin{pmatrix} x' \\ y' \\ z' \\ 1 \end{pmatrix} = B_m B_{m-1} \cdots B_3 B_2 B_1 \begin{pmatrix} x \\ y \\ z \\ 1 \end{pmatrix} = B \begin{pmatrix} x \\ y \\ z \\ 1 \end{pmatrix} \tag{6}$$

in which B is the product of the matrices of the individual mirrors.

Often we are only interested in ray directions and not in the precise location of object and image points in space. Then the 3×3 matrices A_i suffice, as we shall now

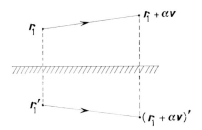

Fig. 2.

show. We can define a ray direction (unit-vector v) by two points on the ray (see fig. 2), such as

$$r_1, \qquad r_1 + \alpha v.$$

Application of eq. (4), (for one mirror) gives:

$$r'_1 = A_i r_1 + 2an,$$
$$r'_2 = A_i(r_1 + \alpha v) + 2an.$$

So the vector αv connecting the two points on the ray is transformed into

$$r'_2 - r'_1 = \alpha A_i v,$$

which shows that ray directions transform according to

$$v' = A_i v.$$

For a sequence of mirrors this gives

$$v' = A_n \cdots A_2 A_1 v_1 = A v_1, \tag{7}$$

where A is the product of the individual 3×3 matrices for each mirror. This 3×3 matrix is identical to the matrix obtained by leaving off the last row and the last column of the 4×4 product matrix B.

We noticed already that, for one mirror, the determinant of both the A and the B matrix is -1. Hence an even number of mirrors leads to a system matrix with a determinant of plus one, and an odd number of reflections leads to a determinant of minus one.

1.3. EXAMPLES

As an example we treat the case of two mirrors intersecting in the z-axis, whose normals make angles of α and β with the positive x-axis (fig. 3). The Cartesian components of the normals are $(\cos \alpha, \sin \alpha, 0)$ and $(\cos \beta, \sin \beta, 0)$ respectively.

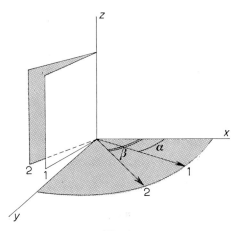

Fig. 3.

Substitution of these values in the 3×3 matrix defined in eq. (4) gives, for the first mirror

$$A_1 = \begin{pmatrix} -\cos 2\alpha & -\sin 2\alpha & 0 \\ -\sin 2\alpha & \cos 2\alpha & 0 \\ 0 & 0 & 1 \end{pmatrix}.$$

The matrix for the second mirror is the same, except for the replacement of α by β. We find the system matrix by multiplying the matrices of the two components:

$$A = A_2 A_1 = \begin{pmatrix} -\cos 2\beta & -\sin 2\beta & 0 \\ -\sin 2\beta & \cos 2\beta & 0 \\ 0 & 0 & 1 \end{pmatrix} \begin{pmatrix} -\cos 2\alpha & -\sin 2\alpha & 0 \\ -\sin 2\alpha & \cos 2\alpha & 0 \\ 0 & 0 & 1 \end{pmatrix}$$

or

or

$$A = \begin{pmatrix} \cos 2(\beta-\alpha) & -\sin 2(\beta-\alpha) & 0 \\ \sin 2(\beta-\alpha) & \cos 2(\beta-\alpha) & 0 \\ 0 & 0 & 1 \end{pmatrix}. \tag{8}$$

This matrix represents a rotation around the z-axis over an angle of $2(\beta-\alpha)$. It appears that the angle of rotation only depends on the difference $\beta-\alpha$, i.e. the angle between the two mirrors. A rotation of the combination around the z-axis does not change the matrix, so every ray that travels in a direction perpendicular to the intersection line of the two mirrors is rotated over the same angle. An important technical application of this principle is found in the pentaprism (fig. 4).

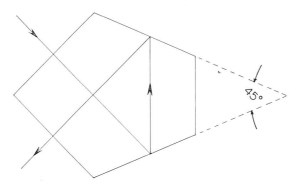

Fig. 4.

In this prism the angle $(\beta-\alpha)$ is 45°, which leads to a constant deviation angle of 90°. We stress that this only holds for rays traveling in a plane perpendicular to the intersection line of the two reflecting surfaces. The error that is introduced by deviating from this plane can be calculated as follows: still assuming that the line of intersection of the mirrors coincides with the z-axis, the matrix for a pentaprism is, according to eq. (8):

$$\begin{pmatrix} 0 & -1 & 0 \\ 1 & 0 & 0 \\ 0 & 0 & 1 \end{pmatrix}.$$

A ray direction including an angle δ with the plane perpendicular to the z-axis can be represented by:

$$v = \begin{pmatrix} \cos \delta \cos \varphi \\ \cos \delta \sin \varphi \\ \sin \delta \end{pmatrix}.$$

The direction of emergence is:

$$v' = \begin{pmatrix} 0 & -1 & 0 \\ 1 & 0 & 0 \\ 0 & 0 & 1 \end{pmatrix} \begin{pmatrix} \cos \delta \cos \varphi \\ \cos \delta \sin \varphi \\ \sin \delta \end{pmatrix} = \begin{pmatrix} -\cos \delta \sin \varphi \\ \cos \delta \cos \varphi \\ \sin \delta \end{pmatrix}.$$

Let the angle between the incident and the emerging ray be $90° + \varepsilon$. The cosine of this angle is equal to the inner product of v and v':

$$\cos(90° + \varepsilon) = -\cos^2\delta \cos\varphi \sin\varphi + \cos^2\delta \sin\varphi \cos\varphi + \sin^2\delta$$

or

$$\sin\varepsilon = -\sin^2\delta. \tag{9}$$

For a small deviation δ we so find for the error ε:

$$\varepsilon = -\delta^2.$$

We see that this error is only a quadratic effect (see table 1).

TABLE 1

δ		ε	
7.6	degrees	1	degree
1	degree	1	minute of arc
10	minutes	2	second of arc
2	minutes	0.07	second of arc

Eq. (9) also holds for large angles: if δ is $90°$ we see that $\varepsilon = 90°$, so that the angle of deviation is zero. This is to be expected for a ray traveling parallel to the line of intersection of the mirrors.

The pentaprism is, as the name implies, usually executed as a prism and not as a combination of two mirrors. The effect of the refraction at the entrance surface is compensated by the refraction at the exit surface. This only obtains when the successive reflections image the normal v_0 on the entrance surface into the normal v_0' on the exit surface. In other words: the entrance and exit surface must be perpendicular to the same ray. This can be brought in formula form as follows:

$$|v_0^T A v_0| = 1.$$

We mention in passing that the calculation of the points of incidence of a ray on the respective mirror surfaces can be easily effected with the methods described in this section. Let r_i be the point of incidence of a ray on the ith surface, and v_i' its direction after this surface. Then the point of incidence on the $(i+1)$st surface is

$$r_{i+1} = r_i + \lambda v_i', \tag{10}$$

where r_{i+1} must satisfy the equation of the $(i+1)$st surface:

$$r_{i+1} \cdot n_{i+1} = a_{i+1}.$$

This linear equation must be solved for λ. Substitution of λ in (10) yields the point of incidence on mirror $(i+1)$.

1.4. THE DESIGN OF A MIRROR SYSTEM WITH A GIVEN MATRIX

The reverse problem of designing a mirror system with a given matrix is considerably more difficult. We shall in this section construct one solution for the case when the A matrix is given, but we must point out in advance that the solution is not unique.

To find this solution we must consider the eigenvalues of the given 3×3 matrix. The eigenvalue equation is of the third degree; hence there must always be one real eigenvalue. We are dealing with orthogonal transformations, hence this eigenvalue must be $+1$ or -1. The other two eigenvalues are complex conjugates (which may be equal and real on occasion), so their product is always positive. The product of the three eigenvalues is equal to the determinant of the matrix. So we are led to the following two cases:

$$\text{determinant } +1, \quad \lambda_1 = +1, \quad \lambda_{2,3} = e^{\pm i\varphi},$$

$$\text{determinant } -1, \quad \lambda_1 = -1, \quad \lambda_{2,3} = e^{\pm i\varphi}.$$

Let us first consider the first case. Assume that we have turned the coordinate system such that the real eigenvector associated with the real eigenvalue coincides with the z-axis. We claim that then the given matrix will be transformed into

$$\begin{pmatrix} \cos \varphi & \sin \varphi & 0 \\ -\sin \varphi & \cos \varphi & 0 \\ 0 & 0 & 1 \end{pmatrix}. \tag{11}$$

This can be seen as follows:
(1) The direction of the z-axis is obviously an eigenvector with eigenvalue $+1$.
(2) The characteristic equation reads

$$\begin{vmatrix} \cos \varphi - \lambda & \sin \varphi & 0 \\ -\sin \varphi & \cos \varphi - \lambda & 0 \\ 0 & 0 & 1-\lambda \end{vmatrix} = 0,$$

or

$$(\cos \varphi - \lambda)^2 (1 - \lambda) + \sin^2 \varphi (1 - \lambda) = 0,$$

so

$$\lambda_1 = +1, \quad \lambda_{2,3} = \cos \varphi \pm i \sin \varphi = e^{\pm i\varphi},$$

which verifies our statement.

The matrix (11) is the rotation matrix that we encountered already in the previous section. Applying the results derived in the previous section we are led to the following conclusion:

Let a 3×3 matrix A be given, with a positive determinant. This matrix can be realized by two mirrors, as follows:
(1) Determine the complex conjugate eigenvalues of the matrix; $e^{\pm i\varphi}$.
(2) Determine the real eigenvector of the matrix. Then the matrix is realized by two

mirrors including an angle $\frac{1}{2}\varphi$ and intersecting in a line parallel to the real eigen-vector.

We wish to stress that the coordinate transformation used in the derivation of this result need not actually be carried out at all.

The case with a negative determinant goes along similar lines, and the result is the same except for one added mirror perpendicular to the real eigenvector.

We mentioned already that these solutions are not unique. Often they are impractical because of added geometrical restrictions. No foolproof method to solve such problems is known to these authors. We mention however one procedure to simplify or complicate mirror systems. This method is cumbersome but leads to useful results occasionally. Consider a sequence of (say) 4 mirrors, numbered 1, 2, 3, 4. We can introduce two parallel mirrors a and b in between any two mirrors of the given sequence, for a and b will have the same matrix, and the product of these matrices will be the unit matrix, so the matrix of the sequence does not change. Let the new sequence be (for instance)

$$1 \quad a \quad b \quad 2 \quad 3 \quad 4.$$

We can now rotate 1 and a jointly around their line of intersection, and similarly b and 2 (or, for that matter, any other combination of two mirrors used in sequence) without changing the system matrix. This leads to new solutions for the same matrix.

In reverse this method can be used to simplify a sequence of mirrors. In any sequence 1, 2, 3, 4 of four plane mirrors we can rotate 1 and 2 jointly and 3 and 4 jointly until the normals of the mirrors 2 and 3 coincide. At this point we can just leave out mirrors 2 and 3. So any sequence of 4 mirrors can be reduced to a sequence of 2 mirrors. Repeated application of this procedure shows that a sequence containing an odd number of mirrors can always be reduced to 3 mirrors, and an even number of mirrors can always be reduced to 2 mirrors. This shows that the solutions constructed by the eigenvalue method are the simplest solutions possible.

We leave the degenerate cases of no mirror and one mirror to the reader.

1.5. EXAMPLES

As an example of the design method set out in the previous section we shall solve the following problem: to design a combination of two prisms P and Q, such that any two parallel rays incident upon P and Q respectively emerge with the same orientation in space, but traveling in opposite directions.

It is clear that if A is the matrix representing prism P, prism Q must be represented by the matrix $-A$. So we need one prism with an odd number of reflections, and one with an even number of reflections. Inspection shows that "no mirror" combined with one mirror does not satisfy the requirements. The next simplest case is one mirror and two mirrors respectively. We can choose the orientation of the single mirror arbitrarily; we take for the direction of its normal $(0, 0, 1)$.

The matrix for this mirror is

$$\begin{pmatrix} 1 & 0 & 0 \\ 0 & 1 & 0 \\ 0 & 0 & -1 \end{pmatrix}.$$

Hence the matrix for the second prism is

$$\begin{pmatrix} -1 & 0 & 0 \\ 0 & -1 & 0 \\ 0 & 0 & 1 \end{pmatrix}.$$

The eigenvalue equation for this matrix is

$$(-1-\lambda)^2(1-\lambda) = 0$$

or

$$\lambda_1 = 1, \qquad \lambda_{2,3} = -1 = e^{\pm i\pi}.$$

The angle between the two mirrors is half the angle occurring in the exponent, i.e. 90°. The intersection line of the two mirrors is parallel to the eigenvector belonging to the eigenvalue $+1$. Let its components be p, q, r. Then we have

$$\begin{pmatrix} -1 & 0 & 0 \\ 0 & -1 & 0 \\ 0 & 0 & 1 \end{pmatrix}\begin{pmatrix} p \\ q \\ r \end{pmatrix} = 1 \cdot \begin{pmatrix} p \\ q \\ r \end{pmatrix}$$

or $p=0$ and $q=0$. So the eigenvalue is parallel to the z-axis. Hence the second prism must have two reflecting surfaces perpendicular to each other and intersecting in a line parallel to the z-axis.

The resulting prism combination can be realized as shown in fig. 5 in a number of projections.

The first ray mentioned in the statement of the problem is reflected by surface ABC. The second ray is first reflected by surface BEFC and then by surface BEDA, or first by BEDA and then by BEFC. These two cases lead to the same result because an angle of 90° is its own supplement.

The system can be executed as an ordinary 45°–45°–90° prism with the sideface ABC silvered. The refractions upon entrance and exit of the ray through surface ADCF cancel when this surface is parallel to the z-axis. For a ray entering perpendicularly to surface ADCF only reverses direction and returns perpendicular to ADCF. According to section 1.3 this is the requirement to make the entrance and exit refraction cancel each other. The ray just mentioned does only reverse direction indeed, for a ray parallel to it, to be reflected by ABC, is parallel to ABC and so does not change direction at all.

In conjunction with an autocollimator this prism can be used to put two mirrors parallel (fig. 6). Two return images can be observed, one from one mirror via ABC, and one from the other mirror via the two reflections by BEDA and BEFC. Only when the two return images coincide the two mirrors are parallel. The adjustment is independent of movements and rotations of the prism. This follows directly from the original statement of the problem.

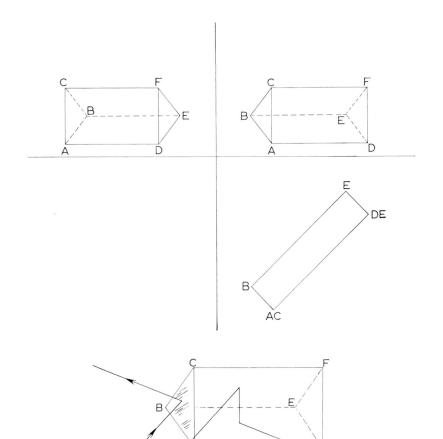

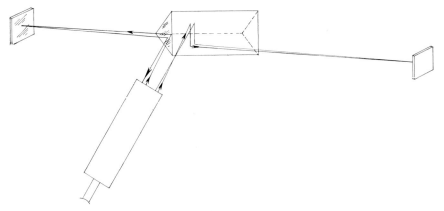

Fig. 5.

Fig. 6.

2. Optical instruments

2.1. INTRODUCTION

In this section we shall discuss the principles governing the design of some important optical instruments. Lack of space does not permit us to enter into questions of mechanical construction, nor can we describe the multitude of instruments currently on the market. For these matters we refer the reader to JOHNSON [1960], KINGSLAKE [1965] and the publications of instrument manufacturers.

An optical instrument can never be discussed separate from the source of the light entering it and the destination of the light emerging from it. For a telescope the source of light is the scene to be observed, and the light emerging from the telescope is observed by the eye. For a spectrograph the source of light may be an electric discharge, and the light emerging from the spectrograph may be detected by a photographic plate, or an array of photosensitive electronic devices. In all cases the optical instrument is an aid to bring the properties of the source into a form compatible with the requirements of the detecting device. In many cases the line that separates the optical instrument from the detector cannot be easily drawn. We shall for instance encounter quite a few cases in which the eye is considered as the detector. The eye itself however is an optical instrument that images the incoming light onto its retina.

The eye is a complicated instrument because its surfaces are not spherical and its media are not homogeneous. For elementary discussions the human eye may be approximated by a single refracting surface with a radius of 5.73 mm. This surface separates the air from a medium with a refractive index of 1.366. The retina of the eye is located in the back focal plane of the eye. Its back focal length f' is 22.78 mm. Due to the difference in the refractive index of the object and the image space the front focal length of the eye is smaller than the back focal length: $f = -17.06$ mm. The diameter of the entrance pupil of the eye varies from 2 to 8 mm, depending on the intensity of the incoming light.

The resolving power of the eye is about 1 minute of arc over a field of a degree or two in the center of the field of view. The sensitive spot in the retina corresponding to this field of high resolution is called the macula lutea. Outside of it the resolution drops severely.

The eye can accommodate its power to form sharp images of objects at a finite distance. The average closest distance of sharp vision is 250 mm.

When the eye motion must be taken into account, the rotation of the eye may be approximated by a rotation around a point 13 mm away from the vertex of the model eye described above.

For further information on the eye we refer to the literature, e.g. LE GRAND [1957] or BERENS and ZUCKERMAN [1946].

2.2. MAGNIFIERS

A magnifier is an optical instrument that presents to the eye an enlarged image of a small object. In the discussion that follows we shall assume that the eye remains accommodated at infinity, so that the object is located in the front focal plane of the magnifier.

In fig. 7 we have sketched a schematic of a general type of magnifier, in which the refractive index at the object side is not necessarily unity. Recalling the definition of the nodal points N and N′, we read from fig. 7 that for an object height h the eye observes an image subtending an angle α' given by the ratio of h and FN. If the

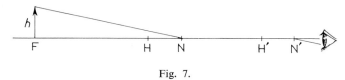

Fig. 7.

same object were viewed without the lens system it would be seen under an angle given by the ratio of h and the closest distance of sharp vision, which has been standardized at 250 mm. This shows that the magnifying power of the instrument is given by

$$M = 250/\text{FN} = 250/\text{H}'\text{F}'. \tag{12}$$

So the magnifying power of a magnifier is given by the ratio of the standard closest distance of sharp vision and the focal length of the instrument in the image space.

The limiting resolution achievable with a magnifier depends on its numerical aperture (fig. 8). This number is defined as:

$$N = n \sin \varphi,$$

where n is the refractive index in the object space and φ is the semi cone angle of the cone of light departing from the center of the object and actually passing through

Fig. 8.

the system. Assuming that the system is aplanatic Abbe's sine rule must hold (ch. 16, section 1.7). When we call the diameter of the exit pupil d', this leads to

$$d'/2f' = n \sin \varphi = N. \tag{13}$$

Note that the diameter of the exit pupil may be determined either by the optical instrument or by the eye.

According to the diffraction theory of aberrations the limiting resolution for periodic objects depends on the wavelength λ of the light and the numerical aperture of the system as follows:

$$P_{\lim} = 1/R_{\lim} = \lambda/2N \qquad (14)$$

provided that there are no aberrations.

$P_{\lim}$ is the period of an object at the limit of resolution; $R_{\lim}$ is the resolution, usually expressed in the number of periods per millimeter. Both quantities are measured in the object plane.

In the image space this limit of resolution must be expressed in angular measure. The limiting period is represented in the image space by an angle $\alpha'_{\lim}$ given by

$$\alpha'_{\lim} = \frac{P_{\lim}}{f'} = \frac{\lambda}{2Nf'} = \frac{\lambda}{d'}, \qquad (15)$$

the last equality following from Abbe's sine rule. In order that this resolution be fully utilized by the eye $\alpha_{\lim}$ must be larger than the resolution limit of the eye, which is about 1 minute of arc, or $1/3438$ radians. For a wavelength of $0.55\ \mu$m we must require that

$$\frac{0.55 \times 10^{-3}}{2Nf'} > \frac{1}{3438}.$$

In this formula we can substitute the magnifying power for f', using eq. (12). This leads to

$$\frac{0.55 \times 10^{-3}}{2N} \frac{M}{250} > \frac{1}{3438}$$

or

$$M > 265N.$$

On the other hand there is no sense in making the magnification of the instrument much larger than this limit. This would lead to empty magnification: the eye can resolve much finer details in the image than the image contains information about the object. Practical limitations are

$$250N < M < 1000N. \qquad (16)$$

The accompanying pupil sizes are

$$7\ \text{mm} > d' > 1.8\ \text{mm}.$$

This is compatible with the actual eye pupil dimensions. Note that this compatibility is not built into our calculations. It is a consequence of the fact that the eye's resolution is just about as good as prescribed by diffraction theory.

The formulas (12), (13) and (14) are vital in the design of magnifying equipment. As an example we mention the design of an instrument to view photographic prints with both eyes simultaneously. Here we must require that the size of the exit pupil is at least 75 mm. Formula (13) shows immediately that the focal length of this instrument cannot be shorter than 37.5 mm divided by the refractive index in the object space. Assuming air in the object space this leads via eq. (12) to the conclusion that the maximum possible magnification is $250/37.5 = 6.7$, no matter the complexity of the system. If a larger magnification is required a separate optical channel for each eye must be used, or other elements must be introduced into the system (e.g. ground glass).

The simplest type of magnifier is a single positive lens. Over a moderate field of view (about 20°) a single lens can be used up to a magnification of about 3. The shape of such a lens is chosen to minimize astigmatism; the pupil must be assumed to lie in the center of rotation of the eye. In the center of the field the resolution of the eye determines the smallest details to be resolved. For larger field angles the aberrations of the lens have a deteriorating effect on the image.

For larger magnifications, up to 12, doublets and triplets must be used to correct for astigmatism, field curvature, distortion and lateral color. Axial color, coma and spherical aberration usually play a minor role due to the small size of the exit pupil.

In the design of these systems the pupil must be chosen in the center of rotation of the eye when the eye is allowed to rotate while the instrument is being used. Allowing a 15 mm distance between the last vertex of the magnifier and the eye, this requires a $15 + 13 = 28$ mm distance from the last vertex of the magnifier to the exit pupil. When the eye is not assumed to rotate 15 mm is sufficient for this distance.

A few representative examples of magnifying glasses are sketched in fig. 9.

Fig. 9.

In principle the simple magnifying glass can be used for much larger magnifications. Van Leeuwenhoek has used small spheres of glass to obtain magnifications as large as $200 \times$, with a resolving power of about 0.5 μm. The use of these instruments is rather awkward, however, as the object and the lens both have to be quite close to the eye. This difficulty is overcome in the microscope.

2.3. MICROSCOPES

The microscope consists of two lens systems with powers A_1 and A_2 respectively. When the distance between the back focal point F_1' of the first system and the front focal point F_2 of the second system is Δ, we have for the system matrix, from the front focal plane of lens 1 to the back focal plane of lens 2:

$$\begin{pmatrix} 0 & -A_2 \\ 1/A_2 & 0 \end{pmatrix}\begin{pmatrix} 1 & 0 \\ \Delta & 1 \end{pmatrix}\begin{pmatrix} 0 & -A_1 \\ 1/A_1 & 0 \end{pmatrix} = \begin{pmatrix} -A_2/A_1 & A_1 A_2 \Delta \\ 0 & -A_1/A_2 \end{pmatrix},$$

where we have assumed the systems are separated by air.

The effective focal length of this system is

$$f' = -\frac{1}{A_1 A_2 \Delta} = -\frac{f_1' f_2'}{\Delta}.$$

Eq. (12) yields for its magnifying power

$$M = \frac{250}{f'} = -\frac{\Delta\ 250}{f_1'\ f_2'}, \tag{17}$$

in which Δ, f_1' and f_2' are expressed in mm. The final image is formed at infinity, so the first optical system must form an intermediate image in the front focal plane of the second optical system. This explains the structure of eq. (17): The factor $-\Delta/f_1'$ is the lateral magnification of the first optical system, and the factor $250/f_2'$ is the magnifying power of the second optical system which is used to observe the intermediate image formed by the first optical system. This situation is further amplified in fig. 10.

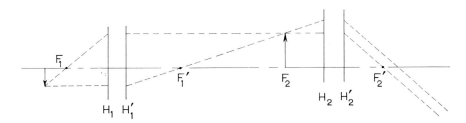

Fig. 10.

The first optical system is called the objective; the second optical system is called the eyepiece.

A very simple numerical example is given in fig. 11.

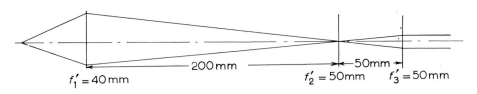

Fig. 11.

The objective is a thin lens with a focal length of 40 mm. The eyepiece consists of two thin lenses, each with a focal length of 50 mm and spaced at a distance of 50 mm. The distance between the objective and the first lens of the eyepiece is 200 mm. A straightforward calculation shows that the matrix for this system is,

$$\begin{pmatrix} -4 & 0.08 \\ 50 & -1.25 \end{pmatrix}$$

when the reference planes are chosen in the first and last lens respectively. We find for the magnification of this system

$$M = \frac{250}{-1/0.08} = -20,$$

indicating at the same time that the image is inverted.

The object must be placed in the front focal point of the system, the location of which is given by

$$f = -\frac{B}{A} = -\frac{-4}{-0.08} = -50 \text{ mm.}$$

So the object is 50 mm in front of the first lens.

In most microscopes the pencil of the image forming light is limited by the objective. The entrance pupil is always quite close to the objective, and the eyepiece must be designed such that this entrance pupil is imaged some 15 mm beyond the last lens of the eyepiece so that the pupil of the eye can be brought to coincide with the exit pupil of the microscope.

Let us assume that, for the microscope of fig. 11, the diameter of the objective lens is 12 mm. Then the fundamental imaging relations

$$B + Al/n = 1/\beta', \qquad C - Al'/n' = \beta',$$

applied to the pupil imagery with $l = 0$ yield

$$l' = 12.5 \text{ mm} \qquad \text{and} \qquad \beta' = -0.25,$$

i.e. the exit pupil is 12.5 mm beyond the last lens, and its size is $-\frac{1}{4} \times 12$ mm $= 3$ mm.

The size of the exit pupil (but not its location) could also have been found from the fundamental relation (13) between the numerical aperture and the diameter of the exit pupil. The numerical aperture is, according to its definition

$$N = \frac{\frac{1}{2} \times 12}{50} = 0.12,$$

disregarding the signs and the small difference between the sine and the tangent. Eq. (13) then yields immediately for the diameter of the exit pupil

$$d' = 2Nf' = \frac{0.12 \times 2}{0.08} = 3 \text{ mm}$$

as found previously.

The next problem of interest is to determine the diameter of the two components of the eyepiece such that a certain field of view can be observed without vignetting. This type of problem occurs quite frequently. We shall here indicate one convenient numerical approach. We shall assume that the required object size is 10 mm. We now use the tabular paraxial ray trace scheme treated in ch. 16, section 2.8 and trace two rays: one through the center of the object and the edge of the pupil, and one through the edge of the object and the center of the pupil.

TABLE 2

Object			x_0	0	5
	t'_1	50	$n_1 L_1$	+0.12	−0.1
Objective	$-a_1$	−0.025	x_1	6	0
	t'_1/n'_1	200	$n_2 L_2$	−0.03	− 0.1
	$-a_2$	−0.02	x_2	0	−20
Eye piece	t'_2/n'_2	50	$n_3 L_3$	−0.03	+ 0.3
	$-a_3$	−0.02	x_3	−1.5	− 5
			$n_4 L_4$	0	+ 0.4

The reader is first of all invited to use the calculation of table 2 to verify the results arrived at earlier: the magnification, the size and location of the exit pupil, and many other properties of the system can be read immediately from table 2.

We now wish to derive from table 2 the required diameters of the eyepiece lenses. To do this we first of all observe that paraxial optics is linear in directions and heights of incidence. This implies that, if two columns of numbers in the table represent rays, then any linear combination of these two columns also represents a ray. A ray intersecting the object plane at a height h_0, and the first lens at a height h_1 is represented by a column obtained by adding together $\frac{1}{5}h_0$ times the first column and $\frac{1}{6}h_1$ times the second column. The size of our object and objective lens are such that the value of h_0 can take any value from -5 to $+5$, and the value of h_1 can vary from -6 to $+6$. So each multiplication factor can vary (and does vary) from -1 to $+1$. This shows that at each lens (or each surface as the case may be), the maximum height of incidence is equal to the sum of the absolute values of the heights in the two columns of the table.

For the first lens of the eyepiece we find: $0+20=20$ mm for the maximum height of incidence, or 40 mm for its diameter. For the second lens of the eyepiece we find $1.5+5=6.5$ mm for the maximum height of incidence, or 13 mm for its diameter.

The distance Δ between the back focal point of the objective and the front focal point of the eyepiece is, for all commercial microscopes, standardized at 160 mm. It is called the optical tube length. The mounting threads are also normalized to allow the use of any objective with every microscope.

When Δ is given the location of the object follows immediately from

$$FF_1 = n f_1'^2 / \Delta,$$

where n is the refractive index of the object space.

The entrance pupil of the microscope is always determined by the objective, and consequently we can speak of the numerical aperture of the objective. A high resolution requires a large numberical aperture. The sine of the aperture angle can never exceed 1, however, which limits the resolution to half a light wavelength as long as the object is in air. To exceed this limit an immersion objective must be used, which

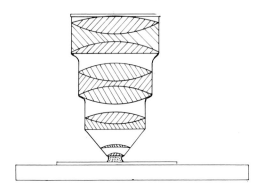

Fig. 12.

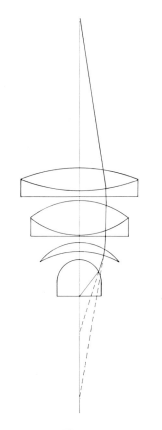

Fig. 13.

is optically connected to the object by a drop of oil (fig. 12). With this technique a numerical aperture of 1.4 can be realized *.

High numerical aperture objectives have one practical disadvantage: the free working distance is quite small, often only a fraction of a millimeter. The depth of field is also small; diffraction theory shows that it is given by $\pm \lambda/2N^2$. This is not necessarily a disadvantage: it can be used to locate a plane very accurately.

The design of microscope objectives centers around the correction of spherical aberration, coma and color. For large numerical apertures the aplanatic points of a spherical surface are used extensively (fig. 13). For large apertures the aberrations depend severely on the magnification, so deviations from the specified optical tube length cannot be tolerated. Neither can the thickness of the cover glass covering the object be neglected.

Some further examples are shown in fig. 14.

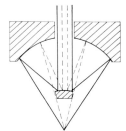

Fig. 14.

In the design of the eyepiece, astigmatism, field curvature, distortion, color and the location of the exit pupil are the main problem areas. Some eyepieces have built-in lateral color to correct for residual lateral color in the objective.

2.4. TELESCOPES

Telescopes are used to present to the eye an image of distant objects enlarged in angular size. Both the object and the image are at infinity, so a telescope has a power of zero. Hence we can write for the matrix of a telescope:

$$\begin{pmatrix} B & 0 \\ -D & 1/B \end{pmatrix}.$$

Disregarding the possibilities of underwater telescopes we assume that both the object and image space have a refractive index of 1. Then two incident pencils of parallel light entering with directions L_1 and L_2 will emerge with directions $L'_1 = BL_1$ and $L'_2 = BL_2$. Hence the matrix element B represents the magnifying power of the telescope, which is its angular magnification.

---

* In the infra red much higher numerical apertures can be attained thanks to the very high refractive index of some of the infra red transmitting materials (germanium has a refractive index of 4).

To discuss the image forming properties of telescopes for finite object distances we shift the matrix reference planes by amounts l and l' respectively. We then find

$$\begin{pmatrix} 1 & 0 \\ l' & 1 \end{pmatrix} \begin{pmatrix} B & 0 \\ -D & 1/B \end{pmatrix} \begin{pmatrix} 1 & 0 \\ -l & 1 \end{pmatrix} = \begin{pmatrix} B & 0 \\ -D+Bl'-l/B & 1/B \end{pmatrix},$$

from which it follows that the lateral magnification is independent of the object distance, and is equal to the reciprocal of the magnifying power. In particular, the ratio of the diameter of the entrance pupil and the exit pupil is equal to the magnifying power of the telescope. Assuming that the diameter of the pupil of the eye may vary from 2 mm to 8 mm, it follows that the diameter of the entrance pupil of a telescope, in mm, must lie in between twice and eight times its magnifying power, i.e. the product of the magnifying power and the exit pupil diameter. The diffraction theory of image formation shows that the limiting angular resolution in the object space is given by the ratio of the wavelength of the light and the diameter of the entrance pupil of the telescope. This is, more precisely, the period of a periodic target at the limit of resolution. For two-point resolution 1.22 times this value is commonly used. Matching this resolution with the resolution of the eye requires again that the

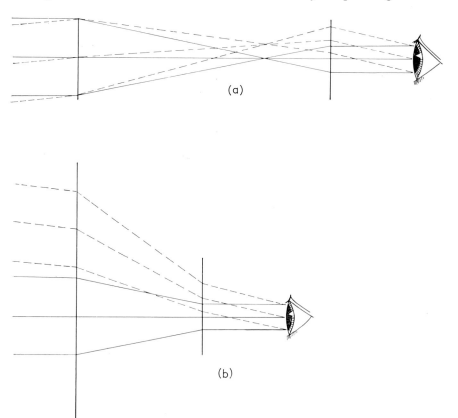

(a)

(b)

Fig. 15.

diameter of the entrance pupil, in mm, be from 2 to 8 times the magnifying power of the telescope.

Telescopes, as microscopes, are usually constructed of two parts: an objective and an eyepiece. Parallel pencils incident upon the objective emerge as parallel pencils from the eyepiece, so the back focal plane of the objective must coincide with the front focal plane of the eyepiece.

Two common forms of telescope are sketched in figs. 15a and 15b. Fig. 15a shows an astronomic telescope, with a positive objective and a positive eyepiece. It gives upside down images. The back focal plane of the objective is usually accessible. Cross hairs can be put in this plane to use the telescope for pointing purposes. The entrance pupil is located in or close to the objective. The eyepiece can be designed such that the exit pupil is at a convenient distance from the last lens of the eyepiece.

Fig. 15b shows a Galilean telescope, with a positive objective and a negative eyepiece. It gives right side up images. The back focal plane is not accessible and the image formed by the eyepiece of the edge of the objective is virtual. So there is no convenient place for the eye. The pupil of the eye itself acts as system pupil, as indicated in fig. 15b, and the objective acts as a field stop.

It is clear that the astronomic telescope is far to be preferred over the Galilean telescope. If the image of an astronomic telescope must be turned right side up two methods are available: prisms (used in binoculars) and an inversion lens system (terrestrial telescope; rifle scopes). For details on the construction and the use of telescopes we refer to KÖNIG and KÖHLER [1959].

Telescope objectives must primarily be corrected for spherical aberration, coma and color. For long focal length objectives the axial color presents a problem: with normal color correction the secondary spectrum amounts to about 1/2000 of the focal length. This problem can be considerably reduced by using special glasses, or be eliminated by using mirrors.

Of the many mirror systems in use, we mention:

1. The parabola, with perfect correction of the spherical aberration but a large amount of coma, fig. 16a.

2. The Ritchey–Chrétien system, in which the spherical aberration and the coma are corrected by using two aspheric mirrors, fig. 16b.

3. The Schmidt system, in which the spherical aberration of a spherical mirror is corrected by placing an aspheric corrector plate in its center of curvature, fig. 16c.

4. The Bouwers system, in which the same result is accomplished by using a refractive element, with a small negative power, concentric with the center of the sphere, fig. 16d.

Both the Schmidt system and the Bouwers system are very well corrected for the off axis aberrations. The residual color is quite small. Both systems have however a curved focal plane with a radius of curvature equal to the focal length of the system.

We note that large telescope objectives of the types described are often themselves called: telescopes. This slight confusion in terminology originated when

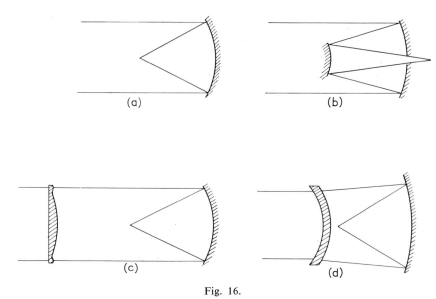

Fig. 16.

astronomers switched from visual observations to photographic work.

What has been said for the correction of simple magnifying glasses and microscope eyepieces holds equally well for telescope eyepieces.

2.5. CONDENSERS

In fig. 17 we have sketched a lens L which forms an image of the transparency T on the screen T′. The rays drawn show that the source of light S illuminates only

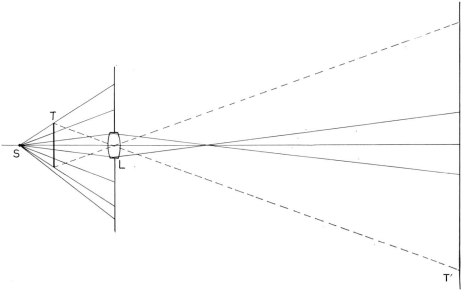

Fig. 17.

the center part of the transparency. In fig. 18 we have inserted the condenser lens C, which images the source in the pupil of the imaging lens. As a result the entire transparency is now illuminated.

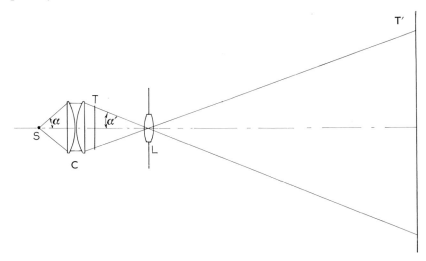

Fig. 18.

Given the imaging lens and its magnification, the most common requirement in the design of a condenser is to achieve the highest possible illumination in the image plane with the smallest possible light source.

To discuss this problem we assume that the source has a uniform brightness. A spherically symmetrical source and a plane Lambertian radiator satisfy this assumption. We must distinguish between two cases.

(A) The source is so large that its image formed by the condenser fills or overfills the pupil of the imaging lens. In this case the solid angle arriving at the image plane is fully determined by the aperture of the imaging lens. This means that for a given imaging lens the illumination in the image plane is fully determined by the brightness of the source (see also chapter 16, section 3.3). Each and every condenser lens will lead to exactly the same illumination in the image plane. In particular the solid angle accepted by the condenser lens from the source is immaterial, as long as the pupil of the imaging lens is filled with light.

Lest the reader be led to the conclusion that any bright point source is a panacea for all illumination problems, we shall discuss this case in some more detail. Using paraxial approximations, let α and α' be the aperture angles for the imaging of the source before and after the condenser lens. Then the ratio between the area of the pupil of the imaging lens and the area of the source is equal tot the square of the ratio of α and α':

$$A_L/A_S = (\alpha/\alpha')^2. \tag{18}$$

The angle α' is fully determined by the size of the transparency and its distance to the imaging lens. So eq. (18) can be solved for α:

$$\alpha = \alpha' \sqrt{(A_L/A_S)}. \tag{19}$$

The angle α cannot usually be made larger than 30°, and consequently eq. (19) sets a lower limit for the size of the source. That this must be so follows of course also from energy considerations. Nevertheless of great practical consequence is the conclusion that if the pupil is filled the details of the operation of the condenser are immaterial. Given the brightness of the source and the aperture of the imaging lens, we can find the upper limit of the illumination in the image plane without considering the details of the condenser design at all.

(B) In the case that the source is not large enough to fill the pupil of the imaging lens, one can only try to make its image as large as possible by increasing the angle α to the largest value that is technically practical. We mentioned already that α cannot usually be made much larger than 30°. An example of the type of condenser useful in this case is shown in fig. 19.

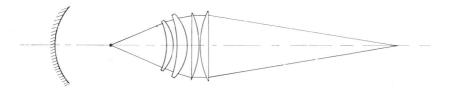

Fig. 19.

The aberration of a condenser system may usually be quite large, but there are a few exceptions. "Filling the pupil" means that every point in the transparency must be connected to every point in the pupil by a light ray. A large amount of spherical aberration may unexpectedly make this impossible. This problem is illustrated in figs. 20a and 20b.

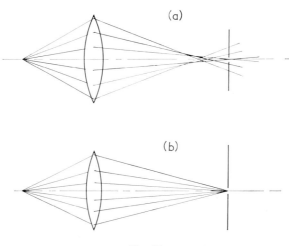

Fig. 20.

In fig. 20a the large spherical aberration makes it impossible to find a location for the small pupil in the ray pattern that passes all the lightrays required. The corrected situation is sketched in fig. 20b. The aberrations of the condenser are also important to acquire a uniform illumination in the image, especially in the case when the brightness of the source varies with the direction in which it is observed. For this problem we refer to LUNEBURG [1964]. Here we shall just treat one simple case. A small source is placed in the front focal point of a lens system to produce a substantially parallel pencil (fig. 21). We assume axial symmetry both for the source

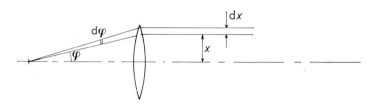

Fig. 21.

and for the lens system. Let $I(\varphi)$ be the candlepower of the source, i.e. its luminous flux emitted per unit solid angle as a function of the angle φ with the axis. We now require that the intensity E (flux per unit area) be uniform over the parallel pencil. Rotating fig. 21 over an angle $d\alpha$ around the axis of symmetry, we have

$$I(\varphi) \cdot \sin \varphi \cdot d\alpha = E dx \cdot x d\alpha$$

or

$$E = I(\varphi) \frac{\sin \varphi}{x} \frac{d\varphi}{dx}. \tag{20}$$

If $I(\varphi)$ is Lambertian, i.e. $I(\varphi) = I_0 \cos \varphi$, this leads to

$$E = I_0 \frac{d(\sin^2 \varphi)}{d(x^2)}.$$

So if E is to be constant Abbe's sine condition must be satisfied, i.e. the lens must be free from coma. If the source is not Lambertian a prescribed amount of coma must be built into the lens. This is, of course, only possible when $I(\varphi)$ is a reasonably smooth function.

2.6. OTHER INSTRUMENTS

The limits of the available space in this chapter forced us to show design principles rather than discuss instrumental details. For a more extensive treatment of instruments we refer to JOHNSON [1960], KINGSLAKE [1965], TWYMAN [1957], BROUWER [1964] and the Ordnance Corps Manual [1952].

3. Design tools

3.1. CALCULATION OF THE THIRD ORDER COEFFICIENTS FROM THE SYSTEM DATA

In ch. 16, section 5, we discussed the physical significance of the third order aberration coefficients. In this section we shall state without proof a procedure that can be followed to calculate the C coefficients from the system data. The derivation of this procedure is rather lengthy and devoid of any interest; we refer the interested reader to BROUWER [1964] and STEWARD [1928].

A special paraxial raytrace procedure must be used, which we shall describe briefly. Let h_i be the height of incidence of a ray on the ith surface of an axially symmetrical system, and ψ_i its direction with respect to the axis before the surface. Then the angle of incidence φ_i on the surface is $\psi_i + \alpha_i$, in which α_i is the angle between the axis and the line connecting the point of incidence with the center of the spherical surface. The angle α_i is equal to $h_i R_i$, in which R_i is the curvature of the surface. So

$$\varphi_i = \psi_i + R_i h_i.$$

Snell's law yields the angle of emergence:

$$\varphi_i' = \frac{n_i}{n_i'} \varphi_i,$$

and finally the direction after the surface follows from

$$\psi_i' = \psi_i - d_i,$$

in which

$$d_i = \varphi_i - \varphi_i'.$$

The height of incidence on the next surface then follows from

$$h_{i+1} = h_i + t_i' \psi_i',$$

in which t_i' is the separation between the surfaces.

This routine is quite easy to execute in the tabular form shown in table 3. In this table two additional quantities have been shown:

$$e_i = \psi_i + \varphi_i', \qquad P_i = \frac{n_i' n_i}{n_i' - n_i}.$$

In order to calculate the C_{ij} coefficients this paraxial raytracing routine must be used twice: once for a ray going through the center of the object, the object ray, and once for a ray through the center of the entrance pupil, the pupil ray. Both rays are chosen such that their direction in the image space is unity. Hence their direction in the object space is G and S respectively, where

$$G = \frac{n'}{n} \beta', \qquad S = \frac{n'}{n} \beta_P'.$$

To distinguish between h, d, and e for the object ray and pupil ray, the latter will be primed.

We further define

$$J = A/nn'.$$

When both of these paraxial ray traces have been performed, the C coefficients follow from:

$$C_{12} = \sum h_i' d_i d_i' e_i' P_i + \frac{S-G}{J}(1-S^2),$$

$$C_{22} = -\sum h_i d_i'^2 e_i P_i,$$

$$C_{23} = \sum h_i d_i d_i' e_i P_i,$$

$$C_{13} - C_{22} = -\left(\frac{S-G}{J}\right)^2 \sum \frac{R_i}{P_i},$$

$$C_{33} = -\sum h_i d_i^2 e_i P_i.$$

The sums are extended over all surfaces. Quantities without the index i refer to the system as a whole. The expression for $C_{13} - C_{22}$ explains the simple behavior of this quantity under a pupil shift, as noted in ch. 16, section 5.3. The meridional and sagittal field curvatures are given by

$$R_m = n'\left(\frac{J}{S-G}\right)^2(C_{13} + 2C_{22})$$

$$= 3C_{22}n'\left(\frac{J}{S-G}\right)^2 - n'\sum R_i/P_i \tag{22}$$

and

$$R_s = n'\left(\frac{J}{S-G}\right)^2 C_{13}$$

$$= C_{22}n'\left(\frac{J}{S-G}\right)^2 - n'\sum R_i/P_i. \tag{23}$$

If $C_{22} = 0$ there is no astigmatism, only field curvature and in that case

$$R_m = R_s = -n'\sum R_i/P_i. \tag{24}$$

The sum $\sum R_i/P_i$ is known as the Petzval sum.

3.2. EXAMPLE OF A THIRD ORDER CALCULATION

As an example we take a single lens with curvatures $+1$ and zero, and a thickness of 0.1. The refractive index be 1.5. For this lens we have

$$f' = 2 \qquad l_{F'}' = 1.93333 \qquad l_{H'}' = -0.06667$$

$$l_F = -2 \qquad l_H = 0.$$

For an object magnification of -0.5 the object distance is -6, so the proper object ray data to enter into table 3 are $\psi_1 = -0.5$, $h_1 = -3$. Assuming a pupil magnification of $+1$ the proper initial data for the pupil ray are $\psi_1 = 1$, $h_1 = 0$.

TABLE 3

	Object ray		Pupil ray	
r	1	∞	1	∞
n	1	1.5	1	1.5
n'	1.5	1	1.5	1
$R = 1/r$	1	0	1	0
n/n'	0.666667	1.5	0.666667	1.5
t'	0.1		0.1	
h	3	−2.933333	0	0.066667
t'	0.066667		0.066667	
h_1	−2.933333		0.066667	
ψ	−0.5	0.666667	1	0.666667
$\dfrac{Rh}{\varphi}$ +	−3	0	0	0
	−3.5	0.666667	1	0.666667
$\dfrac{\varphi'}{d}$ −	−2.333333	1	0.666667	1
	−1.166667	−0.333333	0.333333	−0.333333
ψ	−0.5	0.666667	1	0.666667
$\dfrac{-d}{\psi'}$ +	1.166667	0.333333	−0.333333	+0.333333
	0.666667	1	0.666667	1
$e = \psi + \varphi'$	−2.833333	1.666667	1.666667	1.666667
$P = \dfrac{nn'}{n'-n}$	3	−3		

TABLE 4

	1st surface	2nd surface	$n = 1$	$n' = 1$
h	−3	−2.93333	$G = -0.5$	$S = 1$
h'	0	0.06667	$\dfrac{S-G}{J}(1-S^2)=0$	
d	−1.16667	−0.33333		
d'	0.33333	−0.33333	$\left(\dfrac{S-G}{J}\right)^2 = 9$	
e	−2.83333	1.66667		
e'	1.66667	1.66667		
P	3	−3		
R	1	0		
			sum	
hd^2eP	34.729	1.626	36.355	$C_{33} = -36.355$
$hdd'eP$	−9.910	−1.626	−11.536	$C_{23} = -11.536$
hd'^2eP	2.831	1.628	4.459	$C_{22} = -4.459$
$h'dd'e'P$	0	−0.037	−0.037	$C_{12} = -0.037+0 = 0.037$
R/P	0.333	0	0.333	$C_{13}-C_{22} = 9 \times 0.333 = 3.000$

The table is then completed, and the data so obtained are used to calculate the aberration coefficients, as shown in tables 3 and 4. Once the aberration coefficients are determined, the aberrations can be calculated for any object point and aperture.

As an example we take an object point on the x-axis with a height of 0.30. Then

$$\xi = -0.05, \qquad \eta = 0.$$

Substitution of the values found for the C coefficients and these values for ξ and η in eq. (104) of ch. 16, we arrive at

$$n'x' = Gnx + \tfrac{1}{2}C_{12}\xi^3 + \tfrac{1}{2}(C_{13}+2C_{22})\xi^2\xi_1 + \tfrac{1}{2}C_{23}(3\xi_1^2+\eta_1^2)\xi + \tfrac{1}{2}C_{33}(\xi_1^2+\eta_1^2)\xi_1,$$
$$n'y' = \tfrac{1}{2}C_{13}\xi^2\eta_1 + C_{23}\xi_1\eta_1\xi + \tfrac{1}{2}C_{33}(\xi_1^2+\eta_1^2)\eta_1,$$

or numerically

$$x' = -0.15 - 0.02049\xi_1 + 0.20718(3\xi_1^2+\eta_1^2) - 18.1689(\xi_1^2+\eta_1^2)\xi_1,$$
$$y' = -0.00933\eta_1 + 0.41436\xi_1\eta_1 - 18.1689(\xi_1^2+\eta_1^2)\eta_1.$$

Assuming that the diameter of the lens is 0.60, ξ_1 and η_1 are limited in their value by

$$\sqrt{(\xi_1^2+\eta_1^2)} = 0.10.$$

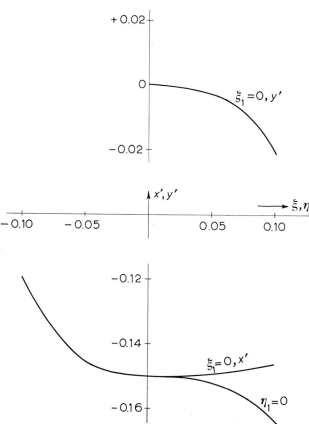

Fig. 22.

In fig. 22 we have plotted two special cases; x' for the rays in the meridional plane, i.e.

$$-0.1 < \xi_1 < 0.1, \qquad \eta_1 = 0,$$

and x' and y' for the "sagittal" rays

$$\xi_1 = 0, \qquad 0 < \eta_1 < 0.1.$$

For η_1 we need to take only half the range of values because of the symmetry of the system about the x–z plane.

For the meridional aberration we have

$$n'x' = nGx + \tfrac{1}{2}C_{13}\xi^3 + \tfrac{1}{2}(C_{13}+2C_{22})\xi^2\xi_1 + \tfrac{3}{2}C_{23}\xi\xi_1^2 + \tfrac{1}{2}C_{33}\xi_1^3,$$

considered as a function of ξ_1. The value for $\xi_1 = 0$ indicates the distortion, and the slope for $\xi_1 = 0$ gives the meridional astigmatism.

For the sagittal curves we have

$$n'x' = nGx + \tfrac{1}{2}C_{12}\xi^3 + \tfrac{1}{2}C_{23}\xi\eta_1^2,$$
$$n'y' = \tfrac{1}{2}C_{13}\xi^2\eta_1 + \tfrac{1}{2}C_{33}\eta_1^3.$$

Hence the x' curve exhibits the distortion and the coma, and the y' curve shows the sagittal astigmatism and the spherical aberration.

When the object magnification or the pupil magnification is zero, the choice of the initial ray data to be entered into the table is not immediately obvious. A limiting procedure shows that the ray must then be chosen parallel to the axis in the object space, with a height of $-n'/A$.

The structure of the formulas given above becomes a little more transparent if one considers the three aplanatic points of a single spherical surface. The aplanatic surfaces proper with $\beta' = (n'/n)^2$ (section 3.7) are characterized by $e=0$. These surfaces are perfectly corrected for spherical aberration, coma and astigmatism; they only suffer from field curvature and distortion. Hence the contribution of a single surface to C_{33}, C_{23} and C_{22} must vanish whenever e is zero for this surface, i.e. the formula must contain e as a factor. The rather more trivial case of the surface itself ($\beta' = +1$) shows absence of the same aberrations which shows that these coefficients must also contain a factor h. Finally the center of the surface, with $\beta' = n/n'$, is characterized by $d=0$, and shows freedom from spherical aberration and coma. So C_{33} and C_{22} must contain a factor d. Although these considerations give some insight into the structure of the formulae, their exact form cannot be determined by these simple arguments.

3.3. ASPHERIC SURFACES

If the system contains aspheric surfaces the formulas given above must be generalized. The sag z of a spherical surface can be written in the form

$$z = r - (r^2 - x^2 - y^2)^{\frac{1}{2}}$$
$$= \tfrac{1}{2}R(x^2 + y^2) + \tfrac{1}{8}R^3(x^2 + y^2)^2 + \ldots$$

We shall only consider aspheric surfaces that can be approximated by

$$z = \tfrac{1}{2}R(x^2+y^2)+\tfrac{1}{8}(1+b)R^3(x^2+y^2)^2. \tag{25}$$

Terms of higher than the fourth degree only affect the higher order aberrations and need not concern us here. In this approximation the surfaces may always be considered as surfaces of revolution generated by a conic section, with

$$
\begin{aligned}
b = 0: &\quad \text{sphere}\\
b > 0: &\quad \text{oblate spheroid}\\
-1 < b < 0: &\quad \text{prolate ellipsoid}\\
b = -1: &\quad \text{paraboloid}\\
b < -1: &\quad \text{hyperboloid.}
\end{aligned}
$$

If the ith surface of a system is aspheric, an aspheric contribution must be added to the formulas given in the previous section. For each aspheric surface these contributions can be calculated as follows:

$$
\begin{aligned}
\Delta C_{12} &= \varepsilon_i h_i h_i'^{\,3}\\
\Delta C_{22} &= -\varepsilon_i h_i^2 h_i'^{\,2}\\
\Delta C_{23} &= \varepsilon_i h_i^3 h_i'\\
\Delta(C_{13}-C_{22}) &= 0\\
\Delta C_{33} &= -\varepsilon_i h_i^4,
\end{aligned}
\tag{26}
$$

in which

$$\varepsilon_i = (n_i'-n_i)b_i R_i^3.$$

As an example we mention that with these formulas any system containing just two surfaces can be corrected for both spherical aberration and coma, if we allow both surfaces to be aspheric. This principle is used in the Schwarzschild and Ritchey–Chrétien telescopes.

3.4. INTERCHANGING OF THE OBJECT AND THE PUPIL

There are occasions when one is interested not only in the aberrations in the object image formation, but also in the aberrations that occur in the image formed by the system of the entrance pupil. It is usually proper to consider the original object and image planes as the "pupils" for the image formation from the real entrance pupil to exit pupil.

The "object" magnification is now S, and the "pupil" magnification G.

Using the routine outlined in the previous sections to calculate the pupil aberrations, we note that there is a great deal of symmetry between the object aberrations and the pupil aberrations. We have the following correspondences:

Object imaging	Pupil imaging
object point location ξ, η	$-\xi_1$, $-\eta_1$
pupil point location ξ_1, η_1	$-\xi$, $-\eta$
rotational invariants w_1, w_2, w_3	w_3, w_2, w_1
object ray and pupil ray	pupil ray and object ray

Hence we have

$$\begin{pmatrix} n' x'_1 \\ n' y'_1 \end{pmatrix} = \frac{n'}{n} \beta'_1 \begin{pmatrix} n x_1 \\ n y_1 \end{pmatrix} - ({}_1C_{12} w_3 + {}_1C_{22} w_2 + {}_1C_{23} w_1) \begin{pmatrix} \xi_1 \\ \eta_1 \end{pmatrix}$$

$$- ({}_1C_{13} w_3 + {}_1C_{23} w_2 + {}_1C_{33} w_1) \begin{pmatrix} \xi \\ \eta \end{pmatrix}.$$

We have given the C coefficients an extra index 1 to show that they describe the pupil aberrations. Inspection of the calculation routine for the aberration coefficients now shows that

$$_1C_{12} = C_{23} + \frac{G-S}{J}(1-G^2)$$

$$_1C_{23} = C_{12} - \frac{S-G}{J}(1-S^2)$$

$$_1C_{13} - {}_1C_{22} = C_{13} - C_{22}.$$

For the spherical aberration of the pupil we obviously have

$$_1C_{33} = -\sum h'_i d'^2_i e'_i P_i,$$

a quantity that is not related to any of the object image aberrations. The only aberration that remains is $_1C_{22}$, which is in fact closely related to C_{22}, although this is not immediately obvious. There is however the following relation

$$_1C_{22} = C_{22} + \frac{S-G}{J}(1-SG).$$

The derivation of this result can only be given in the context of the derivation of the routine presented without proof in the previous sections. We refer to BROUWER [1964] for further details.

Once the C coefficients and $_1C$ coefficients are determined, we know two points, one in the image plane and one in the exit pupil plane, for every image ray corresponding to any given ray in the object space. Hence the image ray of every object ray is fully known, and so the aberrations for any set of object and image planes are, at least in principle, fully determined.

So the third order aberrations of a system are completely known, for any set of object and image planes, if the coefficients C_{12}, C_{22}, C_{23}, C_{13}, C_{33} and $_1C_{33}$ are known for any one given set of object planes and pupil planes. For $_1C_{33}$ we shall write C_{11}, for reasons of symmetry, but also because this coefficient is related to the K_{11} coefficient of the point angle eikonal, as the interested reader can easily verify. Six coefficients are necessary and sufficient; the reason being that the point angle eikonal has only six independent coefficients relating to the third order aberrations.

The next question that naturally arises is: given the coefficients $C_{11}-C_{33}$ for one set of object and pupil planes, how do we calculate these coefficients for another set of object and pupil planes? One way of deriving the required formulae is given by BROUWER [1964]. Here, however, we prefer to use the very concise method developed by T. Smith.

Following his notation, we write

$$D_0 = -C_{11} + \frac{S-G}{J}\left(1 - \frac{S^3}{G}\right), \qquad D_3 = C_{23},$$

$$D_1 = C_{12}, \qquad\qquad\qquad D_4 = -C_{33}. \qquad (27)$$

$$D_2 = -\tfrac{1}{3}(2C_{22} + C_{13}),$$

Overstriping all quantities for the new set of object and pupil magnifications, we write

$$g = \frac{\bar{G}-G}{S-G}, \qquad s = \frac{\bar{S}-S}{S-G}. \qquad (28)$$

Then

$$\bar{D}_i = (D_0, D_1, D_2, D_3, D_4)(1+s, -s)^{4-i}(g, 1-g)^i + \frac{1}{J}(\bar{G}-G)\left\{\frac{\bar{S}^{4-i}\bar{G}^i}{G\bar{G}} - 1\right\} \qquad (29)$$

$(D_0\ldots D_4)(a, b)^{4-i}(c, d)^i$ means: calculate $(a+bt)^{4-i}(c+dt)^i$ and substitute D_i for t^i. This formula is not as complicated as it seems to be; in many cases it reduces to simple relations. If for instance only the pupil magnification is changed we have for the coma coefficient, because $g=0$:

$$\bar{D}_3 = (D_0, D_1, D_2, D_3, D_4)(1+s, -s)^1(0, 1)^3,$$

the additional term being zero because $\bar{G}=G$. Now

$$(1+s-st)(0+t)^3 = (1+s)t^3 - st^4,$$

so

$$\bar{D}_3 = (1+s)D_3 - sD_4,$$

or

$$\bar{C}_{23} = (1+s)C_{23} + sC_{33},$$

compatible with our previous work in ch. 16, section 5.4. The reader will note that no formula has been given for the transformation of $C_{13}-C_{22}$. Its simple relation to the Petzval sum obviates the need for such a formula.

The formulas presented here have numerous applications. If a photographic lens is for instance designed for an object at infinity, i.e. $G=0$, the formulas allow us to get an idea of the performance for finite conjugates. But more importantly, the formulas can be used to establish general properties of lenses with certain geometrical restriction, i.e. concentric lenses, "thin" lenses, symmetric lenses, etc. In the section to follow this will be demonstrated, using methods essentially due to SMITH [1923].

3.5. SPECIAL LENS TYPES

3.5.1. *The concentric system*

A concentric system is characterized by the fact that the centers of curvature of all its surfaces coincide in one point, the center of the system. Putting the pupil of the system in the center we have $S = +1$. A ray going through the center of the system is perpendicular to all surfaces, so for the pupil ray d' is zero for all surfaces. Hence, for $S = +1$ we have

$$C_{12} = C_{22} = C_{23} = 0$$

and

$$C_{13} - C_{22} = -(S-G)^2/J,$$

because it follows from simple paraxial considerations that the Petzval sum of a concentric system equals its power devided by the product of the indices in the object and the image space. Because C_{22} is zero there is no astigmatism, and the field curvature is

$$R_{\mathrm{m}} = R_{\mathrm{s}} = n' \left(\frac{J}{S-G}\right)^2 \left(-\frac{(S-G)^2}{J}\right) = -n'J.$$

Hence, once the power of the concentric system is known and $S = +1$, five of the six aberration coefficients are predetermined, and only the spherical aberration can be controlled in the design. Also, if the spherical aberration coefficient is known for one magnification, it can be calculated for any other magnification. Writing, for $G = -1$: $C_{33} = -4\gamma/J^2$, it can be proved by using the shift formulae of the previous section that for an arbitrary magnification G we have

$$C_{33} = -\frac{(1-G)^4}{4J}\left[\frac{\gamma}{J} - \left(\frac{1+G}{1-G}\right)^2\right]. \tag{30}$$

In fact (and for the derivation we must refer to the literature, in particular HERZBERGER [1958] and WALTHER [1959]) the calculation of the γ coefficient from the system data is very simple. Writing

$$\gamma J^2 + \tfrac{1}{3}J^3 = \Gamma,$$

we have

$$\Gamma = \tfrac{4}{3}\sum_i R_i^3 \left(\frac{1}{n_i'^3} - \frac{1}{n_i^3}\right). \tag{31}$$

Combined with

$$J = \sum_i R_i \left(\frac{1}{n_i'} - \frac{1}{n_i} \right) \tag{32}$$

this leads to a straightforward technique of designing concentric systems.

3.5.2. *The thin system in air*

Thin systems do not exist in practice, but are important as an approximation to "essentially thin" lenses, such as spectacle glasses, simple doublets, etc. They are also important as building blocs in predesigns of more complicated systems. Thin systems are characterized by zero axial thicknesses. Assuming that the pupil coincides with the thin lens system and that the system is in air, the pupil magnification is $+1$. The pupil ray has the special property that h' is zero for all surfaces, so C_{11} and C_{12} are zero. Moreover, $_1C_{22}$ is zero, hence $C_{22} = (1-G)^2/J$. Writing for the Petzval sum $\tilde{\omega}$, this leads to

$$R_{\mathrm{m}} = -3J - \tilde{\omega}, \qquad R_{\mathrm{s}} = -J - \tilde{\omega}.$$

Hence there is always a large amount of astigmatism and field curvature, as for most ordinary glasses $\tilde{\omega}$ is about from 60 % to 75 % of the power of the system. Disregarding this slight freedom in the choice of $\tilde{\omega}$, there are only two degrees of freedom in a thin system, the spherical aberration C_{33} and the coma C_{23}. Again, if these coefficients are known for one particular magnification, then they can be calculated for any other magnification. Writing, for $G = -1$, in order to standardize the notation

$$\begin{aligned} C_{33} &= -4\gamma/J^2 \\ C_{23} &= -4\beta/J^2 \end{aligned} \left.\begin{aligned} & \\ & \end{aligned}\right\} \begin{aligned} S &= +1 \\ G &= -1 \end{aligned}$$

then, for an arbitrary magnification G, and keeping $S=1$, we have

$$C_{33} = -\tfrac{1}{4} \frac{(1-G)^4}{J^2} \{\gamma - 4\beta M + (3J + 2\tilde{\omega})M^2\}, \tag{33}$$

$$C_{23} = -\tfrac{1}{2} \frac{(1-G)^3}{J^2} \{\beta - (2J + \tilde{\omega})M\}, \tag{34}$$

with

$$M = (1+G)/(1-G).$$

Note that the only degrees of freedom are J, $\tilde{\omega}$, β and γ, no matter how many elements the thin system has. Two elements are usually sufficient to realize the required values of β and γ. More elements may be needed for other reasons, such as chromatic aberrations and higher order aberrations.

3.5.3. *The symmetric system*

Almost symmetric lens designs are quite common in photographic objectives; truly symmetric lenses are hardly ever used however for reasons that will be set forth in this section.

A symmetric lens consists of two identical parts, one turned around with respect to the other (fig. 23). We assume that the pupil is located in the plane of symmetry, which makes the pupil magnification equal to unity. We further assume that the object magnification is -1, i.e., the symmetric lens is used symmetrically. Then, for two

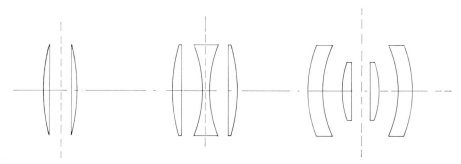

Fig. 23.

corresponding surfaces in the front and rear part, h, d and e' are the same, and e, P, h' and d' are equal except for their signs. Hence C_{12} and C_{23} are zero, and only C_{11}, C_{22} and C_{33} can be chosen at will.

We write for purposes of normalization

$$\left.\begin{array}{c} C_{11} = \dfrac{4}{J^2}(\zeta - J) \\[2mm] -\tfrac{1}{3}(2C_{22} + C_{13}) = \dfrac{4}{J^2}\varepsilon \\[2mm] C_{33} = -\dfrac{4}{J^2}\gamma \end{array}\right\} \quad \begin{array}{l} G = -1 \\ S = +1. \end{array}$$

ζ, ε, γ and the Petzval sum are the only available variables. We can now use the transformation formulas to express the aberrations for an infinite object distance, $G=0$, in the variables ζ, ε and γ. The result of this work is

$$\begin{aligned} \tfrac{1}{2}J^2 C_{12} &= \zeta - J, \\ -J^2 C_{22} &= \zeta + \varepsilon - J - \tfrac{1}{3}\tilde{\omega}, \\ 2J^2 C_{23} &= \zeta + 3\varepsilon - 2J, \\ 4J^2 C_{33} &= -\zeta - 6\varepsilon - \gamma + 4J, \end{aligned}$$

in which $\tilde{\omega}$ is again the Petzval sum and S remains unity. Eliminating ζ and ε from the first three relations we have

$$3C_{22} + C_{12} + C_{23} = -(J - \tilde{\omega})/J^2.$$

In a well corrected photographic objective C_{22}, C_{12} and C_{23} must be small. The relation between the coefficients shows that this is only possible if the Petzval sum is of the same order of magnitude as the power. This however means that the field curvature is large. Hence we have proved that a symmetric system used with an object at infinity cannot be corrected for distortion, astigmatism, field curvature and coma simultaneously.

3.6. RAY TRACING. CONSTRUCTION OF RAYS; APLANATIC POINTS

Ray tracing consists of numerically following a ray through an optical system. With the aid of modern electronic computers the drudgery is taken out of these computations. These computers are so fast that it is entirely possible to include one or more aspheric surfaces in the optical system and to investigate the influence of decentrations of the elements upon the optical image formation. Furthermore, many programs are worked out where the computer analyzes the image quality and makes its own decisions as to what system parameters to change to improve the image. Descriptions of such programs are beyond the scope of this book.

There is often a need to trace a few rays through an optical system; this can be accomplished without tying up a large computer. For this purpose we include the meridional ray trace scheme (table 5), given by T. Smith, which is very convenient when a desk calculator is available. In the example the first six lines are given by the system. The ray described by the quantities h and $\sin \psi$ is shown in fig. 24. We enter $\sin \psi$ three times in our computation table on lines 12, 17 and 22, while h is

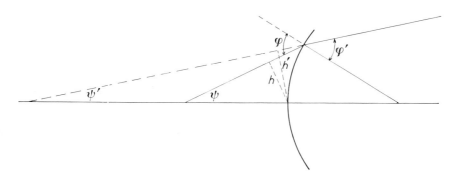

Fig. 24.

entered on line 7. We then compute Rh and enter on line 13 and find $\sin \varphi$ (line 14); we then compute $\sin \varphi'$ (line 15) and d (line 16). We enter $-d$ on line 18 to find $\sin \vartheta$ (line 19). We enter $\sin \varphi'$ on line 23 and compute e (line 24). Then compute N (line 25). Next compute $\cos \psi$, $\cos \varphi$ and $\cos \varphi'$ (lines 26, 27, 28) from $\sin \psi$, $\sin \varphi$ and $\sin \varphi'$. This computation does not have to be done with the same accuracy (the same holds true for lines 29, 30 and 31) since it is used to compute the value of N/D (lines 25 and 31) where N is in most practical cases a small number. The following approximation is found to be extremely practical for this computation:

$$\sqrt{x} = \frac{\tfrac{1}{4}[x(x+6)+1]}{x+1}, \tag{35}$$

TABLE 5

Computation table

1	r	1.000 000	−1.000 000	−1.333 333
2	n	1	1.500 000	1.800 000
3	n'	1.500 000	1.800 000	1.000 000
4	$R = 1/r$	1.000 000	−1.000 000	−0.750 000
5	n/n'	0.666 666	0.833 333	1.800 000
6	t'	0.150 000	0.360 000	
7	h	0.200 000	0.202 692	0.214 752
8	N/D	0.003 167	0.000 624	−0.002 292
	—— +			
9	h'	0.203 167	0.203 316	0.212 460
10	$t' \sin \psi'$	−0.000 475	0.011 436	
	—— +			
11	h'	0.202 692	0.214 752	
12	$\sin \psi$	0.100 000	−0.003 167	0.031 767
13	Rh	0.200 000	−0.202 692	−0.161 064
	—— +			
14	$\sin \varphi$	0.300 000	−0.205 859	−0.129 297
15	$(n/n') \sin \varphi = \sin \varphi'$	−0.200 000	0.171 549	0.232 735
	——————— +			
16	d	0.100 000	−0.034 310	0.103 438
17	$\sin \psi$	0.100 000	−0.003 167	0.031 767
18	$-d$	−0.100 000	0.034 310	−0.103 438
	—— +			
19	$\sin \theta$	0	0.031 143	−0.071 671
20	$-RN/D$	−0.003 167	0.000 624	−0.001 719
	——— +			
21	$\sin \psi'$	−0.003 167	0.031 767	−0.073 390
22	$\sin \psi$	0.100 000	−0.003 167	0.031 767
23	$\sin \varphi'$	0.200 000	−0.171 549	−0.232 735
	—— +			
24	e	0.300 000	−0.174 716	−0.200 968
25	$N = hde$	0.006 000	0.001 215	−0.004 464
26	$\cos \psi$	0.994 987	0.999 994	0.999 495
27	$\cos \varphi$	0.953 939	0.978 581	0.991 605
28	$\cos \varphi'$	0.979 795	0.985 175	0.972 539
	$s = \cos \psi + \cos \varphi + \cos \varphi'$	2.928 721	2.963 750	2.963 639
29	$f = \frac{1}{4} \sin^2 \theta$	0	0.000 242	0.001 284
30	$g = \frac{1}{4}(s^2 - 1)$	1.894 352	1.945 954	1.945 789
	——— +			
31	D	1.894 352	1.946 196	1.947 073

with

$$x = 1 - \sin^2 (\psi, \varphi, \text{ or } \varphi').$$

The error is approximately $(x-1)^4/128$ and thus is small enough for most ray tracing purposes in our case.

We then compute lines 29, 30 and 31. The quantity N/D (line 8) is found and from this h' (line 9). Then $-RN/D$ (line 20) and from this $\sin \psi'$ (line 21).

ψ' is the angle shown in fig. 24 for the refracted ray and therefore the angle ψ for the next surface. The value of $\sin \psi'$ is therefore entered in three places (lines 12, 17 and 22) in the next column. We then compute $t' \sin \psi'$ (line 10) and find h' (line 11), which value is entered in line 7 in the next column. We then have h and $\sin \psi$ for the ray under consideration on the next surface, and we can repeat the whole procedure for this surface.

3.7. APLANATIC POINTS

In general a spherical surface does not form a perfect image of a point. There are, however, a few points that are imaged without aberrations, the so-called aplanatic points.

To investigate these we will use the matrix describing the ray transformation for a single surface given by:

$$\begin{pmatrix} n'L' \\ x' \end{pmatrix} = \begin{pmatrix} 1 + \dfrac{\tau}{n} A & -A \\ \dfrac{\tau\tau'}{nn'} A + \dfrac{\tau'}{n'} - \dfrac{\tau}{n} & 1 - \dfrac{\tau'}{n'} A \end{pmatrix} \begin{pmatrix} nL \\ x \end{pmatrix}.$$

For perfect imagery the equation

$$x' = \left(\frac{\tau\tau'}{nn'} A + \frac{\tau'}{n'} - \frac{\tau}{n} \right) nL + \left(1 - \frac{\tau'}{n'} A \right) x$$

should reduce to

$$x' = \beta' x.$$

When we only consider axial points we have:

$$x = 0$$

and therefore

$$x' = \left(\frac{\tau\tau'}{nn'} A + \frac{\tau'}{n'} - \frac{\tau}{n} \right) nL = 0$$

or

$$\frac{\tau\tau'}{nn'} A + \frac{\tau'}{n'} - \frac{\tau}{n} = 0, \tag{36}$$

with

$$A = \frac{n' \cos \varphi' - n \cos \varphi}{r}. \tag{37}$$

Case 1. It is clear that eq. (36) is satisfied when

$$\tau = \tau' = 0.$$

In other words the vertex of the surface is imaged perfectly onto itself. This conclusion of course holds true for any point on the refracting surface (see fig. 25), and therefore the whole refracting surface is an aplanatic surface.

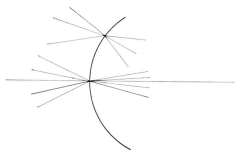

Fig. 25.

Case 2. When we make $\tau = \tau' = r$, or both object and image are in the center of curvature, we find with eq. (36) and (37)

$$\frac{n' \cos \varphi'}{r} - \frac{n \cos \varphi}{r} = \frac{n'}{r} - \frac{n}{r}. \tag{38}$$

However, in this case it is clear that we always have (see fig. 26)

$$\varphi = \varphi' = 0,$$

and therefore eq. (38) reduces to an identity.

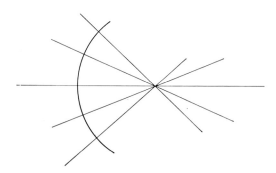

Fig. 26.

Case 3. When we take an object point at a distance

$$r \left(1 + \frac{n'}{n}\right),$$

the paraxial image distance is

$$r\left(1 + \frac{n}{n'}\right).$$

We will now prove that these points are also imaged aplanatically. A ray BAP, going through our object point P (shown in fig. 27) should go through P′ if we

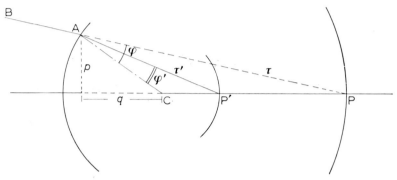

Fig. 27.

presume that P is imaged aplanatically in P′. The triangles ACP and P′CA have the angle ACP in common, and furthermore:

$$\frac{AC}{CP} = \frac{r}{(n'/n)r} = \frac{(n/n')r}{r} = \frac{CP'}{AC},$$

and these triangles are therefore similar. From this it follows that

$$\tau/\tau' = n'/n$$

and

$$\angle\, APC = \varphi', \qquad \angle\, AP'C = \varphi.$$

We still have to prove that AP′ is the refracted ray BAP. The refracted ray should be in the plane defined by BAP and AC and $n' \sin \varphi'$ should be equal to $n \sin \varphi$ according to Snell's law. The first part is obviously true, and the second part is easily proved since

$$n \sin \varphi = n\, p/\tau' = n'p/\tau = n' \sin \varphi'.$$

We have thus proven that any ray going through P will go aberration free through P′. It is also easily shown that eq. (36) holds since in this case

$$\cos \varphi = \frac{q + (n/n')r}{\tau'}, \qquad \cos \varphi' = \frac{q + (n'/n)r}{\tau},$$

and therefore eq. (36) becomes

$$\frac{\tau}{n'}\left(\frac{q}{r} + \frac{n'}{n}\right) - \frac{\tau'}{n}\left(\frac{q}{r} + \frac{n}{n'}\right) + \frac{\tau'}{n'} - \frac{\tau}{n} = 0.$$

These aplanatic points can be used in certain designs (notably microscope objectives). There are basically two possibilities shown in fig. 28a and b.

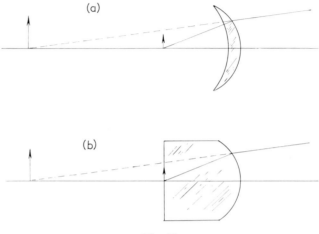

Fig. 28.

In fig. 28a the object is placed in the center of curvature of the first surface while the second refractive surface gives aplanatic imagery according to case 3.

In fig. 28b the first surface is flat and coincides with the object. Usually the object is immersed in a fluid with the same refractive index as the glass of which the lens is fabricated. Recently this last type of lens is used in reverse where in the place of the object an infrared detector is cemented on. For infrared work the lens can be made of germanium with an index of refraction of approximately 4, which results in a detector unit with a very high numerical aperture.

3.8. INITIAL DESIGN PROCEDURES

To initiate the optical design of a system is a difficult procedure since it is impossible to give any standard rules. It proceeds generally along the following lines. First, one has to decide how many elements are needed to achieve the desired image quality. This decision is usually based on the experience of the optical designer. Some conclusions can however be based on deliberations along the following lines. There are a number of conditions the optical system has to fulfill. As an example let us take the case where we want an achromatic image only for a point on the axis. We therefore need to fulfill the following conditions: the system has to have a given power, the color coefficient c_1 has to be zero, and the spherical aberration has to be corrected. The first two conditions need two variables to be simultaneously solved, and, therefore, if we start our design with thin elements, we need the power of two elements as variables to fulfill these conditions. The spherical aberration we can then try to minimize by the distribution of the powers between the surfaces of the elements without changing the power of the elements as a whole. This is called "bending" of the elements. From experience we know that we can indeed find a solution for this problem with two elements, and a doublet will therefore be used. To minimize the spherical aberration the procedure is usually that we first leave our system thin and then bend the elements until a solution is found for which the third order aberration coefficient is approximately zero. Then without changing the radii the elements are given the necessary thicknesses so they can be manufactured. A few rays are then traced and final adjustments made to minimize the spherical aberration, keeping at the same time the color under control.

We notice in this example that we have two elements that we can bend independently if we do not require the elements to be cemented. The above problem could therefore be solved with the additional condition that the shape of the elements be such that we can cement the components.

If we do not require this, we have a degree of freedom at our disposal that we can use for correction of another aberration. The only other aberration that we can improve on is coma. We can therefore bend each element individually and find a combination for which both the third order spherical and third order coma coefficients are zero. We then proceed to give the elements thickness and do the final adjustment with the help of some ray tracing.

It should be noted that we did not use the refractive indices of the glass as variables, and it is indeed possible to find the right refractive index combination so that we can correct both for spherical aberration and coma while we include the cementing condition. For a doublet this is a feasible procedure. In general, however, the use of the refractive index as a variable is a difficult procedure since the availability of only special values makes this a discontinuous variable, and furthermore the dependence of the various aberrations on the refractive index is of a high order, and the effect of changing the refractive index is usually very difficult to control analytically.

In general it is this kind of consideration that leads to the decision concerning the number of elements necessary to accomplish the given task. For instance, in the case of a photographic objective we have the following conditions:

1. given power
2. color correction c_1
3. color correction c_2
4. Petzval sum
5. spherical aberration
6. coma
7. distortion
8. astigmatism.

The first four conditions only involve the number of elements, their power distribution, and their separation. We need therefore at least three elements with two air spaces. In this case we have five variables at our disposal, one more than our four conditions. This leaves us one "structural" degree of freedom. There are three other variables available: the shapes of three elements.

Usually the three bendings are used to control the coma, astigmatism and distortion; the one degree of freedom left in the original layout is then used to control the spherical aberration. We see therefore that the so-called "Cooke" triplet is the simplest lens form for which we can hope to correct all the third order aberrations and indeed for reasonable F-numbers and field sizes this can be done satisfactorily.

The total aberrations of an optical system are, however, not completely described by the third order aberration coefficients; all the higher orders are always present. A good idea of what is happening can be gained by also considering the fifth order aberrations. Let us do this for one particular case, the spherical aberration. The fifth order spherical aberration term will have the form $C\xi_1^5$. So, when the third order coefficient is zero this aberration will be dominant, and the designer is better off to balance the amount of third and fifth order aberration. In fig. 29 we show the fifth

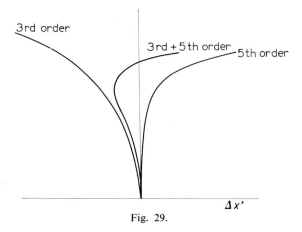

Fig. 29.

order spherical aberration for a given system. By reintroducing the shown amount of third order aberration (usually the third order aberration changes much more rapidly than the higher order aberration when system parameters are changed) of the opposite sign, we can reduce the total aberrations substantially. The shape of the third and fifth order aberration curve is typical for the great majority of actual systems. We see that for a certain value of x_1, less than the maximum value of x_1, we have a maximum in the spherical aberration; this is called the zonal aberration.

The more elements are introduced, the more freedom the designer has, and in general the better he can make his design. Here, however, the experience of the lens designer is the only guide as to how far one needs to go in introducing elements. To give the reader some idea of the corrections attainable, some lens types with their aberration curves are included in this chapter.

Another way to give the designer the necessary freedom, while keeping the number of elements to a minimum, is the use of aspheric surfaces. The recent development of fabrication techniques to produce precision aspheric surfaces has made this approach practicable. The third order theory of aspheric surfaces is included in section 3.3. Since the testing technique for aspheric surfaces is still a difficult one, the number of aspheric surfaces is kept to a minimum, in many cases one. In this case the aspheric surface is usually located near the diaphragm and used to control spherical aberration. This leaves the designer all the other variables to control the other conditions. In the fabrication the aspheric surface quality can be judged by the use of a knife-edge test for the on-axis image. With aspherics it is possible to achieve extremely good image quality since they offer the possibility of correcting zonal aberrations.

3.9. EXAMPLES OF LENS SYSTEMS

We will give some examples of lens systems in the following pages. For each example the following information is supplied.

First the system is given by the values of the successive curvatures (the reciprocals of the radii), the thicknesses of the elements and the air spaces, and the refractive indices. These values are given for a system with a power $+1$. Furthermore, the position of the pupil is given and the paraxial constants b and c (a is always $+1$). For some systems the third order aberration coefficients (as defined by eq. (104), ch. 16) and the color aberration coefficients are given (eq. 67A, ch. 16).

For each system a drawing showing a cross section of the system is given.

Ray trace results of these systems are then graphically represented. This is done by plotting $\Delta x'$ and $\Delta y'$ as a function of the coordinates x_1 and y_1 in the entrance pupil. For rays making an angle α with the axis two sets of rays are traced. For the first set y_1 is zero for all rays. This is called the meridional ray trace. For the intercepts in the paraxial image plane we then have $\Delta y'=0$. The plot of these rays is marked with Δx mer. The second set of rays for the same angle α is chosen such that $x_1=0$ for all rays. The coordinate axis therefore represents y_1 and this leads to two sets of curves, one for $\Delta x'$ and one for $\Delta y'$. These two curves are marked Δx sag and Δy sag, since these rays sometimes are called the sagittal rays.

Example 1. Petzval objective designed by A. Werfeli, U.S. patent 2,744,445; May 8, 1956. This is an *F*:1.4 objective with a total field of 16°, usually used for projection purposes.

Surface #	Curvature	Thickness	Refractive indices e-line	$\nu_e = \dfrac{n_e - 1}{n_{F'} - n_{C'}}$
1	1.108 617	0.175 787	1.680 820	55.26
2	−0.613 741	0.011 552	1.000 000	
3	−0.756 798	0.100 449	1.694 160	30.92
4	+0.272 177	0.841 317	1.000 000	
5	+1.720 865	0.125 562	1.680 820	55.26
6	−1.416 035	0.017 579	1.000 000	
7	−1.660 636	0.025 112	1.747 070	27.50
8	0.000 000	0.000 000	1.000 000	

The pupil is located a distance 0.301 348 behind the fourth surface and the pupil magnification is +1.164 721.

Paraxial constants: $c = +0.377591$, $b = +0.173081$.

The following color aberration coefficients are found

λ	c_1	c_2
0.768 2	0.002 358	−0.001 011
0.656 3	0.001 122	−0.000 668
0.486 1	−0.000 233	0.000 665
0.435 8	0.000 304	0.001 630

The third order aberration coefficients are

$$C_{12} = -1.700\,51$$
$$C_{22} = 0.272\,08$$
$$C_{23} = 0.083\,52$$
$$C_{33} = -0.090\,77$$
$$C_{13} - C_{22} = 1.135\,78$$

The cross section of the system is shown in fig. 30 and the aberration curves in fig. 31.

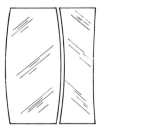

Fig. 30. Petzval objective.

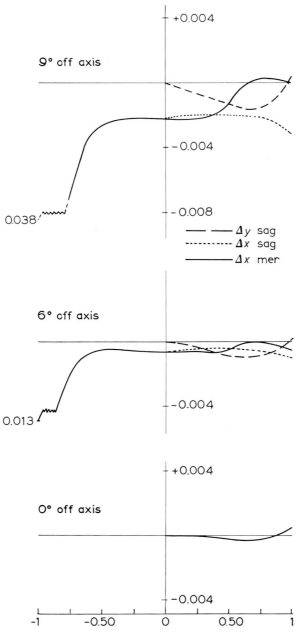

Fig. 31.

Example 2. Triplet designed by Y. Eggert, U.S. patent 3,039,359; June 19, 1962. This is an *F*:2.8 objective with a total field of 29°.

Surface #	Curvature	Thickness	Refractive index e-line	$\nu_e = \dfrac{n_e - 1}{n_{F'} - n_{C'}}$
1	2.314 763	0.063 006	1.641 28	55.24
2	−0.219 977	0.126 513	1.000 00	
3	−2.274 767	0.008 501	1.650 62	33.75
4	2.656 728	0.124 113	1.000 00	
5	+0.598 939	0.070 007	1.622 87	60.06
6	−2.724 721	0.000 000	1.000 00	

The pupil is located a distance 0.040004 behind the 4th surface and has a magnification +1.014050.

Paraxial constants: $c = 0.847296$, $b = 0.683238$.

	Color aberrations	
λ	c_1	c_2
0.768 2	0.003 662	−0.000 004
0.656 3	0.001 547	0.000 033
0.486 1	−0.000 132	−0.000 087
0.435 8	0.001 177	−0.000 276

The third order aberration coefficients are:

$$C_{12} = -0.01646$$
$$C_{22} = 0.08212$$
$$C_{23} = -0.05794$$
$$C_{33} = -1.38060$$
$$C_{13} - C_{22} = 0.33128$$

The cross section of the system is shown in fig. 32 and the aberration curves in fig. 33.

Fig. 32. Projection triplet.

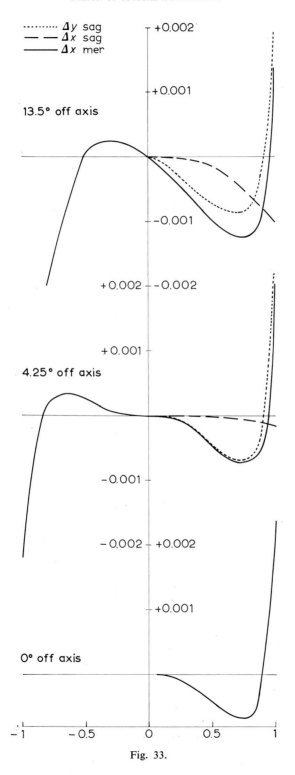

Fig. 33.

Example 3. Tessar objective designed by Jiro Mukai, U.S. patent 2,838,978; June 17, 1958. This is an *F*:2.8 objective with a total field of 45°.

Surface #	Curvature	Thickness	Refractive index e-line	$v_e = \dfrac{n_e - 1}{n_{F'} - n_{C'}}$
1	2.636970	0.097075	1.66104	57.28
2	0.108916	0.720550	1.00000	
3	−1.348962	0.027021	1.59663	35.47
4	3.223519	0.061047	1.00000	
5	0.000000	0.021016	1.51314	60.23
6	2.871790	0.136105	1.69400	54.56
7	−1.819600	0.000000	1.00000	

The pupil magnification is +0.939982 and is located behind the 4th surface. The paraxial constants are: $c = 0.789672$, $b = 0.815632$.

λ	Color aberrations	
	c_1	c_2
0.6563	0.003585	−0.000046
0.4861	−0.001757	−0.000037
0.4358	−0.002309	−0.000181

The third order aberration coefficients are

$$
\begin{aligned}
C_{12} &= -0.15578 \\
C_{22} &= 0.41637 \\
C_{23} &= 1.39666 \\
C_{33} &= 4.68482 \\
C_{13} - C_{22} &= 0.74545
\end{aligned}
$$

The system is shown in fig. 34 and the ray trace results in fig. 35.

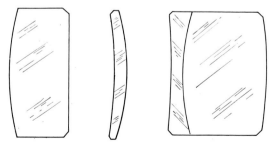

Fig. 34. Tessar objective.

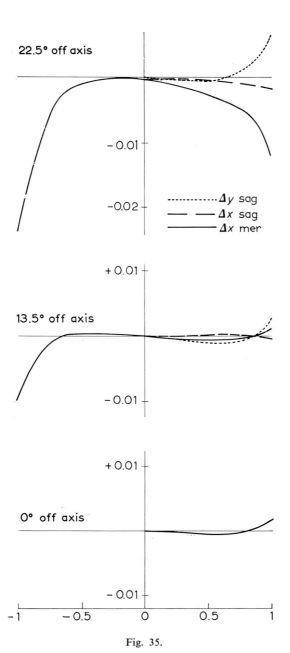

Fig. 35.

Example 4. Gauss objective designed by G. Lange, U.S. patent 3,043,193, July 10, 1962. This is an *F*:2 objective with a field of 36°.

Surface #	Curvature	Thickness	Refractive index e-line	$\nu_e = \dfrac{n_e - 1}{n_{F'} - n_{C'}}$
1	1.531 352	0.078 352	1.693 42	54.60
2	0.667 848	0.001 963	1.000 00	
3	2.627 018	0.133 194	1.614 03	58.37
4	0.080 682	0.035 259	1.588 33	40.56
5	3.988 533	0.293 824	1.000 00	
6	−3.259 972	0.039 176	1.682 12	32.01
7	−0.422 372	0.105 778	1.693 42	54.60
8	−2.444 575	0.001 963	1.000 00	
9	0.535 630	0.133 194	1.693 42	54.60
10	−1.131 974	0.000 000	1.000 00	

The pupil is located behind the 5th surface and has a magnification $+1.298\,931$. The paraxial constants are: $c = 0.624\,778$, $b = 0.299\,436$.

λ	Color aberrations	
	c_1	c_2
0.768 2	0.003 761	0.000 472
0.656 3	0.001 712	0.000 216
0.486 1	−0.000 360	−0.000 040
0.435 8	0.000 377	0.000 056

The third order aberration coefficients are

$$C_{12} = -0.831\,54$$
$$C_{22} = 0.121\,12$$
$$C_{23} = -0.031\,11$$
$$C_{33} = -0.218\,23$$
$$C_{13} - C_{22} = 0.396\,45$$

The system is shown in fig. 36 and the ray trace results in fig. 37.

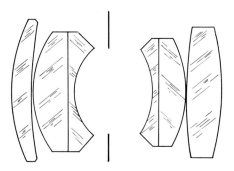

Fig. 36. Gauss objective.

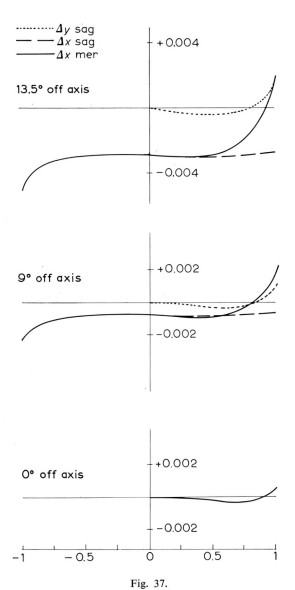

Fig. 37.

Example 5. Ritchey–Chrétien. This system is often used in telescopes since it gives a larger field than the parabolic mirror. It is traced here for an *F*:3 system and for a field of 4°.

Surface #	Curvature	Thickness	Refractive index
1	−0.75	−0.4	−1
2	−0.625	0	1

The surfaces are both aspheric and are given by

$$z = \frac{R\tau^2}{1 + \sqrt{(1 - \alpha R^2 \tau^2)}},$$

where z is the coordinate in the direction of the axis of symmetry where the ray is refracted by the surface, R is the curvature, τ is the distance of the point where the ray is refracted to the axis of symmetry, α is a coefficient describing the asphericity.

For the first surface $\alpha = -0.592\,592$ and for the second surface $\alpha = -64$. The paraxial constants are: $c = 0.4$, $b = 1.5$.

Since this is a reflecting system there are no color aberrations.

This system is designed so that the third order spherical and coma aberration coefficients are zero. It cannot be corrected for astigmatism and field curvature. For this system the meridional field curvature $R_m = -5.75$ and the sagittal field curvature $R_s = -1.75$.

The system is shown in fig. 38 and the results of the ray traces in fig. 39.

Note that the small amount of residual spherical aberration can be corrected by small higher order changes in the asphericity of the primary mirror.

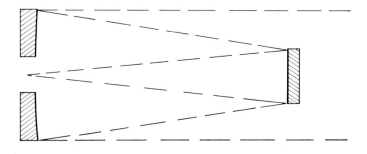

Fig. 38. Ritchey–Chrétien.

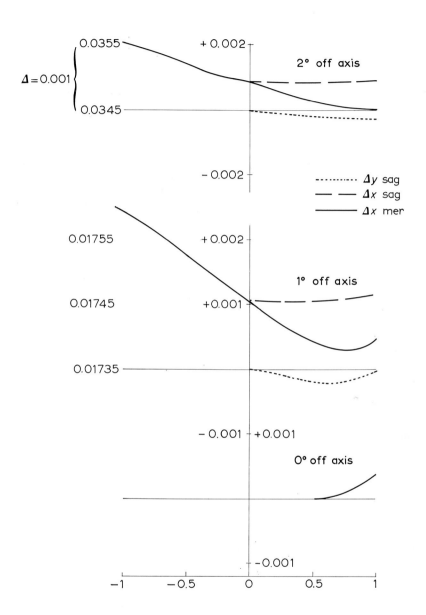

Fig. 39.

Example 6. Concentric System. This system is traced for an *F*:1.5 bundle.

Surface #	Curvature	Thickness	Refractive index d-line	v_d
1	−1.340869	0.184325	1.6034	38.02
2	−1.075141	1.292112	1.0000	
3	−0.450000	0.000000	−1.0000	

The image has a field curvature of 1. The pupil is located in the center of curvature of the system and has a magnification of −1.

	Color aberrations	
λ	c_1	c_2
0.6563	−0.002803	0
0.4861	0.0006410	0

The third order aberration coefficients are

$$C_{12} = -0.00001$$
$$C_{22} = 0.00000$$
$$C_{23} = -0.00002$$
$$C_{33} = -0.02695$$
$$C_{13} - C_{22} = -1.00000$$

The system is shown in fig. 40. Since the system is concentric, including the image plane, we only have to ray trace one field angle. In this example we have done this for three wave lengths. The results are shown in fig. 41.

Fig. 40. Bouwers system.

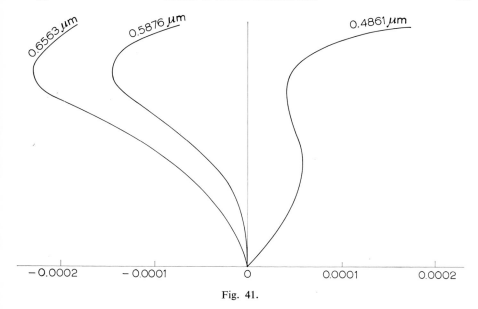

0.6563 μm   0.5876 μm   0.4861 μm

| −0.0002 | −0.0001 | O | 0.0001 | 0.0002 |

Fig. 41.

Example 7. Huygens eyepiece.

Surface #	Curvature	Thickness	Refractive index d-line	v_d
1	0.000000	0.072662	1.6074	56.7
2	−2.163352	1.019280	1.0000	
3	0.000000	0.169544	1.6074	56.7
4	−1.081760	0	1.0000	

The pupil is a distance 0.161470 in front of the system and has a magnification +18.411448 and a diameter of 0.06.

λ	Color aberrations	
	c_1	c_2
0.6563	0.007431	−0.001218
0.4861	−0.017247	0.002893

The third order aberration coefficients are

$$C_{12} = 1026.95$$
$$C_{22} = -115.96$$
$$C_{23} = 306.87$$
$$C_{33} = -163.09$$
$$C_{13} - C_{22} = -552.06$$

The system is shown in fig. 42 and the ray trace results in fig. 43.

Fig. 42. Huygens eyepiece.

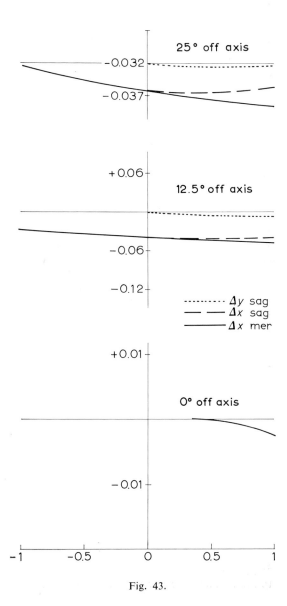

Fig. 43.

References

BERENS, C. and J. ZUCKERMAN, 1946, Diagnostic examination of the eye.

BROUWER, W., 1964, Matrix methods in optical instrument design (W. A. Benjamin, Inc., New York).

HERZBERGER, M., 1958, Modern geometrical optics (Interscience Publishers, New York).

JOHNSON, B. K., 1960, Optics and optical instruments (Dover Publications, New York).

KINGSLAKE, R., 1965, Applied optics and optical engineering (Academic Press, New York).

KÖNIG, A. and H. KÖHLER, 1959, Die Fernrohre und Entfernungsmesser (Springer-Verlag, Berlin).

LEGRAND, Y., 1957, Light, color and vision (Chapman and Hall, London).

LUNEBURG, R. K., 1964, Mathematical theory of optics (Univ. of California Press).

Ordnance Corps Manual, 1952, Design of fire control optics (U.S. Department of Commerce, Washington, D.C.)

SMITH, T., 1923, Optical calculations, in: A dictionary of applied physics, Vol. 4.

STEWARD, G. C., 1928, The symmetrical optical system (Cambridge Univ. Press).

TWYMAN, F., 1957, Prism and lens making (Hilger and Watts, Ltd., London).

WALTHER, A., 1959, Optical applications of solid glass spheres. Thesis, University of Delft, The Netherlands.

CHAPTER 18

MEASUREMENT OF ABERRATIONS
AND OPTICAL TRANSFER FUNCTIONS
OF OPTICAL SYSTEMS

K. ROSENHAUER

Physikalisch-Technische Bundesanstalt,
Abteilung IV,
Bundesallee 100, 33 Braunschweig, Germany

CONTENTS

1. Aberrations

The rays in an optical system do not form point images, i.e. the pencils are not homocentric; aberrations occur and the rays from a point object form a confused image patch. This arises from both aberrations and diffraction effects. The ray deviations can be classified as monochromatic and chromatic aberrations; the former are also known as Seidel aberrations and those of the third order comprise spherical aberration, astigmatism, coma, mean field curvature and distortion; instead of astigmatism and mean field curvature we often specify the meridional and sagittal field curvatures. The chromatic aberrations are 1) the longitudinal chromatic aberration, in which the focal points or image points do not coincide for the different wavelengths, and 2) transverse chromatic aberration, in which the focal lengths differ for different colours, causing a variation of magnification with wavelength.

The Seidel aberrations can be written out as a power series. The terms are of even or odd power according as the longitudinal or transverse ray aberrations are used. For transverse ray aberrations we then have terms of 3rd, 5th, 7th, . . . orders. More recently a different classification from that of Seidel has been made, in connection with which we refer to the work of HERZBERGER [1958].

It is difficult to infer much about the overall effect of aberrations from a consideration of the individual terms. This is because the aberrations alone do not give complete information about the energy distribution in the confusion patch; the spectral distribution in the light, the spectral sensitivity of the detector and the chromatic aberrations must all be considered together in their effect on image quality. Some relevant results are available for spherical aberration only, i.e. they apply to the axial region, not to oblique pencils (ROSENHAUER and ROSENBRUCH [1964a], SHANNON [1964]).

The aberrations may be measured by the classical methods, e.g. those of Foucault, Hartmann and Wetthauer, and also certain others, which however are equivalent to these three in most cases. For transverse ray aberrations we have more recently the application of the spot diagram (HERZBERGER [1957]), in connection with which we refer to work by BAKER and WILLIAMS [1965]. Herzberger worked on the evaluation of spot diagrams. These methods are in a certain sense analytical or differentiating, since they bring out the effects of individual aberrations.

In order to obtain the overall effect of the different image errors it is clear that we want a testing technique which shall be, on the other hand, integrative. Examples of such instruments are wellknown; they are used to determine the resolving power or resolution of an optical system at different points in the fields. The test objects used until recently include the Cobb test chart, a two-line pattern shown in fig. 1 (GARDENER [1941]), the three-line Kodak variation, radial gratings (COLEMAN and HARDING [1947], JEWEL [1949]), and some arbitrarily chosen patterns, letters and grating structures. In this connection we note that it is often possible to resolve the lines of a grating structure, but the contrast between the light and dark parts may be reduced. Further details are given by RECKMEYER [1934], ROEDER [1941], and by HANSEN [1942].

The resolving power may be estimated either visually or photographically; the results thus depend not only on the optical system, but also on the method of observation, i.e. in the photographic case on the quality of the negative, the kind of emulsion, etc.

(a)

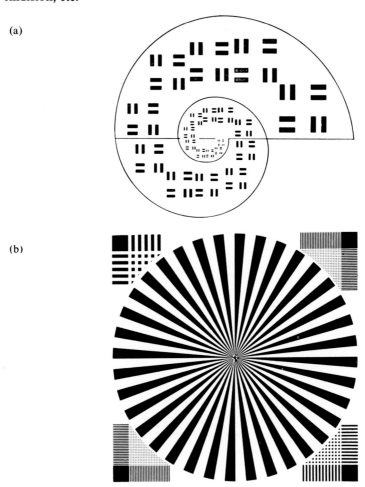

(b)

Fig. 1. (a) Cobb test chart; (b) radial grating, sector star test.

2. The optical transfer function

SCHADE [1948] made the following observation: one can regard an optical system as equivalent to an electrical communication channel, the object and image corresponding respectively to the input and output. A sinusoidal signal, i.e. in the optical case a sinusoidal light distribution, will be reproduced on the output side by linear transformation as again a sinusoidal distribution. The magnification corresponds to a frequency change and when the operation of the system is linear we can represent the modulation as a function of frequency, in this case the spatial frequency. Modulation transfer theory has been developed to a very sophisticated level for communications and it can easily be applied to the optical case.

2.1. PRINCIPLES AND APPLICATION OF OPTICAL TRANSFER FUNCTION THEORY

The application of transfer function theory from information theory to optics provides us with an objective measure of image quality in an *incoherently* illuminated optical system; it is relatively simple to compute and measure it accurately. For coherent and partially coherent illumination see BORN and WOLF [1964]. An optical system is, of course, characterized by not one but many transfer functions, corresponding to many physical parameters such as relative aperture, focus, field angle, kind of illumination, etc. This is an advance over the earlier kinds of measurement, in which the image quality of a system was measured by resolving power, i.e. the degree to which two neighbouring points could be distinguished; such observations are really in the nature of threshold measurements and are therefore subject to large errors. Furthermore it is in general not sufficient for good image quality that neighbouring object points be represented as neighbouring image points, it is also necessary to provide a more or less faithful rendering of the light intensities. Thus quality in an optical image comprises not merely geometrical representation but also true contrast. Optical transfer function theory is analogous to electrical transfer theory in that a one- or two-dimensional array of points in space corresponds to a succession in time of signals. In this way the optical system can be treated as a communication channel or a filter between object and image.

2.2. PROPERTIES OF THE OPTICAL TRANSFER FUNCTION

The characteristic transfer properties of an optical system can be characterized by the so-called optical transfer function (OTF). If we neglect stray light*, transmission losses, etc., it is a function of the aberrations and diffraction properties of the objective. If there are further imaging steps which are in effect incoherent, e.g. a photographic emulsion or projection on a diffusing screen, we can take the intermediate terms, insofar as the processes are linear, and form the product to give the overall transfer function. The resultant image quality is in general determined by the dominant term in this sequence. To simplify the discussion we shall in what follows consider only a unidimensional process of transfer from object to image.

Basically any object light distribution can be represented as a Fourier integral or Fourier sum. Thus the brightness distribution in the object is represented as a superposition of sinusoidal distributions. In other words, for any given object distribution we can find the frequency spectrum. We cannot find a universal form to comprehend the great variety of possible object distributions, so we start with one- or two-dimensional elementary periodic structures with uniform brightness; the spatial frequencies are varied and the contrast transfer properties are computed or measured.

* On the influence of stray light on the OTF see DIEDERICHS [1961, 1958].

The frequency transfer function is then obtained for the complete frequency spectrum up to the resolution limit, giving the amplitude and phase changes by which a given object grating is imaged through the system. The choice of spatial frequency to represent the image formation naturally depends on the kind of object, but some basic form of object grating is always implied, namely a linear structure with a sinusoidally varying light distribution, the so-called sine grating. More complicated structures, for example the square wave grating, are sometimes used, since they are easier to make, and occasionally slits or edges, but the results for a sine grating can always be recovered from the measurements. We shall give later typical forms of contrast transfer curves for optical systems.

The frequency range, or bandwidth, and the contrast, or depth of modulation, depend on the relative aperture and the residual aberrations. We know from a study of the image formation process, which frequencies are important for particular applications of an optical system and which aberrations are most to be avoided, and it is this which makes optical transfer theory important for the lens manufacturer. It must be remembered always that frequency here is not a time-like variable but has the dimension of reciprocal length (line frequency or spatial frequency).

The mathematical principles of transfer function theory for optical systems have been well understood for some considerable time; we shall briefly summarize them below. The basic principles were published by DUFFIEUX [1946] and further developments were made by SCHADE [1948], MARÉCHAL [1947, 1948], and HOPKINS [1953].

The process of image formation in an incoherent illumination can be written as a convolution integral; it is an essential condition that the imagery be isoplanatic and linear. By "linear" we mean that the intensity relations between object and image are mathematically linear, so that they can be described by a convolution integral. In fact the imagery of a corrected optical system is seldom isoplanatic over the whole field; usually only small regions can be taken as isoplanatic. Thus the object must be assumed to be small enough to lie within such a region. On the other hand the aberrations and therefore the form of a point image vary comparatively slowly over the field of a corrected optical system, whereas in order to show detectable changes they would have to vary by appreciable amounts over a distance comparable in size to the diffraction image. Thus it is reasonable to study the image formation of small detail within such an isoplanatic region.

2.3. THEORETICAL FOUNDATIONS OF OPTICAL TRANSFER FUNCTION THEORY

We use normalized coordinates in the object and image planes and in the entrance and exit pupils. Then the image intensity distribution $B'(u', v')$ can be written as a convolution of the object intensity distribution $B(u, v)$ and the intensity point spread function $G(u, v, u', v')$

$$ B'(u', v') = \tfrac{1}{2}\pi \iint_{-\infty}^{+\infty} B(u, v)\, G(u' - u, v' - v)\, \mathrm{d}u\, \mathrm{d}v. \tag{1} $$

The intensity point spread function is determined by the residual aberrations and is proportional to the squared modulus of the amplitude spread function

$$G(u', v') = |F(u', v')|^2. \tag{2}$$

The amplitude spread function can be written as a two-dimensional Fourier transform, starting from the Kirchhoff diffraction integral and using known results

$$F(u', v') = \text{const.} \int\int f(x', y') \exp\{2\pi i(u'x' + v'y')\} \, dx' dy'. \tag{3}$$

The function $f(x', y')$ is called the pupil function and it is the inverse Fourier transform

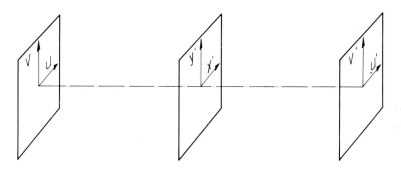

Fig. 2. Coordinate system. u, v in object plane; x', y' in pupil plane; u', v' in image plane.

of the amplitude spread function $f(u', v')$. The following relations hold between the intensities if s', t' are the coordinates of the spatial frequency spectrum.

$$G(u', v') = \int\int g(s', t') \exp\{2\pi i(s'u' + t'v')\} \, ds' dt', \tag{4}$$

$$g(s', t') = \int\int G(u', v') \exp\{-2\pi i(s'u' + t'v')\} \, du' dv'. \tag{5}$$

Substituting these in the convolution integral we obtain finally

$$B'(u', v') = \int\int g(s', t') b(s', t') \exp\{2\pi i(s'u' + t'v')\} \, ds' dt', \tag{6}$$

$$b'(s', t') = g(s', t') b(s', t'). \tag{7}$$

We define as transfer function not the diffraction solid itself, but its inverse Fourier transform, i.e. the spatial frequency spectrum of the intensity of $F(u', v')$

$$g(s', t') = \frac{b'(s', t')}{b(s', t')}. \tag{8}$$

We thus have an exact analogy with the electrical case, since the object, or original function, is represented in frequency space by means of the Fourier transformation and then transferred to the image function. Hopkins proposed to use this quantity, the so-called optical transfer function or OTF, as a measure of image quality for given, simple objects, since for incoherent illumination it can be expressed as the autocorrelation function of the pupil function

$$g(s', t') = \frac{1}{2\pi} \int \int f(x', y') f(x' - s', y' - t') dx' dy'. \tag{9}$$

In order to use this expression it is only necessary to know the wave aberration function of the system; this is given by its constructional data, or it can be measured. Without this application of Fourier transform theory it would be necessary first to calculate the point spread function, then obtain the image intensity by convolution and finally calculate the amplitude and phase of the OTF for each desired frequency. Of course, what is really significant is not the quantity $f(s', t')$ but the relative OTF, normalized to unity at zero frequency

$$D(s', t') = \frac{g(s', t')}{g(0, 0)}. \tag{10}$$

This function is in general complex and it can be expressed as the sum of real and imaginary parts or according to amplitude and phase. As pointed out by Hopkins, we can by symmetry take the displacement from $x' + \frac{1}{2}s'$ and $y' + \frac{1}{2}t'$, so the normalized OTF can be written as follows

$$D(s', t') = \frac{\int \int f(x' + \frac{1}{2}s', y' + \frac{1}{2}t') f(x' - \frac{1}{2}s', y' - \frac{1}{2}t') dx' dy'}{\int \int |f(x', y')|^2 dx' dy'} = \frac{S}{G}. \tag{11}$$

This expression is simply the integral of the product of two pupil functions over their common area when s, the coordinate origin of one, is displaced to the point (s', t'); the integrand is non-zero only in the overlap region. For the special case of an aberration-free objective with a circular pupil the OTF can be computed to be

$$D(s') = \pi^{-1} \{2 \arccos (\tfrac{1}{2}s') - \sin [2 \arccos (\tfrac{1}{2}s')]\}. \tag{12}$$

The pupil function $f(x', y')$ can be written as a function of the wave aberration $W(x', y')$

$$f(x', y') = \exp \{(2\pi i/\lambda) W(x', y')\}. \tag{13}$$

Here $W(x', y')$ is the deviation of the wavefront transmitted by the optical system from the ideal spherical shape, expressed as a function of the pupil coordinates x' and y'.

Eq. (11) can be written as follows

$$D(R) = \frac{\int \int_A \exp (2\pi i/\lambda) \{W(x' + \frac{1}{2}\lambda bR, y') - W(x' - \frac{1}{2}\lambda bR, y')\} dx' dy'}{\int \int_a dx' dy'}, \tag{14}$$

where λ=wavelength of the light, b=radius of the ideal spherical wave from the exit pupil to the image point, R=spatial frequency in lines per millimetre, $\lambda bR=s'$, A=domain of integration, i.e. the region common to the two pupils displaced through $\lambda bR=s'$, a=pupil surface. The direction of spatial frequencies is conventionally taken as perpendicular to the x-axis.

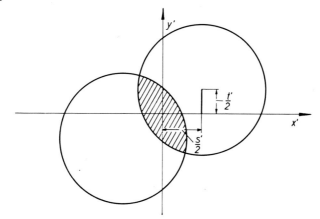

Fig. 3. Domain of integration. The dashed area, the overlapping part of the two sheared pupils, is the domain of integration.

2.4. THE IDEAL SYSTEM

For an ideal system we have $W(x', y')=0$, $f(x', y')=1$ and $D(s')$, the OTF, is in this case equal to the ratio of the common area of the two sheared pupils to the total pupil area, as already explained.

2.5. DEFOCUSSING

For simply defocussing along the optical axis we have $W(x', y')=A'(x'^2+y'^2)$ and as shown by Hopkins the OTF can in this case be computed as

$$
\begin{aligned}
D(s') = (4/\pi\alpha) \cos\left(\tfrac{1}{2}\alpha s'\right)&\{\beta J_1(\alpha)+\tfrac{1}{2}\sin 2\beta[J_1(\alpha)-J_3(\alpha)]+ \\
&-\tfrac{1}{4}\sin 4\beta[J_3(\alpha)-J_5(\alpha)]+ \\
&+\tfrac{1}{6}\sin 6\beta[J_5(\alpha)-J_7(\alpha)]+ \\
&-\ldots\}+ \\
-(4/\pi\alpha) \sin\left(\tfrac{1}{2}\alpha s'\right)&\{\sin \beta[J_0(\alpha)-J_2(\alpha)]+ \\
&-\tfrac{1}{3}\sin 3\beta[J_2(\alpha)-J_4(\alpha)]+ \\
&-\tfrac{1}{5}\sin 5\beta[J_4(\alpha)-J_6(\alpha)]+ \\
&-\ldots\},
\end{aligned}
\tag{15}
$$

where $\alpha=(4\pi/\lambda)A'$, $\beta=\arccos \tfrac{1}{2}s'$, and $J_0, J_1, J_2, \ldots$ are the Bessel functions of successive orders. The series are convergent and suitable for numerical evaluation and the results are shown in fig. 4.

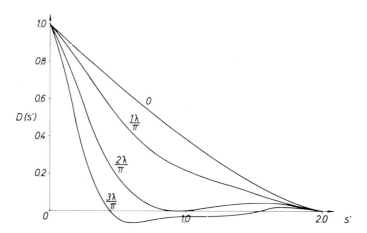

Fig. 4. OTF for a lens with different amounts of defocussing. The numbers on the curves give the wave aberration in fractions of the wavelength λ; 0 gives the curve for a lens free of aberration.

2.6. ABERRATED SYSTEMS

A closed expression for general functions $W(x', y')$ is of course not possible; we shall mention a few of the various approximate methods that have been described. Until recently the optical designer had to be content with experience and some well-tried rules of thumb as guides. The residual aberrations compatible with good image quality could only be computed with difficulty and in a few selected cases.

2.7. DETERMINING THE WAVEFRONT ABERRATION FOR THE COMPUTATION OF THE OTF

In order to compute the OTF it is necessary to determine the residual aberrations in a suitable form, i.e. as wavefront aberration. Many methods are available for existing optical systems.

First, we can determine the wavefront aberration of a sample system interferometrically, by means of the Twyman–Green interferometer or by some other interferometric method. Alternatively we can proceed by computation, integrating the geometrical ray aberrations, and these can be determined experimentally or by computing from the constructional data. Sometimes we can obtain some particular properties of the optical system directly from the wavefront aberration coefficients, without going to the much greater labour of computing the OTF.

A further possibility is then to vary systematically the aberration residuals; thus the wave aberrations may be found for all regions of interest and the correction may be improved by linear interpolation to find the best system. The OTF would be useful here as a merit function, the appropriate line frequency being chosen; however, further research on the relations between aberrations and image quality is needed before this can be done.

2.8. COMPUTING THE OTF; THE GENERAL SOLUTION

Several special methods adapted for electronic computers have been developed for calculating the OTF at a given spatial frequency. An exact method is due to HOPKINS [1957] and GOODBODY [1958]; this was used for some of the examples given below. Among several approximate methods for evaluating the integrals we may mention that of BARAKAT [1962], in which high order Gaussian quadrature is used with Legendre polynomials and non-uniform integration intervals.

The methods so far mentioned involve the use of large electronic computers, but it must not be forgotten that the calculation can be done very quickly and according to the exact formulae by means of analogue computers. For example ROSENHAUER *et al.* [1963, 1966] describe an analogue computer which yields the OTF for spherical aberration of different magnitudes and kinds. Such an instrument permits the rapid, systematic exploration of design parameters to optimize a system, since the aberration coefficients can be set up on a potentiometer. Of course this method has restricted accuracy, perhaps 1 % to 2 %.

2.9. NEGLECTING DIFFRACTION ALONG THE OPTICAL AXIS

All the methods so far considered start from the exact equations for the OTF and they thus take into account both *diffraction* and *aberrations*. However, it is known that the geometrical optics approximation is adequate for dealing with the image quality of systems in which the effect of aberrations is large compared to that of diffraction.

We obtain the geometrical optics approximation by letting the wavelength λ tend to zero in eq. (14). The transition to the limit may be written

$$D(R)_{\text{geom.opt.}} = \lim_{\lambda \to 0} D(R);$$

the transition first affects the limits of integration, for the shear λbR becomes identically zero as $\lambda \to 0$ and the domain of integration is simply the pupil.

Secondly the integrand in eq. (14) changes from its original form, which is

$$\exp (2\pi i/\lambda)\{W(x'+\tfrac{1}{2}\lambda bR, y') - W(x'-\tfrac{1}{2}\lambda bR, y')\}.$$

The limiting process on the exponent gives

$$\lim_{\lambda b \to 0} 2\pi i bR \, \frac{W(x'+\lambda bR, y') - W(x', y')}{\lambda bR} = 2\pi i bR \, \frac{\partial W(x', y')}{\partial x'}, \tag{16}$$

the quotient of differences becoming a differential coefficient. But we have

$$b \frac{\partial W(x', y')}{\partial x'} = Q(x', y'),$$

where $Q(x', y')$ is the transverse ray aberration at image distance b. Consequently we have

$$
D_{\text{geom.opt.}}(R) = (1/\pi)\frac{\displaystyle\iint \exp\left(2\pi i b R\,\partial W/\partial x'\right)\mathrm{d}x'\mathrm{d}y'}{\displaystyle\iint \mathrm{d}x'\mathrm{d}y'}. \tag{17}
$$

For objects on the optical axis the wave aberration depends only on the radius of the exit pupil, $r=(x'^2+y'^2)^{\frac12}$, since there is rotation symmetry. Thus we can put for the wave aberration $W=W(r)$ and similarly $Q=Q(r)$. Let $r_{\max}=h$ at the rim of the pupil. Then in this special case we obtain for the OTF

$$
D_{\text{geom.opt.}}(R) = (2/h^2)\int_0^h J_0[2\pi R Q(r)]r\,\mathrm{d}r. \tag{18}
$$

Here J_0 is the Bessel function of order zero. If we develop J_0 in a power series we have

$$
J_0(z) = 1-(\tfrac12 z)^2+(\tfrac12 z)^4\frac{1}{(2!)^2}-(\tfrac12 z)^6\frac{1}{(3!)^2}+\dots \tag{19}
$$

and thus we obtain

$$
D_{\text{geom.opt.}}(R) = (2/h^2)\left\{\tfrac12 h^2-(\pi R)^2\int_0^h [Q(r)]^2 r\,\mathrm{d}r+(\tfrac14\pi R)^4\int_0^h [Q(r)]^4 r\,\mathrm{d}r+\dots\right\}. \tag{20}
$$

If we take only the first two terms we obtain the approximation of LUKOSZ [1958]

$$
D_{\text{geom.opt.}}(R) \approx 1-2R^2(\pi/h)^2\int_0^h [Q(r)]^2 r\,\mathrm{d}r. \tag{21}
$$

In general $W(r)$ and $Q(r)$ can be written as polynomials in r and the above approximation is then easily evaluated.

2.10. EFFECT OF NEGLECTING DIFFRACTION IN THE OFF-AXIS REGION

Again a closed solution is not possible in the extra-axial region for the geometrical optics approximation; the integral may be evaluated by the Hopkins method but the procedure is simpler since the domain of integration does not change with frequency. We have

$$
D(R, T) = \frac{1}{N}\sum_{i=0}^N \cos\{2\pi[Q(x_i', y_i')R+Q(x_i', y_i')T]
$$

$$
+ i\sin\{2\pi[Q(x_i', y_i')R+Q(x_i', y_i')T], \tag{22}
$$

where $Q(x_i', y_i')$ is the transverse ray aberration at (x_i', y_i'), N is the number of subdivisions in the pupil, and R and T are the spatial frequencies in lines per mm in the x and y direction, respectively. The values $Q(x_i', y_i')$ used in the calculation correspond to the intersection points of the rays in the so-called spot diagram; they can be obtained simply by ray-tracing or they can be calculated analytically as was done by HERZBERGER [1958]. The spot diagram is obtained from the intersections with the image plane of rays from one object point which pass through a uniform mesh of points in the entrance pupil. The density of these points in the image plane is a measure of the intensity distribution in the point image if diffraction is neglected.

The OTF computed as above from a set of points of suitable density is an easily calculated criterion of image quality; however, it is not at present possible to predict which method will ultimately be adopted in practical lens design.

Studies of the relations between spherical aberration and OTF are reported in Applied Optics **5**, 415 (1966) and PTB Mitteilungen **75**, 553 (1965). Studies of the OTF in relation to the spectral sensitivity of the detector, the spectral energy distribution in the light source and chromatic aberration in the optical system are reported in Japanese Journal of Applied Physics **4**, Supplement **1**, 238 (1965).

3. Quality criteria for optical systems

The OTF is defined in relation to the image of an object with sinusoidal light distribution. For such objects it is a direct criterion of image quality. The image forming properties of the system for other objects, e.g. slits or edges, must then be calculated from the OTF. There are thus certain difficulties in defining a generally applicable criterion of image quality. LINFOOT [1960] made a study of this problem and gave precise mathematical formulations for three quality criteria.

3.1. LINFOOT'S QUALITY CRITERIA

The criteria are 1) image fidelity, 2) relative structure content, and 3) image correlation quality. We now give the mathematical relations between these three concepts. The image fidelity M_f is defined by

$$1 - M_f = \frac{\iint [B(u, v) - B'(u', v')]^2 \, du \, dv}{\iint [B(u, v)]^2 \, du \, dv} =$$

$$= \frac{\iint |1 - D(s', t')|^2 \, |b(s', t')|^2 \, ds' \, dt'}{\iint |b(s', t')|^2 \, ds' \, dt'}. \tag{23}$$

Here $D(s', t')$ is the two-dimensional OTF, which, together with the Fourier transform of the object, $b(s', t')$, determines the fidelity.

For the relative structure content M_s we have

$$M_s = \frac{\iint |b(s', t')|^2 \, |D(s', t')|^2 \, ds' \, dt'}{\iint |b(s', t')|^2 \, ds' dt'}. \tag{24}$$

This likewise involves the two-dimensional OTF and the object transform.

The third criterion, the correlation quality M_k is

$$
M_k = \frac{\iint |b(s', t')|^2 D(s', t') \, ds' dt'}{\iint |b(s', t')|^2 \, ds' \, dt'} \tag{25}
$$

The three criteria satisfy the relation $M_f = 2M_k - M_s$. The structure of the object is involved in these expressions as well as the OTF, so that they are relevant to a given object, but they are on that account relatively complicated to use.

3.2. SLEVOGT'S QUALITY CRITERIA

SLEVOGT [1961], KÄMMERER [1959] and HERTEL [1963] proposed other image quality criteria, namely image detail, contour sharpness and contrast content. Contrast content is a measure of the number of distinguishable brightness steps in the middle frequency range. Image detail corresponds essentially to resolving power and contour sharpness is a measure of the accuracy of reproduction of the intensity gradient in an edge. The choice of criterion depends on the kind of object; also aesthetic judgements play an important part in the choice, in fact the whole matter is subjective to a very large extent.

3.3. OTHER QUALITY CRITERIA

HEYNACHER [1963] used similar criteria, following the introduction of the notion of acutance by HIGGINS and WOLFE [1955]. It should also be mentioned that SCHADE [1954] used the structure content as a quality criterion and the work of Heynacher favours this quantity.

In general it can be said that a reduction in image quality is noticeable if frequencies of 5 to 6 lines per millimetre are not reproduced in a well-illuminated image viewed at 25 cm distance. Further investigations on the optimal quality of optical images were carried out by FRIESER and BIEDERMANN [1963]. ROSENHAUER and ROSENBRUCH [1957] determined the line frequency at given contrast (e.g. $K = 0.4$) necessary for good imagery, and conversely they investigated the OTF required to give good images at given frequency (e.g. 30 lines/mm). ROSENBRUCH [1959] estimated the resolving power as the intersection point of the acuity curve of the eye with the OTF curve and he also considered the use of the number of resolvable points and the information content as quality criteria.

The OTF contains all the information needed for a physical analysis of the image formation for any given object, but it is nevertheless far from being an ideal quality criterion. All criteria are to some extent arbitrary in their weighting of the physical properties of the object, so none can satisfy all purposes.

4. Measurement techniques

A great advantage of the OTF for measurement purposes is that it is easy to obtain relative values; this is useful both for testing during manufacture and for final performance testing of optical systems. We shall describe here a few of the many methods for measuring the OTF which have been described over the last 15 years.

4.1. MECHANICAL AND OPTICAL REQUIREMENTS

A stable mounting for the lens under test is essential for the measurement of OTF, just as for aberration measurement; the mounting must have well-controlled fine adjustments so that the necessary displacements of the lens corresponding to the required different image planes, field angles and azimuths may be carried out. The requirements on precision and stability in the mechanical parts of the apparatus vary greatly with focal length and relative aperture. If an objective has relative aperture $f/2$ (numerical aperture 0.25), a displacement of the image plane of only $3\,\mu\text{m}$ can change the OTF by 0.10 and the error will be correspondingly larger for larger apertures.

The OTF has physical significance only for incoherently illuminated objects and it is necessary to take care to ensure that this condition is always complied with by, e.g., using a much larger aperture in the illuminating system, by using diffusing or scattering screens, etc.

As is wellknown, aberrations change with the conjugate distances, so the desired conjugates must be used, or else they must be simulated by optical means; for example a collimator can simulate an indefinitely long conjugate. However, if such auxiliary optical systems are used, it is necessary to ensure that they do not affect the condition of incoherence and that, as imaging systems, they do not change the OTF of the system under test. It is often difficult to check on these points by calculation and thus it is best to avoid the use of auxiliary systems whenever possible; when they must be used they must be of such optical quality that their effect on the lens under test can be neglected.

4.2. THE GENERAL ARRANGEMENT

The general plan of all OTF measuring equipment comprises a light source, the test-object, the optical system to be tested, in its mounting, and an image detector, usually with electronic signal processing gear. The main differences between the various methods are in the form of the test-object and in the details of the electronic data processing to be applied to the measurements.

4.3. DESCRIPTION OF THE PRINCIPAL METHODS

We now describe briefly a few of the principal methods.

4.3.1. *The direct method with a periodic test-object*

The direct measurement of the OTF involves a periodic test-object or grating of sinusoidally varying transmission; it must be illuminated incoherently and the spacing must be variable over the appropriate spatial frequency range. The lens under test forms an image in the required image plane and the light distribution here, also sinusoidal in intensity, can be measured by means of a narrow slit followed by a photomultiplier and associated electronics. The light distributions in the object and in the image have each contrast K defined by the formula

$$K = (J_{max} - J_{min})/(J_{max} + J_{min}).$$

The OTF for the corresponding spatial frequency is then given by the quotient

$$OTF = K_{image}/K_{object}.$$

The different spatial frequencies are obtained from different test-objects arranged in sequence, e.g. on a rotating drum in the object plane (ROSENHAUER and ROSENBRUCH [1956]). In this case the scanning slit in the image plane can be stationary, since the

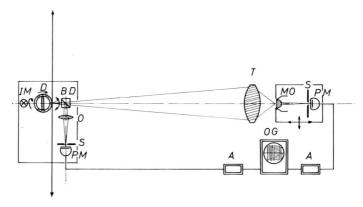

Fig. 5. Direct-scanning of measuring OTF. IM = illumination unit with light source, condenser, filter and ground glass plate; D = rotating drum with grating as test object; BD = beam splitter; T = test lens; MO = microscope objective; S = slit; PM = photomultiplier; O = ideal lens; A = amplifier; OG = oscilloscope.

rotation of the drum provides the scan. The spatial sequence of grating images traversing the slit is transformed by means of the photomultiplier etc., into a temporal sequence of current or voltage variations. The signal from the multiplier can be sent direct to the deflectors of an oscilloscope and the frequency dependent signal appears on the screen in its original spatial sequence. If K_{object} is constant and if the number of periods of different frequencies and the sequence of frequencies are suitably chosen, the envelope of the oscilloscope trace represents the OTF curve, provided the multiplier is linear. The different spatial frequencies correspond to the different temporal frequencies in the oscilloscope, so that the amplifiers and the multiplier must have a suitably broad-band response. There are considerable difficulties in obtaining a test-object with unit contrast and sinusoidal transmission over a wide frequency range.

The test-object is only scanned in one direction and thus various methods have been developed in which the sinusoidal variation is obtained by a suitably shaped mask

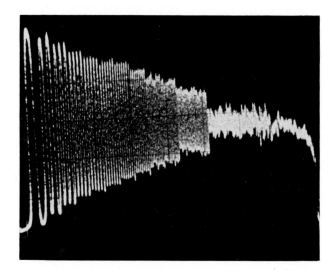

Fig. 6. Oscilloscope trace of the image of the grating test-object. A square-wave test-object, whose spatial frequency becomes stepwise smaller, is imaged by the test lens T and an ideal lens O (see fig. 5).

in the perpendicular direction; a long enough slit is used to ensure integration. In principle the same results must be obtained as for a test-object in which the transmission actually varies.

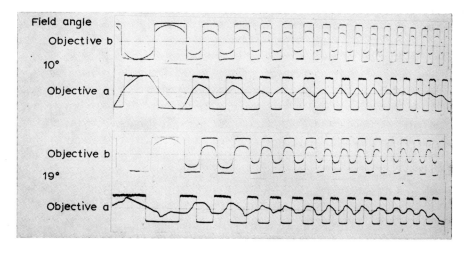

Fig. 7. Time sequence of oscillograms of square-wave grating as imaged by two different objectives at 10° and 19° field angles. The upper row: a good lens at 10° field, the second row: a low-performance lens at 10° field; the third and fourth rows give the same for 19° field.

Square-wave test-objects have often been used instead of sinusoidal test-objects and corrections applied mathematically to the results; COLTMAN [1954] gave formulae suitable for this purpose. This computation can be avoided if the test-object is a star with square-wave transmission; the star is rotated and its image is made to fall on a pinhole, so that in effect the hole scans round a circle of variable radius concentric with the star; the spatial frequency increases inversely with the scan radius but the signal from the multiplier behind the scanning pinhole has a constant temporal frequency, since the angular velocity of the test-object disc is constant (LINDBERG [1954], INGELSTAM et al. [1956]). The harmonics can easily be blocked by suitable electrical filters, so that only the fundamental is transmitted, and this gives the same effect as if the test-object were sinusoidal. A similar effect can be achieved by using a test-object in which the different frequencies are arranged sequentially if the velocity of scanning of each section is made inversely proportional to the spatial frequency; this was done by MURATA [1959, 1960] by means of a cam drive. Again the multiplier

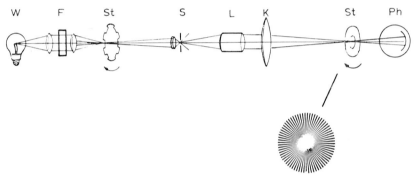

Fig. 8. The star sector method of measuring OTF. W = light source; F = collimating and filtering unit; St = rotating sector with very low spatial frequency to normalize the OTF; S = microscope objective to illuminate a small hole; L = test lens; K = collimator; St = sector star, Ph = photo-multiplier.

output is of constant frequency, independent of the spatial frequency, and it may easily be filtered to give the effect of a sinusoidal form.

The method of LOHMANN [1957] can also be used to obtain an approximately sinusoidal transmission with continuously varying spatial frequency; the test-object is formed by two square-wave gratings of high spatial frequency superimposed at an angle which is variable; moiré fringes are obtained and their spatial frequency depends on the angle between the gratings. If the two gratings are on two contra-rotating discs the moiré fringes spread out from a common diameter of the discs and the lens under test forms an image of them on a slit.

Care must be taken to choose a test-object with the right range of spatial frequencies for the lens to be tested; the extreme values should correspond to OTF values of nearly unity and zero respectively. If the range cannot be encompassed by one test-object, then more than one must be used; a special test-object for the lower frequencies is often used.

4.3.2. *Indirect methods using slits and edges*

The OTF can also be obtained by indirect methods in which non-periodic test-objects of any form are used; the object and image are Fourier analysed and the amplitudes and phases of the individual Fourier components are obtained. Slits and edges are simple and easily made and they are often used in this way.

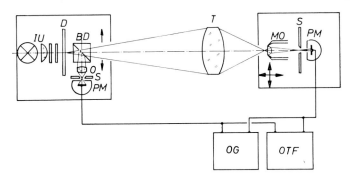

Fig. 9a. OTF measuring method by scanning the edge image with narrow band filters. IU = illumination unit; D = rotating sector disk; T = test lens; MO = microscope objective; S = scanning hole; PM = photomultiplier; O = ideal lens; BD = beam splitter; OG = oscilloscope; OTF = electronic device and plotter.

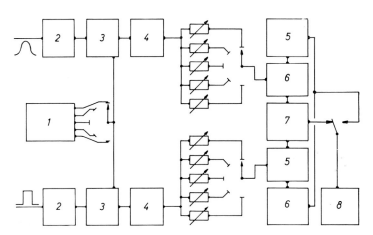

Fig. 9b. Block diagram of electronic circuit of fig. 9a (two-channel analyser). 1 = quartz frequence generators; 2 = preamplifiers; 3 = mixing stage; 4 = 60 kHz filters followed by adjustable resistors; 5 = logarithmic amplifier; 6 = amplifier; 7 = phase meter; 8 = plotter.

The frequency spectra of an edge (or a low-frequency square-wave grating with mark-space ratio 1 : 1) and of a slit (or low-frequency square-wave grating with mark-space ratio about 1 : 1000) are wellknown. The edge or slit is imaged by the lens under test onto a narrow slit followed by a photomultiplier; the image, or rather a time-varying electrical magnitude which is proportional to it, is analysed and so by comparison with the amplitudes and phases in the original object the OTF is obtained.

There are many variations of this method; it avoids the difficulty of generating complicated test-objects, but the subsequent Fourier analysis requires more complex electronics than in the direct methods (ROSENHAUER and ROSENBRUCH [1956, 1964b]).

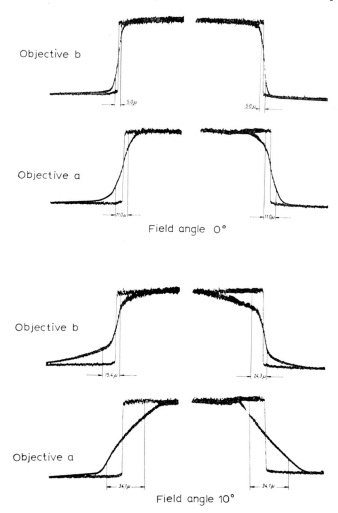

Fig. 9c. Oscillograms of edge images for two objectives at two different field angles.

4.3.3. Indirect methods involving interferometry

A third group of methods involves operations in the plane of the exit pupil, rather than in the image plane. A shearing interferometer is used to produce two coherent images of the pupil sheared through a distance $s = \lambda f R$, where λ is the wavelength of the light, f is the focal length or conjugate distance from the system under test and R is the spatial frequency at which the measurement is to be made. The overlap region of the two pupils is traversed by bright and dark fringes which map the wave aberration $W(x'+\frac{1}{2}s', y')-W(x'-\frac{1}{2}s', y')$, which function is required for calculating the OTF as shown in the theoretical section of this chapter. The total flux in the overlapping regions is measured and this is proportional to the OTF. The best-known method based on this principle is that described by BAKER [1955].

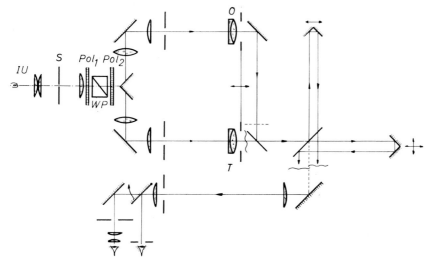

Fig. 10. Baker's shearing interferometer method. IU = illumination unit; S = slit; Pol$_1$, Pol$_2$ = polarizers; WP = Wollaston prism; O = ideal lens; T = test lens.

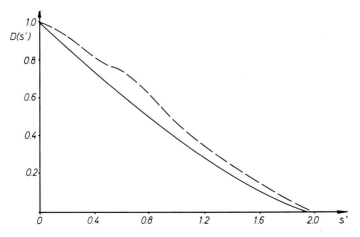

Fig. 11. OTF for an aberrationless lens for sine wave (full curve) and square-wave (dashed curve) test gratings.

The advantage of this method is that the aberrations and the OTF are measured simultaneously; a disadvantage is that monochromatic light must be used. Any method which produces a sheared exit pupil can be applied; usually some form of differential interferometer is used but certain forms in which the ray paths are changed by the interferometer are not suitable; for example, it is inadvisable to use systems in which thick plane-parallel plates are traversed by converging pencils of light.

4.3.4. *Indirect methods based on measurement of the geometrical aberrations*

A last group comprises methods in which the geometrical aberrations are measured

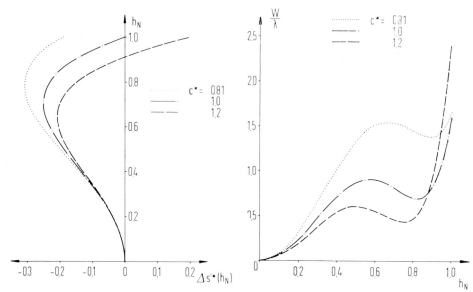

Fig. 12a. Three different spherical aberrations for normalized height of incidence.

Fig. 12b. Wave aberrations of fig. 12a for optimal focussing.

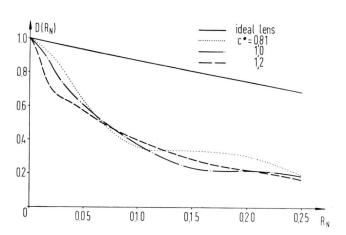

Fig. 12c. OTF curves calculated from the wave aberrations of fig. 12b.

and the OTF is computed by means of the formulae derived above. The aberrations can be measured by any of the usual methods, e.g. those of Hartmann, Wetthauer, Väisilä, Foucault, Ronchi and others.

All the methods described can be used to determine the ensemble of OTF curves in the region of interest for studying the image quality and then the quality criteria described above can be applied.

5. Experimental results

The OTF relates to a sinusoidal test-object. If the test-object is a square-wave grating we obtain different values of the transfer factors and these can be transformed back by the wellknown formulae of Coltman. The difference between the two sets of values is shown in fig. 11 for an aberration-free system. In the examples which follow, which are

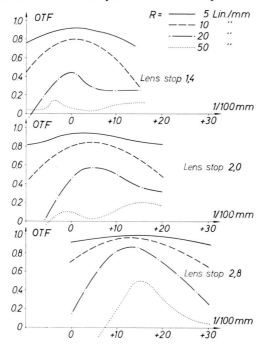

Fig. 13. OTF values for different spatial frequencies R as functions of the image plane positions, for three stop settings.

chosen from many OTF measurements on objectives, the transfer function always refers to a sinusoidal object, i.e. we are dealing with the normal OTF.

The OTF is a measure of the image-degrading effects of aberrations and diffraction, so that different kinds of aberrations produce different OTF curves. Fig. 12a shows longitudinal spherical aberration of different kinds but of equal magnitudes; the curves for $C^* = 0.81$, 1.00 and 1.20 correspond respectively to undercorrection, correction and overcorrection. Fig. 12b shows the corresponding wave aberrations, referred to the best focal plane, and fig. 12c shows the OTF curves. It can be seen that the undercorrected aberration gives the best OTF at lower frequencies, while over-correction is better for the middle frequency range. Thus by controlling the spherical

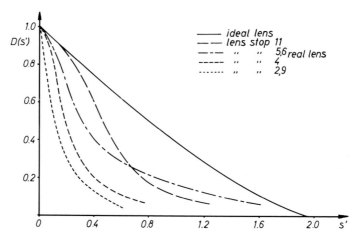

Fig. 14. OTF curves for different apertures; the image plane for the best curve at full aperture is the same as that at small aperture.

aberration we can obtain the desired OTF in the axial region. In each case the OTF was measured for the best image plane. Fig. 13 shows for another objective how the OTF varies with focus and stop setting; this figure shows not the actual OTF curves, but the OTF at certain chosen spatial frequencies as a function of the axial focus position. The objective is heavily overcorrected for spherical aberration at full aperture. It can be seen from the figure that by suitable stopping down the aperture, it is possible to increase the maximum as well as change its position. In most commercial photographic objectives the spherical aberration is large enough to make it necessary to stop down considerably before the performance is diffraction limited. Fig. 14

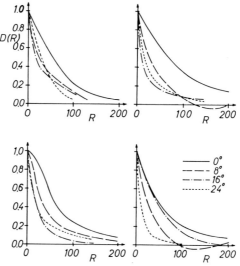

Fig. 15. Dependence of OTF curves on field angle for 4 different objectives; the spatial frequency R is in lines per mm.

shows how this occurs in a 50 mm $f/2$ miniature camera objective; in this example the best image plane at full aperture does not change on stopping down, so that the effects of spherical aberration and defocussing act against each other.

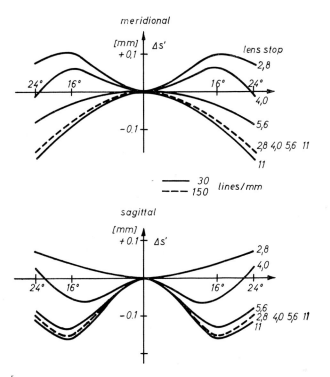

Fig. 16a. The best image surface as function of aperture (lens stop) and azimuth (direction of gratings) for a 35 mm $f/2.8$ objective. $\lambda = 546$ nm.

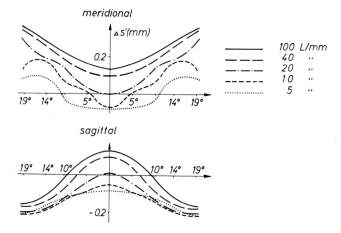

Fig. 16b. Dependence of the best image surface on spatial frequency R and azimuth for a 50 mm $f/2$ objective.

The relations between OTF and aberrations on-axis are easy to visualize and to study experimentally, but in the off-axis region the interactions between the multiplicity of aberration types and vignetting make the analysis difficult. Fig. 15 shows the OTF for a few 50 mm $f/2$ objectives, at full aperture, in the best axial focal plane and for meridional grating lines. The question of the contributions of individual aberrations to the complete curve is not relevant to the assessment of the image quality of the complete objective, but is of interest to the manufacturer who wishes to know how to improve his products. It is useful to know how the locations of the image positions for best OTF change on going from the axis, as a function of field angle, azimuth, spatial frequency of the test-object and aperture of the objective. For vanishingly small aperture we obtain simply the meridional and sagittal field curvatures. For larger apertures the asymmetric aberrations come into play, e.g. coma and other effects which cause an apparent displacement of the image position. Fig. 16a shows

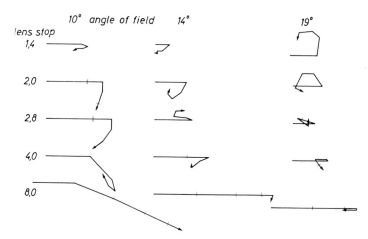

Fig. 17. Complex OTF values represented vectorially for some field angles and stop settings of an objective.

the effects of aperture change on meridional and sagittal grating lines, for a 50 mm $f/2$ miniature camera objective. Fig. 16b shows how the shape of the best image surface depends on spatial frequency.

As can be seen from eq. (14), the OTF is in general a complex quantity; the imaginary part is zero only if the wave aberration is rotation symmetric, e.g. as on the axis, where there is pure spherical aberration. We can represent the OTF either by its real and imaginary parts or in terms of its amplitude and phase. The amplitude of the OTF is called the modulation transfer function (MTF). The oblique aberrations such as coma and distortion, which are asymmetric, produce a lateral displacement of the image of the grating which is a function of the spatial frequency; this appears as a phase shift additional to the amplitude change. In the best image position, i.e. when distortion and defocus are allowed for, the magnitude of the phase shift is only significant when the MTF is less than 0.2. Thus the MTF alone is usually adequate to characterize the off-axis image quality. However, many methods of measurement, e.g. that in which an edge test-object is used, give the MTF and the phase shift at the same time. The vector representation can be used to show both these quantities together; vectors are drawn of length proportional to the MTF and with direction

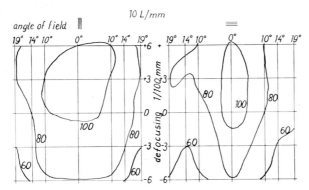

Fig. 18a. Contrast mountains for spatial frequency of 10 lines per mm for meridional and sagittal azimuths of a photographic lens. The numbers at the curves give the contrast transfer factor which is reached at this curve. The dashed domain marks the reversal of the sign of contrast transfer.

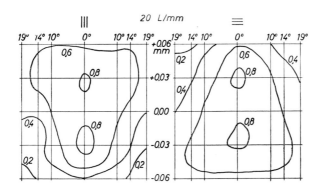

Fig. 18b. Contrast mountains for 20 lines per mm (see fig. 18a).

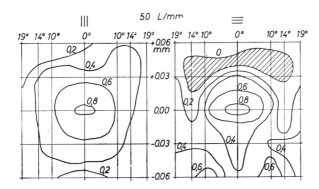

Fig. 18c. Contrast mountains for 50 lines per mm (see fig. 18a).

corresponding to the phase angle, as in fig. 17. To show phase and amplitude together as functions of spatial frequency we need a three-dimensional coordinate system and this cannot be represented in the usual way in a two-dimensional diagram. Fig. 17 shows the vectorial representation of the complex OTF for an $f/1.4$ photographic objective; the measurements were made in the best focal plane for the axial region at $f/2$, with stop settings down to $f/8$ and with sagittal grating lines. The vectors for spatial frequencies of 5, 10, 15, 20 and 25 lines per mm are placed end to end for the field angles 10°, 14° and 19°.

To characterize the performance of a wide-angle objective so that the image quality can be assessed, the OTF must be known for several field angles and image planes and for both line directions. Another way of plotting the OTF is often used to display all these values; the axial image plane displacement in, e.g. microns, is plotted along one axis of a coordinate system and the field coordinate, e.g. field angle in degrees, is plotted along the other axis; then level lines or contours of constant contrast are plotted. Figs. 18a, b and c show such curves; they may be interpreted as map contours of contrast in the image space of the optical system. The contours are plotted for spatial frequencies 10, 20 and 50 lines per mm and for meridional and sagittal gratings. The numbers on the curves indicate the percentage contrast; the shading indicates regions of contrast reversal. The optical system was a very wide aperture 50mm photographic objective; it had to be stopped down to $f/2$ to give measurable contrast transfer and even then no detail finer than 20 lines per mm could be seen off-axis, as is clear from the graphs.

References

BAKER, L. R., 1955, Proc. Phys. Soc. (London) B **68**, 871.
BAKER, L. R. and T. L. WILLIAMS, 1965, Appl. Opt. **4**, 285.
BARAKAT, R., 1962, J. Opt. Soc. Am. **52**, 985.
BORN, M. and E. WOLF, 1964, Principles of optics (London, 1964).
COLEMAN, H. S., and S. W. HARDING, 1947, J. Opt. Soc. Am. **37**, 263.
COLTMAN, J. W., 1954, J. Opt. Soc. Am. **44**, 486.
DIEDERICHS, E., 1961, Dissertation Techn. Hochschule, Braunschweig.
DIEDERICHS, E. and A. LOHMANN, 1958, Optik **15**, 751.
DUFFIEUX, P., 1946, L'intégral de Fourier et ses applications à l'optique (Rennes).
FRIESER, H. and K. BIEDERMANN, 1963, Optik **20**, 5.
GARDENER, I. C., 1941, Natl. Bur. Std. Circ. C 428.
GOODBODY, A. M., 1958, Proc. Phys. Soc. (London) **72**, 411.
HANSEN, G., 1942, Zeiss-Nachr. **4**, 129.
HERTEL, J., 1963, Dissertation Techn. Univ., Berlin.
HERZBERGER, M., 1957, J. Opt. Soc. Am. **47**, 548.
HERZBERGER, M., 1958, Modern geometrical optics (Interscience, New York).
HEYNACHER, E., 1963, Zeiss-Mitt. **3**, 32.
HIGGINS, G. C. and R. N. WOLFE, 1955, J. Opt. Soc. Am. **45**, 121.
HOPKINS, H. H., 1953, Proc. Roy. Soc. (London) A **217**, 408.
HOPKINS, H. H., 1955, Proc. Roy. Soc. (London) A **231**, 91.
HOPKINS, H. H., 1957, Proc. Phys. Soc. (London) B **70**, 449.
INGELSTAM, E., E. DJURLE and B. S. SJØGREN, 1956, J. Opt. Soc. Am. **46**, 707.

JEWELL, L. E., 1949, J. Opt. Soc. Am. **3**, 51.

KÄMMERER, J., 1959, Dissertation Techn. Univ., Berlin.

LINDBERG, P., 1954, Opt. Acta **1**, 80.

LINFOOT, E. H., 1960, Qualitätsbewertung optischer Bilder (Vieweg, Braunschweig).

LOHMANN, A., 1957, Optik **14**, 510.

LUKOSZ, W., 1958, Dissertation Techn. Hochschule, Braunschweig.

MARÉCHAL, A., 1947, Rev. Opt. **26**, 257.

MARÉCHAL, A., 1948, Rev. Opt. **27**, 73, 269.

MURATA, K., 1959, J. Appl. Phys. (Japan) **28**, 276.

MURATA, K., 1960, Optik **17**, 152.

RECKMEYER, 1934, Am. Annual Photography p. 220.

ROEDER, 1941, Phot. Ind. **29**, 371.

ROSENBRUCH, K.-J., 1959, Optik **16**, 135.

ROSENHAUER, K. and K.-J. ROSENBRUCH, 1956, Opt. Acta **4**, 21.

ROSENHAUER, K. and K.-J. ROSENBRUCH, 1957, Z. Instrumentenk. **65**, 83.

ROSENHAUER, K. and K.-J. ROSENBRUCH, 1959, Z. Instrumentenk. **67**, 179.

ROSENHAUER, K. and K.-J. ROSENBRUCH, 1964a, Japan. J. Appl. Phys. **4**, Suppl. **1**, 238.

ROSENHAUER, K. and K.-J. ROSENBRUCH, 1964b, Optik **21**, 652.

ROSENHAUER, K., K.-J. ROSENBRUCH and H. SIEMS, 1963, Z. Instrumentenk. **71**, 14.

ROSENHAUER, K., K.-J. ROSENBRUCH and F. A. SUNDER-PLASSMANN, 1966, Appl. Opt. **5**, 415.

SCHADE, O. H., 1948, RCA Rev. **9**, 245.

SCHADE, O. H., 1954, Natl. Bur. Std. Circ. 526.

SHANNON, R. R., 1964, Japan. J. Appl. Phys. **4**, Suppl. **1**, 231.

SLEVOGT, H., 1961, Optik **18**, 506.

AUTHOR INDEX